NUCLEAR PHYSICS

ROBERT A. HOWARD

University of Oklahoma

NUCLEAR PHYSICS

WADSWORTH PUBLISHING COMPANY, INC.

Belmont, California

L.C. Cat. Card No.: 62-17901

Printed in the United States of America

Preface

In the study of mechanics, one finds that a very few unifying concepts can be used to explain virtually all observed mechanical phenomena. The same thing can be said of thermodynamics and electricity, except that here there are more basic principles than in mechanics. Nuclear physics, by contrast, is not so neatly structured. Many of the basic laws—laws that might, for example, explain the binding together of nuclear particles—are still lacking. In mechanics, thermodynamics, and electricity it is most efficient, from a pedagogical viewpoint, to state the established laws and then develop their many consequences in an orderly fashion. Such a presentation requires that the student make a separate study of the historical development of the field if he is to gain an insight into the ways in which our present ideas have evolved, and such an insight is indispensable if the student is some day to carry on investigations of his own on the frontiers of scientific knowledge.

Nuclear physics presents a most unusual opportunity to learn the factual matter and its historic setting with little sacrifice in efficiency. The reason is that the field is evolving rapidly, so one must know the background of our present tentative ideas in order to appreciate new theories and developments when they arise. For example, an excellent book published in 1955 stated flatly that the parity of an isolated system is always conserved, thereby leaving the student completely unprepared for the discovery, which soon followed, that parity is *not always* conserved.

In the present book the historical development is followed as much as possible, but whenever this approach seems too cumbersome, ideas are presented in whatever order appears conducive to an understanding of the present status of our concepts.

It has been my observation that beginning graduate students are usually appalled upon discovering their own experiments to be so much more difficult than they had been led to believe by the schematic drawings of equipment and the casual descriptions of procedures given in texts. It is hoped that the

v

occasional lengthy discussions of misinterpreted experiments as well as the detailed descriptions of certain pieces of apparatus will give the student a more realistic background for beginning his own investigations.

Educators are keenly aware of the high degree of compartmentalization of knowledge that is brought about by the methods of teaching presently employed in most colleges and universities, but find it difficult to alter the situation. As a partial solution to this unhappy state of affairs many of the problems in this book have been deliberately constructed to give the student an opportunity to utilize what he has learned in other subject areas.

An attempt has been made to confine the subject matter of this book to the *physics* of nuclear physics. Chapter 4, "Methods of Detecting Nuclear Radiations," was felt to be a necessary digression enabling the reader to understand the experimental techniques used by various investigators and thus to evaluate their conclusions. The complex engineering of charged particle accelerators, although not absolutely essential to an understanding of the experiments in which they are used, is a fascinating subject and one that the student may find is not covered in any other course. For this reason, Appendix A has been devoted to a discussion of these important devices. I have found, in several years of teaching, that although most students have had courses in particle mechanics, they are not as facile in the subject as they need to be to handle the many collision problems arising in nuclear physics. The lack is particularly evident when the collisions must be treated relativistically. For this reason, the subject of collision dynamics is treated in Chapter 10. This chapter could well be read at any time during the course, but has been placed just before the chapter on high energy physics because relativistic collisions are so much a part of the latter subject. Nuclear reactors are not a proper part of nuclear physics but certainly represent the most important commercial application of nuclear physics. The interested reader will find an introduction to the physics of nuclear reactors in Appendix B.

It is assumed that the reader is familiar with quantization concepts from previous courses in modern physics or atomic physics, but that he is not necessarily familiar with the formal methods of wave mechanics. With seeming perversity, relativistic wave mechanics is mentioned in Chapter 7, but only for the purpose of enabling the reader to understand the terms used in the literature of beta decay. For the curious reader, a brief wave-mechanical treatment of barrier penetration is given in Appendix C.

The advisability of using only mks units was seriously considered but finally decided against for two reasons. In the first place, the literature uses a variety of units, with preference given to such quantities as gauss-cm, and ergs per gauss. Secondly, the student at the level for which this text is intended should no longer find conversion of units an obstacle to his understanding. He should view such conversions as are necessary in the problem sections not merely as nuisances (which they admittedly are) but also as opportunities to improve his facility in this very necessary process.

A rather complete list of original papers is given at the end of each chapter. I have found great pleasure in reading these papers and would like to share this pleasure with the readers of this book, for it is inevitable that in the process of condensation necessary to keep the book to a reasonable size, much interesting detail has been omitted. Some of the papers, especially those of Rutherford, are models of scientific clarity. It is hoped that the student will find time to read at least a few of these original papers both for their historical interest and to obtain a better perspective of the developments they report.

My indebtedness extends to many people, but especially to the students who used a preliminary version of this book. A specific acknowledgment is due Albert E. Wilson, who carefully read the appendix on nuclear reactors and made a number of suggestions for the improvement of the presentation. Thanks are also due Professors Harry T. Easterday of Oregon State University, J. A. Jungerman of the University of California at Davis, and William W. Watson of Yale University for their helpful comments and suggestions in the manuscript stage. It would have been impossible to write this book without the sacrifices, the patience, and the understanding of my wife, Jane.

R.A.H.

Contents

7 BETA DECAY 210

8 ELECTROMAGNETIC RADIATION 255

9 NUCLEAR STRUCTURE 282

10 COLLISION DYNAMICS 322

THE BIRTH OF NUCLEAR PHYSICS

1-1 Early Ideas of Atomism

The idea of atomism—that all matter consists of minute, indivisible particles—began, as far as is known, with the Greeks. Leucippus is credited with founding the Greek School of Atomism at Abdera during the fifth century B.C. His pupil Democritus developed the atomic hypothesis further about 420 B.C., and their ideas were still further developed by Aristotle (384–322 B.C.).

William Higgins, on the basis of determinations of relative combining weights of elements forming chemical compounds, enunciated a theory of combination of definite numbers of atoms, such as two oxygen atoms with one carbon atom to form carbon dioxide. This theory, advanced in 1789, was generally ignored. Not until 1808–10, when John Dalton independently published an almost identical theory, did it receive any serious attention. The experimental fact of combination in definite proportions does not prove that

1

matter consists of atoms, but it is at least in agreement with such a hypothesis, whereas the atoms of Democritus were products of pure speculation, unsupported by experimental evidence of any kind.

In 1815 Prout hypothesized that all the elements were built up of hydrogen atoms. He was led to this conclusion by the fact that most of the known atomic weights were approximately integral multiples of the atomic weight of hydrogen. However, as atomic weights became known more accurately, nonintegral atomic weights such as that of chlorine, 35.5, thoroughly discredited the now famous "Prout's hypothesis."

1-2 Discovery of Radioactivity

Prior to 1895 it was known that some fluorescent bodies, after activation by sunlight, were capable of blackening photographic plates even when the plates were wrapped in black paper. When Roentgen discovered, in 1895, that x-rays could also blacken photographic plates wrapped in black paper, a number of investigators, among them Henri Becquerel, set out to search for some connection between the two phenomena. In February of 1896 several days of cloudy weather prevented Becquerel from exposing a particular fluorescent substance (a double sulfate of potassium and uranium) to the sun's rays. When he placed it near photographic plates wrapped in black paper (1)* he found that the plates were blackened just as they were by fluorescent materials that had been activated by sunlight. He found subsequently that exposure to sunlight had no effect on the phenomenon. It was also observed that the radiation that blackened the plates was capable of penetrating thin sheets of metal and other substances opaque to visible light. Becquerel soon discovered that the penetrating radiation was associated with the uranium, that it was independent of the state of chemical combination of the uranium, and that there was no connection between it and fluorescence. Somewhat later it was found that the radiations were capable of ionizing air and discharging an electroscope, properties which x-rays had also been found to possess.

G. C. Schmidt (24) and Marie Sklodowska Curie† independently observed in 1898 that thorium gave off radiations similar to those emitted by uranium.

Madame Curie (5) made tests on the activities‡ of various compounds of uranium and thorium and found that the activity was independent of the

* Numbers in parentheses refer to the bibliography at the end of the chapter.

† Madame Curie (5) also erroneously concluded that cerium, niobium, and tantalum were slightly radioactive. She observed a high "activity" from yellow phosphorus but correctly suspected that this was not true radioactivity since red phosphorus and phosphates showed no activity whatsoever.

‡ Activity refers to some quantity that measures the intensity of the radiation. In the case of ionization measurements, the rate of discharge of an electroscope is directly proportional to the activity. Activity and photographic blackening are not so simply

state of chemical combination, thus confirming and extending the results of Becquerel. She concluded from this fact that radioactivity, as the phenomenon has come to be called, was an *atomic* phenomenon. She also found that the activity of natural pitchblende [$U(UO_4)_2$] surpassed that of freshly prepared pure uranium oxide, and that natural chalcolite [$Cu(UO_2)_2(PO_4)_2 \cdot 8H_2O$] was more active than the same substance prepared in the laboratory. From this she concluded that there must be some extremely radioactive ingredient in natural pitchblende and chalcolite that was not present in pure uranium, and she set herself the task of isolating this unknown substance.

Working with her husband, Pierre Curie (6), Madame Curie found that a bismuth sulfide (Bi_2S_3) could be separated from pitchblende which showed an activity 400 times that of the same quantity of pure uranium, while ordinary bismuth sulfide showed no activity whatever. They assumed that this precipitate contained a new radioactive element, which they named polonium. In collaboration with G. Bemont (7) they found that a barium sulfate precipitate from pitchblende carried down a substance which could be converted to the chloride and then separated from barium chloride by fractional crystallization. The separated crystals darkened a photographic plate in half a minute, whereas several hours' exposure was required to obtain the same degree of blackening with pure uranium or thorium. It was assumed that yet another new element had been discovered, and it was given the name radium. The atomic weight of radium was found to be greater than that of barium.

1-3 Separation of Rays into α, β, and γ Components

After numerous erroneous results had been published by various investigators it was found by F. O. Giesel (9) and by S. Meyer and E. von Schweidler (10) that the radiations could be partially resolved by a magnetic field perpendicular to the beam of radiation. Rutherford (15) suggested the names α rays for the easily absorbed undeviated component, and β rays for the deviated rays. P. Villard (26) showed that the undeflected portion of the beam could be partially absorbed by thin layers of material but that the remainder of the beam was capable of penetrating thick layers of matter. He suggested the name γ rays for the penetrating component of the undeviated rays. He found that the deflected portion of the beam was negatively charged and behaved like a beam of electrons.

---

related, but the activity can be obtained from the blackening by the same methods used to interpret blackening in terms of light intensity. One such method makes use of the fact that blackening is (to a good approximation) a function of the product of intensity and exposure time, so that if it takes twice as long to produce a given amount of blackening with one source as it does with another source, one infers that the first source is only half as active as the second.

It was suggested by both Strutt (25) and Sir William Crookes (4) that since the β rays were negatively charged it was likely the α rays were positively charged. Rutherford (16) was led to the same conclusion by the following facts:

1. The decrease in intensity (as measured for example by the rate of discharge of an electroscope) is approximately proportional to the density of the material traversed by the rays. Since this was known to be true for β rays, it seemed reasonable to assume that α rays too were charged.

2. The decrease in intensity per unit thickness of traversed material increases with the thickness of material previously passed through. Since this is not characteristic of x-rays, it seemed doubtful that the rays could be electromagnetic waves.

3. Although the failure of the rays to be deflected by a magnetic field would seem to rule out the possibility of charged particles, he pointed out that q/M (the ratio of charge to mass) for H^+ ions is about 10^4 emu/gm, some thousand times smaller than the estimated value for electrons, so that if the "particles" were as massive or more massive than H^+ ions their deviation would be minute compared with that of an electron moving with the same velocity.

Rutherford (17) verified his theory by use of the apparatus shown schematically in Fig. 1-1. The radium salt was placed at the bottom of the lower box, which also contained the collimating plates. The top of the box was covered by an aluminum foil 0.00034 cm thick, and dry electrolytic hydrogen gas was forced slowly through this foil to prevent any radium emanation (a radioactive substance coming from radium, now called *radon*) from entering the ionization chamber above. A magnetic field applied perpendicular to the paper in the figure deflected the negatively charged radiation sideward, thus preventing it from passing through the collimating plates. Since a part of the undeviated radiation was known to be easily absorbed, it was advantageous to use a light gas such as hydrogen rather than air in the collimating chamber in order to reduce the absorption of the undeviated radiation. The smaller absorption by hydrogen in the ionization chamber was compensated for by making the chamber quite tall. The magnetic field was produced by the field magnet of an Edison dynamo whose pole faces were each 1.90×2.50 cm. The magnetic flux density at the pole faces was 8370 gauss and the fringing field was 2460 gauss near the bottom of the radium container.

The radium was placed 1.4 cm below the 25 collimator plates, each of which was 3.70 cm long by 0.7 cm wide. The results shown in Table 1-1 were obtained. These results prove that the α rays, which are not easily deflected by a magnetic field, are nevertheless deflected slightly by a *strong* magnetic field. The experiment, while presumably proving that the α rays consist of charged particles, gives no information as to whether they are positively or negatively charged.

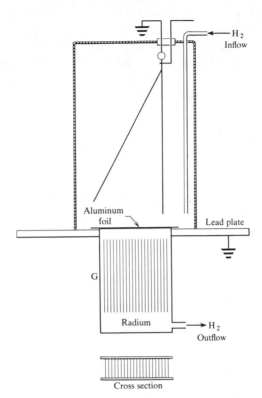

Fig. 1-1. Apparatus by means of which Rutherford proved that alpha rays are charged particles. A magnetic field perpendicular to the page was applied to the right of G.

Table 1-1

Condition	Electroscope discharge rate (volts/min)
Without magnetic field (residual magnetic field believed to deflect β rays)	8.33
With magnetic field	1.72
With magnetic field but radium covered with 0.01 cm thick mica plate to absorb α rays	0.93
Without magnetic field but radium covered with 0.01 cm thick mica plate to absorb α rays	0.92

Rutherford was able to determine the sign of the charge by a slight modification of the experiment. As shown in Fig. 1-2, a grid was placed over the collimating plates, thus partially blocking the openings between them.

The plates were spaced 1 mm apart and the unblocked openings were about 0.5 mm wide. When a magnetic field somewhat less than enough to deflect all the charged particles from the beam was applied in such a direction as to deflect positively charged particles toward the right, no noticeable change in ionization took place in the chamber. When a field of the same strength was

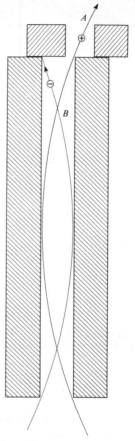

Fig. 1-2. Details of the modification made in the collimating plates of Fig. 1-1 to determine the sign of the charge borne by alpha particles. *A* is the trajectory of a positively charged particle with just sufficient energy to pass through the collimator under deflection produced by a given magnetic field. *B* is the trajectory of a negatively charged particle with the same magnitude of q/m and the same momentum as the positively charged particle whose trajectory is labeled *A*.

established in the opposite direction, that is, in a direction such as to cause positively charged particles to be deflected toward the left, the ionization was reduced to about one-fourth of its original value. This confirmed the suspicions of Crookes, Strutt, and Rutherford that the α rays were positively charged particles.

1-4 Determination of q/M for Alpha Particles

Rutherford next investigated electrostatic deflection of the α rays by insulating the collimating plates from each other and applying a potential difference of 600 volts between each pair of plates. This produced a 7%

decrease in ionization. Early attempts to go to higher potential differences simply resulted in sparking between the plates, but in a later experiment he was able to increase the effect to 45% when the potential was applied. The data on electrostatic deflection, plus the fact that the value of $B\rho$* (where B is magnetic flux density and ρ is the radius of curvature of the path) for complete deviation of the rays was 390,000 gauss-cm, enabled him to give rough values for the velocity and for the ratio of charge to mass of the α particles. For the velocity, he obtained 2.5×10^9 cm/sec and for q/M 6×10^3 emu/gm, values which he felt gave the correct orders of magnitude only.

In 1903 Th. des Coudres (8), confirming similar work done by Becquerel (2) in air, observed the magnetic deflection of α rays by allowing the radiation from radium to pass through a slit covered by an aluminum foil 0.004 mm thick into an evacuated chamber, at one end of which was placed a photographic plate. The upper part of the plate, as shown in Fig. 1-3, was covered

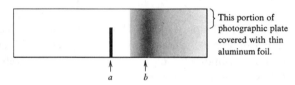

Fig. 1-3. Representation of des Coudres' photographic plate. In the absence of a magnetic field the collimated beam of radium radiations would be normal to the page and would strike at a. The entire apparatus was evacuated so that the radiations would not be absorbed by the air. A weak magnetic field directed from the upper edge toward the lower edge of the photographic plate deflected a part of the radiations to region b. That part of the *undeflected* radiation which produced photographic blackening was completely absorbed by the thin aluminum foil while the deflected beta radiation was not appreciably absorbed by the foil. The broad band at b requires that the beta rays vary in mass, charge, velocity, or some combination of these.

by an aluminum foil 0.01 mm thick. The undeviated α rays made a dark line on the uncovered part of the photographic plate, but failed to penetrate the aluminum foil. The β rays, on the other hand, produced nearly as much blackening under the foil as elsewhere. When des Coudres heard of Rutherford's work, he repeated his experiment with stronger magnetic fields. Figure 1-4 depicts the results he obtained when he first applied a 76-gauss field to deflect the β rays and then applied a 2500-gauss field to deflect the α rays. An interesting feature of the plate he obtained is that the deflected α rays form a sharp

---

* This quantity is called the "magnetic rigidity" of the particle and is often given as $H\rho$ in the literature.

line, while the β rays form a spectrum, indicating either variation in velocities or variation in values of q/M for the latter particles. He also made measurements on the electrostatic deflection of the α rays, using the apparatus depicted

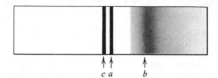

Fig. 1-4. Representation of a second photographic plate obtained by des Coudres. The line at *a* is caused by radiation undeflected by a 76-gauss magnetic field which deflected beta rays to *b*. When the magnetic field was increased to 2500 gauss, line *c* was formed. This shows that the alpha rays striking at *c* were positively charged. The beta rays were deflected beyond the right end of the photographic plate by the 2500-gauss field.

schematically in Fig. 1-5. The plates I and II acted both as the electrodes and as a collimator. From these measurements of magnetic and electrostatic deflection des Coudres obtained 1.65×10^9 cm/sec for the velocity of an α particle, and 6.4×10^0 emu/gm for q/M.

Rutherford and his coworkers (18, 19, 20) made several determinations of v and of q/M for α rays, the one published in 1914 being, perhaps, the most

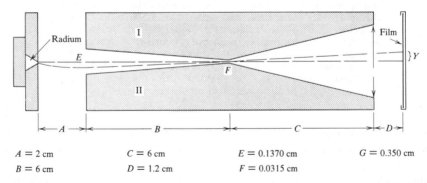

$A = 2$ cm	$C = 6$ cm	$E = 0.1370$ cm	$G = 0.350$ cm
$B = 6$ cm	$D = 1.2$ cm	$F = 0.0315$ cm	

Fig. 1-5. Schematic diagram of the apparatus used by des Coudres for electrostatic deflection of alpha rays.

easily understood. Using an apparatus in principle like that of Fig. 1-6, in which the magnetic field is perpendicular to the paper in the figure, the particles were first deflected toward the right; the magnetic field was then reversed and the particles deflected toward the left. The distance between the two resulting spots on the photographic plate was measured and used to compute the quantity

$$\frac{Mv_0}{q/c} = B\rho, \tag{1-1}$$

where M = the mass of the particle,

$\quad v_0$ = its initial velocity,

$\quad q/c$ = its charge in emu,

$\quad q$ = its charge in esu,

$\quad c$ = a conversion factor numerically equal to the velocity of light in vacuo in cm/sec,

$\quad B$ = the magnetic flux density in gauss,

$\quad \rho$ = the radius of curvature of the trajectory followed by the particle in cm.

A schematic diagram of the apparatus they used for electrostatic deflection

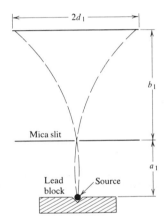

Fig. 1-6. Schematic diagram of Rutherford's magnetic deflection apparatus.

of the α particles is shown in Fig. 1-7. For this arrangement, when d_2 is small compared with b_2,

$$\frac{Mv_0^2}{q/c} = 10^8 E \frac{a_2 b_2}{2d_2}, \tag{1-2}$$

where $10^8 E$ = the electric field intensity between the deflecting plates in abvolts/cm,

$\quad E$ = the electric field intensity in volts/cm,

$\quad a_2, b_2, d_2$ are in cm.

Dividing Eq. (1-2) by Eq. (1-1), one obtains the initial velocity of the particle,

$$v_0 = \frac{10^8 E a_2 b_2}{2B\rho d_2}, \tag{1-3}$$

and substituting (1-3) back into (1-1),

$$\frac{q/c}{M} = \frac{10^8 E a_2 b_2}{2 B^2 \rho^2 d_2}.$$ (1-4)

In this way they found that for α particles from radium C,

$$v_0 = 1.922 \times 10^9 \text{ cm/sec},$$

$$\frac{q/c}{M} = 4.82 \times 10^3 \text{ emu/gm}.$$

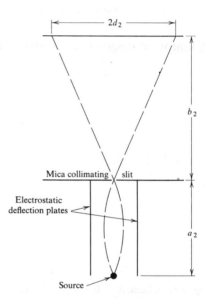

Fig. 1-7. Arrangement similar to one used by Rutherford for electrostatic deflection of alpha particles.

1-5 Radioactive Decay

In 1900, Crookes (3) found that he could precipitate a carbonate free of uranium from a uranium solution, and that its activity was many times that of uranium. Moreover, the residual uranium had lost its power to blacken a photographic plate. Rutherford and Soddy (23) carried out similar separations from solutions of both uranium and thorium salts. They called the separated substances uranium X and thorium X, respectively. The activities of these substances as well as the residual uranium and thorium are shown as functions of the elapsed time in Figs. 1-8 and 1-9. The activities shown are the β activities, as it is the β rays that are most effective in blackening photographic plates; the α rays produce a negligible amount of blackening by comparison. It will be noticed that the activities of uranium X and thorium X

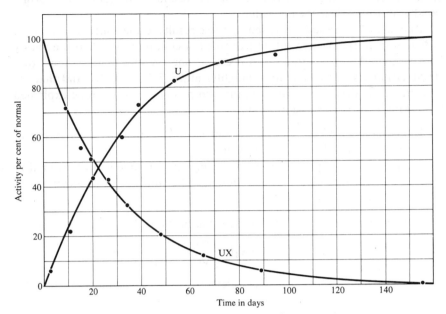

Fig. 1-8. Uranium X decay curve and uranium build-up curve.

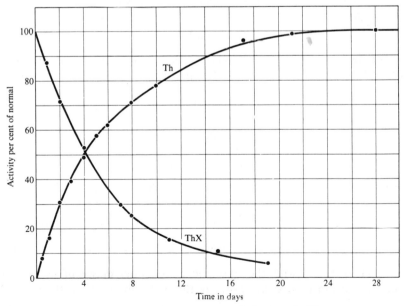

Fig. 1-9. Thorium X decay curve and thorium build-up curve.

soon die away, while the activities of the residual uranium and thorium rapidly return to their former values.

Rutherford and Soddy were led by these results to the conclusion that the radiation from radioactive substances was not continuous, as had previously been thought, but was a random process. If one assumes that a parent atom (U or Th) decays, gives rise to a daughter atom (UX or ThX), and that the daughter atom decays in turn, then the two pairs of curves can be explained by making two further assumptions:

1. The activity of the parent element is proportional to the number of parent atoms decaying in unit time.
2. The number of parent atoms decaying per unit time is proportional to the number of parent atoms present. The constant of proportionality is called the *decay constant*.

These assumptions may be expressed mathematically as

$$\Phi = k_1\left(-\frac{dN}{dt}\right),\qquad(1\text{-}5)$$

where Φ is the activity of the parent element, k_1 is a constant, N is the total number of parent atoms present, and t is the time, and

$$-\frac{dN}{dt} = \lambda N,\qquad(1\text{-}6)$$

where λ is the decay constant for the element under consideration. It follows at once* that

$$\Phi = (k_1\lambda)N,\qquad(1\text{-}7)$$

and since the activity is proportional to the number of parent atoms, it suffices to find how N varies with t. From (1-6),

$$\frac{dN}{N} = -\lambda\,dt.$$

Integrating this expression, one obtains

$$\ln N = -\lambda t + C.\qquad(1\text{-}8)$$

When $t = 0$, $\ln N = \ln N_0 = C$, and (1-8) becomes

$$\ln\left(\frac{N}{N_0}\right) = -\lambda t$$

or
$$N = N_0 e^{-\lambda t}.\qquad(1\text{-}9)$$

Equation (1-9) agrees with the observed exponential decay of activity of uranium X and thorium X, but how are the build-up curves of the residual

---

* The activity due to any daughter atoms present is not included here in Φ.

uranium and thorium to be explained? Evidently the observed (β) activity of normal uranium is not to be traced in any appreciable degree to the uranium itself, for removal of uranium X eliminates its activity. This indicates that the observed activity is due to uranium X, which is somehow formed from or by the uranium.

The rate of *increase* in the number of daughter atoms due to decay of parent atoms is $N_p\lambda_p$, while the rate of *decrease* in the number of daughter atoms due to their decay (to "granddaughter" atoms) is $N_d\lambda_d$, where the subscripts p and d refer respectively to parent and daughter atoms. From these considerations we can write down the differential equation

$$\frac{dN_d}{dt} = -N_d\lambda_d + N_p\lambda_p = -N_d\lambda_d + \lambda_p N_{p0}e^{-\lambda_p t} \tag{1-10}$$

or

$$\frac{dN_d}{dt} + N_d\lambda_d = \lambda_p N_{p0}e^{-\lambda_p t}. \tag{1-11}$$

If we now multiply through by $e^{\lambda_d t}$, the left side of (1-11) becomes a perfect differential. Thus

$$e^{\lambda_d t}\frac{dN_d}{dt} + e^{\lambda_d t}N_d\lambda_d = \frac{d}{dt}(N_d e^{\lambda_d t}) = N_{p0}\lambda_p e^{(\lambda_d - \lambda_p)t}. \tag{1-12}$$

On the parent atom build-up curve, $N_d - 0$ at time $t = 0$, if, as has been assumed, the activity is entirely due to daughter atoms. Integration of (1-12) then yields, with the initial condition $N_d = 0$ at $t = 0$,

$$N_d e^{\lambda_d t} = \frac{N_{p0}\lambda_p}{\lambda_d - \lambda_p}[e^{(\lambda_d - \lambda_p)t} - 1] \tag{1-13}$$

or

$$N_d = \frac{N_{p0}\lambda_p}{\lambda_d - \lambda_p}(e^{-\lambda_p t} - e^{-\lambda_d t}). \tag{1-14}$$

For sufficiently small values of $\lambda_p t$ the quantity $e^{-\lambda_p t} \cong 1$, so that, where $\lambda_d \gg \lambda_p$, one may write

$$N_d \cong \left(\frac{\lambda_p N_{p0}}{\lambda_d}\right)(1 - e^{-\lambda_d t}), \tag{1-15}$$

which is exactly the form of equation required to explain the observed build-up curves for uranium and thorium beta activities. On the other hand, when t is large, $e^{-\lambda_d t}$ rapidly approaches zero if $\lambda_d \gg \lambda_p$, and (1-14) becomes

$$N_d \cong \frac{\lambda_p N_{p0}}{\lambda_d}e^{-\lambda_p t} = \frac{\lambda_p}{\lambda_d}N_p \tag{1-16}$$

or

$$\lambda_d N_d = \lambda_p N_p, \tag{1-17}$$

a result which could have been obtained directly from (1-10) by setting dN_d/dt equal to zero. Equation (1-17) states that after a long interval the rate of growth of daughter atoms is just equal to their rate of decay and their number remains substantially constant, decreasing slowly as the number of parent atoms slowly decreases. Such a state is known as "secular equilibrium," and is to be distinguished, for example, from chemical equilibrium, which has to do with reversible processes.

The "half-life period" of an element, which is usually called simply its "half-life," does *not* give one-half the lifetime of an atom, but rather the length of time required for one-half of a given (large) number of atoms to decay. Thus, if $t_{1/2}$ is the half-life of the element,

$$\frac{N_0}{2} = N_0 e^{-\lambda t_{1/2}}, \tag{1-18}$$

from which

$$t_{1/2} = \frac{\ln 2}{\lambda} = \frac{0.693}{\lambda}. \tag{1-19}$$

If one expresses the condition for secular equilibrium in terms of half-lives rather than decay constants, then

$$\frac{N_d}{N_p} = \frac{t_{d1/2}}{t_{p1/2}}. \tag{1-20}$$

The "mean lifetime," t_a, of an atom of a radioactive element may be found by adding the lifetimes of all atoms and dividing by the total number of atoms. In equation form,

$$t_a = \frac{\int_{N_0}^{0} t(-dN)}{N_0} = \frac{1}{N_0} \int_0^\infty t\left(\frac{-dN}{dt}\right) dt$$

$$= \frac{1}{N_0} \int_0^\infty t\lambda N_0 e^{-\lambda t} \, dt,$$

$$t_a = \frac{1}{\lambda}. \tag{1-21}$$

It is seen that the mean lifetime* of an atom is not the same as the half-life of an element, but instead is equal to the reciprocal of the decay constant of the element.

The relationship between $t_{1/2}$ and t_a is shown graphically in Fig. 1-10.

When the natural logarithm of the activity of a substance is plotted against time it is sometimes found that a curve rather than a straight line results, as shown in Fig. 1-11. This indicates that the substance consists of a mixture of radioactive species. If the curve has a straight portion for large values of t,

---

* The atoms at the time that we arbitrarily take as $t = 0$ may already be incredibly ancient, but this fact does not enter into our computation. The term "mean lifetime" as used here means the average lifetime of all atoms measured from any arbitrary time. If the radioactive atoms were all created at time $t = 0$ the result would not differ from that derived above. The reason lies in the assumption (Assumption 2 and Eq. 1-6) that the probability that an atom that exists now will decay in a time t is not influenced by its past history.

the slope* of this straight portion is the negative of the decay constant of the long half-life component, and by the following process it is possible to determine the half-lives of the individual species.

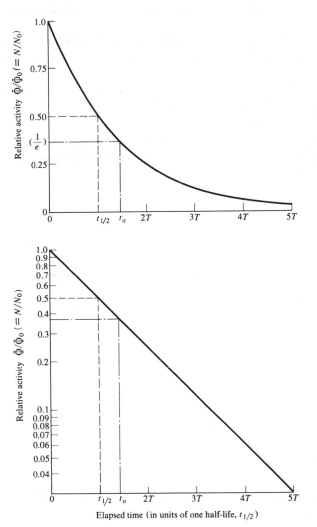

Fig. 1-10. Radioactive decay curves, showing relative activity as a function of elapsed time. The upper curve is plotted on linear coordinates while the lower is plotted on semi-log paper. Note that in each period of time equal to the half-life the activity decreases to half of what it was at the beginning of that period.

* Logarithms to base ten rather than natural logs may be used if desired. In this case the decay constant will be the negative of 2.3 times the slope.

1. Extrapolate the straight line corresponding to the long half-life species back to $t = 0$.
2. Take the difference between the total activity and that due to the long half-life component for several values of t.
3. Plot the difference found from step 2 on a semi-logarithmic graph like the original plot.
4. If the resulting plot has a straight portion for the larger values of t, the slope is the negative of the decay constant of the component having the second longest half-life.
5. If the graph plotted in step 3 still has a curved portion for small t, repeat steps 2, 3, and 4 to determine the decay constant of the third longest half-life component, etc.

It should be noted that the use of this method is not always feasible. If the half-lives of the components are not markedly different, the log activity

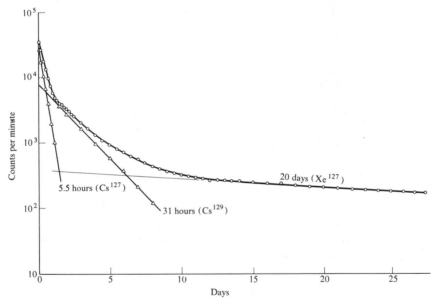

Fig. 1-11. Decay curve of a mixture of radioactive substances having different half-lives, showing how the half-life of each is determined. [From R. W. Fink, F. L. Reynolds, and D. H. Templeton, *Phys. Rev.*, **77**, 614 (1950)].

vs. time plot will have no straight portion for any reasonable value of t. If the initial activity of the short half-life component is not comparable with or greater than that of the longer half-life component, then one must take small differences between large numbers (step 2), and the experimental errors will be so large that the half-life of the component having the smaller half-life cannot be determined with sufficient accuracy to be useful.

1-6 Identification of α Particle with He

It was well known prior to 1900 that helium is always present in radio-active minerals, and at that time it had never been found elsewhere on earth. It had even been suggested (22) that He might be the inert end product of a series of radioactive disintegrations. Canal ray experiments had shown the q/M for H^+ ions was approximately 10,000 emu/gm, while deflection experiments had shown that q/M for α particles was about 6000 emu/gm. This suggested that α particles might be either H_2^+ ions or He^{++} ions, either of which would have q/M values of about 5000 emu/gm.

In 1903 Ramsay and Soddy (11) obtained the spectrum of helium from a gas (which also contained radium emanation) released by a solution of 30 mg of radium bromide in water. They repeated the experiment, but this time passed the gas through a liquid air-cooled trap to condense out carbon dioxide and radium emanation, and obtained a nearly complete spectrum of helium. Later (12), using 50 mg of radium bromide, they condensed the radium emanation in a liquid air trap and then flushed out with oxygen all other gases that might be present. When the liquid air was removed from the trap so that the radium emanation could evaporate, a spectrum was obtained which contained no helium lines but did contain some new lines which were believed to be those of the emanation. After four days, however, the He spectrum reappeared, indicating that helium comes from radium emanation but differs from the emanation. Three facts bear out this conclusion:

1. Helium is not radioactive, but the emanation is.
2. The spectrum of helium differs from that of the emanation.
3. The molecular weight of emanation (determined from diffusion experiments) is large, but that of helium is small.

Rutherford (13, 14) summed up as follows the arguments in favor of the view that helium coming from radioactive disintegration is the α radiation rather than the end product of a series of radioactive disintegrations:

1. The successive ejection of several α particles would still leave an element of large atomic weight.
2. Helium appears in quantity before appreciable amounts of radium can completely decay. Long-lived links in the radioactive decay chain (as Rutherford pictured it) would prevent any large quantity of end product from being formed, whereas previous disintegrations would supply ample α particles.
3. The value of q/M for an α particle is about right for an He^{++} ion.

Direct proof of the identity of helium and α particles came in 1909 in an experiment performed by Rutherford and ·Royds (21). They placed a large amount of radium emanation in a thin-walled glass tube which had been previously tested and found impermeable to helium. The thin-walled tube was surrounded by a heavy-walled glass tube and the space between the two evacuated. A means was provided for compressing any gas collected between the two glass tubes into a capillary discharge tube. After two days the yellow line of helium could be seen, and after six days the entire spectrum was visible.

Since it had been found previously that the value of q/M for α particles is about one-half that of H^+ ions, the proof that α particles are He ions shows that the ions are doubly charged. This result was in accord with Rutherford's view that a heavy element, such as uranium, expels an α particle and becomes a slightly lighter element with properties different from those of the original element.

PROBLEMS

1-1 Prove, with reference to Fig. 1-6, that the radius of curvature of the trajectory is given by

$$\rho = \frac{\sqrt{(b_1^2 + d_1^2)[(a_1 + b_1)^2 + d_1^2]}}{2d_1}.$$

1-2 Assuming that α particles bear two positive electronic charges, what is the energy in ergs of an α particle from RaC? (Use Rutherford's values $v = 1.922 \times 10^9$ cm/sec, $q/M = 4.82 \times 10^3$ emu/gm.)

[*Ans.* 1.23×10^{-5} erg.]

1-3 Prove Eq. (1-2) for electrostatic deflection of a charged particle in the apparatus sketched in Fig. 1-7.

1-4 Make a plot of the ratio of the number of daughter atoms to the original number of parent atoms as a function of time if the half-life of the parent atoms is five days and the half life of the daughter atoms is ten days. When does true secular equilibrium occur in this case?

1-5 Derive an expression for the number of "granddaughter" atoms as a function of time if the granddaughter atoms are also radioactive. Let the original number of daughter and granddaughter atoms be zero.

1-6 The activity of a radioactive material was measured with the results given in the table below. How many radioactive species are present, and what is the half-life of each?

Elapsed time	Activity	Elapsed time	Activity
0	9.00	4 hr	2.98
30 min	4.90	24 hr	2.89
60 min	3.57	48 hr	2.78
90 min	3.18	96 hr	2.59
2 hr	3.05	192 hr	2.26

[*Ans.* $T_1 = 19.5$ days, $T_2 = 18$ min.]

1-7 A certain radionuclide may decay either by α or by β emission, and a decay constant may be assigned to each process. Only the β activity was measured, with the results tabulated below. How long will it take for half of a given number of atoms to decay, taking account of those which decay both by α and β emission?

β Activity	Elapsed time		β Activity	Elapsed time
1000	0 min		398	4 min
795	1 min		251	6 min
632	2 min		159	8 min

[*Ans.* 3.01 min.]

1-8 The specific activity of U^{235} has been found to be 4774 ± 72 disintegrations per minute per milligram. [E. H. Fleming, Jr., A. Ghiorso, and B. B. Cunningham, *Phys. Rev.*, **82**, 967 (1951).] What is the half-life of U^{235} as determined from this measurement?   [*Ans.* $(7.07 \pm 0.11) \times 10^8$ years.]

REFERENCES

1. Becquerel, H., *Compt. Rend.*, **122**, 501, 689 *et seq.* (1896).

2. Becquerel, H., *Compt. Rend.*, **136**, 199 (1903).

3. Crookes, W., *Proc. Roy. Soc.*, **66**, 409 (1900).

4. Crookes, W., *Proc. Roy. Soc.*, **69**, 413 (1902).

5. Curic, M., *Compt. Rend.*, **126**, 1101 (1898).

6. Curie, P., and Curie, M., *Compt. Rend.*, **127**, 175 (1898).

7. Curie, P., Curie, M., and Bemont, G., *Compt. Rend.*, **127**, 1215 (1898).

8. des Coudres, Th., *Physik. Z.*, **4**, 483 (1903).

9. Giesel, F., *Wiedemann's Annalen der Physik und Chemie*, **69**, 834 (1899).

10. Meyer, S., and von Schweidler, E. R., *Physik. Z.*, **1**, 90 (1899).

11. Ramsay, W., and Soddy, F., *Nature*, **68**, 246 (1903).

12. Ramsay, W., and Soddy, F., *Proc. Roy. Soc.*, **72**, 204 (1903).

13. Rutherford, E., *Radioactivity* (2d ed.; Cambridge: Cambridge University Press, 1905).

14. Rutherford, E., *Nature*, **65**, 366 (1903).

15. Rutherford, E., *Phil. Mag.*, **47**, 109 (1899).

16. Rutherford, E., *Phil. Mag.*, **5**, 95 (1903).

17. Rutherford, E., *Phil. Mag.*, **5**, 177 (1903).

18. Rutherford, E., *Phil. Mag.*, **12**, 348 (1906).

19. Rutherford, E., and Hahn, O., *Phil. Mag.*, **12**, 371 (1906).

20. Rutherford, E., and Robinson, H., *Phil. Mag.*, **28**, 552 (1914).

21. Rutherford, E., and Royds, T., *Phil. Mag.*, **17**, 281 (1909).

22. Rutherford, E., and Soddy, F., *Phil. Mag.*, **4**, 569 (1902).

23. Rutherford, E., and Soddy, F., *Phil. Mag.*, **5**, 445, 576 (1903).

24. Schmidt, G. C., *Wiedemann's Annalen der Physik und Chemie*, **65**, 141 (1898).

25. Strutt, R. J., *Trans. Roy. Soc.*, **196**, 507 (1901).

26. Villard, P., *Compt. Rend.*, **130**, 1178 (1900).

2

THE NUCLEAR ATOM

2-1 The Rutherford Model of the Atom

J. J. Thomson conceived of the atom as consisting of electrons embedded in a spherical matrix of positive charge. He was able to demonstrate that the electrons could be so placed as to be in stable static equilibrium. Dynamic theories of atomic construction had been considered, but the known fact that acceleration of a charged particle gives rise to electromagnetic radiation made such theories untenable. Atoms are not observed to radiate energy continuously, and if they did, what was to supply the energy radiated away? The Thomson model of the atom, being a static model, did not encounter this difficulty and therefore seemed a more reasonable one.

In 1909, the same year that the identity of α particles with He^{++} ions was completely established, Geiger and Marsden (9) found that when α particles were passed through gold foil 0.00004 cm thick, about 1 in 8000 was deflected through an angle greater than 90°. This result is not consistent with the Thomson model, as will be shown in the following discussion.

One can get an approximate figure for the volume occupied by a single atom in a solid piece of gold by assuming that the solid is built by stacking up gold atoms like blocks. Since gold has an atomic weight of 197.2 and a specific gravity of 19.32 near room temperature, the volume of one of the cubical blocks is

$$V = \frac{197.2 \ (\text{gm/GAW})^*}{19.32 \ (\text{gm/cm}^3) \times 6.02 \times 10^{23} \ (\text{atoms/GAW})}$$

$$= 17 \times 10^{-24} \ \text{cm}^3.$$

The radius of a spherical gold atom that would just fit into this cube is evidently

$$r = \tfrac{1}{2}(17 \times 10^{-24})^{1/3} = 1.28 \times 10^{-8} \ \text{cm}.$$

Now the force that a Thomson atom of this size would exert on an α particle outside of it would be essentially zero since the atom is electrically neutral. Only if the α particle passed through the interior of the atom would it encounter an appreciable electrical field. But even if one ignores the electrons and considers only the positive charge of the atom, the electric fields are still too small to cause any appreciable deflection of the α particle, because the electric field would have its maximum value at the surface of the atom and would decrease linearly to zero at the center of the atom. In other words the maximum electrical deflection force experienced by an α particle is roughly that which it would experience if it came within 10^{-8} cm of a point charge of the same magnitude as the total positive charge in a gold nucleus. Now, as will be seen in what follows, this force is several thousand times too small to deflect an α particle through more than 90°. Since the α particles could not be deflected through the observed angle by a single encounter, the only other explanation consistent with the Thomson atom is that they were scattered successively through small angles until the total deflection became large. Rutherford was able to show rather easily that the probability of such an event, since the total probability is the *product* of the probabilities of each particular interaction, is wholly negligible.

Rutherford (23) then revived the idea of a nuclear atom, that is, one in which the charge of one sign is concentrated at the center, or nucleus, of the atom. He assumed that the positive charge and most of the mass of the atom are concentrated in a sphere whose radius is not more than 3×10^{-12} cm, and that the electrons are disposed about the nucleus at distances of the order of 10^{-8} cm from it. Gaseous conduction experiments had already shown that the positively charged ions were relatively massive, while the negatively charged ions were usually electrons, so that it was reasonable to

* GAW = gram-atomic weight.

associate the mass of the atom with the positive charge. Like the Thomson atom, this atom would have no appreciable electric field outside the atom, but, quite unlike the Thomson atom, it would have a very intense field close to the nucleus. Because of the very small mass of the electron, α particles would not be scattered appreciably by encounters with electrons, so that one may treat the atom as a point charge of positive electricity in calculating the large-angle scattering of α particles.

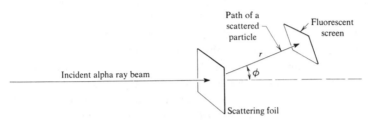

Fig. 2-1. Schematic diagram of Rutherford scattering experiment. The thin scattering foil was normal to the incident alpha-particle beam, while the fluorescent screen was normal to *r*. Each alpha particle that was scattered through an angle near φ produced a scintillation on the fluorescent screen. Dark-adapted observers counted the number of scintillations produced in a given time interval.

Rutherford was able to show* that if a narrow pencil of α particles were incident on a thin scattering foil, then the number of particles, $N_\alpha \, dP/dS$, which would be scattered through an angle $\phi \pm \delta\phi$ and strike unit area of a fluorescent screen oriented perpendicular to the path of the deflected particles at a distance *r* from the scattering point on the foil is given by

$$N_\alpha \frac{dP}{dS} = \frac{N_\alpha N_a b q_1^2 q_2^2}{4M^2 v_0^4 r^2 \sin^4 \phi/2},$$ (2-1)

where N_α is the number of α particles striking the scattering foil, dP/dS is the probability, per unit area of the fluorescent screen, that a single α particle be scattered through some angle between $\phi - \delta\phi$ and $\phi + \delta\phi$ and strike the screen, N_a is the number of scattering (foil) atoms per unit volume, *b* is the thickness of the scattering foil, q_1 is the charge on the nucleus, q_2 is the charge on the α particle, *M* is the mass of the α particle, and v_0 is the initial velocity of the α particle.

Geiger and Marsden (10) reported in 1913 on a new set of experiments in which α particles were scattered by thin foils. The experiments were performed for the specific purpose of testing Rutherford's theory. They were able to verify three of the predictions of Eq. (2-1):

* See Appendix D.

(a) $\qquad N_\alpha \dfrac{dP}{dS}$ is proportional to $\dfrac{1}{\sin^4 \phi/2}$,

(b) $\qquad N_\alpha \dfrac{dP}{dS}$ is proportional to the foil thickness, b,

(c) $\qquad N_\alpha \dfrac{dP}{dS}$ is proportional to $\dfrac{1}{v_0^4}$.

They could not check directly the dependence on q_1, since the nuclear charge was not known. It was believed at that time to be roughly proportional to the atomic weight, and they showed that $N_\alpha\, dP/dS$ is approximately proportional to the square of the atomic weight, which would be consistent with proportionality to q_1^2. From the fraction of α particles scattered out of the beam and onto a 1-mm² screen at 45° by a thin gold foil, they deduced that the numerical magnitude of the nuclear charge of gold (measured in units of the charge of an electron) must be about half of the numerical magnitude of its atomic weight.

2-2 Bohr's Modification of Rutherford's Model

Niels Bohr (3) was able to explain the observed spectrum of hydrogen by utilizing the Rutherford nuclear atom model with the following assumptions:

1. The electron describes a circular orbit about the nucleus, obeying the classical laws of mechanics and electrostatics but not obeying the classical law of electromagnetic radiation from an accelerated charged particle.

2. Only certain discrete orbits are allowed, which are determined by the quantization of angular momentum condition. This is the requirement that the line integral of the angular momentum about the orbit must be an integer times Planck's constant, or in equation form

$$\int p_\phi \, d\phi = nh, \qquad (2\text{-}2)$$

where p_ϕ is the orbital angular momentum of the electron and must be a constant in a radial force field, ϕ is the angular coordinate of the electron, n is an integer, and h is Planck's constant. Thus

$$p_\phi = \frac{nh}{2\pi} = n\hbar \qquad (2\text{-}3)$$

where $\qquad\qquad\qquad\qquad \hbar \equiv h/2\pi.$

3. Transition of the electron from a higher energy orbit to an orbit of lower energy gives up energy in the form of a photon according to the law of conservation of energy. Thus

$$hv = W_{n_2} - W_{n_1}, \tag{2-4}$$

where v is the frequency of the radiation associated with the photon, W_{n_2} is the energy of the electron in a higher energy orbit, and W_{n_1} is the energy of the electron in a lower energy orbit.

The success of this theory firmly established the nuclear atom model and also demonstrated the correctness of the assumption made by Rutherford, but not proved by his experiments, that the nucleus was positively charged. Although the electron-nucleus system must rotate about its common center of mass, the nucleus is so much more massive than the electron that only a very small error results if the nucleus is considered fixed. If this approximation is made, the mass of the nucleus does not enter the equations of motion at all and it is seen that the *mass* of the nucleus has an almost negligible effect on the distribution of its orbital electrons. On the other hand, the electrostatic attraction that the nucleus exerts on an orbital electron is directly proportional to the charge on the nucleus, so that the number of positive electronic charges on the nucleus is of extreme importance.

In the same year that the Bohr hypothesis of atomic structure was advanced, Moseley (18) found a remarkable regularity in the K lines of the x-ray spectra of various elements, as shown in Fig. 2-2. This regularity he

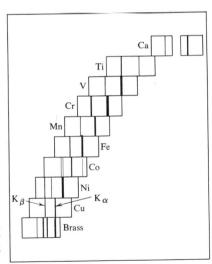

Fig. 2-2. The K_α and K_β x-ray spectrum lines of various elements obtained by Moseley. This is a drawing of a photograph appearing in *Phil. Mag.*, **26**, 1024 (1913).

showed to be consistent with the idea that the K spectrum lines are excited when the innermost electrons of atoms have been removed, since he found that for the K lines

$$\nu = 0.248 \times 10^{16}(Z - 1)^2, \tag{2-5}$$

where Z is an integer that usually denoted the position of the element in the periodic series at that time. If one assumes that there are two K electrons, then the removal of one will leave a nucleus with, say, Z positive electronic charges on it surrounded by one electron in the K shell. On the average, the negative charge on the electron will reduce the effective charge on the nucleus by about one (electronic charge unit) for points beyond the K orbit. If one uses the Bohr equation for a hydrogenlike atom with an effective nuclear charge of $(Z - 1)$, the frequency of a photon emitted when an electron falls from the L shell to the vacant site in the K shell is given by

$$\nu_B = 0.246 \times 10^{16}(Z - 1)^2. \tag{2-6}$$

The remarkable agreement between the observed and the approximate calculated values of ν lends great weight to the idea that Z, which is called the atomic number of the element, not only is the number of positive electronic charges on the nucleus but also determines the position of the element in the periodic system.

2-3 Isotopes

In 1886 Crookes advanced the idea that all atoms must have integral atomic weights and that those elements which appeared to have nonintegral atomic weights were, in reality, mixtures. Thus he conceived of chlorine (at. wt 35.46) as a mixture of atoms having atomic weights of 34, 35, and 36 in proper proportion to give the observed average atomic weight.

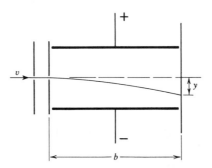

Fig. 2-3. Schematic diagram of the electrostatic deflection component of Thomson's apparatus. A magnetic field parallel to the electric field produced a deflection at right angles to the page (Fig. 2-4) and thus produced the parabolic traces on the photographic plate shown in Fig. 2-5.

J. J. Thomson (26, 27) later made an extensive study of canal rays, the positive ions formed when electricity is discharged through a gas. One experimental arrangement he used allowed a collimated beam of positive ions to pass through a region in which parallel electric and magnetic fields were imposed. For simplicity, consider the photographic plate to be at the end of the accelerating electric and magnetic fields, as shown in Fig. 2-3. Let the collimated beam of positive ions move along the x-axis from left to right. An ion entering the field will be accelerated by the electric field according to the equation

$$\ddot{y} = Eq/M, \tag{2-7}$$

where E is the electric field intensity between the plates and q/M is the charge-to-mass ratio of the ion. Integrating, this becomes

$$\dot{y} = (Eq/M) \cdot t + \dot{y}_0,$$

but since $\dot{y}_0 = 0$,

$$\dot{y} = (Eq/M) \cdot t. \tag{2-8}$$

A second integration gives

$$y = \frac{Eq}{M} \cdot \frac{t^2}{2} + y_0,$$

and if y_0 be taken as zero,

$$y = \frac{Eq}{M} \cdot \frac{t^2}{2}. \tag{2-9}$$

But since the ion also travels a distance b in the x-direction in the time t at a velocity v, one may write

$$t = \frac{b}{v} \tag{2-10}$$

and

$$y = \frac{Eqb^2}{M \cdot 2v^2}. \tag{2-11}$$

If a magnetic field of intensity B is parallel to the electric field, then a positive ion will be deflected upward along a curved path (Fig. 2-4) whose radius of curvature, ρ, can be found from the relation*

$$\frac{Bqv}{c} = \frac{Mv^2}{\rho}$$

or

$$\frac{Bq}{cM} = \frac{v}{\rho}. \tag{2-12}$$

---

* The introduction of c ($= 3 \times 10^{10}$) into this equation assumes that E is to be expressed in electrostatic units, while B is in gauss, and q is in esu.

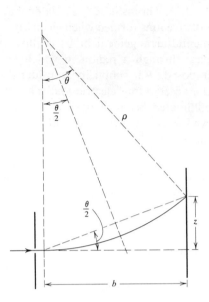

Fig. 2-4. Schematic diagram of magnetic deflection of a charged particle in Thomson's apparatus.

Let z be the upward deflection of the ion. Then

$$z = b \tan \frac{\theta}{2} \cong b \tan \frac{b}{2\rho} \cong \frac{b^2}{2\rho} \qquad (2\text{-}13)$$

if the deflection is small, and from (2-12),

$$z = \frac{Bqb^2}{2cMv}. \qquad (2\text{-}14)$$

Elimination of v between (2-11) and (2-14) yields the relation

$$z^2 = \frac{B^2b^2(q/M)}{2Ec^2}\, y. \qquad (2\text{-}15)$$

Thus the locus of all ions having the same value of q/M but varying velocities is a parabola on the photographic plate. Figure 2-5 shows such a set of parabolas obtained by Thomson for atmospheric neon, and it will be noticed that in addition to the main neon parabola corresponding to an atomic weight of 20 there is a faint subsidiary parabola corresponding to an atomic weight of about 22. Here, for the first time,* was the experimental evidence in favor of Crookes' conjecture that the atoms of a single element are mixtures of different species, each of which has an integral atomic weight.

---

* It was already known that the atomic weight of lead recovered from uranium ore is lower than the atomic weight of ordinary lead, but the work of Thomson and Aston tied such differences down to the individual atoms.

CO Ne^β Ne^α

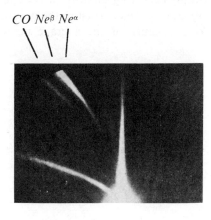

CO Ne^β Ne^α

Fig. 2-5. Parabolas obtained by Thomson in 1913 and published by Aston in 1920 [*Phil. Mag.*, **39**, 449 (1920)] Ne^α is Ne^{20}, Ne^β is Ne^{22}. The lower photograph represents a longer exposure than the upper, and brings out the weak Ne^{22} trace which is just barely visible in the upper photograph.

Aston devised a more effective deflection device, to which he gave the name "mass spectrograph." This instrument had the property of bringing to a focus ions with the same value of q/M but varying velocities. A schematic diagram of the apparatus is shown in Fig. 2-6.

Mass spectra obtained by Aston in 1920 are shown in Fig. 2-7. Aston introduced the term *isotopes* to describe those nuclear species having the same atomic number, and therefore the same chemical properties, but different masses. The word was constructed from the two Greek words, *isos*, meaning "the same," and *topos*, meaning "place." Thus isotopes are varieties of atoms that belong in the same place in the periodic table of the elements. The word *nuclide* is often used synonymously with isotope, but nuclide has a somewhat more restricted meaning (see Glossary). A quantity comparable to atomic weight but applying to a single isotope of an element rather than a naturally occurring mixture of isotopes is the isotopic weight, or better, the *isotopic mass.* In contrast to the unit of atomic weight, which may be defined as one-sixteenth of the average mass of an oxygen atom* in a naturally

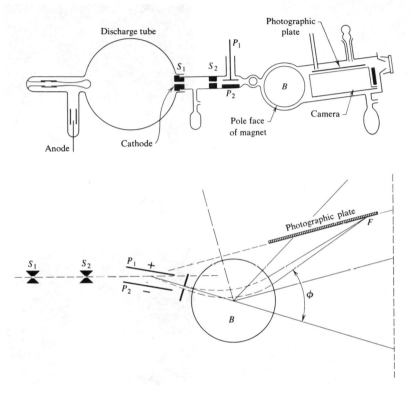

Fig. 2-6. Above, a diagram of Aston's first mass spectrograph [*Phil. Mag.*, **39**, 612 (1920)]. Below, a schematic diagram of the mass spectrograph showing how it focuses ions of the same value of q/M [*Phil. Mag.*, **38**, 707 (1919)]. The ions are collimated by slits S_1 and S_2, deflected electrostatically in the field between P_1 and P_2, deflected again in the magnetic field indicated by the circle at B, and brought to a focus at F.

occurring mixture of the oxygen isotopes O^{16}, O^{17}, and O^{18}, the unit of isotopic mass (amu) is defined as one-sixteenth of the mass of an O^{16} atom. Because naturally occurring oxygen contains very small amounts of O^{17} and O^{18} in addition to the principal isotope O^{16}, the ratio of the masses of one

---

* The chemist usually defines the atomic weight of an element as 16 times the *ratio* of the weight of one gram-atom of the element to the weight of one gram-atom of oxygen. This corresponds to his method of measurement. The atomic weights are numerically the same by either definition.

atomic weight unit* to one amu is 1.000275 ± 0.000005. In September of 1960 the Tenth General Assembly of the International Union of Pure and Applied Physics recommended the adoption of the exact number 12 as the relative nuclidic mass of the carbon isotope C^{12}. They suggest the use of the symbol u for this unit. Where not specified otherwise, isotopic masses in this book are in amu.

Isotopic masses differ only slightly from integers. For example, the isotopic mass of H^1 is 1.008144, while that of U^{238}, which differs from an integral number more than any other naturally occurring isotope, is 238.12522.

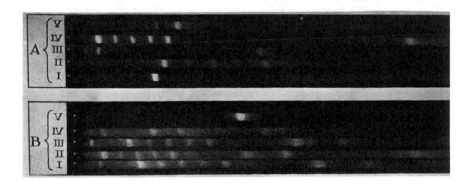

Fig. 2-7. Mass spectra obtained by Aston in 1920. The regular spacing of the bright lines shows the approximately linear M/q dispersion of this mass spectrograph [*Phil. Mag.*, **39**, 499 (1920)].

The integer that is nearest the isotopic mass is called the *mass number* of the element. This is the integer that has been used above as a superscript, as in U^{238}. The fact that the isotopic masses differ from each other by essentially integral values caused a revival of Prout's hypothesis. The ejection of electrons from the nucleus in radioactive β decay seemed to prove that the nucleus was made up of protons (hydrogen nuclei) equal in number to the mass number, and a number of electrons equal to the difference between the mass number and the atomic number. The ejection of an electron from the nucleus would then increase the effective positive charge of the nucleus and hence its atomic number. Since the atomic number is increased by one unit, one extra-nuclear electron must be added to make the new atom electrically

* Atomic weights are sometimes said to be given on the chemical scale while isotopic masses are called atomic weights on the physical scale.

neutral. Thus the nucleus loses an electron while the number of orbital electrons is increased by one, so that the total number of electrons would be constant and there should be no change in isotopic mass as a result of β decay. There was still the small discrepancy between an actual isotopic weight and the sum of the isotopic weights of a number of hydrogen atoms equal to the mass number of the isotope to be explained. This point will be discussed a little later. *The theory of nuclear structure just given has since been discarded* (see Sec. 2-5).

While the existence of isotopes was discovered by means of the mass spectrograph, some important isotope discoveries were made by other means. Urey, Brickwedde, and Murphy (28) discovered the existence of H^2 (deuterium) by the small shift in the spectral lines caused by different energies of rotation of nuclei of different masses about the centers of mass of their electron-nucleus systems. If the motion of the nucleus is taken into account in the Bohr model of the atom, the frequency of the light that gives rise to a spectral line is given by

$$\nu = \frac{2\pi^2 \hat{M} Z^2 e^4}{h^3} \left(\frac{1}{n_1^2} - \frac{1}{n_2^2} \right), \tag{2-16}$$

where $\hat{M}$, the *reduced mass*, is given by

$$\hat{M} = m_e \left(\frac{1}{1 + m_e/M} \right), \tag{2-17}$$

m_e is the mass of an electron, and M is the mass of the nucleus. Since all the other quantities in the equation are identical for a given spectral line, the ratio of the frequency of a deuterium line to that of the frequency of a hydrogen line is given by

$$\frac{\nu_{H^2}}{\nu_{H^1}} = \frac{\hat{M}_2}{\hat{M}_1} = \frac{1 + m_e/M_1}{1 + m_e/M_2} \simeq 1.0003. \tag{2-18}$$

Small though the difference between this number and unity is, it is still large enough to be measured. In the case of the heavier elements, however, it will be seen at once that the effect is negligible, so that this is not a generally applicable method for finding isotopes.

In molecular spectra, the nuclear masses are more important than they are in atomic spectra. An H_2 molecule, for example, may be thought of crudely as looking something like the model shown in Fig. 2-8. The electronic energy levels might be something like those of He, but now the two nuclei may rotate about each other and may vibrate back and forth as well. The momenta of these motions will be quantized, and therefore the total energy of the molecule will be the sum of a number of these smaller energies and the large electronic energies. This results in groups of closely spaced spectrum lines or bands. Since the same amount of momentum of the nuclear motion will result in different amounts of energy, depending on the masses of the nuclei, the spacing of the lines within a band will be different for molecules containing one kind of nucleus than for molecules of the same chemical compound containing nuclei of different mass number. The accuracy of this method decreases as the isotopic mass increases, and in addition there are other effects which give rise to small changes in the energy of a molecule.

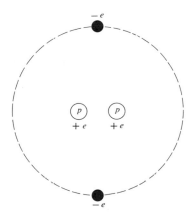

Fig. 2-8. Crude model of a H_2 molecule. The quantized rotations of the two nuclei about their common center of mass give rise to closely spaced energy levels superposed on the rather large electronic energy differences. These small energy differences depend directly on the nuclear mass.

Nevertheless $_6C^{13}$, $_7N^{15}$, and $_8O^{18}$ were discovered by this means in the period 1929–1931. Figure 2-9 shows the stable isotopes that are now known.

Proof of the existence of isotopes, taken together with Moseley's discovery of the meaning of atomic number and the identification of α particles with He^{++} ions, made it clear that Rutherford's ideas of successive disintegration schemes were certainly correct. The ejection of an α particle would reduce the mass number of the isotope by four units and the atomic number by two units, while the ejection of a β particle would leave the mass number unchanged but would increase the atomic number by one. The disintegration scheme for U^{238} is shown in Fig. 2-10, where the mass number minus the atomic number, $A - Z$, is plotted against the atomic number for each isotope in the sequence. Figures 2-11 and 2-12 give the disintegration schemes for two other naturally occurring radioisotopes, $_{92}U^{235}$ and $_{90}Th^{232}$.

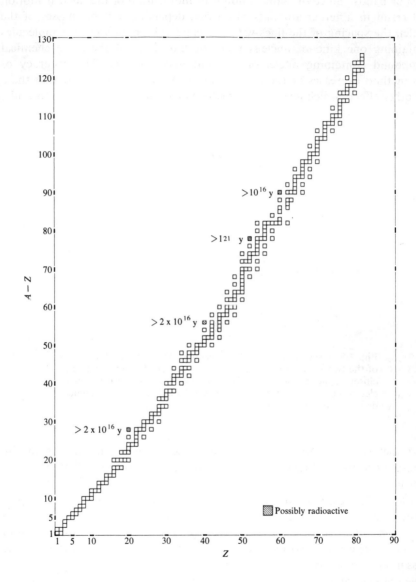

Fig. 2-9. Chart of known stable nuclei. The difference between mass number and atomic number, $A - Z$, is plotted against the atomic number, Z.

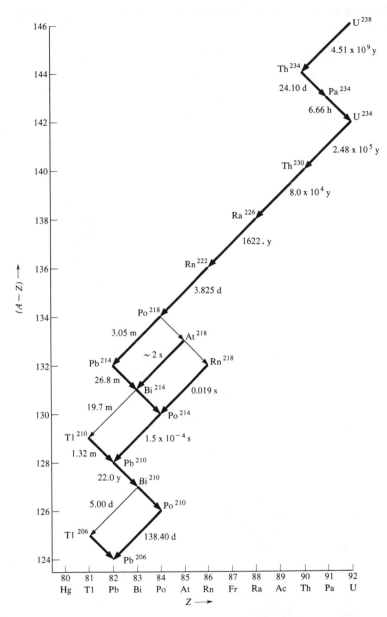

Fig. 2-10. The uranium–radium decay series, sometimes referred to as the $4n + 2$ series since the mass number of every member of the series is given by $4n + 2$ where n is an integer. The series ends at Pb^{206} which is nonradioactive. Some atoms of Th^{234} decay to Pa^{234} in its normal state while others decay to Pa^{234} in an excited state. The excited Pa^{234} may either emit a γ ray and become normal Pa^{234} or it may emit a β ray and become U^{234}. The half-life of excited Pa^{001} is 1.175 minutes. Where alpha and beta decay are alternative or competing processes, as is the case in Po^{218}, the dominant decay mode is shown by a heavy arrow. The half-life of Bi^{214} (19.7 minutes) is the time required for one-half of the Bi^{214} atoms to decay by the competing processes of α and β emission.

There are a few weakly radioactive naturally occurring isotopes of atomic number less than 80:

Isotope	Half-life	Radiation emitted
$_{75}Re^{187}$	$4 \times 10^{12} y$	β
$_{71}Lu^{176}$	$7 \times 10^{10} y$	β, α
$_{62}Sm^{152}$	$1.4 \times 10^{11} y$	α
$_{37}Rb^{87}$	$5 \times 10^{10} y$	β, γ
$_{19}K^{40}$	$4.5 \times 10^{8} y$	β, γ

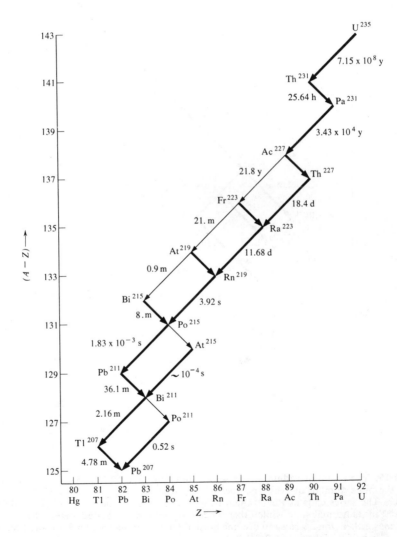

Fig. 2-11. The uranium–actinium or $4n + 3$ decay series.

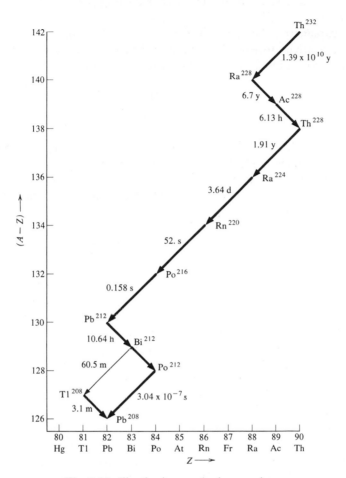

Fig. 2-12. The thorium or 4*n* decay series.

2-4 Energy Released in Radioactive Decay

Rutherford and Soddy pointed out early (24) in the study of radioactivity that the energy liberated per gram of matter is enormous, and might be the seat of the sun's source of energy. They were able to calculate roughly the energy released from the measured energy of the charged particles (knowledge of γ-ray energies came a little later), and the measured number of disintegrations per unit mass per unit time. The calculated energies were so much greater than those involved in known chemical reactions that it was difficult to offer any reasonable explanation for them. The α particle emitted by

Po^{212}, for example, has an energy of 8.776 Mev,* whereas the heat of combustion of C and O to form CO_2 is 94,000 calories per mole, or 4.1 ev per molecule.

The explanation lay close at hand, for Einstein announced his special theory of relativity (6)† in 1905 and according to this theory the mass, M, of a moving object differs from its mass at rest, M_0, according to the relation

$$M = \frac{M_0}{\sqrt{1 - v^2/c^2}}, \qquad (2\text{-}19)$$

where v is the velocity of the body relative to the observer and c is the velocity of light in vacuo, which in the relativity theory is taken as a universal constant for all observers and the maximum possible observable velocity. Conservation of energy then leads to the result that the kinetic energy of a body, W_k, is given by

$$W_k = Mc^2 - M_0c^2 = M_0c^2 \left(\frac{1}{\sqrt{1 - v^2/c^2}} - 1\right), \qquad (2\text{-}20)$$

which for very small velocities is approximately $\frac{1}{2}M_0v^2$. Einstein advanced the hypothesis that the term M_0c^2 was to be interpreted as the energy due to mass alone, or *rest energy*, as it is often called, the quantity M_0 being referred to as the *rest mass*. If this idea is correct, then very small changes in mass could easily account for the relatively large energies released in radioactive disintegration. For example, the conversion of one gram of mass to energy would yield 9×10^{20} ergs or 25.02×10^6 kwhr. The conversion of one mass unit (a little less than the mass of a single hydrogen atom) to energy would give 931 Mev. Thus if the isotopic mass of an α emitter is 0.004 mass unit greater than the combined isotopic masses of the daughter product and an He atom, there will be 3.724 Mev of energy appearing. If all this energy were given to the α particle, the kinetic energy of the α particle would be 3.724 Mev. Actually, conservation of momentum requires that a small fraction of the energy be imparted to the recoiling daughter nucleus.

The deviation of isotopic masses from what might be expected from

* An electron-volt (ev) is the amount of energy given to a particle with a single electronic charge when it falls through a potential difference of one volt. It is equal to 1.6×10^{-12} erg. In nuclear physics, one usually uses a unit that is a million times larger (Mev): 1 Mev = 1.6×10^{-6} erg. Other commonly used units are the Kev and the Bev: 1 Kev = 10^3 ev; 1 Bev = 10^9 ev.

† "The mass of a body is a measure of its energy content; if the energy changes by L, the mass changes in the same sense by $L/(9 \times 10^{20})$, the energy being measured in ergs and the mass in grams.... It is not impossible that with bodies whose energy content is variable to a high degree (e.g., with radium salts) the theory may be successfully put to the test."

Prout's hypothesis is clearly shown by a plot of packing fraction* against mass number. Packing fraction is defined as

$$\frac{\text{isotopic mass} - \text{mass of } A \text{ particles of unit isotopic mass}}{A},$$

where A is the mass number. The unit usually used is 10^{-4} atomic mass unit

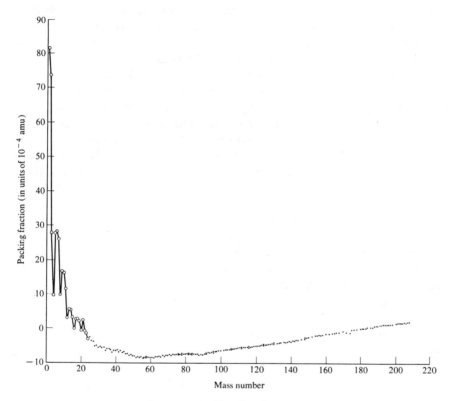

Fig. 2-13. Packing-fraction curve.

per (hypothetical) particle, so that one may write

$$\text{p.f.} = \frac{(M - A)}{A} \cdot 10^4,$$

where M is the isotopic mass of the isotope in question. A plot of packing fractions is shown in Fig. 2-13. Because O^{16} is arbitrarily taken to have an isotopic mass of 16, its packing fraction is zero. It is evident from the curve

---

* A similar, but physically more meaningful, quantity that is generally used now in place of packing fraction is the "average binding energy per nucleon." This is discussed in detail in Chap. 9.

that the elements of minimum or most negative packing fraction are those whose mass numbers are in the vicinity of 53.

It might appear to be more logical if we defined the packing fraction as

[(isotopic mass) − (sum of isotopic masses of the hydrogen atoms necessary to form the isotope according to Prout's hypothesis)]

divided by the number of hydrogen atoms necessary to form the isotope under Prout's hypothesis. The only difference between a curve of this type and the usual packing-fraction curve is that the line of zero packing fraction would be shifted upward so that the packing fraction of H^1 would be zero and that of any other stable isotope would be negative.

The principal problem of nuclear physics today is to elucidate the forces that bind the nuclear particles together into stable assemblages. It is evident that something holds the nucleus together, for most of the elements are non-radioactive and therefore stable. Even the radioactive elements are meta-stable or they would not exist. Dynamic stability implies a minimum in the potential energy of a system. If a nucleus composed of a number of nucleons (nuclear particles) is stable, then it must have less energy than the constituent particles would have if they were far removed from each other; otherwise the nucleons would move away from each other and the nucleus would disintegrate. The fact that the nuclear assemblage is in a state of minimum energy also means, in view of the mass-energy relationship, that its mass is less than that of its constituent particles. The most stable nuclei, then, evidently belong to those elements having mass numbers between 48 and 85, the most naturally abundant of these being iron, with mass numbers of 54, 56, 57, and 58. Those elements of high mass number, Tl, Pb, Bi, Po, At, Rn, Fr, Ra, Ac, Th, Pa, U, have larger packing fractions and are therefore less stable than elements of lower mass number, so that it is not surprising that most of the isotopes of these elements are radioactive. From energy considerations alone, it may seem surprising that we do not find radioactivity in nearly all the elements. This point will be discussed again later.

2-5 Nuclear Spin and Magnetic Moment

If one imagines an electron in an atom to be moving in a Bohr orbit about the nucleus of the atom, then the motion of the charge borne by the electron will produce a magnetic field. The average value of the magnetic field so produced at any point would be that which one would calculate for the current equivalent to the moving charge and flowing around the same path. If the observable angular momentum of the electron is $l\hbar$, then one can easily show (see Probs. 2-7 and 2-8) that the observable magnetic dipole moment associated with the electron's motion is

$$\mu = \frac{el\hbar}{2m_e c}, \tag{2-21}$$

where e is the charge of the electron and m_e is the mass of the electron. The unit of magnetic moment ($eh/2m_e c = 0.9274 \times 10^{-20}$ erg/gauss)* is called a *Bohr magneton*.

The word "observable" has been used here because of the way in which the angular momentum quantum numbers arise from the solutions of the Schrödinger wave equation. Experimentally, one can gain information about the energy of the atom, which includes a term that is proportional to the square of its angular momentum, by observing the photons emitted when there is a transition from a higher to a lower energy state of the atom. In order to find out something about the angular momentum of the atom, since angular momentum is a vector quantity, one must establish some preferred direction in space (through the creation of a magnetic field, for example) and one then determines only the *component* of the angular momentum about an axis in this preferred direction. According to quantum mechanics if the maximum value of the component of the angular momentum about some specified axis (considering a particle that moves in a potential field that is a function only of the distance from some fixed point) is $l\hbar$, then the possible values that the specified angular momentum component may have are

$$l\hbar, \quad (l-1)\hbar, \quad (l-2)\hbar, \cdots, \quad (-l+1)\hbar, \quad -l\hbar,$$

where l can have only *integral* values.

Classically, the kinetic energy of a rigid body that rotates about a principal axis is given by

$$W_K = \frac{1}{2} G\omega^2 = \frac{(G\omega)^2}{2G} = \frac{H^2}{2G}, \tag{2-22}$$

where G is the moment of inertia of the body about the principal axis in question, ω is the angular velocity of the body about this same axis, and H is the angular momentum about this axis. In the solution to the Schrödinger equation there arises a quantized energy term proportional to

$$\hbar^2 l(l+1).$$

It is possible to show, furthermore, that the expectation value of the square of the magnitude of the total angular momentum of the particle is given by $H^2 = \hbar^2 l(l+1)$. One is thus led to a result that seems anomalous from the standpoint of classical mechanics, namely, that the maximum value (l) of the component of angular momentum about any specified axis is always less than the square root (H) of the expectation value of the square of the magnitude of the total angular momentum. Since one can never observe the vector **H** no matter what direction in space he chooses, it is called *unobservable*. The

---

* This enigmatic unit could be expressed in a physically more understandable form as the torque per unit flux density or cm-dyne/gauss. The erg/gauss is the unit most commonly given in the literature, however.

only vector quantity that can be observed is $l\hbar$ or some smaller quantity that is an integral multiple of $\hbar$ such as $(l - 2)\hbar$.

In the vector model of the atom, this situation, known as spatial quantization, is represented as shown in Fig. 2-14(a). It is customary to refer to the angular momentum quantum numbers, such as l, as the angular momenta.

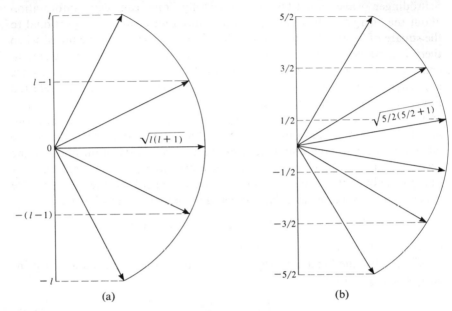

(a)   (b)

Fig. 2-14. (a) Observable angular momentum quantum numbers of a particle having a maximum observable angular momentum quantum number l, where l is an integer. According to wave mechanics, the angular momentum vector has a length $\sqrt{l(l + 1)}\,\hbar$ but this is not an observable quantity.

(b) Similar to (a) except that the maximum observable angular momentum quantum number is 5/2. When the spin is half-integral, as in this example, there is no state in which the observable angular momentum is zero.

This corresponds to the choice of a system of units in which $\hbar = 1$. In what follows, this custom will be followed wherever there seems to be little danger of misunderstanding.

Now a charged particle revolving about an axis exhibits a magnetic dipole moment which may be represented by a vector collinear with the angular momentum vector. We might, therefore, think of a total magnetic moment vector having a length $\sqrt{l(l + 1)}\,(e\hbar/2m_ec)$ associated and collinear with a total angular momentum vector **H**. This vector must be unobservable to be consistent with the unobservability of **H**. The observable magnetic moment would have a maximum possible value of $l(e\hbar/2m_ec)$. Since it is only the observable magnetic moments and angular momenta whose quantum numbers are integers, the word *observable* will hereafter be omitted where this can be done without risk of confusion.

The electron also possesses an angular momentum about its own axis, which is called an intrinsic angular momentum or *spin*. The magnitude of the observable electron spin has been found to be $\hbar/2$. If one assumes some particular form of electronic structure such as a sphere with uniform mass and charge distribution throughout its volume, then one can calculate the expected magnetic dipole moment of the electron due to its spin. Such models are of doubtful physical significance since they require a distribution of charge, whereas all experimental evidence indicates that charges smaller than the electronic charge do not exist. According to the Dirac relativistic wave mechanics the electron should have an observable spin of $\hbar/2$ and an observable magnetic moment of one Bohr magneton. Experiments (15) have shown, however, that the intrinsic observable magnetic moment of the electron is 1.00116 Bohr magnetons. The energy of an atom depends to a very slight extent on the relative orientation of the intrinsic magnetic moment of an electron and the magnetic field of the other electrons. The allowed orientations thus give rise to a group of closely spaced energy levels so that transitions involving these levels result in a group of closely spaced spectrum lines. This effect is known as *fine structure* in atomic spectroscopy. A good example is the well-known sodium D doublet.

If a nucleus contained a proton that moved in an orbit with observable angular momentum $\hbar$, then one would expect the nucleus to exhibit an observable magnetic moment, due to the motion of the proton, of

$$\frac{e\hbar}{2M_p c} = \frac{0.9274 \times 10^{-20}}{1835.98} = 0.5051 \times 10^{-23} \text{ erg/gauss,}$$

where M_p is the mass of the proton. The magnetic dipole moment calculated in this way has been adopted as the unit of measurement for nuclear magnetic moments, and is called a *nuclear magneton*. As anticipated, the magnetic moments of nuclei are very small.

Since a torque is exerted on a magnetic dipole when its axis is not parallel to the ambient magnetic field, work must be done on the dipole if it is turned through some angle θ against this torque. The torque (an unobservable) would be

$$T = \mu_t B \sin \theta,^* \tag{2-23}$$

where μ_t is the total (unobservable) magnetic moment, B is the magnetic flux density, and θ is the angle which the magnetic dipole axis makes with the

---

* This equation and some of the equations on the following pages are more commonly expressed in terms of the magnetic intensity H, in which case the dipole moment, μ, is expressed in different units than ergs/gauss as above. It is more convenient to use B and express μ in ergs/gauss when the dipole moment is due to a revolving charge and this choice has accordingly been made here.

direction of the magnetic field. The work that must be done to turn the dipole from some angle θ_1 to some larger angle θ_2 is then

$$\Delta W = \int_{\theta_1}^{\theta_2} T \, d\theta = \int_{\theta_1}^{\theta_2} \mu_t B \sin \theta \, d\theta = \mu_t B(\cos \theta_1 - \cos \theta_2)$$

$$= (\mu_t \cos \theta_1 - \mu_t \cos \theta_2)B = (\mu_1 - \mu_2)B, \qquad (2\text{-}24)$$

where μ_1 and μ_2 are the observable magnetic moments corresponding to θ_1 and θ_2 respectively. Thus the energy differences, which we might look upon as being due to the different spatial orientations of the axis of rotation, involve only the observable magnetic moments.

If we consider the dipole to consist of two monopoles of opposite sign separated by a distance b, then the work done on one monopole in bringing it from infinity to a point on a line perpendicular to the local magnetic field direction will be the negative of that done on the monopole of opposite sign in bringing it to a point on this same line. In other words, the energy of the dipole is zero when $\theta = 90°$. On the other hand, if the final position of the dipole makes an angle θ with the magnetic field direction, the work done on the positive monopole (strength $\hat{m}$) is less than before by an amount $\hat{m}B(b/2) \cos \theta$, and the magnitude of the negative work done on the negative monopole is increased by $\hat{m}B(b/2) \cos \theta$. Therefore the total energy of the dipole is

$$W = -B\hat{m}b \cos \theta = -B\mu_t \cos \theta.$$

Actually, there is no potential energy associated with the motion of a charged particle in a steady magnetic field, so that what appears here as a potential energy term must in fact be a change in the kinetic energy of the moving charge associated with the establishment of the magnetic field. If one starts with the charged particle revolving in a circle with no external magnetic field and gradually increases the field to some value, then during the time the field is increasing there will be a time rate of change of magnetic flux through the orbit of the particle producing an emf which will accelerate or decelerate the charged particle. The magnitude of this emf will clearly be proportional to the flux through the orbit and therefore to the area of the orbit projected onto a plane normal to the direction of the magnetic field. The effect is then proportional to the cosine of the angle between the angular momentum vector and the magnetic flux density vector, and will be zero when this angle is 90°. Thus if the normal to the plane of the orbit is at right angles to the magnetic field vector, there will be no change in the kinetic energy of the charged particle when the magnetic field is established.

The same result can be obtained in a somewhat different way. It will be shown soon (Eq. 2-31) that the torque exerted on the equivalent dipole will cause the angular momentum vector to precess about the magnetic field vector with a precessional angular velocity given by $\Omega = \mu B/H$ where H is the instantaneous value of the angular momentum about the spin axes. Ω will be a vector in the direction of **(B)** and will have a component along the spin axis of $-\Omega \cos \theta$. The effective instantaneous angular velocity about the spin axis will then be

$$\omega = \omega_0 - \Omega \cos \theta, \tag{2-25}$$

where ω_0 is the spin angular velocity in the absence of the magnetic field. The altered kinetic energy of rotation about the spin axis will then be

$$W_0 + \Delta W = \tfrac{1}{2} G \omega^2 = \tfrac{1}{2} G (\omega_0 - \Omega \cos \theta)^2$$
$$= \tfrac{1}{2} G (\omega_0^2 - 2\omega_0 \Omega \cos \theta + \Omega^2 \cos^2 \theta).$$

Since $\Omega \ll \omega$ we may neglect the term in Ω^2, so that

$$W_0 + \Delta W = \tfrac{1}{2} G \omega_0^2 - G \omega_0 \Omega \cos \theta = W_0 - G \omega_0 \Omega \cos \theta. \tag{2-26}$$

Thus
$$\Delta W = - G \omega_0 \Omega \cos \theta = - H \Omega \cos \theta = - H \frac{\mu_t B \cos \theta}{H}$$
$$= -\mu_t B \cos \theta. \tag{2-27}$$

Again we see that the change in kinetic energy is zero when the orbit lies in a plane containing the magnetic flux density vector. If we are to treat the orientation energy as that of the potential energy of the equivalent dipole we must take this potential energy to be zero when the dipole is at right angles to the magnetic field. The orientation energy may then be written

$$W = -\mu_t \cos \theta B = -\mu_{\text{eff}} B \tag{2-28}$$

where $\mu_{\text{eff}} \equiv \mu_t \cos \theta$.

Since the magnetic moments of nuclei are so much smaller than those of electrons, the energy differences associated with orientation are correspondingly very small compared with those which give rise to fine structure. The close spacing of certain groups of spectrum lines associated with nuclear magnetic moments is known as *hyperfine structure*. Instruments of extremely high resolving power are required to resolve such a multiple line into individual lines and measure their separations, but this has been done. The fact that measured nuclear magnetic moments are as small as they are shows that electrons cannot exist as such in nuclei, since electrons have very much larger magnetic moments.

Thus far the spin of the nucleus has been discussed in terms of its associated magnetic moment. The angular momentum of the nucleus is also responsible for an alternation of intensities of lines in the band spectra of homonuclear diatomic molecules.* The band spectrum lines originate in transitions from higher to lower electronic energy states accompanied by simultaneous changes in the rotational state of the molecule. Transitions are not possible between all energy states, but there may be several pairs of states between which

---

* Molecules consisting of two identical atoms.

transitions are possible for which the energy difference is the same. Transitions between these pairs of states will then result in photons of the same wavelength, which therefore contribute to the same spectrum line. Now if all possible rotational states had equal population densities, that is, if the probability of finding a molecule in one rotational state were the same as that of finding it in any other rotational state, then one can show from a consideration of the symmetry properties of the wave functions involved that the intensities of one set of spectrum lines would be greater than the intensities of the interspersed lines by a factor $(I + 1)/I$, where I is the observable angular momentum quantum number (usually called the *nuclear spin*) of either nucleus. Actually, the rotational states are populated according to the Boltzmann population factor, but for energy levels that are closely spaced, as are the rotational energy levels, this factor varies slowly from one energy level to the next so that by taking the average of the intensities of the two "strong" lines adjacent to a "weak" line the effect of the variable population densities can be made negligible.

The nuclear spins of many isotopes have been determined in this way, but it is clear that the measured values become unreliable for large values of I, as the intensities of the lines become very nearly equal in this case. When $I = 0$ the ratio becomes infinite, which means that every other line is entirely missing.

It is also possible to obtain the same information, and often with greater accuracy, from microwave spectroscopy (11, 17). In this method the electromagnetic waves are generated by a vacuum tube oscillator, such as a velocity modulation tube (a klystron), usually with frequencies in the range 1500 to 300,000 megacycles per second. Since the waves are essentially "monochromatic" no dispersing element such as a prism or grating is needed. The spectra are usually obtained by observing the frequency dependence of the attenuation or absorption of the waves in passing through a region filled with the material to be studied in its gaseous state. In optical spectra, there must always be an orbital electronic transition involved in order that the energy difference between the initial and final states be great enough to correspond to a photon whose wavelength lies in or near the visible region of the spectrum. In microwave spectra, on the other hand, where the photon energy is low, the observed transitions do not ordinarily involve such orbital electronic transitions. With the exception of Na^{22}, the spin of each of the nuclei listed in Table 2-1 was determined by one or more of the methods discussed above.

Table 2-1

Nucleus	Spin	Nucleus	Spin	Nucleus	Spin
$_1H^1$	$\frac{1}{2}$	$_7N^{15}$	$\frac{1}{2}$	$_{17}Cl^{35}$	$\frac{3}{2}$
$_1H^2$	1	$_{11}Na^{22}$	3	$_{17}Cl^{36}$	2
$_2He^4$	0	$_{16}S^{32}$	0	$_{34}Se^{80}$	0
$_6C^{13}$	$\frac{1}{2}$	$_{16}S^{33}$	$\frac{3}{2}$	$_{36}Kr^{83}$	$\frac{9}{2}$

The first thing one notices when he inspects Table 2-1 is that the proton (nucleus of H^1), like the electron, has a spin of $\frac{1}{2}$. The second thing one notices is that those nuclides with even mass numbers, A (second and third rows), have integral (0, 1, 2, 3) spins while those with odd mass numbers (first and fourth rows) have half-integral ($\frac{1}{2}$, $\frac{3}{2}$, $\frac{9}{2}$) spins, and that in neither case does it matter whether the atomic number, Z, is odd or even. In the particular case where both A and Z are even, however (third row), the spin is always zero. In a molecule like H_2 we know that the exchange energy of the two nuclei is so great that the nuclear spins must be aligned either parallel (both spin vectors pointing in the same direction) or antiparallel (spin vectors pointing in opposite directions). We also know that the orbital electrons of atoms tend to pair off with antiparallel spins, and that such a pair, having neither a net spin angular momentum nor a net intrinsic magnetic moment, exhibit no spin interaction with the remaining particles of the system. Since the observed spins of nuclei of large A are not much greater than those of nuclei of small A, it is likely that such a pairing of like particles also occurs in the nucleus. In any event, if one assumes that the spins of all unpaired nuclear particles are aligned either parallel or antiparallel, then all observed nuclear spins can be explained by assuming a nucleus to be made up of A particles, each having a spin of $\frac{1}{2}$. The observed nuclear spins cannot easily be reconciled with the theory of nuclear structure that requires A protons and $(A - Z)$ electrons, since when Z is even this would result in an even number of particles which if aligned parallel or antiparallel would lead to integral spins in rows 3 and 4, and when Z is odd would result in an odd number of particles, and therefore lead to half-integral spins, in rows 1 and 2. Since any orbital motions of the nuclear particles would be expected to lead to integral angular momenta, such motions would contribute to the observed nuclear "spin" but would not affect our arguments about integral or half-integral spins. (If the arguments above are not obvious to the reader, he should convince himself of their validity by trying various combinations of spins for the constituent particles of some of the nuclei listed in the table.) Nuclear spin data thus cast further very serious doubts on the correctness of the proton-plus-electron theory of nuclear structure.

Hyperfine structure studies do not provide a very satisfactory means for determining nuclear magnetic moments. Molecular beam studies, on the other hand, enable one to determine nuclear magnetic moments with considerable precision. This method, which was developed by Rabi and his collaborators, depends upon the force exerted on a magnetic dipole by a non-uniform magnetic field and upon the quantum mechanical effect of *space quantization* discussed above and depicted in Fig. 2-14(a) and (b).

If a short magnet of pole strength $\hat{m}$ and length b is located in a uniform magnetic field, the force exerted on its north pole is equal and opposite to that exerted on its south pole, so that no net force acts to accelerate its center of mass, although there may be a torque acting that tends to align the magnet with the direction of the magnetic field. On the other hand, if the magnet is located in a *nonuniform* magnetic field, the force exerted on its north pole is not equal to that exerted on its south pole and it will suffer an acceleration in any given direction proportional to the gradient of the component of the magnetic field in that direction. For example (Fig. 2-15), let the x-component

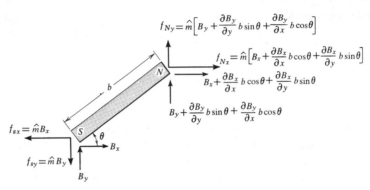

$$f_{Ny} = \hat{m}\left[B_y + \frac{\partial B_y}{\partial y} b \sin\theta + \frac{\partial B_y}{\partial x} b \cos\theta\right]$$

$$f_{Nx} = \hat{m}\left[B_x + \frac{\partial B_x}{\partial x} b \cos\theta + \frac{\partial B_x}{\partial y} b \sin\theta\right]$$

$$B_x + \frac{\partial B_x}{\partial x} b \cos\theta + \frac{\partial B_x}{\partial y} b \sin\theta$$

$$B_y + \frac{\partial B_y}{\partial y} b \sin\theta + \frac{\partial B_y}{\partial x} b \cos\theta$$

$$f_{sx} = \hat{m} B_x$$

$$f_{sy} = \hat{m} B_y$$

Fig. 2-15. Illustration of the force exerted on a short magnet by an inhomogeneous magnetic field. The pole strength of either pole is $\hat{m}$, and the product $\hat{m}b = \mu$ is the dipole moment of the magnet. The dipole moment is a vector quantity, μ, which points from the S to the N pole of the magnet.

of the magnetic field be B_x at the south pole of the magnet. Then the x-component of the field at the north pole will be

$$B_x + \frac{\partial B_x}{\partial x} b_x + \frac{\partial B_x}{\partial y} b_y + \frac{\partial B_x}{\partial z} b_z.$$

where b_x, b_y, and b_z are the projections of b on the x-, y-, and z-axes, respectively. The force exerted on the magnet is then the sum of the forces acting on its two extremities, or

$$f_x = \hat{m}\left(B_x + \frac{\partial B_x}{\partial x} b_x + \frac{\partial B_x}{\partial y} b_y + \frac{\partial B_x}{\partial z} b_z\right) - \hat{m} B_x,$$

$$f_x = \hat{m}(\mathbf{b} \cdot \nabla B_x) = \mu \cdot \nabla B_x, \tag{2-29}$$

where $\mu = \hat{m}\mathbf{b}$ is the magnetic moment of the magnet, and ∇B_x is the gradient of B_x (a vector quantity). Equation (2-29) is more general than the case for which it was derived, and may be applied to find the force acting on any magnetic dipole—for example, that produced by a revolving charge. The force acting on a dipole in the x-direction is then proportional to the magnetic moment, μ, of the dipole, to the magnitude of the gradient of B_x, and to the cosine of the angle between the vectors μ and ∇B_x.

If a nucleus or nuclear particle possessing both an angular momentum and a magnetic moment, the two vectors being collinear, is aligned at an angle to a magnetic field it will precess about the field lines or field direction with a large precessional velocity. One can calculate the expected precessional velocity from strictly classical mechanics. From (2-23) the torque exerted on the dipole is $T = \mu_t B \sin \theta$. If the instantaneous angular momentum about the spin axis is H, then the component perpendicular to the field lines is $H \sin \theta$, and it is this component that precesses. If the precessional angular velocity is Ω, then

$$T = \mu_t B \sin \theta = \text{time rate of change of angular momentum} = \Omega H \sin \theta.$$
$$(2\text{-}30)$$

Thus
$$\Omega = \frac{\mu_t B}{H},$$
$$(2\text{-}31)$$

and, if we consider only the observable components of μ_t and H along the direction of the field lines,

$$\Omega = \frac{\mu B}{I\hbar}.$$
$$(2\text{-}32)$$

A consequence of this *Larmor precession* is that the force acting on the dipole at right angles to the field lines continually rotates about the field lines so that the average value of the force at right angles to the field lines is zero. Another way of saying this is that the time average of the component of dipole moment perpendicular to the field lines will be zero as a result of the Larmor precession. This would mean that only the component of the dipole moment in the direction of the field lines could be measured and this component is therefore, as previously stated, the observable dipole moment.*

Frisch and Stern (8) first succeeded in measuring the magnetic dipole moment of the proton by observing the deflection of a beam of cold (95°K) hydrogen molecules in an inhomogeneous magnetic field. Specific heat measurements (5) and intensity alternations in band spectra had shown that diatomic hydrogen must exist in two forms, called *orthohydrogen* when the nuclear spins are parallel and *parahydrogen* when the nuclear spins are antiparallel. In either type of hydrogen molecule in its electronic ground state, the two electron spins are antiparallel and the electron orbital angular momentum is zero so that the electrons do not contribute to the magnetic moment of the molecule. In the lowest energy state of the orthohydrogen molecule, the protons revolve about their common center of mass with an angular

---

* This is a classical approach to a quantum mechanical effect. It is probably preferable simply to state, as was done earlier, that only the component in the direction of the magnetic field is observable, but this classical argument may make it easier for the reader to accept a statement that is made here without proper quantum mechanical proof.

momentum of $\hbar$ and therefore would be expected to have a magnetic moment, due to this motion only, of one nuclear magneton. In addition, the intrinsic magnetic moments of the two protons add, since the spins are parallel. In the strong fields used (about 20,000 gauss) the interactions of the two internal magnetic fields with each other are small compared with the interaction with the external magnetic field. The two dipole moments (spin and rotational) then respond independently to the external field or, in the language of quantum mechanics, the spins are decoupled from the orbital motion. On the other hand, the large exchange forces between the protons prevent the spin of one proton from being decoupled from the spin of the other proton by the external magnetic field so that orthohydrogen is not transformed to parahydrogen or vice versa. According to the space quantization rules of quantum

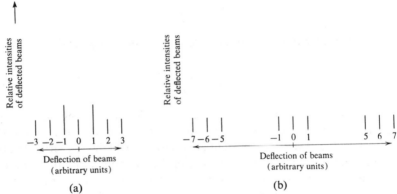

(a)   (b)

Fig. 2-16. (a) Split-up of beam of monoergic cold orthohydrogen molecules to be expected if the intrinsic magnetic moment of a proton were one nuclear magneton.

(b) Split-up anticipated if the magnetic moment of the proton were three nuclear magnetons. Both (a) and (b) assume that the magnetic field is sufficiently strong to cause complete decoupling of nuclear rotation and nuclear spin. The undeflected beams strike at 0.

mechanics, the rotational and spin angular momenta could each be oriented with respect to the magnetic field lines to have observable angular momenta of 1, 0, or -1. If the proton had a magnetic dipole moment of one nuclear magneton, the dipole moment of the molecule could have values of $(2 + 1)$, $(2 + 0)$, $(2 - 1)$, $(0 + 1)$, $(0 + 0)$, $(0 - 1)$, $(-2 + 1)$, $(-2 + 0)$, $(-2 - 1)$ or, in other words, 3, 2, 1, 0, -1, -2, -3. If a monoergic beam containing molecules having these dipole moments were passed through an inhomogeneous field the beam would be split up as shown in Fig. 2-16(a). On the other hand, if the proton moment were three nuclear magnetons, the beam would be split as shown in Fig. 2-16(b).

At very low temperatures nearly all parahydrogen molecules are in their ground state, in which state they have zero rotational angular momentum and consequently zero rotational magnetic moment. Since the proton spins are antiparallel their intrinsic magnetic moments cancel out, so that parahydrogen molecules that issue from a low-temperature cavity suffer no deflection in an inhomogeneous magnetic field. A beam containing both types of hydrogen molecules with a Maxwellian velocity distribution when passed through an inhomogeneous magnetic field would then give a single broad peak if the proton had a magnetic dipole moment of one nuclear magneton and a peak with wings if its magnetic moment were appreciably greater than one. The latter was observed by Frisch and Stern as shown in Fig. 2-17, and this led them to the conclusion that the magnetic dipole moment of a proton must lie between two and three nuclear magnetons.

Rabi and his collaborators devised a great improvement over the method

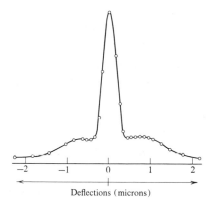

Fig. 2-17. Intensity as a function of deflection in a transverse inhomogeneous magnetic field as observed by Frisch and Stern [*Z. Physik*, **85**, 4 (1933)]. Ordinary hydrogen (a mixture of ortho- and para-) at 95°K was used. The central peak includes all of the parahydrogen. The width of the central peak is attributable almost entirely to the finite resolving power of the detector.

of Frisch and Stern. They passed particles through two consecutive inhomogeneous magnetic fields, such that the first deflected the particles in one direction and the second deflected them in the other. Thus with the two fields properly adjusted, particles passed through to the detector without any net deflection.

The conditions for zero deflection, moreover, are independent of the velocity of the particle. The reason is that the times spent in the two inhomogeneous deflecting fields are each inversely proportional to the velocity of the particle so that the ratio of these two times is a constant. Thus the accuracy of this method, in contrast to the experiments of Frisch and Stern, does not suffer from the spread in velocities of particles emerging from the oven.

This method was first applied to neutral hydrogen atoms (12). The ground state of the neutral hydrogen atom has an electronic orbital angular momentum of zero and an electron spin of $\frac{1}{2}$. It thus has a magnetic moment of approximately one Bohr magneton due to its electron. If one used strong magnetic fields, as in the Frisch and Stern experiment, so that the nuclear spin was completely decoupled from the electron spin, then one would have the problem of observing deflection effects due to the nuclear magnetic moment in the presence of the much larger deflection effects associated with the much larger electron magnetic moment. On the other hand, if smaller magnetic fields are used, the effective magnetic moment of the atom is very sensitive to the relative orientation of nuclear and electronic spins.

The argument that led to Eq. (2-24) shows that one might define the effective magnetic moment of an atom in a magnetic field as

$$\mu_{\text{eff}} = -\frac{\partial W}{\partial B},\qquad(2\text{-}33)$$

where W is the orientation energy of the atom in the magnetic field B. The total instantaneous orientation energy of the atom may be written semi-classically as the sum of the interaction energies of the nuclear and electron magnetic moments and the interaction energy of each magnetic moment with the external magnetic field. Thus

$$-W = \mu_{It}B_J\cos\theta + \mu_{It}B_0\cos\phi + \mu_{Jt}B_0\cos\alpha$$

$$= \frac{\sqrt{I(I+1)}}{I}\,\mu_I B_J\cos\theta + \frac{\sqrt{I(I+1)}}{I}\,\mu_I B_0\cos\phi$$

$$- \frac{\sqrt{J(J+1)}}{J}\,\mu_J B_0\cos\alpha,\qquad(2\text{-}34)$$

where μ_{It} is the total (unobservable) magnetic moment along the nuclear spin axis,

$$\mu_{It} = \frac{\sqrt{I(I+1)}}{I}\,\mu_I,\qquad(2\text{-}35)$$

μ_{Jt} is the total magnetic moment along the electron spin axis,

$$\mu_{Jt} = -\frac{\sqrt{J(J+1)}}{J}\,\mu_J,$$

the negative sign occurring because a revolving negatively charged particle, such as an electron, produces a magnetic moment vector whose sense is opposite to the angular momentum vector of the particle,

μ_I is the maximum observable nuclear magnetic moment,

μ_J is the maximum observable electron magnetic moment,

B_J is the magnetic field strength at the nucleus due to the magnetic moment of the electron,

B_0 is the external magnetic field strength,

θ is the angle between the direction of the "total" electron spin and the total nuclear spin vectors,

ϕ is the corresponding angle between the total nuclear spin and external magnetic field vectors,

α is the corresponding angle between the total electron spin and external magnetic field vectors,

I is the maximum observable nuclear spin, and

J is the maximum observable electron spin.

This would be a fairly simple equation to evaluate if it were not for the quantity B_J. To evaluate B_J one must know the electron current density distribution about the nucleus. This is equivalent to saying that we must know the wave function for the orbital electron of the hydrogen atom in its ground state. Fortunately, the hydrogen atom with its single electron is simple enough that the electron wave function can be calculated theoretically. Even after B_J has been calculated we have only an instantaneous value of the orientation energy, while we need to know the quantity that can be observed, which is the *average* value of the orientation energy. To get at this, the precession of the various total angular momentum vectors must be considered. In the absence of an external magnetic field the total angular momentum vector **F** (see Fig. 2-18) would remain fixed in space and the interaction of the

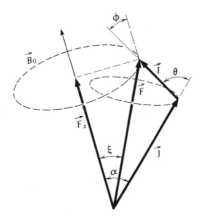

Fig. 2-18. Vector model diagram of a hydrogen atom in a weak magnetic field. For convenience, the figure is drawn to represent that instant in which **I** and **J** lie in the plane of **B₀** and **F**. The angle between **F** and **J** will always be equal to this momentary value of $(\alpha - \xi)$.

nuclear and electronic magnetic fields would cause **J** and **I** to precess together about **F**. If a weak external magnetic field is applied we expect that **I** and **J** will continue to precess rapidly about **F** while **F** precesses slowly about **B**$_0$. Thus, to find the average interaction energy of the nuclear magnetic moment and the external magnetic field, one should first find the projection of μ_{It} on **F**, since this is the average value of the nuclear magnetic moment that is precessing about **B**$_0$, and then take the projection of this average value onto **B**$_0$. The average value of W may then be written

$$-W = \frac{\sqrt{I(I+1)}}{I} \mu_I B_J \cos\theta + \frac{\sqrt{I(I+1)}}{I} \mu_I B_0 \cos(\phi + \xi) \cos\xi$$

$$- \frac{\sqrt{J(J+1)}}{J} \mu_J B_0 \cos(\alpha - \xi) \cos\xi. \qquad (2\text{-}36)$$

From the geometry of the figure and the law of cosines

$$\cos(\phi + \xi) = \frac{I(I+1) + F(F+1) - J(J+1)}{2\sqrt{I(I+1)F(F+1)}}, \qquad (2\text{-}37)$$

$$\cos(\alpha - \xi) = \frac{J(J+1) + F(F+1) - I(I+1)}{2\sqrt{J(J+1)F(F+1)}}, \qquad (2\text{-}38)$$

$$\cos\xi = \frac{F_z^*}{\sqrt{F(F+1)}} \equiv \frac{m}{\sqrt{F(F+1)}}, \qquad (2\text{-}39)$$

and $$\cos\theta = \frac{F(F+1) - J(J+1) - I(I+1)}{2\sqrt{I(I+1)J(J+1)}}, \qquad (2\text{-}40)$$

so that

$$-W = \frac{\sqrt{I(I+1)}}{I} \mu_I B_J \frac{F(F+1) - J(J+1) - I(I+1)}{2\sqrt{I(I+1)}\sqrt{J(J+1)}}$$

$$+ \frac{\sqrt{I(I+1)}}{I} \mu_I B_0 \frac{I(I+1) + F(F+1) - J(J+1)}{2\sqrt{I(I+1)}\sqrt{F(F+1)}} \cdot \frac{m}{\sqrt{F(F+1)}}$$

$$- \frac{\sqrt{J(J+1)}}{J} \mu_J B_0 \frac{J(J+1) + F(F+1) - I(I+1)}{2\sqrt{J(J+1)}\sqrt{F(F+1)}} \cdot \frac{m}{\sqrt{F(F+1)}},$$

$$-W = \frac{F(F+1) - J(J+1) - I(I+1)}{2I\sqrt{J(J+1)}} \mu_I B_J$$

$$+ \frac{I(I+1) + F(F+1) - J(J+1)}{2IF(F+1)} m\mu_I B_0$$

$$- \frac{J(J+1) + F(F+1) - I(I+1)}{2JF(F+1)} m\mu_J B_0. \qquad (2\text{-}41)$$

* The projection of the "total" angular momentum vector onto an axis parallel to the magnetic field is called the "magnetic quantum number," m.

Then

$$\mu_{\text{eff}} = -\frac{\partial W}{\partial B_0} = \frac{m}{2F(F+1)}\left\{[I(I+1) + F(F+1) - J(J+1)]\frac{\mu_I}{I}\right.$$

$$\left. - [J(J+1) - I(I+1) + F(F+1)]\frac{\mu_J}{J}\right\}. \quad (2\text{-}42)$$

In weak magnetic fields, therefore, the effective magnetic moment is not dependent on the field strength and is not sensitive to μ_I because μ_I is so small compared to μ_J. In fields of intermediate intensity the semiclassical derivation given above is no longer valid. A wave mechanical derivation has been carried out by Breit and Rabi (4) for the case of $J = \frac{1}{2}$ which leads to

$$W = -\frac{\Delta W}{2(2I+1)} - \frac{\mu_I}{I} B_0 m \pm \frac{\Delta W}{2}\left(1 + \frac{4m}{2I+1}x + x^2\right)^{1/2}, \quad (2\text{-}43)$$

where

$$x = \frac{\left(\dfrac{-\mu_J}{J} + \dfrac{\mu_I}{I}\right)}{\Delta W} B_0, \quad (2\text{-}44)$$

and ΔW is the energy difference between hyperfine structure levels.

The $+$ sign is used before the third term in W for $F = I + \frac{1}{2}$ and the $-$ sign when $F = I - \frac{1}{2}$.

Fermi (7) and others have calculated ΔW for $J = \frac{1}{2}$ and find

$$\Delta W = \left(\frac{2I+1}{2}\right)\cdot\frac{16}{3}\pi\mu_0\frac{\mu_I}{I}|\psi(0)|^2, \quad (2\text{-}45)$$

where $\psi(0)$ is the electron wave function at the nucleus.

For the normal hydrogen atom, where $I = \frac{1}{2}$,

$$\Delta W = 3.36 \times 10^{-18}\frac{\mu_p}{\mu_{NM}}, \quad (2\text{-}46)$$

where μ_p/μ_{NM} is the magnetic moment of the proton in nuclear magnetons, and ΔW is in ergs.

If one neglects μ_I in comparison to μ_J, then

$$x \cong -\frac{\mu_J}{J\Delta W}B_0 = \frac{2\mu_0 B_0}{\Delta W}, \quad (2\text{-}47)$$

where $\mu_0 = \dfrac{e\hbar}{2mc}$,

$$\mu_{\text{eff}} = -\frac{\partial W}{\partial B_0} = \frac{\mu_I m}{I} - (\pm)\frac{\Delta W}{4}\frac{\left(\dfrac{4m}{2I+1} + 2x\right)\dfrac{\partial x}{\partial B_0}}{\left(1 + \dfrac{4m}{2I+1}x + x^2\right)^{1/2}}, \quad (2\text{-}48)$$

and one obtains for the case $I = \frac{1}{2}$,

$$\mu_{\text{eff}} \cong 2m\mu_I - (\pm)\frac{(m + x)}{(1 + 2mx + x^2)^{1/2}}\mu_0 \tag{2-49}$$

$$\cong -(\pm)\frac{m + x}{(1 + 2mx + x^2)^{1/2}}\mu_0. \tag{2-50}$$

When $m = 0$,

$$(\mu_{\text{eff}})_0 \cong -(\pm)\frac{x}{(1 + x^2)^{1/2}}\mu_0, \tag{2-51}$$

and when $m = \pm 1$,

$$(\mu_{\text{eff}})_{\pm 1} \cong \begin{cases} -\mu_0 & \text{if } m = +1. \\ +\mu_0 & \text{if } m = -1. \end{cases}$$

These values are plotted in Fig. 2-19.

By making the second inhomogeneous field such that it has a different ratio of field to gradient of field than the first inhomogeneous field it is possible

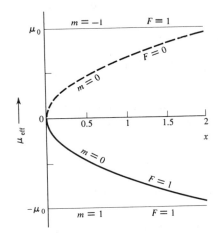

Fig. 2-19. Effective magnetic moment of a hydrogen atom with nuclear spin $\frac{1}{2}$. The nuclear magnetic moment has been taken to be positive. If the nuclear magnetic moment were negative, the solid and the dotted $m = 0$ curves would be interchanged. x is proportional to the imposed external magnetic flux density, B_0 [see Eq. (2-44)].

to have the two deflections at two different values of x. The ratio of the two μ_{eff} values can then be found and, from this, a relationship between x_1 and x_2. The ratio of x_1 to x_2 may be calculated from Eq. (2-51). Having found, say,

x_1, Eq. (2-47) can be used to obtain ΔW, and the magnitude of the proton magnetic moment follows immediately from (2-46).

One might think that it would be more difficult to apply the atomic beam method to the deuterium atom, but it actually turns out to be simpler. Figure 2-20 shows how μ_{eff}/μ_0 varies with x for the deuterium atom. It will be noted that these curves possess a property not shared by the hydrogen curves, namely, that two of the curves cross the x-axis. This means that all atoms for

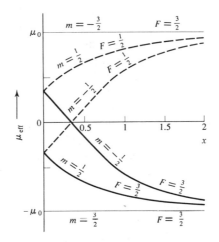

Fig. 2-20. Effective magnetic moment of a deutcrium atom with nuclear spin 1. The nuclear magnetic moment has been taken to be positive as in Fig. 2-19.

which $m = -1$ will be undeflected at this value of x. Since x is proportional to B_0 one can vary the magnetic field until he gets a sudden increase in detector current due to the undeflected atoms. Since these atoms suffer no deflection, it is not necessary to measure the magnetic field gradient as one must do in the case of hydrogen atoms.

To determine the sign* of the magnetic moment, it is necessary to introduce an oscillating field between the two deflecting fields. If the oscillating field quanta are of the correct energy to allow the atom to change from one possible spatial orientation to another, "nonadiabatic" transitions may occur. If such transitions take place, the effective magnetic moment of the atom will be altered and the deflection in the second steady inhomogeneous field will not be of the correct amount to cause the atom to enter the detector. If a

---

* If the magnetic moment corresponds to that expected of a positive charge rotating in the direction of the spin angular motion, it is called a positive magnetic moment. If it is in the direction to be expected of a rotating negative change, it is called a negative magnetic moment.

selector slit is properly positioned just after the first deflecting field, only atoms whose effective magnetic moments are negative are passed. Now if the nuclear magnetic moment is positive, atoms for which $m = 0$ have an angular momentum (F value) of 1 and hence three possible spatial orientations ($m = 1$, $m = 0$, $m = -1$). Nonadiabatic transitions may therefore be induced in the intermediate field. On the other hand, if $m = 0$ and the nuclear magnetic moment is negative, $F = 0$ and nonadiabatic transitions cannot occur since m may have only the value zero. It was thus possible to show that the proton has a positive magnetic moment. In a similar way (taking account of the energies of the radio-frequency quanta that can produce transitions) it was possible to show that the deuteron also has a positive magnetic moment.

Later, the method was applied to molecular beams (13). Here, as in the Frisch and Stern experiments, one may often choose molecules that have zero electronic magnetic moment, so that the nuclear magnetic moments can be measured rather directly. In these experiments there is a steady homogeneous intermediate magnetic field and an oscillating electric (or magnetic) intermediate field. One adjusts the deflecting fields until molecules pass with no *net* deflection to the detector. Then one varies either the magnitude of the steady intermediate field until the energy difference between two orientation states is equal to the energy of a quantum of the oscillating field, or the frequency of the oscillating field until its quanta are equal to the energy difference between two possible orientation states. In either case, when equality is reached, nonadiabatic transitions will take place, the effective moments of the molecules in the second deflecting field will be altered, and those molecules which have undergone such transitions will no longer reach the detector.

If the "oscillating" field is actually a rotating field, then the probability of transition is great only if the field rotates in the same direction and in synchronism with the Larmor precession of the molecule. Since the direction of precession depends on the sign of the magnetic moment, one can select by a suitable slit those molecules which have, say, an effective positive magnetic moment in the first deflecting field, and then, from the direction of rotation of the intermediate field necessary to produce transitions, ascertain whether the magnetic moment of the molecule is actually positive or negative.

If molecules or atoms undergo spatial reorientation as a result of absorption of quanta of energy from the oscillating field, then to the circuit of which the oscillating field coil or loop is a part, the impedance of the loop should appear to have a greater resistance component at the frequency at which transitions are induced. Purcell, Torrey, and Pound (21) have been able to observe such resonance absorptions, not in beams, but in gases, liquids, and solids placed in magnetic fields. This method is known as a magnetic resonance absorption method.

Bloch, Hansen, and Packard (2) devised a somewhat different method in which, at resonance, a signal is generated in a coil that is at right angles to and therefore not normally coupled to the exciting coil. There are many complications to the interpretations of these last two methods. For a more complete discussion the reader is referred to the original papers or to one of the review articles such as that by Pake (19), or to the books by Ramsey (22) and by Kopfermann (14).

2–6   Nuclear Electric Quadrupole Moment

If the charge distribution in a nucleus were spherically symmetric, the charge q would act as though it were concentrated in a point at the center of the nucleus, and the electrostatic potential exterior to the nucleus at any point distant r from the center of the nucleus would simply be

$$U = \frac{q}{r}. \tag{2-52}$$

A slightly more general type of charge distribution would be a figure of revolution about the spin axis of the nucleus, or in other words a charge distribution which is not a function of the azimuth angle ϕ. The potential could then be written in terms of Legendre polynomials, P_n, as

$$U(r, \theta) = \frac{1}{r} \sum_{n=0}^{\infty} \frac{a_n}{r^n} P_n(\cos \theta), \tag{2-53}$$

where $P_0 = 1$,
   $P_1 = \cos \theta$,
   $P_2 = \frac{3}{2} \cos^2 \theta - \frac{1}{2}$,
   $P_3 = \frac{5}{2} \cos^3 \theta - \frac{3}{2} \cos \theta$, etc.,

where θ is the angle between the radius vector r and the spin axis of the nucleus. The ($n = 0$) term is the coulomb term corresponding to (2-52). The ($n = 1$) term would represent the electric dipole field of the nucleus, but as these have never been observed and are not to be expected from theory, we may assume that $a_1 = 0$. The ($n = 2$) term is the electric quadrupole term. By definition, the electric quadrupole moment is $Q = 2a_2/q$. By comparing the potential computed along the axis of spin ($\theta = 0$) with (2-53), it can be shown that

$$Q = \frac{1}{q} \int (3z_n^2 - r_n^2) D(r_n, \theta_n) \, dV_n, \tag{2-54}$$

where the integration is over the volume of the nucleus, dV_n is a nuclear volume element (for example, the ring-shaped volume element $2\pi r_n^2 \sin \theta_n \, d\theta_n \, dr_n$), $z_n (= r_n \cos \theta_n)$ is the distance of the nuclear volume element from the center of the nucleus along the spin axis, and $D(r_n, \theta_n)$ is the charge density at the point (r_n, θ_n, ϕ_n) in the nucleus. The physical import of the quadrupole moment may be easily illustrated by a two-dimensional nucleus (Fig. 2-21).

A spherical distribution of charge within the nucleus (i.e., a distribution which is a function of r_n only) can easily be shown to give $Q = 0$ by application of Eq. (2-54). A distribution that is more elongate (prolate) along the z axis will weight the $3z^2$ term more heavily and give a positive quadrupole moment, whereas a distribution that is flattened (oblate) in the direction of the z axis will lead to a negative quadrupole moment.

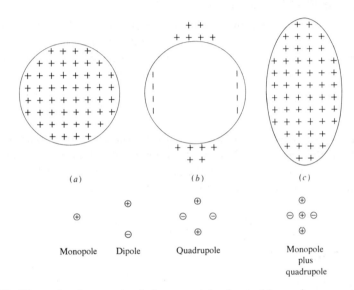

Fig. 2-21. Illustrating how a circularly symmetric charge (a) can be converted to an elliptical charge distribution (c) by the addition of positive and negative charges in equal numbers as shown in (b). The circular distribution acts as a monopole or concentrated charge, while the added charges act, to a first approximation, as a quadrupole.

Thus far the discussion has been classical. If we adopt the viewpoint of the vector model, then the internal magnetic field of the atom should cause the spinning nucleus to precess about an axis parallel to the magnetic field direction. If the charge distribution about the unobservable total angular momentum axis is elongate, which classically would give a positive quadrupole moment, the time average charge distribution about the precession axis would be effectively more flattened. If one lets l be the projection of the total spin vector onto some arbitrary z-axis and I the maximum possible value of l, then it can be shown (1) that the quadrupole moment is

$$Q_l = C[3l^2 - I(I + 1)], \qquad (2\text{-}55)$$

where C is a constant of proportionality that depends on the actual charge distribution within the nucleus. If $I = \frac{1}{2}$, then $l = \pm\frac{1}{2}$ and it follows from

(2-55) that $Q_i = 0$. Thus only nuclei with spins of 1 or greater can exhibit electric quadrupole moments.

It can be shown further that if the nuclear charge distribution has three axes of symmetry (not necessarily a unique set) that are orthogonal to each other, then the nucleus cannot have an electric dipole moment.

The interaction of the nuclear electric quadrupole moment with the electric field of the orbital electrons gives rise to a small change in the energy of the atom which is proportional to the gradient of the electric field strength at the nucleus and to the quadrupole moment. Schüler and Schmidt (25) were able to show in 1935 that this effect could explain an apparent anomaly in the hyperfine structures of Eu^{151} and Eu^{153}. In recent years a number of electric quadrupole moments have been determined by the techniques of microwave spectroscopy. The difficulty in establishing the magnitude of the electric field gradient at the nucleus seriously limits the accuracy of such determinations. Measured electric quadrupole moments vary from about 7×10^{-24} cm^2 for Lu^{176} to $(-1.2 \pm 0.2) \times 10^{-24}$ cm^2 for Sb^{123}. Extensive lists of electric quadrupole moments have been published by Poss (20) and by Mack (16). A more recent tabulation appears in Kopfermann's book (14).

Table 2-2 MAGNETIC MOMENTS OF NUCLEI

Nucleus	Magnetic moment (in nuclear magnetons)	Nucleus	Magnetic moment (in nuclear magnetons)
$_1H^1$	2.7935	$_4Be^9$	-1.1776
$_1H^2$	0.85761	$_{13}Al^{27}$	3.6394
$_1H^3$	2.9795	$_{21}Sc^{48}$	4.8
$_2He^4$	(zero)*	$_{23}V^{51}$	5.1407
$_3Li^6$	0.82210	$_{48}Cd^{113}$	-0.65
$_3Li^7$	3.2567	$_{49}In^{113}$	5.461

* No detectable magnetic moment has ever been found for a nucleus whose spin is zero.

PROBLEMS

2-1 If a charged particle is traveling in a plane that is perpendicular to a uniform magnetic field, show that the time required to make one complete revolution is independent of the energy of the particle, provided the particle moves with a nonrelativistic speed.

2-2 How close will an 8.776-Mev α particle from Po^{212} get to a U nucleus in a head-on collision before being turned back? Neglect the recoil of the U nucleus. (This gives us some idea of the maximum possible size of the U nucleus.) [*Ans.* 3.02×10^{-12} cm.]

2-3 According to Bainbridge and Nier ["Relative Isotopic Abundances of the Elements," Preliminary Report No. 9, Nuclear Science Series, National

Research Council (1950)], tin has naturally occurring stable isotopes with the isotopic abundances listed below. (a) Compute the average isotopic mass of tin, neglecting packing. (b) Correct for packing fraction, using Fig. 2-13, and, taking account of the fact that the atomic weight unit is 1.000275 times the unit of isotopic mass, compute the atomic weight of tin.

Isotope	% Abundance	Isotope	% Abundance
Sn^{112}	0.95	Sn^{118}	24.01
Sn^{114}	0.65	Sn^{119}	8.58
Sn^{115}	0.34	Sn^{120}	32.97
Sn^{116}	14.24	Sn^{122}	4.71
Sn^{117}	7.57	Sn^{124}	5.98

[*Ans.* (a) 118.84, (b) 118.75. This may be compared with the 1956 chemical value of 118.70.]

2-4 Show that for a velocity v, small compared with the velocity of light c, the kinetic energy of a particle of rest mass M_0 given by the relativity formula reduces to $\frac{1}{2}M_0v^2$.

2-5 What is the velocity of an electron that, starting from rest, (a) falls through a potential difference of 2 volts, (b) falls through a potential difference of 10^7 volts?   [*Ans.* (a) 8.39×10^7 cm/sec, (b) 2.9955×10^{10} cm/sec.]

2-6 From the fact that the earth, which is about 92.9 million miles from the sun, receives 0.033 calories of radiant energy per second per square cm of area normal to the sun's rays, compute the number of tons of the sun's mass that must be converted to energy in one year.   [*Ans.* 1.47×10^{14} tons.]

2-7 Prove that two protons revolving in a circular orbit about their common center of mass with an angular momentum of $\hbar$ produce a magnetic moment of one nuclear magneton by this motion. The magnetic moment of a current i (abamperes) in a circular wire loop of radius a cm is $\pi a^2 i$ (ergs/gauss).

2-8 If a proton were a sphere of uniform density with a uniform volume density of charge having an angular momentum $\hbar/2$, what would be its magnetic moment, assuming applicability of the classical laws of electromagnetism?   [*Ans.* $\frac{1}{2}$ nuclear magneton.]

2-9 Find the force exerted on a magnetic dipole of strength μ in the plane of a two-dimensional radial magnetic field. Let the dipole axis be oriented at an angle θ to the direction of the magnetic field..
     [*Ans.* If $B = B_a$ at $r = a$, then $f = -(\mu a B_a \cos \theta/r^2)$.]

2-10 How far would a "cold" orthohydrogen molecule be deflected by a magnetic field having a gradient of 10^5 gauss/cm if the pole pieces were 10 cm long? Take the velocity of the molecules to be 60,000 cm/sec.
     [*Ans.* 13.8×10^{-3}, 11.8×10^{-3}, 9.7×10^{-3}, 2.1×10^{-3}, or 0.0 cm.]

2-11 Starting from Eq. (2-54), show that the electrical quadrupole moment of a spherical charge distribution is zero.

REFERENCES

1. Blatt, J. M., and Weisskopf, V. F., *Theoretical Nuclear Physics* (New York: John Wiley & Sons, 1952).

2. Bloch, F., Hansen, W. W., and Packard, M., *Phys. Rev.*, **69**, 127 (1946).

3. Bohr, N., *Phil. Mag.*, **26**, 1 (1913).

4. Breit, G., and Rabi, I. I., *Phys. Rev.*, **38**, 2082 (1931).

5. Cornish, R. E., and Eastman, E. D., *J. Am. Chem. Soc.*, **50**, 627 (1928).

6. Einstein, A., *Ann. Physik*, **17**, 891 (1905); **18**, 639 (1905).

7. Fermi, E., *Z. Physik*, **60**, 320 (1930).

8. Frisch, R., and Stern, O., *Z. Physik*, **85**, 4 (1933).

9. Geiger, H., and Marsden, E., *Proc. Roy. Soc.*, **A82**, 495 (1909).

10. Geiger, H., and Marsden, E., *Phil. Mag.*, **25**, 604 (1913).

11. Gordy, W., *Rev. Mod. Phys.*, **20**, 668 (1948).

12. Kellogg, J. M. B., Rabi, I. I., and Zacharias, J. R., *Phys. Rev.*, **50**, 472 (1936).

13. Kellogg, J. M. B., Rabi, I. I., Ramsey, N. F., and Zacharias, J. R., *Phys. Rev.*, **56**, 728 (1939).

14. Kopfermann, H., *Nuclear Moments* (New York: Academic Press, 1958).

15. Lamb, W. E., and Retherford, R. C., *Phys. Rev.*, **72**, 241 (1947).

16. Mack, J. E., *Rev. Mod. Phys.*, **22**, 64 (1950).

17. Miner, R. W., ed., "Microwave Spectroscopy," *Ann. N.Y. Acad. Sci.*, **55**, 743 (1952).

18. Moseley, H. G. J., *Phil. Mag.*, **26**, 1024 (1913).

19. Pake, G., *J. Chem. Phys.*, **16**, 327 (1948); *Am. J. Phys.*, **18**, 438, 473 (1950).

20. Poss, H. L., *Spins, Magnetic Moments, and Electric Quadrupole Moments*, BNL-26, October 1, 1949. See also Mack, J. E., *Rev. Mod. Phys.*, **22**, 64 (1950).

21. Purcell, E. M., Torrey, H. C., and Pound, R. V., *Phys. Rev.*, **69**, 37 (1946).

22. Ramsey, N. F., *Nuclear Moments* (New York: John Wiley & Sons, 1953).

23. Rutherford, E., *Phil. Mag.*, **21**, 669 (1911).

24. Rutherford, E., and Soddy, F., *Phil. Mag.*, **5**, 576 (1903).

25. Schüler, H., and Schmidt, T., *Z. Physik*, **94**, 457 (1935).

26. Thomson, J. J., *Rays of Positive Electricity* (2nd ed.; London: Longmans, Green & Co., 1921).

27. Thomson, J. J., *Phil. Mag.*, **13**, 561 (1907); **24**, 209 (1912).

28. Urey, H. C., Brickwedde, F. G., and Murphy, G. M., *Phys. Rev.*, **39**, 164 (1932); **40**, 1 (1932).

3

INTERACTION OF CHARGED
PARTICLES WITH MATTER

3-1 Introduction

The penetration of matter by charged heavy particles (mass at least as great as that of a proton) of moderate energies (i.e., less than about 12 Mev) is the principal topic treated in this chapter. Since α particles were the only such particles available in the earlier days of nuclear physics, most of the discussion centers around α particles, but the results are applicable to other charged heavy particles as well. The extension of the discussion to much higher energies is reserved for a later chapter. The penetration of matter by electrons is discussed briefly, emphasizing those aspects in which electron penetration differs from heavy particle penetration.

In the above, one is concerned only with the interaction of the swift charged particle with the electrons of the material through which it moves. The latter part of the chapter is an introduction to the subject of the interaction of charged particles with nuclei. Later in the book this matter is

65

discussed further, especially in those sections dealing with particles of very great energy.

3-2 Concept of Range

Madame Curie, using apparatus like that shown schematically in Fig. 3-1, measured the ionization produced in the ionization chamber by α rays from a polonium source, as a function of the separation between the ionization

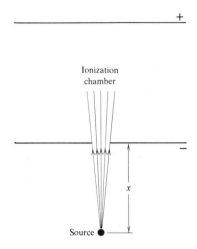

Fig. 3-1. Schematic representation of method used by Madame Curie to determine the ranges of (monoergic) α particles. When x is equal to the range of the particles, they no longer reach the ionization chamber, so that the ionization drops nearly to zero.

chamber and source. The ionization decreased, of course, as the source was moved away, owing partly to the divergence of the beam and partly to energy lost by the particles in ionizing the gas outside the chamber, but at 4 cm the ionization dropped rather suddenly to zero. One says, then, that the "range" of the polonium α particle in air at normal temperature and pressure is 4 cm. Not all α emitters exhibited the property of well-defined range, but it was suspected, and has since been demonstrated, that these radionuclides emit two or more groups of α particles, each having a definite* energy and range. The phenomenon of range is in sharp contrast to the absorption of x-rays and other forms of electromagnetic radiation, where the decrease in intensity of the beam is an exponential function of the thickness of absorber traversed, so that the intensity approaches zero asymptotically as the absorber thickness becomes infinite. The *mean ranges* in air at NTP of the α particles from

---

* Neglecting small statistical fluctuations in range, a phenomenon discussed in Sec. 3-4.

various substances, as given by Holloway and Livingston (16), vary from 2.653 cm for U^{238} to 11.580 cm for Po^{212}.

When the air pressure is doubled, or more exactly, when the density is doubled, the α particle ranges are cut in half. In general, if the range is expressed in units of mass per unit cross section (i.e., the mass of a column of air of unit cross section and of length equal to the range of the particle) rather than as a distance, the range will be found to be independent of the density of the air. The range, even when expressed in mg/cm^2, is not the same for different absorber materials, however. In the case of the elements, the range in mg/cm^2 increases roughly as the square root of the atomic weight, as will be seen by an inspection of the last columns of Tables 3-1 and 3-2.

In the case of a mixture or compound, the range (in mg/cm^2) may be approximated by taking an average value of the range constant (about 0.8 for 4-Mev alphas, as seen from the last column of Table 3-2) and multiplying by the weighted average value of the square roots of the atomic weights of the constituents. Within the limits of accuracy of such an approximation, the range in air may be taken to be the same as that in oxygen. Such rough calculations are useful in estimating the maximum thickness that a window of material may have and still transmit α particles, or in finding the minimum thickness of absorber that will completely remove the α particles from a beam of mixed radiation.

Table 3-1 RANGES OF α PARTICLES FROM Bi^{214}
(Ranges and densities of gases at 15°C, 760 mm Hg)

Z	Element	At. wt M_a	Range (cm)	Density (gm/cm^3)	Range (mg/cm^2)	Range constant $(mg/cm^2)/M_a^{1/2}$
1	H	1.0080	30.93	0.0000852	2.63	2.62
2	He	4.003	32.5	0.000168	5.46	2.73
3	Li	6.94	12.91×10^{-3}	0.534	6.90	2.61
8	O	16.00	6.26	0.00135	8.33	2.08
12	Mg	24.32	5.78×10^{-3}	1.74	10.06	2.04
13	Al	26.97	4.06×10^{-3}	2.699	10.94	2.10
20	Ca	40.08	7.88×10^{-3}	1.55	12.20	1.93
26	Fe	55.85	1.87×10^{-3}	7.86	14.7	1.96
28	Ni	58.69	1.84×10^{-3}	8.90	16.4	2.14
29	Cu	63.57	1.83×10^{-3}	8.94	16.4	2.05
30	Zn	65.38	2.28×10^{-3}	7.14	16.3	2.01
47	Ag	107.88	1.92×10^{-3}	10.50	20.2	1.95
48	Cd	112.41	2.42×10^{-3}	8.65	20.9	1.97
50	Sn	118.70	2.94×10^{-3}	7.31	21.5	1.97
78	Pt	195.23	1.28×10^{-3}	21.37	27.4	1.96
79	Au	197.20	1.40×10^{-3}	19.32	27.0	1.93
81	Tl	204.39	2.33×10^{-3}	11.85	27.6	1.93
82	Pb	207.21	2.41×10^{-3}	11.35	27.3	1.90

SOURCE: H. Rausch von Traubenberg, *Z. Physik*, **2**, 268 (1920); T. S. Taylor, *Phil. Mag.*, **26**, 402 (1913).

Table 3-2 RANGES OF 4-MEV α PARTICLES IN VARIOUS ELEMENTS

Z	Element	At. wt. M_a	Range (mg/cm²)	Range constant (mg/cm²)/$M_a^{1/2}$
13	Al	26.98	4.2	0.81
14	Si	28.09	4.5	0.85
29	Cu	63.54	7.0	0.88
32	Ge	72.60	7.2	0.85
47	Ag	107.88	8.2	0.79
79	Au	197.0	12.7	0.90

SOURCE: G. W. Gobeli, *Phys. Rev.*, **103**, 275 (1956).

If a thin sheet of material is placed in a beam of α rays such that the beam is incident normally on the sheet, then the range (in air at NTP) of the rays will be reduced by a certain amount. The reduction in range in centimeters may be defined as the "stopping power" of the sheet of material. The "relative stopping power" of the material with respect to air may be defined as the stopping power of the sheet divided by the stopping power of a sheet of air at NTP of the same thickness. An equivalent definition is that it is the reciprocal of the thickness of material necessary to reduce the air range by one centimeter. The "relative atomic stopping power" is the ratio of the average stopping power per atom of the material to the average stopping

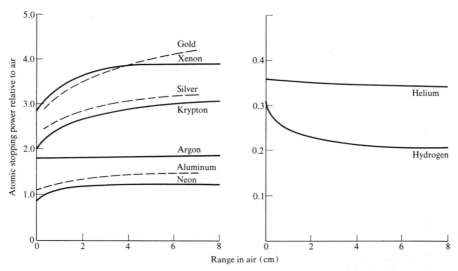

Fig. 3-2. Relative atomic stopping power of various elements as a function of the range of the α particle in air at NTP. It is seen that the relative atomic stopping powers are practically constant for particles whose energies correspond to air ranges greater than 4 cm.

power per atom of some reference material. If a sheet of material of thickness b, density D, and atomic weight M_a produces the same decrease in range as a sheet of thickness b_0 of the reference material, which has a density D_0 and atomic weight M_{a0}, then the relative atomic stopping power s is given by

$$s = \frac{b_0 D_0 M_a}{b D M_{a0}}. \tag{3-1}$$

Although s for a given material is relatively constant for α particles having air ranges greater than 4 cm, it is subject to variations characteristic of the elements involved for lower-energy α particles. This is well illustrated by Fig. 3-2.

3-3 Collision Cross Section

Suppose an α particle of radius r_1 is fired through a group of stationary air molecules, each having a radius r_2. Then, if we treat the α particle and air molecules as hard spheres (which, we shall see, is a very poor assumption), the region in which a collision can take place, as illustrated in Fig. 3-3, is the

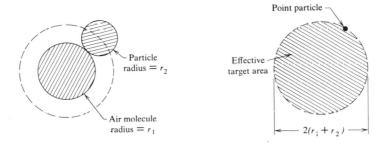

Fig. 3-3. Upper diagram represents grazing collision of a particle with another (stationary) particle such as an air molecule. Lower diagram represents effective target area in which collision is certain. The impinging particle is now treated as a geometrical point.

same as the target area that a sphere of radius $(r_1 + r_2)$ would present to a point (zero-radius) α particle. The target area of a single such sphere will be $\pi(r_1 + r_2)^2$ and, if there are N_m molecules per cm^3, then the total target area* per cm^2 in a slab of air of thickness (measured in the direction of the α-particle trajectory) dx will be $N_m \pi(r_1 + r_2)^2 \, dx$. The probability that an α particle will collide with an air molecule in passing through the slab of air

---

* Neglecting cases where the target area of one molecule obscures part of the target area of another molecule. This approximation becomes better, the lower the number of air molecules per cm^3 and the smaller the thickness of the slab of air.

is equal to the target area of the molecules in the slab divided by the cross section of the slab, which has been taken to be unity. It is therefore given by $N_m\pi(r_1 + r_2)^2\,dx$. Now, suppose a collimated beam of N_α particles is incident on the slab of air and that all of those particles which collide with an air molecule are removed from the beam. Then we may write

$$-dN_\alpha = N_\alpha \cdot N_m\pi(r_1 + r_2)^2\,dx \tag{3-2}$$

or (see Sec. 1-5)

$$N_\alpha = N_{\alpha 0}e^{-N_m\pi(r_1 + r_2)^2 x}, \tag{3-3}$$

where $N_{\alpha 0}$ is the number of particles incident on a slab of air of thickness x, and N_α is the number of particles that pass through the slab without undergoing a collision. The average distance traveled by an α particle before suffering a collision is then given by

$$\Lambda = \frac{\int_{N_{\alpha 0}}^{0} x(-dN_\alpha)}{N_{\alpha 0}} = \frac{1}{N_m\pi(r_1 + r_2)^2}. \tag{3-4}*$$

(The calculation here for the *mean free path*, Λ, will be recognized as being identical with that used to calculate the mean lifetime of a radionuclide in Sec. 1-5). Since the radius of an air molecule is somewhat greater than 10^{-8} cm while the radius of an α particle is negligible by comparison, and $N_m = 2.705 \times 10^{19}$ molecules/cm^3 at NTP, a maximum value for the mean free path to be expected on the assumption that air molecules act like hard spheres is

$$\Lambda_{hs} = \frac{1}{2.705 \times 10^{19} \times 3.14 \times (10^{-8})^2} \cong 10^{-4} \text{ cm.}$$

Since the observed ranges are measured in centimeters and since the tracks in photographic emulsions and in cloud chambers are nearly straight lines, as shown in Figs. 3-4 and 3-5, it follows that air molecules and their constituent atoms are highly transparent to α particles; this fact is also demonstrated by the scattering experiments of Geiger and Marsden, which showed that the interaction of an α particle and a nucleus obeys the known laws of electrostatics even for large-angle deflections where the α particle approaches within 3.2×10^{-12} cm of the nucleus. If we treat the nucleus as a hard elastic sphere of radius 3.2×10^{-12} cm, rather than as a charged body, we obtain a mean free path for nuclear collision of more than 10^3 cm. This shows that, except in the rare instance of large-angle scattering, the α particle does not lose any appreciable energy through collisions with nuclei.

Because the collision cross section is closely related to the probability of collision, it is customary in nuclear physics to use the term *cross section*. For example, suppose a large number, N, of particles impinge perpendicularly

* Note that this expression gives a mean free path that is independent of the energy of the particle.

Fig. 3-4. Photomicrograph of alpha particle tracks in a nuclear photographic emulsion which was soaked in a dilute uranyl acetate solution. Some of the V-shaped tracks may be the result of successive alpha decays.

Fig. 3-5. Cloud-chamber photograph of alpha-particle tracks from radium-bearing self-luminous paint of clock hand.

upon a thin layer of absorber of thickness dx, and that $-dN$ of them* suffer collisions. Then the probability that a single particle will suffer a collision is $-dN/N$, so that the target area per cm^2 must also be $-dN/N$. But the target area per cm^2 is the product of the target area per atom (its cross section, σ) and the number of atoms in the volume dx. Thus

$$\frac{-dN}{N} = N_s \sigma \, dx, \qquad (3\text{-}5)$$

where N_s is the number of scattering atoms per cm^3, or

$$\sigma = \frac{-dN/dx}{NN_s}. \qquad (3\text{-}6)$$

It should be noted that σ is strictly a conceptual quantity. It is not a property of the target atoms, but a property of the specific interaction between projectile and target atoms. The cross section is usually a function of the energy of the impinging particle. Thus (3-5) cannot be exactly integrated unless, from range-energy relationships, σ can be given as a function of the thickness of material traversed, x. The measured cross section often turns out to be of the same order of magnitude as the geometrical cross section of a nucleus, namely, about 10^{-24} cm^2. One therefore defines a unit of cross section, called the *barn*, which is equal to 10^{-24} cm^2. In some processes it is convenient to use the *millibarn* (mb) which is 10^{-27} cm^2.

The collision cross section is related to the total probability that a particle be scattered. It is often desirable to be more specific. One then defines a *differential cross section* which is related to the probability that an event takes place within a restricted range of values of some parameter. For example, one might ask, "What is the probability that a particle be scattered through an angle between θ and $\theta + d\theta$ in passing through a thickness, dx, of scatterer?" If $P(\theta)$ is the probability density per unit angle, this could be written

$$P(\theta) \, dx \, d\theta = \sigma(\theta) N_s \, dx \, d\theta, \qquad (3\text{-}7)$$

or it could be written in terms of the probability density per unit solid angle, $P'(\theta)$, as

$$P'(\theta) \, dx \, d\Omega = \sigma'(\theta) N_s \, dx \, d\Omega, \qquad (3\text{-}8)$$

where $d\Omega$ is the element of solid angle into which the particle is scattered. Since the solid angle encompassed between θ and $\theta + d\theta$ is $2\pi \sin \theta \, d\theta$ steradians, the two differential cross sections are related by

$$\sigma(\theta) = 2\pi \sin \theta \sigma'(\theta). \qquad (3\text{-}9)$$

---

* The minus sign is introduced here as in Eq. (3-2) to take care of the case where a collision removes the particle from the beam. The usual convention, that dN represents an *increase* in the number of particles in the beam, demands that the number of particles *removed* from the beam be $-dN$.

We shall use the concept of cross section later on, not only for scattering, but also for many other kinds of nuclear interaction.

3-4 Ionization by Heavy Particles

The first accurate determination of the total ionization produced by an α particle was made by Geiger (14). He measured the total ion current produced in air by α particles from Bi^{214}, and by using the values $q = 2 \times 4.65 \times 10^{-10}$ esu for the charge on an α particle and $N_\alpha = 3.57 \times 10^{10}$ particles/sec-gm Ra, he deduced that 2.37×10^5 ion pairs are produced per α particle. If presently accepted values of q and N_α are used, his results give 2.2×10^5 ion pairs/Bi^{214} α. Fonovits-Smereker (13) obtained a value of 2.20×10^5 ion pairs/Bi^{214} α, and this was later confirmed by I. Curie and F. Joliot (10). If the energy of a Bi^{214} α particle is taken as 7.68 Mev, then the average energy loss by the α particle, per ion pair formed in air, is about 35 ev. Since the atomic ionization potential for nitrogen is 14.48 volts and for oxygen is 13.55 volts, a considerable proportion of the α-particle energy must be expended in processes other than single ionization of atoms. Some of the energy must go into dissociation of the diatomic gas molecules O_2 and N_2, some into excitation of the atoms or molecules, and some into double or

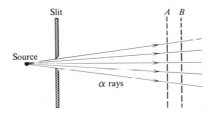

Fig. 3-6. Schematic diagram of a possible experimental method for measuring ionization as a function of the distance traveled by α particles. Only ionization produced in the volume between the screen electrodes A and B is measured. The slit guarantees that the same number of α particles pass through the volume AB regardless of how far it is from the source, unless particles come to rest or suffer large-angle scattering before reaching A.

multiple ionization of an atom (which requires more energy per electron released than single ionization).

The ionization per unit path length along the path of an α particle may be measured by using the scheme shown in Fig. 3-6. The collimated beam of α particles ionizes the air between the screens A and B. By keeping the separation between A and B constant and moving both away from the source, the ionization can be obtained as a function of the distance of *AB* from the source. Results obtained by I. Curie in this way are shown in Fig. 3-7.

If the ionization is plotted as a function of *residual range* (i.e., the distance the particles can go from the point where their ionization is being measured

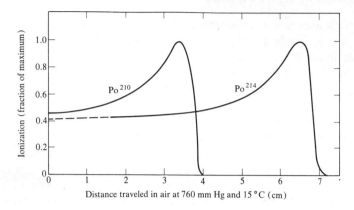

Distance traveled in air at 760 mm Hg and 15 °C (cm)

Fig. 3-7. Ionization as a function of the distance the thin ionization chamber is placed from the source (see Fig. 3-6). While the range of Po^{214} alpha particles is much greater than that of Po^{210} alpha particles, the shapes of the curves are very nearly the same. The ionization produced by a single alpha particle per unit length of path increases as the particle slows down. Straggling causes the *number* of particles entering the chamber to decrease near the end of the range so that the measured ionization decreases.

before they will all be brought to rest) the two curves are very nearly identical. This is what one would expect if all the particles lose energy continuously through ionization as they progress through the gas, for then an α particle from Po^{210} with enough energy remaining to go one more centimeter before being brought to a stop does not differ from a Po^{214} α particle with the same residual energy.

Henderson (15) made very precise ionization measurements near the end of the range of α particles by allowing *A* and *B* to remain at fixed distances from the source and measuring the ionization between *A* and *B* as a function of the air pressure in the chamber. His results are shown in Fig. 3-8. It will be noted that the curve approaches the axis asymptotically, so that the maximum range is rather an indefinite quantity. To avoid this vagueness, Marsden and Perkins (20) suggested that the virtually straight, sloping portion of the ionization *vs.* range curve just before the tail (region *CB* in Fig. 3-8) be extrapolated to the range axis. The intersection of this straight line with the range axis is then defined as the "extrapolated range."

Cloud-chamber photographs of α-particle tracks show that the particles all have nearly, but not exactly, the same range and that the ionization as indicated by fog droplet density increases up to the end of the track. The shape of the ionization-range curve near maximum range is therefore to be ascribed to the variation in range of α particles from the same source, which effect is called *straggling*. The variation in range (6, 11) about some mean value is found to be nearly gaussian, so that the fraction

$$\frac{\text{number of particles having ranges between } x \text{ and } x + dx}{\text{total number of particles}}$$

is given by

$$N(x)\,dx = \frac{e^{-[(R_0 - x)/\alpha]^2}}{\pi^{1/2}\alpha}\,dx, \qquad (3\text{-}10)$$

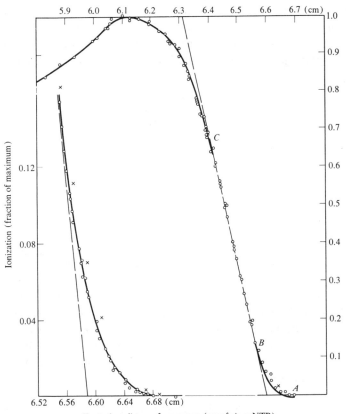

Fig. 3-8. Ionization produced by Bi^{214} α particles per unit path length as a function of the equivalent air distance from the source. Actually, Henderson kept the distance between source and ionization chamber constant and varied the air density by varying the pressure. The curve at the left is an expanded plot of the portion BA of the curve at the right. A straight line drawn through CB intersects the axis at about 6.58 cm. This distance is called the extrapolated range.

where R_0 is the mean range of the particles and α, the range straggling para-meter, is the half-width of the range distribution curve at $1/e$ of its maximum. It is thus apparent that the mean range of an α particle will correspond to a point on the specific ionization curve at approximately half the maximum, and that this will be appreciably smaller than the extrapolated range. Since both types of range are reported in the literature, it is important to distinguish between the two.

3-5 Theory of Ionization by Heavy Particles

A crude theory of specific ionization by a charged heavy particle can be constructed, which, although leading to incorrect results, gives a qualitative understanding of the observed phenomena. Suppose a charged particle of kinetic energy W_k, mass M, and charge Ze, where Z is an integer and e is the electronic charge, passes near an electron of mass m at a distance b from the path of the particle, as shown in Fig. 3-9. If we assume that the energy lost

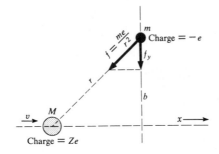

Fig. 3-9. Diagram of a rapidly moving charged particle interacting with an electron of the absorber to produce ionization.

by the moving particle is relatively small in such a single encounter, then it is simpler to find the energy given to the electron than to find directly the energy lost by the particle. Let the particle be moving so swiftly that the electron does not move appreciably during the encounter. Then the sum of the impulses given to the electron in the x-direction will be zero,* while the sum in the y-direction will be

$$p_y = \int f_y \, dt = \int_{-\infty}^{\infty} \frac{bZe^2}{(b^2 + x^2)^{3/2}} \frac{dx}{v} = \frac{2Ze^2}{vb}. \tag{3-11}$$

* The error that we make by neglecting the x-component of the momentum p_x given to the electron will be only about 1% if p_x is as great as 10% of p_y, since the energy (3-12) is given by

$$W_e = \frac{p^2}{2m} = \frac{p_x^2 + p_y^2}{2m}.$$

The situation is depicted graphically in Fig. 3-10.

The energy given to the electron can then be computed from its momentum:

$$W_e = \frac{p_y^2}{2m} = \frac{2Z^2e^4}{mv^2b^2}. \tag{3-12}$$

If there are NZ_m effective electrons per unit volume, then the energy given to the electrons in a cylindrical shell of radius b and thickness db as the moving charge goes from $x = -a$ to $x = +a$ is

$$dW_e \cong 2a \cdot 2\pi b \, db \cdot NZ_m \cdot \frac{2Z^2e^4}{mv^2b^2}, \tag{3-13}$$

the approximation being good if $a \gg b$ so that the region in which (3-11) does not hold is small. The energy per unit path length is then

$$\frac{dW_e}{dx} = \frac{2a \, 2\pi b \, db \, NZ_m}{2a} \frac{2Z^2e^4}{mv^2b^2}, \tag{3-14}$$

and the total energy per unit path length given to electrons in a cylinder of inner radius b_1 and outer radius b_2 is

$$\frac{dW_{et}}{dx} = \frac{4\pi Z^2 e^4 NZ_m}{mv^2} \int_{b_1}^{b_2} \frac{db}{b} \tag{3-15}$$

$$= \frac{4\pi Z^2 e^4 NZ_m}{mv^2} \ln \frac{b_2}{b_1}. \tag{3-16}$$

When a is allowed to become infinite, the approximation becomes very good, provided b_2 is kept finite (as it must be if the energy loss is to be finite), and

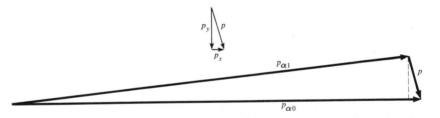

Fig. 3-10. Diagram illustrating momentum conservation in the ionization process and showing that it is reasonable to neglect the x component of momentum given to the electron. The relative magnitude of the electron momentum has been greatly exaggerated for purposes of illustration.

(3-16) gives what will hereafter be referred to as the "space rate of loss of energy" by the moving charged particle. Then*

$$\frac{dW}{dR} = \frac{4\pi Z^2 e^4 NZ_m}{mv^2} \ln \frac{b_2}{b_1}. \tag{3-17}$$

* The quantity dW/dR is positive if R is the *residual range*, for then W decreases as R decreases.

It is clear that b_1 cannot be allowed to go to zero as this would make dW/dR infinite and negative. We see, therefore, that for Eq. (3-17) to have meaning, b_1 cannot go to zero and b_2 cannot become infinite. Arguments can be given for definite choices of b_1 and b_2, but they are not very satisfactory, and it is even possible that b_2/b_1 is a function of the particle velocity.

If one assumes, nevertheless, that b_2/b_1 is a constant, then the actual value of the fraction is not essential to our discussion as we are more interested in comparative than in absolute values of range. With the assumption of constant b_2/b_1, one obtains

$$R = \int dR = \int_0^W \frac{mv^2}{4\pi Z^2 e^4 N Z_m \ln b_2/b_1} \, dW. \tag{3-18}$$

Making use of the fact that

$$W = \tfrac{1}{2} M v^2, \tag{3-19}$$

$$dW = Mv \, dv, \tag{3-20}$$

and

$$R = \frac{mM}{4\pi Z^2 e^4 N Z_m \ln b_2/b_1} \int_0^v v^3 \, dv \tag{3-21}$$

$$= \frac{mMv^4}{16\pi Z^2 e^4 N Z_m \ln b_2/b_1}. \tag{3-22}$$

It is observed experimentally, in the case of alpha particles, that

$$R = kv^w, \tag{3-23}$$

where k is a constant of proportionality and w is not a true constant but a slowly varying function of v. For energies encountered in natural alpha decay, w is approximately 3, which is clearly not in very good agreement with (3-22).

A great number of attempts* have been made to deduce, theoretically, an exact relationship between ionization, velocity, and range of charged particles. Although no generally applicable formula has been derived, several satisfactory approximations have been made for special cases. Some things that could cause the oversimplified derivation used above to lead to erroneous results are:

1. Neglect of momentum imparted to the electron in the x-direction.
2. The fact that energy transfer in amounts less than the ionization potential must be quantized.
3. The wave-mechanical effect (29) of resonance, in which appreciable energy is transferred to a distant electron, in contrast to the classical treatment in which energy transfer to distant electrons is negligible.

* See Refs. 1, 4, 5, 7, 11, 12, 17, 21, and 27.

4. Neglect of the momentum transferred to the nucleus, especially where quantum considerations will not allow the energy of the electron to be altered.

5. Bremsstrahlung, or radiation caused by acceleration or deceleration of the charged particle. This effect should be negligible, however, for the interaction of such a heavy particle as the α particle with electrons.

6. Variation of b_2/b_1 with velocity.

7. Near the end of its range, a charged particle may pick up an electron, thus reducing its effective charge and hence its rate of energy loss. The picked-up electron is usually lost again before the particle has moved very far. This pick-up and loss may alternate several times before the particle comes to rest, but it is clear that the process extends the range beyond that contemplated for a particle of the initial charge.

Equation (3-24), due to Livingston and Bethe (18), gives the space rate of energy loss, from ionization effects only, of fast particles:

$$\frac{dW}{dR} = \frac{4\pi e^4 Z^2}{mv^2} \, NZ_m \left[\ln \left(\frac{2mv^2}{I} \right) - \ln (1 - \beta^2) - \beta^2 \right], \qquad (3\text{-}24)$$

where NZ_m is the effective number of electrons per unit volume of stopping material of atomic number Z_m, β is the ratio of the velocity of the particle to the velocity of light in free space, and I is the mean excitation potential of the atoms in the stopping material.

This formula is valid only for particle velocities much greater than the velocity of orbital electrons in the K shell of the atoms of the stopping material. Effects such as radiation, nuclear interaction, and so on are not taken into account in this formula. The relativistic terms (30) (those involving β) arise from the effect of the Lorentz contraction of the field of the moving particle on distant electrons. The first term in the expansion of $\ln (1 - \beta^2)$ is $(-\beta^2)$, so the last two terms within the brackets may be neglected when β is small.

Figure 3-11 shows how the space rate of energy loss, calculated from the Bethe and Livingston formula, varies with the ratio of the kinetic energy to the rest energy of a charged particle. It will be noted that each of the curves passes through a minimum. The minimum space rate of energy loss is independent of the mass of the moving particle, but is proportional to the charge squared. Thus an α particle will lose energy, and hence produce ionization, at a minimum rate four times as great as the minimum rate for protons. This fact often makes it possible to determine the charge of particles of very high energy.

If we assume that the oversimplifications involved in the derivation of (3-22) will not change its form except for the power of v (which will be taken to be 3 for alpha particles in the energy range involved in this discussion), then we may write

$$R = k' \frac{Mv^3}{Z^2},$$ (3-25)

where k' is a proportionality constant. It may be shown that the maximum velocity (see Prob. 3-7) that can be given by an α particle to a proton in a collision is $v_p = 1.6v_\alpha$. If we use this relation together with (3-25) to calculate

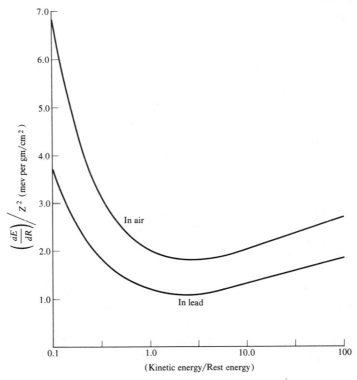

Fig. 3-11. Space rate of energy loss curve calculated from the Bethe and Livingston formula (3-24). The space rate of energy loss in Mev per gm/cm² is Z^2 times the ordinate, where Z is the number of electronic charges on the moving particle. The kinetic energies are expressed in units of M_0c^2. Since the ionization rate is nearly in direct proportion to the rate of energy loss, the minimum ionization will occur at approximately the same energy as the minimum rate of energy loss. For an alpha particle the minimum occurs at a little over 10 Bev.

the maximum range of a recoil proton relative to the maximum range that the impinging α particle would have in the absence of a collision, we obtain

$$\frac{R_p}{R_\alpha} = \frac{M_p}{M_\alpha} \left(\frac{Z_\alpha}{Z_p}\right)^2 \left(\frac{v_p}{v_\alpha}\right)^3 = \frac{1}{4}\left(\frac{2}{1}\right)^2 \left(\frac{1.6}{1}\right)^3 = 4.1,$$

which is in reasonably good agreement with the value of 4 found by Marsden (19) in scintillation experiments. Equations (3-22) and (3-24) are in qualitative agreement with the following experimentally observed facts:

1. The range of a proton is greater than the range of a deuteron, which is greater in turn than that of an α particle if they all have the same energy.
2. Alpha particles are less penetrating than β particles of the same energy.
3. The tracks of electrons observed in cloud chambers and nuclear emulsions are generally lighter (smaller ionization per unit range) than the tracks of protons, which are in turn lighter than the tracks of α particles, while the tracks of highly ionized heavy atoms are very dense.
4. The tracks of very-high-energy light particles are very faint or not detectable at all.

Since nearly all methods of observing charged particles rest ultimately on their ability to ionize, the range-energy and rate-of-energy loss *vs.* energy relations are of considerable importance in studying nuclear phenomena. For example, the tracks of charged particles in nuclear emulsions are due to the fact that the silver halide grains are ionized by the charged particle and thus become developable in the same way as light-activated grains. The great density of the emulsion, compared to air, means that many more ions are produced per unit path length, so that the tracks are very short compared to cloud-chamber tracks but the range-energy curves are of the same form, as will be seen by an inspection of Fig. 3-12.

If one has an experimentally determined range-energy curve for a particle of given mass and charge, it is possible to construct a range-energy curve for a second particle that has a different mass and charge. To do this, it is necessary only to assume that the space rate-of-energy loss is a function of velocity alone for particles bearing the same charge and that it varies as the square of the charge for particles of differing charge moving with the same speed. In equation form,

$$\frac{dW}{dR} = Z^2 f(v). \tag{3-26}$$

But
$$W = Mc^2 \left(\frac{1}{\sqrt{1 - v^2/c^2}} - 1 \right)$$

so that v is a function only of W/M. Equation (3-26) may then be rewritten as

$$\frac{dW}{dR} = Z^2 F\left(\frac{W}{M}\right), \tag{3-27}$$

where F is some, as yet unspecified, function of W/M. By integrating Eq. (3-27), one may obtain R. Thus

$$R = \int_0^R dR = \frac{1}{Z^2} \int_0^W \frac{dW}{F(W/M)} = \frac{M}{Z^2} \int_0^{W/M} \frac{d(W/M)}{F(W/M)},$$

or
$$R = \frac{M}{Z^2} \mathscr{F}\left(\frac{W}{M}\right), \tag{3-28}$$

where
$$\mathscr{F}\left(\frac{W}{M}\right) = \int_0^{W/M} \frac{d(W/M)}{F(W/M)}.$$

Equation (3-28) may be rewritten as

$$\frac{RZ^2}{M} = \mathscr{F}\left(\frac{W}{M}\right). \tag{3-29}$$

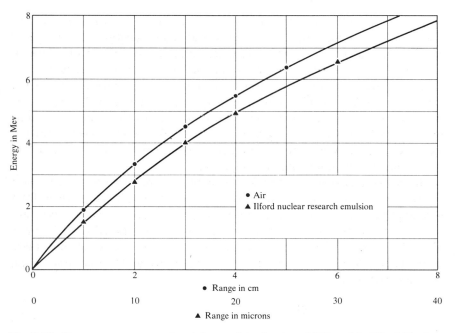

Fig. 3-12. Range-energy curves for alpha particles in air at NTP and in Ilford Nuclear Research emulsion. The relatively very great density of emulsion makes the corresponding ranges much shorter than in air, but the shapes of the curves are nearly identical.

To obtain the range-energy curve of a particle of mass M_2 and charge Z_2 from that of a particle of mass M_1 and charge Z_1, one then goes through the following steps:

1. Select a point on the known range-energy curve (i.e., a pair of values of R_1 and W_1).

2. Calculate the corresponding values of $R_1 Z_1^2 / M_1$ and W_1 / M_1.
3. The value of $\mathscr{F}$ depends only on the ratio W/M. Therefore the same value of $\mathscr{F}$ will apply to a pair of points on the new curve if

$$\frac{W_1}{M_1} = \frac{W_2}{M_2}. \tag{3-30}$$

This relationship is used to calculate a value W_2 on the new curve.
4. Since $\mathscr{F}_1$ has been made equal to $\mathscr{F}_2$,

$$\frac{R_1 Z_1^2}{M_1} = \frac{R_2 Z_2^2}{M_2} \tag{3-31}$$

from Eq. (3-29). This expression may be used to calculate R_2. One now has a pair of points (R_2, W_2) on the new curve corresponding to the pair (R_1, W_1) on the original curve for the same value of $\mathscr{F}$.

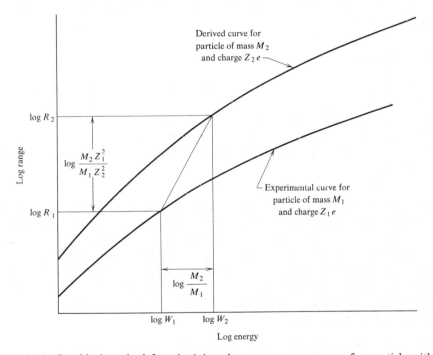

Fig. 3-13. Graphical method for obtaining the range-energy curve of a particle with mass M_2 and charge $Z_2 e$ from the known range-energy curve of a particle of mass M_1 and charge $Z_1 e$. If $Z_1 = Z_2$ the line joining corresponding points on the two curves will have a slope of 45°. Thus if one can determine the range-energy curve of a particle of unknown mass but the same charge as that of a particle of known mass for which a range-energy curve exists, the ratio of the energies of two corresponding points on the two curves which are connected by a 45° line will give the ratio of the masses of the particles.

5. Repetition of the above steps will transform the original range-energy curve to a range-energy curve for the second particle.

The process of constructing the new range-energy curve is greatly simplified if the curves are plotted on logarithmic coordinates. Then Eq. (3-30) becomes

$$\log W_2 = \log W_1 + \log \left(\frac{M_2}{M_1}\right) \tag{3-32}$$

and (3-31) becomes

$$\log R_2 = \log R_1 + \log \left(\frac{M_2 Z_1^2}{M_1 Z_2^2}\right). \tag{3-33}$$

As shown in Fig. 3-13 each point on the new curve is simply displaced upward by an amount $\log (M_2 Z_1^2 / M_1 Z_2^2)$ and to the right by an amount $\log (M_2/M_1)$ from the corresponding point on the original curve. An approach like that just outlined has proved to be very useful in the analysis of nuclear emulsion tracks.

3-6 Ionization by Electrons

A swift electron, in moving through matter, loses energy in much the same way as a charged heavy particle does, but there are some important differences. For one thing, the sidewise momentum given to the moving charged particle is much more significant in the case of a moving electron than it is in the case of a moving heavy particle. This is because, as seen from the equation

$$p = (2mW)^{1/2},$$

the momentum of an electron is much smaller than that of a heavy particle having the same kinetic energy. In particular, an electron will have only about $\frac{1}{86}$ the momentum of an α particle if both have the same energy.

Another difference arises when the scattering and scattered particles are indistinguishable. In this case one cannot tell, after a collision, which is the scattered particle. Bethe (25), arbitrarily calling the particle with the larger energy the scattered particle, obtains the following formula for the space rate of energy loss by electrons:

$$\frac{dW}{dR} = \frac{2\pi e^4 N Z_m}{mv^2} \left[\ln \frac{mv^2 W}{2I^2} - \ln (1 - \beta^2) \right.$$

$$\left. - (2\sqrt{1 - \beta^2} - 1 + \beta^2) \ln 2 + 1 - \beta^2 + \frac{1}{8} (1 - \sqrt{1 - \beta^2})^2 \right]. \tag{3-34}$$

This formula gives only the energy loss through what might be called ordinary collisions. It does not include energy loss through radiation (bremsstrahlung).

According to classical electromagnetic theory, when a charged particle of charge e suffers an acceleration of magnitude a, it radiates electromagnetic energy at a rate given by

$$\frac{dW}{dt} = \frac{2}{3} \frac{e^2}{c^3} a^2.$$ (3-35)

Since $a = f/M$, it is evident that for a given force acting on a moving charged particle the rate of radiation is inversely proportional to the square of the mass of the particle. Thus a proton would radiate at a rate about 3×10^{-7} that of an electron. The space rate of radiative energy loss increases nearly linearly with the kinetic energy, W, of the electron and approximately as the square of the atomic number, Z_m, of the scattering material. Bethe and Heitler (2) show that the ratio of radiative to ordinary collision loss is

$$\frac{(dW/dR)_{\text{rad}}}{(dW/dR)_{\text{col}}} \cong \frac{WZ_m}{800},$$ (3-36)

where W is given in Mev. Thus in mercury ($Z_m = 80$), bremsstrahlung losses would equal ordinary collision losses for an electron of 10 Mev kinetic energy.

The relativistic terms in (3-34) cause the space rate of energy loss, which is decreasing with increasing energy at small kinetic energies, to pass through a minimum and start increasing as β approaches unity. Another effect not taken account of in the derivation of (3-34) comes into play as β becomes appreciable, namely, polarization of the dielectric (the medium through which the electron is passing) by the moving electron. This causes the rate of energy loss to rise much more slowly with increasing energy than (3-34. would indicate.

3-7 Nuclear Disintegration by Bombardment

Rutherford and his coworkers found that when α emitters were mounted on metal plates, long-range particles were observed. These particles had approximately the same range as the recoil protons observed when α particles from these same emitters were passed through hydrogen gas. It was believed therefore that these long-range particles must be recoil protons from hydrogen occluded on the metal surface. In 1919, however, Rutherford (22) reported a set of experiments that required a very different explanation.

An intense Bi^{214} source was placed in a metal box about 3 cm from an opening at one end. This opening was covered by a silver plate whose stopping power was about equal to 6 cm of air. A zinc sulfide scintillation screen was placed 1 mm outside of the box so that absorbing foils could be introduced between the silver plate and screen. The whole apparatus was placed in a strong magnetic field to deflect any β rays out of the beam. When the air in the box was exhausted and absorption measurements were made with aluminum foils, Rutherford found, as in his earlier experiments, that some scintillations were observed even when the aluminum absorber corresponded to a much greater range in air than that of the α particles from the source. When dry oxygen or dry carbon dioxide was introduced into the box, the number of long-range particles reaching the screen was reduced, as expected, because of the extra thickness of absorber. When dry air was introduced, however, the number of scintillations *increased*! With absorber equivalent to 19 cm of air, the number of scintillations with dry air in the box was double the number observed when the box was evacuated. Since it was known from earlier works that recoil singly ionized oxygen and nitrogen atoms have a range of about 9 cm (see Prob. 3-8), the increase could not be due to heavy recoils. Moreover, the absence of such an increase in oxygen and CO_2 indicated that the effect was traceable to the nitrogen in dry air, or else to some other rarer constituent of dry air, such as argon. To test this hypothesis, Rutherford prepared pure nitrogen from NH_4Cl and $NaNO_2$. With pure nitrogen in the box the number of scintillations was 1/4 greater than with dry air. Since air is 4/5 nitrogen, this is just the increase to be expected if the effect is due to nitrogen.

When gold or aluminum foils were placed close to the source, the range of the secondary particles was cut down in proportion to the decreased range of the α particles after traversing these foils. This showed that the long-range particles were actually due to collisions of the α particles with nitrogen atoms in the volume of the gas rather than to some effect at the source brought about through introduction of the nitrogen. The range of the particles, together with the fact that they produced weak scintillations which appeared to be the same as those produced by recoil protons, led Rutherford to conclude that the long-range particles produced by α bombardment of nitrogen are protons.*

Rutherford and Chadwick (23) repeated and extended these experiments with superior optical equipment for observing the scintillations and found that the particles from nitrogen had a range of 40 cm of air compared with the maximum recoil proton range of 29 cm. Using absorbers equivalent to 32 cm of air, they observed long-range particles (believed to be protons) from α bombardment of several elements, as shown in Table 3-3. They failed to observe any long-range particles from a number of other elements, but had no way of knowing whether they emitted shorter-range particles under bombardment. In these experiments they made the significant observation that the particles were emitted in all directions.

---

* In the article cited above (22), Rutherford makes the following prophetic statement: "Considering the enormous intensity of the forces brought into play, it is not so much a matter of surprise that the nitrogen atom should suffer disintegration as that the α particle itself escapes disruption into its constituents. The results as a whole suggest that if α particles—or similar projectiles—of still greater energy were available for experiment, we might expect to break down the nucleus structure of many of the lighter atoms."

The nondirectionality was not completely understood at the time, but it is strong evidence that the α particle is absorbed or captured by the nucleus. The new nucleus then decomposes into a proton and a residual nucleus. Since the residual nucleus is much more massive than the proton, the proton may be emitted in any direction and still conserve momentum.* If the α particle simply chipped a loosely bound proton from the nitrogen nucleus, then no protons could be ejected at angles of more than 90° with respect to the direction of motion of the incident α particle.

The discovery of nondirectionality enabled Rutherford and Chadwick (24) to revise their experimental technique so that only particles emitted at a 90° angle to the α beam were observed. With this arrangement they obtained practically no background scintillations (which are mostly due to proton recoils in the direction of the beam due to hydrogen contamination) and could observe short-range disintegration particles. In this way they found that in addition to the elements listed in Table 3-3, neon, magnesium, silicon, sulfur, chlorine, argon, and potassium emitted particles with ranges greater than 7 cm of air.

Table 3-3 RANGES OF PROTONS PRODUCED BY α-PARTICLE
BOMBARDMENT OF VARIOUS ELEMENTS

Element	Maximum range of particles in cm of air
Boron	~ 45
Nitrogen	40
Fluorine	> 40
Sodium	~ 42
Aluminum	90
Phosphorus	~ 65

Blackett (3) succeeded in obtaining cloud-chamber tracks showing proton emission by N under α bombardment. Since this is a fairly rare event he had to take 23,000 photographs containing 415,000 tracks to obtain eight examples of the event. In each case there are only two prongs to the fork in the track, showing that the α particle is absorbed into the nucleus and that a proton is emitted. This is made even more certain by the fact that each set of tracks is coplanar, which would not be the case if a third particle were emitted but failed to leave a track. Blackett suggested the reaction

$$_7N^{14} + _2He^4 \rightarrow _8O^{17} + _1H^1,$$

although $_8O^{17}$ had not been discovered at that time.

While a number of artificial disintegrations were induced by α-particle bombardment of light elements, it is clear that more and more energy is

---

* As will be seen in a later chapter, this is true only when the energy of the α particle is not too great.

required to overcome the repulsive coulomb force of the nucleus as its atomic number increases. This fact seemed to indicate that exceedingly energetic bombarding particles would be required to produce artificial disintegrations in the heavier elements. As we shall see in Chap. 5, however, Gamow, in 1928, put forward a theory that explains α-particle decay of naturally radioactive substances. This theory also implies that nuclei may be disintegrated by particles with insufficient energy to surmount the coulomb potential barrier. For this reason, Cockcroft and Walton (8) constructed, in 1932, a high-voltage machine for the purpose of bombarding nuclei with electrically accelerated particles such as protons. This Cockcroft-Walton generator, as it is now known, was used by its inventors to accelerate protons down a vertical series of evacuated tubes. The swift protons were allowed to impinge on a plane target of the material being studied arranged at an angle of 45° to the proton beam. Disintegration particles (α particles in every case, as far as the experimenters could tell) leaving the target at 90° to the beam struck a zinc-sulfide screen at one side of the apparatus. The resulting scintillations were observed through a microscope.

Cockcroft and Walton (9) bombarded targets of Li, Be, B, C, O, F, Na, Al, K, Ca, Fe, Co, Ni, Cu, Ag, Pb, and U. Scintillations were observed in every instance, but it was suspected that the scintillations in the case of the elements of large atomic number must be traceable to contamination of the heavy elements by lighter elements.

When a Li target was used, a beam current of 1 microampere and an accelerating potential difference of 125 kilovolts produced about 5 scintillations per minute. Figure 3-14 shows that the number of counts per minute, recorded by a type of proportional counter, per microampere of beam current, increased rapidly as the accelerating voltage was increased. The ranges of the α particles remained essentially constant over this voltage range, indicating that the energy of the α particle was derived primarily from the nuclear energy released in the disintegration. They believed that the reaction was

$$_3Li^7 + {}_1H^1 \rightarrow {}_2He^4 + {}_2He^4.$$

The occurrence of simultaneous α particles was confirmed by using a thin target and observing simultaneous scintillations on screens on opposite sides of the target. The measured α ranges gave a total energy liberation of 17.2 Mev, which was in fair agreement with the energy expected (14.3 ± 2.7 Mev) from the known masses of the atoms involved.

When fluorine in the form of powdered CaF_2 was used as a target, the assumed reaction was

$$_9F^{19} + {}_1H^1 \rightarrow {}_2He^4 + {}_8O^{16}$$

and the energy of the emitted α particle was found to be 4.15 Mev. The mass values then available gave, after allowing for the energy imparted to the recoiling O nucleus, an expected α-particle energy of 4.3 Mev.

In addition to α particles and protons, deuterons ($_1H^2$ nuclei), tritons ($_1H^3$ nuclei), and many other nuclei have since been used successfully as bombarding particles to produce nuclear disintegrations.

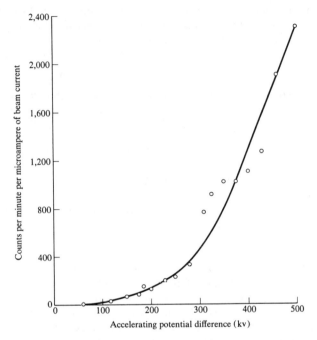

Fig. 3-14. Reaction rate of the Li (p, α) reaction as a function of the energy of the impinging proton. These results were obtained by Cockcroft and Walton (9) with a thick target. Consequently, not all reactions are produced by protons of energy corresponding to the accelerating potential difference.

No nuclear reaction has ever been observed in which a bombarding electron is absorbed by the nucleus. The interaction of electrons with nuclei is discussed further in Chap. 7.

Gamma rays have been shown to produce nuclear disintegrations, but a discussion of this type of reaction is deferred until Chap. 8.

PROBLEMS

3-1 Estimate, using a "range constant" of 0.8, the maximum thickness of a film of cellulose tetranitrate $C_{12}H_{16}O_6(NO_3)_4$ with a specific gravity of about 1.66, that a 4-Mev α particle can penetrate.   [*Ans.* 0.0014 cm.]

3-2 If a Pb nucleus could be considered to be a hard uncharged sphere of radius 9×10^{-13} cm and the α particle considered to be a point, how many α particles from Bi^{214} out of each million would strike a nucleus before coming to rest in a Pb absorber? Take the range of a Bi^{214} α particle in lead to be 2.41×10^{-3} cm, and the density of lead to be 11.35 gm/cm³.

[*Ans.* 202.]

3-3 Find the force exerted by an Au^{197} nucleus on an α particle at a distance of 10^{-12} cm from the nucleus (center to center) (a) due to gravitational attraction and (b) due to electrostatic repulsion.

[*Ans.* (a) 1.45×10^{-28} dyne, (b) 3.64×10^7 dynes.]

3-4 A 4-Mev α particle, in passing near a free electron, imparts to it an energy of 35 ev. How much momentum is transferred to the electron (a) in the forward or x-direction and (b) in the transverse or y-direction?

[*Ans.* (a) 4.03×10^{-20} gm-cm/sec, (b) 3.17×10^{-19} gm-cm/sec.]

3-5 In Eq. (3-11), one could have written

$$P_y = \int_{-\infty}^{\infty} eE_y \, dt = e \int_{-\infty}^{\infty} E_y \, dt,$$

where E_y is the y-component of the electrical field intensity at $x = 0$, $y = b$ when the moving charge is at x. By use of Gauss' theorem, obtain the result without actually having to carry out the integration.

3-6 A cloud-chamber track has a maximum radius of curvature of 20 cm. The track has a total length of 10.4 cm. The cloud chamber is in a magnetic field (which is perpendicular to the plane of the track) of 11,520 gauss. A 4-Mev α particle from a Th^{232} source is found to have a range of 2.55 cm in the cloud chamber. Identify the particle that made the 10.4-cm track and find its initial speed. [*Note:* A unique answer cannot be obtained, but a few trial values for the charge borne by the particle will show that one such value is more reasonable than the others.]   [*Ans.* Speed $= 2.2 \times 10^9$ cm/sec.]

3-7 Show that the maximum velocity that can be imparted to a proton at rest by an impinging α particle is 1.6 times the initial velocity of the α particle.

3-8 Find the maximum range, in air at NTP, of a recoiling singly charged nitrogen atom that results from the collision of a 7.06-cm-range (in air at NTP) α particle with a nitrogen atom that is initially at rest.

[*Ans.* 8.67 cm.]

3-9 Show that when a nucleus collides elastically with another nucleus (which is initially at rest) of the same mass, the two particles move away from each other along paths that are at right angles to each other.

3-10 Show that the space rate of change of the radius of curvature of a cloud-chamber track whose plane is perpendicular to the magnetic field is related to the instantaneous radius of curvature, ρ, and residual range, R, by the expression

$$\frac{d\rho}{dR} = \frac{\rho}{wR},$$

where w is the coefficient of v in Eq. (3-23).

3-11 Determine the cross section for the reaction $N^{14} + \alpha \rightarrow p + O^{17}$ from Blackett's results. Assume an α-particle range in the cloud chamber at NTP of 7.06 cm. Assume that the cross section is not a function of the α-particle energy. [*Ans.* 63.2 mb.]

REFERENCES

1. Bethe, H. A., *Ann. Physik*, **5**, 532 (1930); *Z. Physik*, **76**, 293 (1932).

2. Bethe, H. A., and Heitler, W., *Proc. Roy. Soc. Lond.*, **A146**, 83 (1934).

3. Blackett, P. M. S., *Proc. Roy. Soc.*, **107**, 349 (1925).

4. Bloch, F., *Ann. Physik*, **16**, 285 (1933); *Z. Physik*, **81**, 363 (1933).

5. Bohr, A., *Kgl. Danske Videnskab. Selskab, Mat.-fys. Medd.*, **24**:19 (1948).

6. Bohr, N., *Phil. Mag.*, **30**, 531 (1915).

7. Bohr, N., *Phil. Mag.*, **25**, 10 (1913); **30**, 581 (1915); *Z. Physik*, **34**, 142 (1925); *Naturwiss.*, **16**, 245 (1928); *Phys. Rev.*, **58**, 654 (1940); **59**, 270 (1941); *Kgl. Danske Videnskab. Selskab, Mat.-fys. Medd.*, **18**:8 (1948).

8. Cockcroft, J. D., and Walton, E. T. S., *Proc. Roy. Soc.*, **A136**, 619 (1932).

9. Cockcroft, J. D., and Walton, E. T. S., *Proc. Roy. Soc.*, **A137**, 229 (1932).

10. Curie, I., and Joliot, F., *Compt. Rend.*, **187**, 43 (1928).

11. Darwin, C. G., *Phil. Mag.*, **23**, 901 (1912).

12. Fermi, E., *Z. Physik*, **29**, 315 (1924); *Phys. Rev.*, **57**, 485 (1940).

13. Fonovits-Smereker, H., *Wien. Ber.*, **131**, 355 (1922).

14. Geiger, H., *Proc. Roy. Soc.*, **A82**, 486 (1909).

15. Henderson, G. H., *Phil. Mag.*, **42**, 538 (1921).

16. Holloway, M. G., and Livingston, M. S., *Phys. Rev.*, **54**, 18 (1938).

17. Kramers, H. A., *Physica*, **13**, 401 (1947).

18. Livingston, M. S., and Bethe, H. A., *Rev. Mod. Phys.*, **9**, 267 (1937).

19. Marsden, E., *Phil. Mag.*, **27**, 824 (1914).

20. Marsden, E., and Perkins, P. B., *Phil. Mag.*, **27**, 690 (1914).

21. Møller, Chr., *Ann. Physik*, **14**, 53 (1932).

22. Rutherford, E., *Phil. Mag.*, **37**, 581 (1919).

23. Rutherford, E., and Chadwick, J., *Phil. Mag.*, **42**, 809 (1921).

24. Rutherford, E., and Chadwick, J., *Nature*, **113**, 457 (1924).

25. Segrè, E., ed., *Experimental Nuclear Physics*, vol. I (New York: John Wiley & Sons, 1953), p. 254, in section by Bethe and Ashkin.

26. Taylor, T. S., *Phil. Mag.*, **26**, 402 (1913).

27. Thomson, J. J., *Conduction of Electricity through Gases* (2nd ed.; Cambridge: Cambridge University Press, 1906).

28. Von Traubenberg, H. Rausch, *Z. Physik*, **2**, 268 (1920).

29. Williams, E. J., *Proc. Roy. Soc.*, **130**, 328 (1931).

30. Williams, E. J., *Proc. Roy. Soc.*, **A139**, 175 (1933).

4

METHODS OF DETECTING
NUCLEAR RADIATIONS

4-1 Ionization Chamber

Most detection methods rest ultimately on the process of ionization. An α particle from Bi^{214} will produce about 2.2×10^5 ion pairs in air before being brought to rest. Since each ion (of a given sign) bears a charge of 4.8×10^{-10} esu, the total amount of charge of one sign produced by one Bi^{214} α particle would be about 10^{-4} esu. If this charge were communicated to a measuring instrument of 50 statfarad (55.5 $\mu\mu f$) capacitance, the potential difference would be 6×10^{-4} volt. If the measuring instrument (such as a Compton electrometer) had a sensitivity of 10^4 divisions/volt, then a single α particle from Bi^{214} would produce a deflection of six divisions. Hoffman observed deflections due to single α particles, using a sensitive binant electrometer. Ziegert (28) measured the total ionization produced by a single α particle in this way. However, the slow response of the electrometer makes this method impractical for counting α particles.

93

4-2 Proportional Counter

When a relatively small potential difference exists between the electrodes of a tube filled with gas (usually at reduced pressure), the *size* of the electrical pulse that results when an ionizing particle passes through the tube is proportional to the total number of primary ions produced by the particle. As the potential difference is increased, the size of the pulse increases but, up to a point, remains proportional to the total number of primary ions produced by the particle. A tube operated in this region is called a *proportional counter* and can be used to distinguish between particles of different energies or differing ionizing power. By selecting pulses within a given range of sizes, it also counts fewer cosmic ray particles and thus lowers the "background count."

As shown in Fig. 4-1, when the potential difference is raised still further, the pulse size ceases to be proportional to the amount of primary ionization.

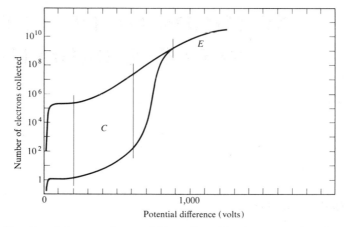

Fig. 4-1. Number of electrons that would be collected by the center wire of a cylindrical Geiger tube as a function of the potential difference between the electrodes. The upper curve is for an initial ionization of 10^5 ion pairs, while the lower is for an initial ionization of 1 ion pair. In the region C the curves have the same shape. Since the vertical coordinate is plotted on a logarithmic scale, the ratio of charges collected in the two cases is constant in region C. This is the "proportional region," the region where the tube is operated if it is to be used as a proportional counter. The region E is the "Geiger region." In this region the charge collected is independent of the number of ions produced by the ionizing particle. [From C. G. Montgomery and D. D. Montgomery, *Franklin Institute Journal*, **231**, 447 (1941).]

If the potential difference is made sufficiently great, the pulse height attains a constant size independent of the amount of primary ionization. Within the proportional region, the pulse size is very sensitive to the potential difference between electrodes, indicating that a very well-regulated source of potential must be used with proportional counters if the pulse size is to be used as a measure of the ionization of a particle passing through the tube.

4-3 Geiger Counter

A gas tube operated in the region where pulse size is independent of primary ionization is called a Geiger-Müller (10, 19) (usually shortened to Geiger or GM) tube. Originally the electrical pulses generated by the GM tube were detected by a quadrant electrometer or a string electrometer. These devices respond very slowly, making them unsuitable for measuring large pulse rates. It is now standard practice to use an electronic amplifier and an electronic scaling circuit in conjunction with a mechanical register. A scaling circuit is one in which one output pulse is produced for some fixed number of input pulses. In a binary or scale-of-two unit, for example, two input pulses produce one output pulse. It is evident that if the output of one binary unit is fed into a second and this into a third, etc., n units will require 2^n input pulses to produce one output pulse.

Now any such device requires some minimum pulse size before a count will be registered. If one then observes the number of counts registered per unit time, from a given amount of radioactive material at a fixed distance from the GM tube, as a function of the potential difference between the electrodes of the tube, he obtains a curve like that shown in Fig. 4-2. A certain minimum

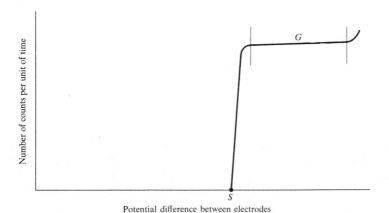

Fig. 4-2. Number of counts recorded as a function of potential difference between the electrodes of a cylindrical GM tube. The strength of the source is constant, and the position of the source relative to the GM tube is fixed while the potential difference is being changed. The number of counts per unit time depends not only on the source strength, but also on the sensitivity and resolving time of the associated electronic circuits. S is the "starting potential," and G is the plateau or "Geiger region" of the tube. The potential differences may vary from a few hundred to a few thousand volts depending upon gas pressure and diameters of the electrodes. A common value for S is about 800 volts, while the region G is typically about 200 volts long with a slope of about 1% per 100 volts.

potential difference must be applied between the electrodes before any counts are obtained. The potential difference at which counts first begin to be registered is called the *threshold potential difference*. As the potential difference is raised still further, more and more ionizing events produce pulses large enough to be counted so that the count rate rises very rapidly with increasing potential difference. At potential differences greater than threshold, any isolated ionizing event in the main part of the counter (usually referred to as the *sensitive volume*) will produce a pulse of maximum size and will therefore be counted. As the potential difference is raised still further, a larger fraction of ionizing events taking place within the counter tube but outside the sensitive volume (e.g., near the ends of the central wire in most cylindrical Geiger counters) will produce pulses large enough to be counted. The relatively flat portion of the curve in Fig. 4-2 is referred to as

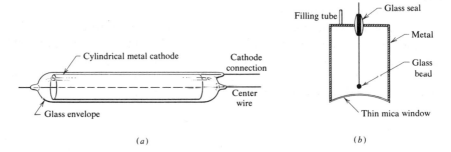

(a)   *(b)*

Fig. 4-3. Diagrams of two fairly typical GM tubes. Type (a) could be used for detecting gamma rays but has walls which are too thick to admit most beta rays. Alpha and low-energy beta particles can be counted with an end-window counter like (b).

the *plateau* or the *Geiger region*. The fact that it is not perfectly flat is explained, in part, by those ionizing events mentioned above, which take place outside the sensitive volume. In the Geiger region the total ionization is several thousand times the primary ionization and is therefore relatively easy to measure. Because the count rate is relatively insensitive to potential difference in the Geiger region, it is not necessary to use a well-regulated power supply for the large potential difference applied to the tube.

When a charged particle passes through the gas of a GM tube it generally creates a rather large number of ion pairs, the actual number being primarily dependent upon the nature and density of the gas, the velocity of the charged particle, and the distance the charged particle travels through the gas. The negative ions are mostly electrons, which, because of their small mass, are given a large acceleration toward the anode. The positive ions, being much more massive, are given a much smaller acceleration toward the cathode. When an electron gets close enough to the anode wire that the potential gradient allows it to acquire an amount of energy in one ionization mean free path length (i.e., the mean radial distance an electron travels through the gas between collisions with gas molecules) sufficient to ionize a gas molecule, the electrons released in this secondary ionization are also accelerated toward the anode and they in turn are given enough energy to ionize other gas molecules. Soon an avalanche of electrons is moving toward the anode wire. The flow of electrons to the anode reduces the positive charge on it and leaves a slowly expanding cloud of positive ions in the region surrounding the anode wire. Application of Gauss' theorem then shows that the electric field intensity is much reduced at the anode wire and although it may reach a maximum value at some distance from the surface of the anode wire this maximum will be less than the maximum field before the electron avalanche took place. The electron multiplication process is taken advantage of in both proportional counters and GM tubes. In proportional counters the total number of elec- trons flowing to the anode is sufficiently small that positive ion space charge effects are negligible, but in GM counters the total electron current is limited by the build-up of space charge and the consequent halting of the avalanche process with the result that the output pulse is independent of the number of ions initially created by the charged particle passing through the gas.

Unless the ionizing event produces ion pairs along the entire length of the anode, the radial electric field will produce an avalanche only along a part of the anode wire. Some electrons will combine with positive ions before reach- ing the anode, and photons will be emitted in the recombination process. In a tube filled with a pure gas such as argon very few of these photons will have sufficient energy to ionize an argon atom, but they may eject photoelectrons from the cathode. Some of these photoelectrons will then initiate avalanches along the remaining parts of the anode. Most counter tubes now in use con- tain a rare gas such as argon and a second gas with a smaller ionization poten- tial. Photons emitted from the avalanche region are strongly absorbed in the surrounding region with the result that many molecules of the second gas are photoionized. This causes the avalanche to spread along the anode wire. In the average counter, if the anode wire is 10 cm long, it takes about 1 μsec for the avalanche to spread the full length of the anode.

When a rare-gas ion, such as an argon ion, reaches the cathode, there is a rather high probability that it will cause the ejection of an electron. The positive ion sheath will now have moved far enough from the anode that, if the potential difference between electrodes has not changed, the electric field intensity will again be great enough to cause an avalanche. Thus a second discharge will occur and this in turn will lead to a third, etc. To avoid this one may use a condenser and high resistance as shown in Fig. 4-4, but the time constant for the recharging of the condenser must be greater than the time required for the positive ions to reach the cathode. Since the drift time of the positive ions is a few hundred microseconds, it is clear that a considerable time will elapse before the electric field intensity near the anode is again large enough to produce an avalanche and that during this time a second ionizing event cannot be detected. The time constant of the external circuit can be effectively reduced by electronic circuits such as the Neher-Harper or the Neher-Pickering, but nearly all GM tubes now used are internally quenching or "self-quenching." In these tubes a quenching gas is added to a rare gas such as argon. The quenching gas may be an organic vapor such as alcohol or ethyl formate, or a halogen (Cl_2 or Br_2). Argon ions formed in the

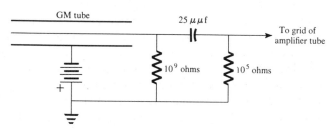

Fig. 4-4. GM circuit in which a 10^9-ohm resistor is used to prevent continuous discharge in a tube of the nonself-quenching type.

avalanche process now undergo charge exchange with molecules of the quenching gas, so that argon ions no longer reach the cathode. When a quench-gas ion reaches the cathode, the energy that it gives up on being neutralized goes into dissociating the quench-gas molecule rather than into liberation of secondary electrons from the cathode. Since no large external drop in potential is required to prevent repeated discharges with the self-quenching counter, a new ionizing event can produce a new avalanche before the positive ions have reached the cathode.

The largest current in the external circuit is associated with the motion of the electrons in the gas, but the time would be extremely short if it were not for the propagation time of the avalanche down the anode wire. Even so, it is usually only of the order of 1 μsec as seen in Fig. 4-5. The current in the external circuit associated with motion of the positive ions is much smaller, but the total charge transferred in the external circuit is primarily associated with motion of the positive ions.

Until the positive ion sheath has moved far enough from the anode wire to re-establish a large electric field intensity in this region the avalanche process cannot again be started and therefore a second ionizing event cannot produce a pulse. This period is called the *dead time* of the tube. The time required to elapse before a second ionizing event will produce a pulse equal to that produced by the previous ionizing event is called the *recovery time* of the tube. The minimum time interval between two successive ionizing events that will still allow both events to be counted is called the *resolving time* of the tube and its associated circuits. For most GM counting systems the resolving time is of the order of 10^{-4} sec. When the number of particles being detected per unit time is large, a statistical correction must be made for the "counting loss" resulting from the finite resolving time of the detector.

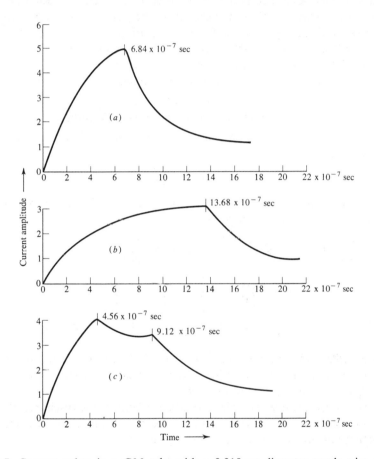

Fig. 4-5. Current pulses in a GM tube with a 0.015-cm diameter anode wire and a 1.8-cm diameter cylindrical cathode. The tube was filled with argon (to a partial pressure of 64 mm Hg) and alcohol (to a partial pressure of 16 mm Hg). The potential difference between electrodes was 1100 volts. In (a), alpha particles were passed through the center of the counter (i.e., at midlength and perpendicular to the axis of the counter). In (b) they were passed through the end, while in (c) they were passed through a point one-third of the length of the counter from one end. In (a) the avalanche propagates in both directions so that the current builds up to a high value in a short time. In (c) the pulse builds up as in (a) until the avalanche reaches the near end of the tube. Current decay in the established part of the discharge then outweighs current growth caused by propagation of the avalanche in the longer part of the tube. When the avalanche reaches the more distant end of the tube, the current begins to decay more rapidly.

Since the α particle has only a very small range (i.e., is not very penetrating), α-particle emitters must be placed inside of the GM tube, or else the tube must have a very thin window (a thin sheet of mica, for example) that the α particles are capable of penetrating. The same is true of β rays, except that very energetic β particles can penetrate thicker windows than can α particles. Radiation that does not consist of charged particles, such as γ radiation, often ejects charged particles of high energy from the gas or, more often, from the electrodes, and these produce sufficient ionization to cause a count. Geiger counters will count nearly 100 per cent of the α and β particles but only 1 to 2 per cent of the γ rays that enter their sensitive volumes.

The *efficiency* of a counter is defined by the relation

$$\epsilon = \frac{\text{number of counts}}{\text{number of particles traversing detector}}. \tag{4-1}$$

If the probability of forming N ion pairs is given by the Poisson distribution function, then

$$P(N) = \frac{e^{-\bar{N}}\bar{N}^N}{N!}, \tag{4-2}$$

where $\bar{N}$ is the average number of ion pairs formed. The total probability of forming some number of ion pairs is

$$\sum_{N_i=0}^{\infty} P(N_i) = \sum_{N_i=0}^{\infty} \frac{e^{-\bar{N}}\bar{N}^{N_i}}{N_i!} = e^{-\bar{N}} \sum_{N_i=0}^{\infty} \frac{\bar{N}^{N_i}}{N_i!}$$

$$= e^{-\bar{N}} \left[\frac{\bar{N}^0}{0!} + \frac{\bar{N}^1}{1!} + \frac{\bar{N}^2}{2!} + \cdots \right]$$

$$= e^{-\bar{N}} \left[1 + \frac{\bar{N}}{1} + \frac{\bar{N}^2}{2!} + \cdots \right] = e^{-\bar{N}} \cdot e^{\bar{N}} = 1.$$

Thus the total probability is unity (as it should be for a properly normalized probability function), as any ionizing event is certain to produce some number of ion pairs between zero and infinity.

Now if only a single ion pair is required to initiate the discharge of a GM tube, then only events producing *no* ion pairs will fail to be counted. The probability of producing *no* ion pairs is given by

$$P(0) = \frac{e^{-\bar{N}}\bar{N}^0}{0!} = e^{-\bar{N}}.$$

The probability of a count must then be

$$1 - P(0) = 1 - e^{-\bar{N}}.$$

But the probability of being counted is just the counter efficiency as defined above. Hence

$$\epsilon_1 = 1 - e^{-\bar{N}} \tag{4-3}$$

if only a *single* ion pair is required to produce a discharge.

If two ion pairs are required to produce a discharge, then all events will be counted except those that produce zero or one ion pair. The efficiency is, therefore,

$$\epsilon_2 = 1 - P(0) - P(1) = 1 - e^{-\overline{N}} - \frac{e^{-\overline{N}}\overline{N}^1}{1!}$$
$$= 1 - e^{-\overline{N}} - \overline{N}e^{-\overline{N}}. \tag{4-4}$$

The extension to any number of required ion pairs is obvious. It is also clear that any event that produces, on the average, a fairly large number of ion pairs within the detector is almost certain to be counted in the absence of overlapping discharges caused by ionizing events closely spaced in time.

4-4 Spark Counter

In this device, which may consist, for example, of a fine wire suspended parallel and very close to a flat metal plate, a sufficiently ionizing particle that passes close to the wire will produce a visible spark. In some forms it can be made to respond only to alpha particles, even in a considerable flux of beta and gamma radiation. This type of counter is usually used in the open air, and therefore operates at atmospheric pressure, which requires a potential difference between the electrodes on the order of 2500 to 3000 volts.

4-5 Crystal Conduction Counter

It was observed soon after the discovery of x-rays (23) that dielectrics could be made slightly conductive by irradiation with x-rays and gamma rays. Van Heerden (24) was the first to describe the use of a crystal to detect single particles. He used silver chloride crystals and found that it was necessary to cool them to liquid nitrogen temperature to obtain satisfactory operation. Wooldridge et al. (26) in 1947 observed electrical pulses produced by single ionizing particles in a diamond at room temperature. No great use has thus far been made of such detectors.

In 1951 McKay (17) reported the use of a germanium p-n junction diode as an alpha-particle counter. Further development of the germanium junction diode detector is described by Bomal et al. (3). More recently (9, 14), silicon p-n junction counters have been developed. In the junction counter, a schematic diagram of which is shown in Fig. 4-6, a reverse bias is applied so that only a very small steady current (generally less than 1 microampere) flows through the device. Under these conditions, most of the potential drop occurs across the depletion region, a zone that extends some distance into the p-type material. If a charged particle enters the crystal through the thin n-type layer and comes to rest in the depletion region, the electrons and holes produced by the charged particle will be swept apart, resulting in a drop in potential across the device. This sudden drop in potential is communicated to an amplifier. It has been found that the output pulses are proportional to the energy of the particle as long as the particle comes to rest within the depletion region, so that the junction counter can be used in place of a proportional counter to measure energies. The rise time of the output pulse

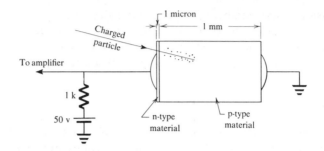

Fig. 4-6. Schematic diagram of a crystal conduction counter. The circuit and dimensional values are usable ones where the semiconductor is silicon, but optimum values will depend both on the nature of the material and on the exact use to which it is to be put.

is typically less than 3.5×10^{-9} sec, but the decay time, which depends on the circuit constants (the capacitance of the diode itself, for one), is usually much greater.

Junction counters have been used most successfully thus far in detecting alpha particles, protons, and other "heavy" particles. Their use as detectors for beta particles and gamma rays is still in the development stage. In principle, one should be able to operate the diode so that avalanches are produced, thus giving what might be loosely called a solid-state Geiger counter. The advantages of the junction counter are small size, fast response, and lack of need for a high voltage supply.

4-6 Scintillation Counter

It was observed by Crookes and by Elster and Geitel in 1903 that a screen coated with ZnS crystals fluoresced when bombarded with α particles. They observed further that when the screen was viewed through a microscope, minute individual flashes of light could be seen. It was assumed at the time, and proved later, that a single flash resulted from the impact of a single α particle. It was observed that when a single small crystal of ZnS, viewed under 800-power magnification, was struck by an α particle, the entire crystal was lighted up.

Geiger (11), using a microscope, observed the "track" of light produced by an α particle in passing through a willemite crystal, and Chariton and Lea observed such tracks in a thin flake of diamond. It was found that the light generated lay in a broad spectral region with maxima at 4500 Å and 5200 Å, and that although the eye is sensitive to as little as 30 photons of green light, about 1200 photons per scintillation are required for accurate visual counting of scintillations.

Much early work was done by visual observation of scintillations, but for this purpose the human eye has since been replaced by the photomultiplier tube. The combination of scintillating material and photomultiplier tube is called a *scintillation counter*. The scintillation counter generally has a smaller resolving time than the Geiger counter, varying from about 10^{-6} sec for some of the inorganic crystals to about 10^{-9} sec for some of the organic scintillators, and has the additional advantage that, unlike the GM tube, the scintillating material may be placed very close to an α emitter or low-energy β emitter without requiring the use of a thin window transparent to these particles.

The pulse size produced by singly charged particles that come to rest in NaI(Tl) (thallium-activated sodium iodide) crystals is almost exactly in direct proportion to the energy of the impinging particle. This linear relationship does not hold for organic scintillators nor for multiply charged particles in NaI(Tl) crystals, but it is still true that the pulse height increases with particle energy, so that with suitable calibration procedures the energy of a particle may be determined from the size of the pulse. Scintillation counters may therefore be used in the same way as one uses proportional counters.

The efficiency of counting those gamma rays which strike the scintillator depends to some extent on the size of the scintillator and its disposition relative to the source as well as upon the nature of the scintillator material. Table 4-1 demonstrates how the efficiency of a 1.5-in. diameter by 1-in. thick

Table 4-1 VARIATION OF NaI(Tl) SCINTILLATOR EFFICIENCY WITH GAMMA-RAY ENERGY*

$W(Mev)$	Efficiency
0.1	100%
1.0	38%
10.0	27.5%

NaI crystal with the source in contact with the crystal on the cylinder axis at one face varies with gamma-ray energy. Not all the scintillation pulses will be of the same size, the fraction of small pulses tending to become larger at greater gamma-ray energies. If the scintillation detector is to be used as an energy measuring instrument, therefore, the effective efficiency is much lower

* More complete calculations of gamma-ray detection efficiency are given in National Bureau of Standards Report No. 1003.

than that given in Table 4-1 at the higher energies. For example, full-energy pulses will be produced by only about 7 per cent of the incident 1-Mev gamma rays in the crystal configuration specified for Table 4-1. The fraction of 1-Mev gamma rays giving full-energy pulses in a 3-in. diameter by 3-in. thick NaI crystal, by contrast, is about 22 per cent. This is an important gain over the 1 to 2 per cent efficiency of GM tubes. A number of substances have been used to yield the scintillations, among them anthracene, naphthalene, phenan-threne, stilbene, and thallium-activated sodium iodide crystals. Solutions and polystyrene plastic containing *p*-terphenyl have also been used.

Since the electrons that move from dynode to dynode of the photomulti-plier tube would be deflected from their normal trajectories by an appreciable magnetic field, the tube must be adequately shielded from such fields. Where it is essential that the particle be detected in a region where the magnetic field is large, as is often the case in experiments using particles accelerated in a cyclotron or synchrotron, for example, the scintillating material may be placed as desired and the light brought out in a clear plastic "light pipe" to the photomultiplier which is placed outside of the disturbing magnetic field.

4-7 Čerenkov Counter

The Čerenkov counter (5) utilizes a photomultiplier tube to detect the Čerenkov radiation from a moving charged particle. Čerenkov radiation is produced when a charged particle passes through a dielectric with a velocity greater than the phase velocity of a light wave in the dielectric, and is the electromagnetic counterpart of the shock waves produced in a gas by an object traveling with a speed greater than sound. The conditions for reinforce-ment are thus the same as those for the bow wave of a ship passing through water with a speed greater than the wave velocity, as shown in Fig. 4-7. The

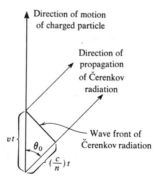

Fig. 4-7. Čerenkov radiation is emitted whenever the velocity, v, of a charged particle is greater than the phase velocity of a light wave in the medium through which the particle is moving. The radiation is generated by polarization of the dielectric by the moving charged particle.

result is that light of a given wavelength is emitted with a sharp, narrow angular distribution whose maximum intensity is at an angle θ_0 with the path of the particle given by

$$\cos \theta_0 = \frac{\text{velocity of light wave in dielectric}}{\text{velocity of particle}} = \frac{c/n}{v} = \frac{c}{nv} = \frac{1}{n\beta}, \quad (4\text{-}5)$$

where $\beta = v/c$, and n is the index of refraction of the dielectric medium.

If the dielectric is relatively thin, the light emerges in a cone whose axis lies along the path of the charged particle.

There would be Čerenkov radiation but no Čerenkov cone if the dielectric were thin compared to a wavelength of the emitted light, as the Čerenkov cone is an interference effect. The continuous generation of the wave by the moving charged particle is equivalent to the optical case of a plane wave incident at a glancing angle θ_i, equal to the Čerenkov cone angle, on a slit of width equal to the path length L of the particle in the dielectric. The diffraction pattern intensity (13) then varies as

$$\frac{\sin^2 [\pi L(\cos \theta_i - \cos \theta)/\lambda]}{[\pi L(\cos \theta_i - \cos \theta)/\lambda]^2} = \frac{\sin^2 [\pi L(c/nv - \cos \theta)(nv/c)]}{[\pi L(c/nv - \cos \theta)(nv/c)]^2},$$

where λ is the wavelength and v the frequency of the emitted light, and θ is the angle between the path of the particle and the direction of emission of the light. This fraction has its maximum value when

$$\frac{c}{nv} - \cos \theta_0 = 0 \quad \text{or} \quad \cos \theta_0 = \frac{c}{nv},$$

which is just the bow-wave equation obtained earlier. To get an idea of how very narrow the angular width of the diffraction maximum is, consider the case where $\beta = 1$, $\lambda = 5000$ Å, and $L = 1$ mm. Then the first minima in the diffraction pattern occur where

$$\cos \theta = \frac{1 \pm 0.0005}{n}.$$

If the index of refraction of the medium gives $\theta_0 = 30°$, for example, then the first minima lie within 3 minutes of arc of the maximum. The complete expression for the energy flow per unit frequency interval, Φ, across unit area, S, perpendicular to the energy flow at a distance r from the midpoint of the path along which the radiation originates is

$$\frac{d\Phi(v, \theta)}{dS} dv = \frac{\pi n e^2 L^2 v^2}{2c^3 r^2} \sin^2 \theta \frac{\sin^2 \left[\pi v L \left(\frac{1}{v} - \frac{n \cos \theta}{c}\right)\right]}{\left[\pi v L \left(\frac{1}{v} - \frac{n \cos \theta}{c}\right)\right]^2}, \quad (4\text{-}6)$$

where n is the index of refraction of the medium for light of frequency v, e is the electronic charge in esu, L is the path length through the dielectric in cm, c is the velocity of light in a vacuum in cm/sec, and v is the velocity of the charged particle in cm/sec.

The light emitted in the Čerenkov process has a broad spectral distribution, but lies mostly in the visible region. The spectral distribution, according to the theory given by Frank and Tamm, is given by

$$N(v) \, dv = 4\pi^2 \frac{Z^2 e^2}{hc^2} \sin^2 \theta \, dv, \qquad (4\text{-}7)$$

where v is the frequency, Ze is the charge borne by the moving particle, and $N(v) \, dv$ is the number of photons with frequencies between v and $v + dv$ emitted in unit path length by the moving charged particle. It will be noticed that this expression does not contain the mass of the particle, so that the radiation process here is quite distinct from that of bremsstrahlung (see Chap. 7). A singly charged particle moving through water with a velocity approximately that of light will emit about 320 photons per cm in the visible region of the spectrum. Since a moving charged particle produces a circular magnetic field concentric with the direction of motion of the particle, and since the Poynting vector must make an angle θ with the direction of motion of the particle, it is to be expected that the Čerenkov radiation will be plane polarized since the electric field vector must be perpendicular to both the magnetic field and Poynting vectors. This has been observed to be the case by Mather (16).

Since the number of photons produced depends on $\sin^2 \theta$, and hence on $1 - 1/\beta^2 n^2$, there will be no radiation produced when $\beta < 1/n$. The Čerenkov counter can, therefore, be used to discriminate against particles whose velocities are less than c/n. Gases, for which the index of refraction, n, is only slightly greater than unity, have been used as Čerenkov radiators to discriminate against all but extremely relativistic ($\beta \simeq 1$) particles. Unfortunately, the number of photons generated per unit path length in this case is also very small so that it is difficult to distinguish Čerenkov pulses from spurious effects.

Because the radiation is propagated in the forward direction of motion of the charged particle, a Čerenkov detector can be made to detect only those particles that enter it from a restricted solid angle. This directionality is not achievable with GM and scintillation counters.

4-8 Cloud Chamber

A visual rather than electrical method of detecting charged particles is provided by the cloud chamber. Wilson (25) found that if the air in a closed chamber was saturated with water vapor and then subjected to a sudden (adiabatic) expansion, the cooling caused water vapor to condense out in a fog of fine droplets. In ordinary air there are always sufficient dust particles to act as condensation nuclei for these droplets, but in clean air ions act as the condensation centers. In particular, he found that for an expansion ratio (expanded volume/compressed volume) of greater than 1.25 but less than 1.31, the negative ions alone act as condensation nuclei. When the expansion ratio lies between 1.31 and 1.38, ions of both signs are effective. If the expansion ratio is made greater than 1.38, a dense cloud forms even in the absence of ions. If a chamber filled with water-saturated air is operated at an expansion ratio between 1.31 and 1.38, the ions produced by a charged particle that has traversed the chamber act as the condensation nuclei and the track followed by the particle is made evident by a thin line of water droplets.

For gases other than air or condensable vapors different from water vapor, drops may form first on positive ions. The critical expansion ratios may be lowered by using argon instead of air, or, more effectively, by using an alcohol-water mixture rather than pure water as the condensable vapor.

To stop or slow down particles of high energy, plates of dense material (lead, copper, gold, etc.) are sometimes placed in the chamber. Another scheme that has been used is to raise the gas pressure within the chamber to as much as 300 atmospheres. The ratio of momentum to charge of charged particles may be determined by placing the cloud chamber in a uniform magnetic field and observing the curvature of the cloud track caused by magnetic deflection of the charged particle.

A disadvantage of the expansion cloud chamber is that it is sensitive only during a very small part of the whole expansion–recompression cycle. The *diffusion cloud chamber* (6, 18, 21), on the other hand, is continuously sensitive. In the diffusion chamber the condensable vapor is evaporated from a warm upper plate and condenses on a cold lower plate. There is thus set up a temperature gradient in the chamber, and as the vapor diffuses into the colder region it becomes supersaturated and capable of condensing on the ions produced by a swiftly moving charged particle. This type of chamber has not yet been brought to the high state of perfection that has been achieved with expansion chambers but may become more widely used as improvements in technique are evolved.

4-9 Bubble Chamber

A device that bears many similarities to a cloud chamber is the bubble chamber (12). In this, the gas of the cloud chamber is replaced by a liquid. When the pressure in the vessel containing the liquid is dropped below the vapor pressure corresponding to the temperature of the liquid, there is a tendency for bubbles to form. Like the droplets in a cloud chamber, however, (see Probs. 6, 7, and 8) bubbles cannot form unless there are ions upon which to start their growth. The bubbles, growing on the ions produced by passage of a charged particle through the liquid, delineate the path of the particle. The chief advantage of the bubble chamber is the much greater density of its liquid compared to that of the gas in a cloud chamber. This more dense liquid has the ability to slow down energetic charged particles and so make them more easily indentifiable. To achieve maximum density one may use liquid xenon. At the other extreme of density, liquid hydrogen has been used extensively to study interactions of charged particles with protons.

The bubble chamber has a much smaller "sensitive time" (i.e., time interval during which the particle must traverse the chamber to produce a useful track) than the cloud chamber has. For this reason it has not found favor in cosmic ray research, but it is almost ideally suited for use with the ultrahigh-energy pulsed particle accelerators as it can be electrically triggered to expand just when the pulse of particles or their secondaries reach the chamber.

Still other devices that are somewhat competitive with the cloud chamber in function have been and are being developed. One such scheme uses a matrix of neon flash tubes (1) to delineate the path of the charged particle. Another device uses layers of plastic fibers. When a charged particle passes through one of these fibers the fiber scintillates. In this way one obtains a "track" of scintillating fiber ends. Interlarded layers of fibers with their axes at right angles to each other would be necessary to obtain a three-dimensional trajectory.

4-10 Nuclear Emulsion

In end results, photographic emulsion (20) is similar to a bubble chamber as a device for charged-particle detection. Great progress has been made (2, 4, 15, 22) in producing photographic emulsions that are extremely sensitive to the ionization produced within the emulsions by the transit of charged particles. After a charged particle has passed through the emulsion, the plate is developed and fixed in a manner similar to that used in ordinary photography. A fine string of silver grains is produced along the path that was followed by the particle. The track is ordinarily too fine to be seen by the unaided eye, but it is quite clear when viewed through a microscope at a magnification of 100 or more. The nuclear emulsion has the advantages of simplicity, continuous sensitivity, small size, and great density, the latter making it especially useful for detecting particles of very high energy which would not be slowed down appreciably in passing through the gas of a cloud chamber. Its chief disadvantage, compared with a cloud or bubble chamber, is that the chronological order of events cannot always be determined. Where the charged particle passes through more than one emulsion it is often possible to determine the approximate time at which the event took place from the displacement of the track in an emulsion that is moved by a clock mechanism. Yngve (27) states that a motion of $\frac{1}{4}$ mm per hour will make it possible to determine the time within a few minutes. While the momentum of the particle that produces the track can be determined rather well from small-angle scattering measurements, the sign of the charge borne by the particle cannot generally be determined unless the particle has been deflected by a magnetic field. Deflection in the air space between two emulsions by a magnetic field perpendicular to the emulsion surfaces has been used by Franzinetti (8) but the technique of associating tracks in the two plates is rather involved. Magnetic deflection within the plate itself is intrinsically difficult because of simultaneous small-angle scattering. Dilworth et al. (7) have used this technique with a magnetic field of 34,000 gauss, but it appears that fields of at least 100,000 gauss will be necessary to make the method sufficiently reliable to be attractive. When used with particle accelerators it is fairly common practice to deflect the particles in a magnetic field before they impinge on the emulsion. In this way only those particles with a known ratio of momentum to charge reach the emulsion. This information, together with information gained from the emulsion tracks, often makes possible an unambiguous interpretation of the event observed.

4-11 Counting Losses

In any counting system there will be a time τ, sometimes called the "resolving time,"* which must elapse after one event is counted in order that the next event be able to produce a large enough electrical pulse to be counted. If the events are randomly distributed in time, then the probability that a second shall occur within some small time t after the initial event is

$$\frac{t}{1/\bar{N}} = \bar{N}t,$$

where $\bar{N}$ is the average number of events per unit time (e.g., the average number of particles passing through the gas of a GM tube). The probability that a second event will not occur during the interval t following the first event is then

$$P(t) = 1 - \bar{N}t. \tag{4-8}$$

The probability that an event will not occur in an interval nt after the first event, where n is an integer, is the product of the probabilities that it will not occur in each interval t, and hence

$$P(nt) = (1 - \bar{N}t)^n. \tag{4-9}$$

---

* Often called "dead time." The latter term usually refers, however, to the time that must elapse before the next event will produce a measurable electrical output pulse and is therefore generally a shorter time than the "resolving time."

If we take n such that $nt = \tau$, this expression becomes

$$P(\tau) = \left(1 - \frac{\bar{N}\tau}{n}\right)^n = 1 - \frac{n\bar{N}\tau}{n} + \frac{n(n-1)(\bar{N}\tau)^2}{2!n^2} + \cdots \quad (4\text{-}10)$$

By permitting t to approach zero, n approaches infinity and

$$P(\tau) = 1 - \bar{N}\tau + \frac{(\bar{N}\tau)^2}{2!} + \cdots = e^{-\bar{N}\tau}. \quad (4\text{-}11)$$

The probability that no event shall occur in the time τ is, therefore, $e^{-\bar{N}\tau}$, and hence the probability that one or more events occur in time τ is $1 - e^{-\bar{N}\tau}$. But events that occur in the time τ after the initial event are not counted, so the probability that an event will not be counted is $1 - e^{-\bar{N}\tau}$. We conclude that the probability that the event *will* be counted is $e^{-\bar{N}\tau}$. The expected average count rate is then

$$\bar{N}_c = \bar{N}e^{-\bar{N}\tau}. \quad (4\text{-}12)$$

Where τ is known, one can make a plot of $\bar{N}_c$ vs. $\bar{N}$. In an experiment, if one measures a certain count rate ($\bar{N}_c$), the true number of events per unit time ($\bar{N}$) can be ascertained from the above plot. $\bar{N}_c$ is equal to zero when $\bar{N} = 0$ and when $\bar{N} = \infty$, and one therefore expects it to have a maximum at some value of $\bar{N}$ between 0 and ∞. This maximum can be found by differentiating with respect to $\bar{N}$ and equating to zero. Thus

$$\frac{d\bar{N}_c}{d\bar{N}} = e^{-\bar{N}\tau} - \tau\bar{N}e^{-\bar{N}\tau},$$

whence

$$1 - \tau\bar{N}_{max} = 0$$

or

$$\bar{N}_{max} = \frac{1}{\tau}, \quad (4\text{-}13)$$

where $\bar{N}_{max}$ is the number of events per unit time at which the counting rate reaches a maximum. The corresponding maximum counting rate is

$$\bar{N}_{c_{max}} = \frac{1}{\tau}e^{-\tau/\tau} = \frac{1}{e\tau}, \quad (4\text{-}14)$$

so that τ can be determined, in principle, by varying the source strength until the counting rate reaches a maximum. Unfortunately, τ changes at high count rates, so this is not a practical method for its determination. The qualitative result that the count rate passes through a maximum, however, is valid.

Another method for determining τ is to measure the count rate produced by an initially strong radionuclide with a relatively short half-life. The logarithm of the count rate plotted against time as shown in Fig. 4-8 will then yield a curve that approaches a straight line of constant slope as the count rate becomes small. By extending the straight line back to small values of t, as shown, one can read off the values of $\bar{N}$ and $\bar{N}_c$ at any value of t and from these determine τ by means of Eq. (4-12).

A third method uses two radioactive sources. The count rates are measured with each source by itself and then with both sources present at the

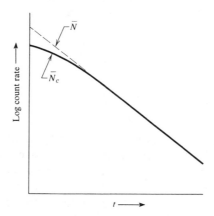

Fig. 4-8. A plot of the logarithm of the average number of counts per second *vs.* the time. At low count rates there is no counting loss, so the curve approaches a straight line. By extending this straight line back to small values of t, one can find what the counting loss was as a function of the count rate. The resolving time, τ, can then be calculated from Eq. (4-12).

same time. One then has three equations like (4-12). These are sufficient to determine the two unknown true event rates and τ.

4-12 Background Effects

Nuclear decay is well represented by the Poisson distribution

$$P(N) = \frac{e^{-\bar{N}}\bar{N}^{N}}{N!},$$

where $P(N)$ is the probability of N decays in a time t_u when the average number of decays in time t_u over a long time is $\bar{N}$ (assuming that the rate does not change appreciably during this time, or in other words that $t_{1/2} \gg t_u$). If a GM counter is used to register some fraction of these decays, then the same law will hold, where now $P(N)$ is the probability of N counts in time t_u and $\bar{N}$ is the average number of counts in time t_u. Statistical theory shows that if one records a total number of counts $\bar{N}t$ in a time t, where now t_u has been taken to be unit time interval, then the *standard deviation* in the average, $\bar{N}$, is

$$\sigma_{\bar{N}} = \sqrt{\frac{\bar{N}}{t}}, \tag{4-15}$$

where σ_N is defined for a large number of independent determinations of $\bar{N}_i$ as

$$\sigma_N = \left(\frac{\sum\limits_{i=1}^{n} (\bar{N}_i - \bar{N})^2}{n} \right)^{1/2}. \tag{4-16}$$

As an example, suppose one obtains 100 counts in 5 seconds. Then the average count rate is $\bar{N} = \frac{100}{5} = 20$ counts/sec, while the standard deviation is

$$\sigma_N = \sqrt{\frac{\bar{N}}{t}} = \sqrt{\frac{20}{5}} = 2,$$

and one might then write the count rate as

$$20 \pm 2 \text{ cps.}$$

In counter measurements there is always a background count, a count that one obtains in the absence of the sample being tested. It is usually possible to make the background count over an extended period of time so that the average rate can be determined to a very small uncertainty. Background still introduces an appreciable extra uncertainty in the determination of the average count rate ascribable to the sample; the reason is that the actual number of background counts during the determination is a statistical quantity, so that subtracting the *average* background rate from the observed total rate will not generally give the actual number of counts due to the sample. If the total number of counts (sample plus background) is $\bar{N}_t t$ in a time t, then the standard deviation in $\bar{N}_t$ is $\sqrt{\bar{N}_t/t}$. Suppose that the background count during a time t_b is $\bar{N}_b t_b$ with a standard deviation $\sqrt{\bar{N}_b/t_b}$. The count rate due to the sample alone is then $\bar{N}_s = \bar{N}_t - \bar{N}_b$ but the standard deviation of $\bar{N}_s$ is

$$\sigma_{\bar{N}_s} = \sqrt{\frac{\bar{N}_t}{t} + \frac{\bar{N}_b}{t_b}} = \sqrt{\frac{\bar{N}_s}{t} + \frac{\bar{N}_b}{t} + \frac{\bar{N}_b}{t_b}}. \tag{4-17}$$

The last term, $\bar{N}_b/t_b$, can be made as small as one pleases by making t_b large, but the term $\bar{N}_b/t$ still remains. As an example, suppose that one measures 400 background counts in 20 seconds. A sample is then brought up to the counter and 375 counts are obtained in 5 seconds. Then

$$\bar{N}_b = \frac{400}{20} \pm \sqrt{\frac{400}{20 \times 20}} = 20 \pm 1 \text{ cps,}$$

$$\bar{N}_t = \frac{375}{5} \pm \sqrt{\frac{375}{5 \times 5}} = 75 \pm 3.9 \text{ cps,}$$

$$\bar{N}_s = (75 - 20) \pm \sqrt{\frac{75 - 20}{5} + \frac{20}{5} + \frac{20}{20}} = 55 \pm 4 \text{ cps,}$$

whereas a measurement with no background present that gave the same average count rate would have given $\bar{N}_s = 55 \pm \sqrt{\frac{5.5}{5}} = 55 \pm 3.3$ cps. On the other hand, extending the background count over an infinite time, thus making the last term in the computation of $\sigma_{\bar{N}_s}$ zero, would only reduce $\sigma_{\bar{N}_s}$ to the value of $\sigma_{\bar{N}_t}$ (i.e., slightly less than 3.9 cps instead of 4 as calculated above). It is clear that our ability to measure the activity of weak sources is limited almost solely by background. Shielding the counter from outside radiation does not completely eliminate background, in part because the shielding material itself always contains some small amount of radioactive impurities.

PROBLEMS

4-1 In the Geiger counter circuit of Fig. 4-3, a discharge causes the potential of point A to drop to $-U$ volts before conduction ceases in the counter gas. How long will it take for the potential of point A to rise to $-0.05U$ in the absence of further discharges?   [*Ans.* 1.5×10^{-3} sec.]

4-2 A cylindrical Geiger tube has a central wire 0.2 mm in diameter and an outer electrode 5 cm in diameter. With 1400 volts potential difference between the electrodes, what is the electric field intensity at the central wire and at the outer electrode?

       [*Ans.* 25,355 volts/cm at the wire; 101.4 volts/cm at the cathode.]

4-3 The "ionization mean free path" of an electron in the gas of a typical GM tube is about 10^{-3} cm [S. A. Korff, *Electron and Nuclear Counters* (New York: D. Van Nostrand Co., 1946)]. What minimum potential difference between the electrodes of Prob. 4-2 will suffice to give a primary electron enough kinetic energy in moving this distance to produce secondary ionization if the tube is filled with argon? The ionization potential of argon is 15.68 volts.   [*Ans.* 909 volts.]

4-4 A "point source" of α particles is placed 0.01 inch (along the axis) from the thin mica window at the end of a GM tube 1 inch in diameter. The mica is so thin that all the α particles that strike it pass through and produce counts. In this position 2400 counts per minute are registered. The background count is 18 counts per minute. (a) What is the strength of the source in disintegrations per second? (b) What count is to be expected when the source is moved out along the axis of the tube until it is 1 inch from the mica window?   [*Ans.* (a) 81.1 disintegrations/sec, (b) 274 counts/min.]

4-5 Lucite has an index of refraction of about 1.5. (a) What should be the cone angle ϕ of Fig. 4-9 (page 114) in order that Čerenkov radiation from a 10.9-Mev electron may emerge parallel to the axis? (b) Will the light be totally reflected from the conical surface?

       [*Ans.* (a) 24.1°, (b) yes, since critical angle = 41.8°.]

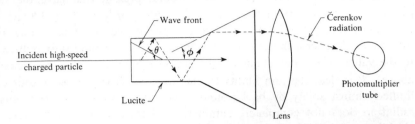

Fig. 4-9. Čerenkov counter used by R. H. Dicke [*Phys. Rev.*, **71**, 737 (1947)]. As the speed of the particle approaches that of light, the angle θ approaches a limiting value. The angle ϕ, which the sides of the conical part of the acrylic plastic make with the axis of the device, can then be chosen so that the rays emerge parallel to the axis. On passing through the lens, these parallel rays will be brought together at its focal point. The active surface of the photomultiplier tube is placed at the point to which the rays converge.

4-6 Show that the vapor pressure Π_r of a droplet of radius r, such as is formed in a cloud chamber, is related to the vapor pressure Π_∞ over a flat surface of the same liquid by the formula

$$\ln \frac{\Pi_r}{\Pi_\infty} = \frac{2M}{R\Theta D}\left[\frac{\gamma}{r} + (\Pi_r - \Pi_\infty)\right],$$

where M is the molecular weight of the liquid, R is the gas constant, Θ is the absolute temperature, D is the density of the liquid, and γ is the surface tension of the liquid. This may be done by carrying w grams of the liquid through the following isothermal cycle:

(a) Pump w grams of liquid from beneath a flat surface of liquid into droplets of radius r such that r is not increased appreciably during the operation. Take the liquid to be incompressible.

(b) Allow w grams of liquid to evaporate from the droplets at their vapor pressure, Π_r. Assume that the vapor obeys the perfect gas law.

(c) Expand the w grams of vapor isothermally from Π_r to Π_∞.

(d) Compress the w grams of vapor at Π_∞ to liquid at Π_∞.

4-7 Show that in the case of a water droplet formed about a singly charged ion at its center, the expression derived in Prob. 4-6 becomes

$$\ln \frac{\Pi_r}{\Pi_\infty} + \frac{2M}{R\Theta D}\left[\frac{\gamma}{r} + (\Pi_r - \Pi_\infty) - \frac{K-1}{K}\frac{e^2}{16\pi r^4}\right],$$

where K is the relative permittivity of the liquid. [*Hint:* Consider the energy stored in the electric field. Take the derivative of this with respect to r to find the effective pressure due to the charge.]

4-8 The term $(\Pi_r - \Pi_\infty)$ in Probs. 4-6 and 4-7 is ordinarily negligible compared with the other terms in the bracket. (a) Find the radius of a charged droplet that will not evaporate in a space where the vapor is at a pressure Π_∞. Take γ for water to be 76 dynes/cm and K to be 81. (b) What would the ratio of the partial pressure of the vapor to Π_∞ have to be in order to prevent evaporation of an uncharged water droplet of this size at 27°C?

[*Ans.* (a) 3.92×10^{-8} cm, (b) 16.4.]

4-9 Show from the Poisson distribution formula [Eq. (4-2)] that the average number of ion pairs formed is N.

REFERENCES

1. Ashton, F., Kisdnasamy, S., and Wolfendale, A. W., *Nuovo Cimento*, **8**, 615 (1958).

2. Berriman, R. W., *Nature*, **161**, 432 (1948).

3. Bomal, R., Koch, L., Van Dong, N., and Schneider, C., *L'électronique nucléaire* (Vienna: Agence international de l'énergie atomique, 1959), p. 137.

4. Brown, R., Camerini, U., Fowler, P. H., Muirhead, H., Powell, C. F., and Ritson, D. M., *Nature*, **163**, 47 (1949).

5. Čerenkov, P. A., *C. R. Acad. Sci. URSS*, **2**, 451 (1934); *Phys. Rev.*, **52**, 378 (1937).

6. Cowan, E. W., *Rev. Sci. Instr.*, **21**, 991 (1950).

7. Dilworth, C. C., Goldsack, S. J., Goldschmidt-Clermont, Y., and Levy, F., *Phil. Mag.*, **41**, 1032 (1950).

8. Franzinetti, C., *Phil. Mag.*, **41**, 86 (1950).

9. Friedland, S. S., Mayer, J. W., and Wiggins, J. S., *Nucleonics*, **18**:2, 54 (1960).

10. Geiger, H., and Müller, W., *Physik Z.*, **29**, 839 (1928); **30**, 489 (1929).

11. Geiger, H., and Werner, A., *Z. Physik*, **8**, 191 (1922).

12. Glaser, D. A., *Phys. Rev.*, **91**, 762 (1953).

13. Houstoun, R. A., *A Treatise on Light* (London: Longmans, Green & Co., 1930).

14. Jones, A. R., *Nucleonics*, **18**:10, 86 (1960).

15. Lattes, C. M. G., Muirhead, H., Occhialini, G. P. S., and Powell, C. F., *Nature*, **159**, 694 (1947).

16. Mather, R. L., *Phys. Rev.*, **84**, 181 (1951).

17. McKay, K. G., *Phys. Rev.*, **84**, 829 (1951).

18. Needles, T. S., and Nielsen, C. E., *Rev. Sci. Instr.*, **21**, 976 (1950).

19. Rutherford, E., and Geiger, H., *Proc. Roy. Soc.*, **A81**, 141 (1908).

20. Shapiro, M. M., *Rev. Mod. Phys.*, **13**, 58 (1941). See also Demers, P., *Ionographie* (Montreal: Les Presses Universitaires de Montreal, 1958).

21. Shutt, R. P., *Rev. Sci. Instr.*, **22**, 730 (1951).

22. Spence, J., Castle, J., and Webb, J. H., *Phys. Rev.*, **74**, 704 (1948).

23. Thomson, J. J., and McClelland, J. A., *Proc. Camb. Phil. Soc.*, **9**, 126 (1896).

24. Van Heerden, P. J., "The Crystal Counter," Utrecht Dissertation (1945).

25. Wilson, C. T. R., *Proc. Roy. Soc.*, **A85**, 285 (1911); **87**, 277 (1912); **104**, 1 (1923).

26. Wooldridge, D. E., Ahearn, A. J., and Burton, J. A., *Phys. Rev.*, **71**, 913 (1947).

27. Yngve, V. H., *Phys. Rev.*, **92**, 428 (1953).

28. Ziegert, H., *Z. Physik*, **46**, 668 (1928).

GENERAL REFERENCE

1. Dabbs, J. W. T., and Walter, F. J. *Semiconductor Nuclear Particle Detectors* (Washington, D.C.: National Academy of Sciences—National Research Council, 1961).

5

NUCLEAR ENERGY LEVELS

5-1 Half-Lives of Alpha Emitters

Rutherford (29) pointed out in 1907 that there seemed to be a rough correlation between the half-life of an α emitter and the range of the emitted α particle, but the half-lives were not known accurately enough at that time to determine whether the exceptions were real or only apparent. In 1911 Geiger and Nuttall (10), after more careful determination of the ranges of various α emitters, discovered a very simple empirical relationship between the ranges and decay constants of α emitters. Their results are shown in Fig. 5-1. The straight-line relationship may be written analytically as

$$\log R = C + k \log \lambda, \tag{5-1}$$

where R is the range of the alpha particle emitted by a nuclide whose decay constant is λ. Since

$$\lambda = 0.693/t_{1/2}$$

this may be written in the alternative form,

$$\log R = C' - k \log t_{1/2}, \tag{5-2}$$

where C and C' are constants characteristic of the series and k is a positive constant which is approximately the same for all series. Since R was found to be proportional to $W^{3/2}$, one would also get a straight-line plot if log W were plotted against log $t_{1/2}$. It is seen from (5-2) that if the range is very small then the half-life must be very long, or from (5-1) that if the range is very small the decay constant would be so small that it would be virtually impossible to detect the radioactivity. Thus there may be many undiscovered

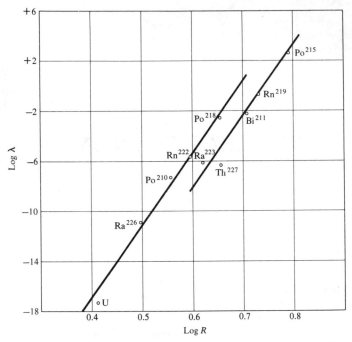

Fig. 5-1. Relationship found by Geiger and Nuttall between the decay constants and the ranges of the α particles emitted by several natural radionuclides.

weakly radioactive nuclides. A more recent compilation (24) of half-lives and energies of α emitters is shown in Figs. 5-2, 5-3, and 5-4. Figure 5-2 shows the relation between α-particle energies and half-lives of even-even nuclides, that is, those which have both even atomic numbers and even mass numbers. Figure 5-3, which gives a comparable plot for those α-emitting nuclides having even atomic numbers and odd mass numbers, and Fig. 5-4, which shows the relation between half-life and α-particle energy for nuclides having odd atomic numbers and either even or odd mass numbers, disclose a very remarkable fact, namely, that the even-even nuclides exhibit a degree of regularity not shared by even-odd, odd-odd, or odd-even nuclides. It will

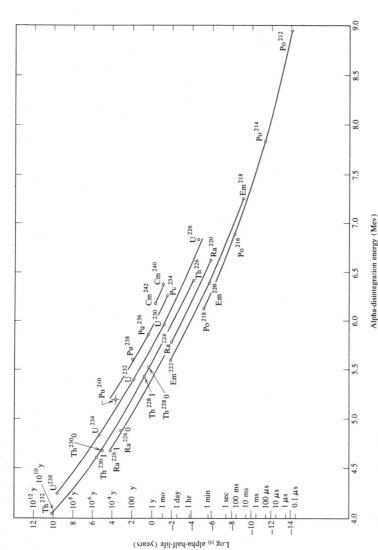

Fig. 5-2. Relationship between half-lives and α-particle energies for nuclides that have both even atomic numbers and even mass numbers. The Roman numeral I following a nuclide symbol (such as Th²²⁸ I) indicates that the point represents the "partial half-life" associated with a short-range group of α particles. The symbol 0 indicates a "partial half-life" associated with transitions to the ground state. These curves are like the Geiger–Nuttall curves (Fig. 5-1) except that the energies are not plotted on logarithmic coordinates. [From I. Perlman, A. Ghiorso, and G. T. Seaborg, *Phys. Rev.*, **77**, 26 (1950).]

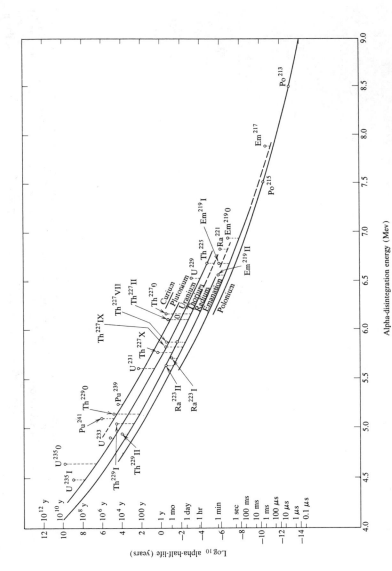

Fig. 5-3. Relationship between half-lives and α-particle energies for nuclides that have even atomic numbers and odd mass numbers. [From I. Perlman, A. Ghiorso, and G. T. Seaborg, *Phys. Rev.,* **77**, 26 (1950).]

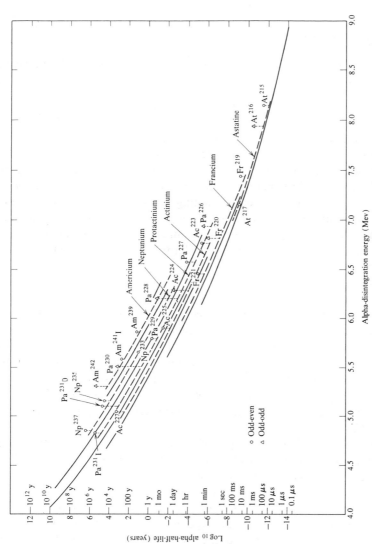

Fig. 5-4. Relationship between half-lives and α-particle energies for nuclides that have odd atomic numbers and either even or odd mass numbers. The solid lines are taken from Fig. 5-2. The dashed lines, interpolated between the solid lines, are where one might expect the data points to lie if the transitions were not forbidden. [From I. Perlman, A. Ghiorso, and G. T. Seaborg, *Phys. Rev.*, **77**, 26 (1950).]

be remembered from Sec. 2-5 that even-even nuclei have no nuclear angular momentum. The greater regularity displayed in Fig. 5-2 is attributable to the fact that both parent and daughter nuclei in this group are even-even. This fact will be considered further in the next section.

5-2 Theory of Alpha Decay

From the Coulomb law of interaction between charged particles in vacuo, namely,

$$f = \frac{q_1 q_2}{r^2}, \tag{5-3}$$

it would follow that an α particle would be repelled by the nucleus with a force that increases without limit as the separation between the nucleus and the α particle approaches zero. Since most natural nuclei do not disintegrate spontaneously, and since many α emitters have a considerable degree of stability, it must follow that the force acting on an α particle changes from a repulsive to an attractive force at points close to a nucleus. The potential* of the α particle in the field of the nucleus must then be something like that shown in Fig. 5-5(a), although the exact shape of the curve near the nucleus is not known. If an α particle with a total energy W, as shown in the figure, could somehow be moved to a point outside the nucleus at a distance b or greater from it, this could be done without doing any net work on the particle. Having gotten outside of the nucleus, it would be repelled by the nucleus and, at a large distance from the nucleus, would have a kinetic energy W since its potential energy would then be practically nil. According to classical mechanics, however, the particle would get out of the nucleus only by going over the top of the potential barrier, and this would require that it be given an additional amount of energy $(U_m - W)$. It would then have a total energy U_m and at a large distance from the nucleus would have a kinetic energy of U_m.

It was found (30) that when α particles from Po^{214} were scattered by uranium the scattering was in accord with the Coulomb law up to 3.2×10^{-12} cm from the nucleus, whereas the α particle *emitted* by U^{238} (the abundant isotope of uranium) has an energy corresponding to the potential energy of an α particle 6.3×10^{-12} cm from the nucleus. It is evident, therefore, that the α particle emitted by U^{238} does not escape by going over the top of the potential barrier. Rutherford advanced the explanation that a neutral particle consisting of an α particle and two electrons moved outside the nucleus far

---

* *Potential* is used here to mean the potential energy of the charged particle in some field of force. This is in contrast to the custom in electrostatics of defining the potential as the potential energy of a *unit* charge in the force field. There is thus no real conflict in definitions, but the unit of charge used here is a bit unusual.

enough to account for its low kinetic energy and then broke up, the electrons being attracted back to the nucleus and the α particle being repelled by the nucleus. We have noted in Chap. 2 that the nuclear spins and magnetic moments are inconsistent with the existence of free electrons in the nucleus. Rutherford's explanation therefore became untenable when these facts were established. (One might have asked, even earlier, why other electrons were not regularly absorbed by nuclei if this sort of process were possible.)

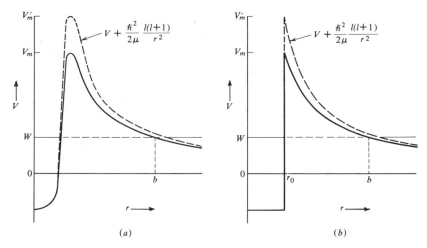

Fig. 5.5. (a) The potential function of a nucleus for a charged particle must be something like this to exhibit coulomb fields at short distances from the nucleus and yet have a stable nuclear assemblage. W is the total energy of the charged particle within the nucleus; b is the closest distance (according to classical theory) that a particle with total energy W could approach to the nucleus from outside.

(b) A "square well potential." This idealization of the nuclear potential function is often used in theoretical work, as it can be handled more simply mathematically. r_0 is defined as the radius of the nucleus in the theory discussed in this section. The dotted curves include the "centrifugal barrier" for a nucleus in which the alpha particle has a reduced mass μ and spin I.

According to wave mechanics (see Appendix C) there is a certain probability that a particle will be found outside the nuclear potential barrier even though it has insufficient energy to surmount its top. Gamow (9) and Gurney and Condon (11) showed that the half-lives of α emitters could be successfully predicted from wave mechanical calculations. The theory shows that as long as the α particle has a positive energy within the nucleus, the nucleus is unstable, and the rate of decay is a function of the width of the potential barrier which the α particle must cross to escape from the nucleus. If the α particle has a negative energy within the nucleus the probability that it will escape is zero, so that the nucleus is completely stable as far as α emission is concerned.

As shown in Appendix C, the probability of transmission (or the transmission coefficient) of a one-dimensional rectangular potential barrier like that shown in Fig. 5-6 whose height is greater than the kinetic energy of the incident particle is given by

$$P_{tr} = \frac{16(W - U_1)(U_2 - W)T^2}{4(W - U_1)(U_2 - W)(1 + T^2)^2 + (2W - U_1 - U_2)^2(1 - T^2)^2},$$
(5-4)

where
$$T^2 = e^{(2/\hbar)\sqrt{2M(U_2 - W)}\cdot a},$$
(5-5)

and where a is the thickness of the barrier, W is the total energy of the particle, U_1 is the potential outside the barrier, U_2 is the potential within the barrier, and M is the mass of the particle.

The potential barrier of a nucleus, of course, cannot be one-dimensional. About the simplest potential barrier one can imagine is that shown in Fig.

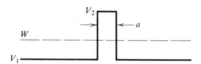

Fig. 5-6. A one-dimensional rectangular potential barrier. There is a finite probability that a particle with total energy W, approaching from the left, say, can penetrate the barrier. According to classical mechanics this probability is zero.

5-5(b) where the potential is a function of the radius only. While the wave equation can be written in spherical coordinates easily enough, the solution for even such a simple potential function as that shown is not easily obtained. An approximate transmission coefficient can be obtained by treating the curved (coulomb) portion of the potential function as a series of narrow rectangular barriers whose heights decrease with increasing r. This leads to the result

$$P_{tr} = e^{-\gamma},$$
(5-6)

where

$$\gamma = \frac{2}{\hbar} \int_{r_0}^{b} \sqrt{2\hat{M}(U - W)} \, dr$$
(5-7)

$$= \frac{\sqrt{8\hat{M}Z_\alpha Z_n e^2}}{\hbar} \int_{r_0}^{b} \sqrt{\frac{1}{r} - \frac{W}{Z_\alpha Z_n e^2}} \, dr,$$
(5-8)

$$\gamma = \frac{1}{\hbar} \sqrt{8\hat{M}Z_\alpha Z_n e^2 b} \left[\cos^{-1} \sqrt{\frac{r_0}{b}} - \sqrt{\frac{r_0}{b} - \frac{r_0^2}{b^2}} \right],$$
(5-9)

where $\hat{M}$ is the reduced mass of the α nucleus system, $Z_\alpha e$ the charge of the α particle, $Z_n e$ the charge of the residual nucleus, and b the classical distance of closest approach to a point charge $Z_n e$ for an α particle with total energy W. (See Prob. 2-2.)

The reduced mass is introduced so that the problem can be reduced to the motion of a particle about an infinitely massive or "fixed" nucleus. Where the energy of the α particle is small compared with the maximum height of the potential barrier, $b \gg r_0$ and

$$\gamma = \frac{2\pi Z_\alpha Z_n e^2}{hv}, \tag{5-10}$$

where v is the velocity of the α particle far from the nucleus and the difference between $\hat{M}$ and the mass of the α particle has been neglected.

The probability of escape per second for the α particle, which is essentially the decay constant, is the product of the probability of transmission in a single encounter with the potential barrier multiplied by the number of encounters per second. If the time between encounters is τ, then the mean lifetime (which is just the reciprocal of the decay constant) is

$$t_a = \frac{1}{e^{-\gamma}(1/\tau)} = \tau e^\gamma. \tag{5-11}$$

The bouncing back and forth of the α particle may be represented by a spherical standing wave within the potential well. To get an estimate of the time τ, one may consider the analogous case of a particle in a one-dimensional rectangular well. If the barrier height were infinite, the standing wave would have to be of such length that it would be an integral number of half wavelengths from one side of the well to the other. Ignoring the fact that the barrier height is not actually infinite, one may obtain an approximate value for the wavelength, λ, from

$$\frac{\lambda}{2} = 2r_0. \tag{5-12}$$

The de Broglie wavelength of the α particle is

$$\lambda = \frac{h}{Mv_i}, \tag{5-13}$$

where v_i is the velocity of the α particle within the nucleus. From (5-12) and (5-13) one obtains

$$v_i = \frac{h}{4Mr_0}. \tag{5-14}$$

If the nuclear radius is taken to be 10^{-12} cm, then, according to (5-14), v_i is about 10^8 cm/sec and τ is about 10^{-20} sec.

If one assumes that the heavy nuclei have nearly identical potential functions, then the greater the total energy of the α particle within the nucleus, the thinner is the part of the potential barrier through which the particle must pass in order to escape from the nucleus. This means that since the potential barrier is effectively both lower and thinner, the probability of escape is greater. But a large total energy of the α particle implies a large kinetic energy of the emitted particle. One would expect, therefore, that the shorter the half-life the greater would be the energy of the emitted α particle, and this is precisely what the Geiger–Nuttall curves demonstrate.

This theory* predicts half-lives that are usually of the correct order of magnitude, but that occasionally differ from observed half-lives by factors that may be as great as 10^3. This may be due in part to the fact that the calculated value of the half-life is extremely sensitive to the nuclear radius. Conversely, the calculated nuclear radius is rather insensitive to the half-life, so that measured half-lives may be used to calculate nuclear radii. In this case r_0 is the nuclear radius *by definition*. There are other ways of defining what one means by "nuclear radius." The radii obtained on the basis of these other definitions are usually within 10 to 20 per cent of each other, but sometimes differ by a factor of 1.5 or even more.

Angular momentum must be conserved during α emission as in other processes. The effect of the angular momentum of the α particle may be most readily handled theoretically by simply adding a "centrifugal potential" to the ordinary potential function. If the α particle has a maximum observable angular momentum of $l\hbar$, the centrifugal potential is

$$U_{\text{cent}} = \frac{\hbar^2}{2\hat{M}} \frac{l(l+1)}{r^2} \tag{5-15}$$

and acts to increase the apparent height of the potential barrier as shown by the dotted curves in Fig. 5-5. It is estimated that even as large a value as $l = 5$ will only change the half-life by a factor of 10. In order to avoid this complication it is convenient to confine our attention to daughter nuclei with zero spin (i.e., the even-even nuclei). Table 5-1 lists a number of such computed nuclear radii for even-even nuclides. Since the α particle has zero spin, this means that the parent nuclei in these cases will also have zero spin.

The alpha-decay theory presented here makes the implicit assumption that the α particle exists as such within the nucleus. If it does not, then one must multiply the escape probability per second by the probability that an α particle will be formed within the nucleus (i.e., the fraction of time during which the nucleus contains an alpha-particle grouping). The probability of alpha emission would be smaller in this case than for a nucleus that always has an alpha-particle group present. The potential barrier would then actually

* For a more recent modification of this theory, see H. J. Mang, *Phys. Rev.*, **119**, 1069 (1960).

Table 5-1 NUCLEAR RADII DETERMINED FROM HALF-LIVES
AND ENERGIES OF ALPHA PARTICLES EMITTED BY NUCLEI
OF SPIN ZERO

Parent nucleus	Daughter nucleus	Calculated nuclear radius	Value of r_1 to satisfy $r_0 = r_1 A^{1/3}$
$_{92}U^{238}$	Th^{234}	9.34 ($\times 10^{-13}$ cm)	1.52 ($\times 10^{-13}$ cm)
$_{92}U^{234}$	Th^{230}	9.21	1.51
$_{90}Th^{230}$	Ra^{226}	9.26	1.52
$_{86}Rn^{222}$	Po^{218}	9.28	1.54
$_{84}Po^{218}$	Pb^{214}	9.14	1.53
$_{84}Po^{210}$	Pb^{206}	8.27	1.40
$_{88}Ra^{224}$	Rn^{220}	9.29	1.54
$_{86}Rn^{220}$	Po^{216}	9.28	1.55
$_{84}Po^{216}$	Pb^{212}	9.12	1.53

SOURCE: M. A. Preston, *Phys. Rev.*, **71**, 865 (1947).

be thinner and the nuclear radius smaller than the value calculated according to the Gamow theory. It is also possible that the nucleus might simultaneously contain more than one permanent or transient α particle. If such were the case, the rate of decay would be greater and the nuclear radius would be underestimated if one used the Gamow theory.

5-3 Nuclear Energy Levels

It will be noted that the α particle in Fig. 5-5 is assumed to have a greater energy than that corresponding to the bottom of the potential well. If the α particle is looked upon as a definite and invariable object (i.e., one ignores the possibility that the α particle itself might be an aggregation of particles that could exist in excited states) then the nucleus can be looked upon as containing an α particle that is moving about the remainder of the nucleus with a certain amount of total energy (kinetic plus potential). Just as an electron may occupy any one of many quantized energy states of an atom, so one might expect that an α particle could occupy any one of a number of possible quantized energy states of a nucleus. There would then be a lowest possible energy state, which could be called the ground state, and several or many discrete energy levels above this. When a nucleus emits an α particle, the residual nucleus may then be left in an excited state in which another of its constituent α particles occupies an energy level above the ground state. By analogy with optical spectra, one might anticipate that this α particle would drop to a lower energy state of the host nucleus with the emission of a gamma ray. An example of such excited states where both α and γ energies have been measured is shown in Fig. 5-7, and the degree of agreement compared in Table 5-2.

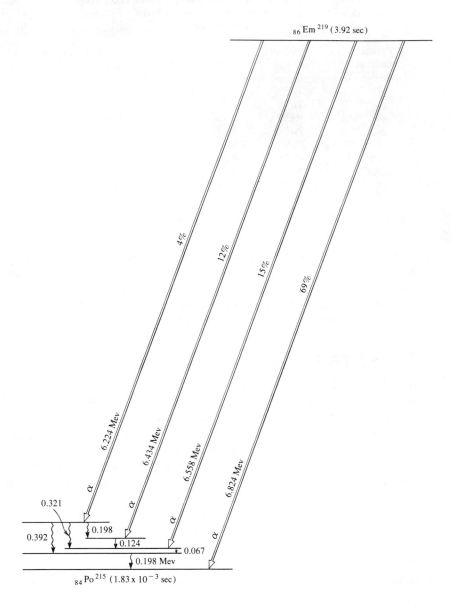

Fig. 5-7. Probable nuclear energy levels of Po²¹⁵ deduced from γ-ray spectrum of excited Po²¹⁵ and α-particle energies from decay of Em²¹⁹. The energy levels at the left are actually for (Po²¹⁵ + He⁴).

Table 5-2 COMPARISON OF OBSERVED GAMMA-RAY ENERGIES WITH CORRESPONDING DIFFERENCES IN MEASURED ENERGIES OF ALPHA PARTICLES FROM RN^{219}

γ	$\alpha_m - \alpha_e$	W_γ (Mev)	$W_{\Delta\alpha}$ (Mev)
$\gamma_1 + \gamma_6$	$\alpha_4 - \alpha_1$	0.590	0.600
γ_2 $\gamma_3 + \gamma_4$	$\alpha_3 - \alpha_1$	0.321 0.322	0.334
$\gamma_5 + \gamma_6$	$\alpha_4 - \alpha_3$	0.265	0.266
γ_3	$\alpha_2 - \alpha_1$	0.198	0.210
γ_4	$\alpha_3 - \alpha_2$	0.124	0.124

SOURCE: *Nuclear Data*, National Bureau of Standards Circular 499, Washington, D.C. (1950).

Actually, it is not at all necessary to assume that the excited states are excited states of an α particle in the nucleus. It is sufficient to say that the nucleus is in an excited state. This excited state *may* be due to excitation of a single nucleon, such as a proton, or it may involve several nuclear particles. Commonly the largest number of alpha particles are those emitted with greatest energy, as one might be led to expect from the Gamow theory, but there are exceptions, such as Bi^{212}, to this rule.

Table 5-3 ENERGY SPECTRUM OF BI^{212}

Energy of emitted α particle (Mev)	5.601	5.620	5.762	6.044	6.083
Relative frequency of decay mode	1.10%	0.16%	1.80%	69.8%	27.2%

SOURCE: *Nuclear Data*, NBS Circular 499.

Where the alpha decay constant of the daughter nucleus is large, an alpha particle may be emitted while the nucleus is in an excited state. An example of this is Po^{212}. Since the decay constant for γ emission is much larger than that for α emission from these excited states, it follows that α emission usually takes place from the ground state and only infrequently from an excited state. The decay schemes for Bi^{212} and the energy levels of its daughter products, Po^{212} and Tl^{208}, are shown in Fig. 5-8.

Evidence for the existence of nuclear energy states also comes from nuclear reactions in which a target nucleus is struck by a high-velocity particle such as a proton. Figure 5-9 shows how the gamma-ray intensity varies with bombarding energy in the C^{14} (p, γ) reaction. The gamma rays measured here were only those whose energies exceeded 3.8 Mev. It will be noticed that the difference between the excitation levels of the resulting N^{15} and the excess of

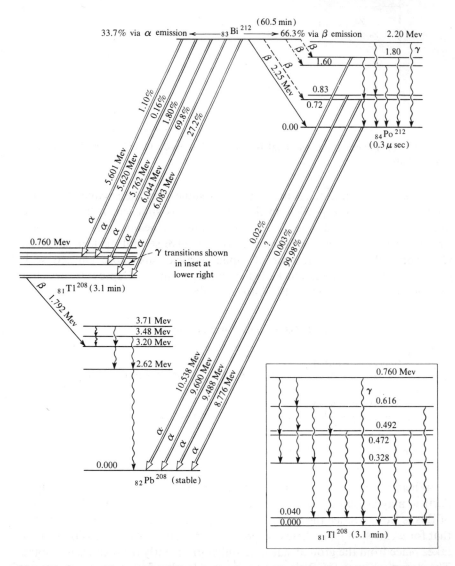

Fig. 5-8. Decay scheme of Bi^{212} and daughters with inferred energy levels of Po^{212}, Tl^{208}, and Pb^{208}. The energy levels of Po^{212}, etc., are actually for $(Po^{212} + He^4)$, etc.

the mass energies of $C^{14} + H^1$ over that of N^{15} (10.214 Mev) is less than the corresponding kinetic energies of the bombarding protons. The reason is that conservation of momentum requires the N^{15} nucleus to have a small amount of kinetic energy so that the excitation energy is correspondingly lessened. In this case (see Prob. 5-5) about $\frac{14}{15}$ of the proton kinetic energy is available for nuclear excitation.

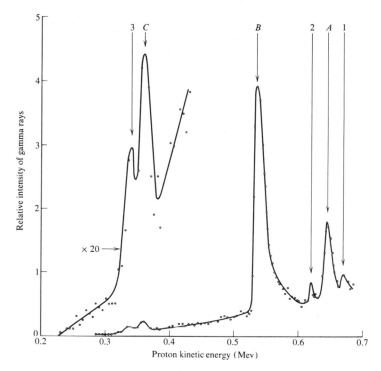

Fig. 5-9. Gamma-ray intensity as a function of the kinetic energy of impinging protons. A carbon target with a slight fluorine contamination was used. The peaks A, B, and C are from the C^{14} (p, γ) reaction, while 1 and 3 are from the F^{19} $(p, \alpha\gamma)$ reaction. The origin of peak 2 is unknown. The fluorine peaks were used to calibrate the equipment. Peak A corresponds to the 10.806 Mev, peak B to the 10.706 Mev, and peak C to the 10.543 Mev levels of Fig. 5-10. [From G. A. Bartholomew, F. Brown, H. E. Gove, A. E. Litherland, and E. B. Paul, *Can. J. Phys.*, **33**, 441 (1955).]

The resonance peaks occur when the proton energy is exactly the right amount to produce an allowed state of excitation of the product nucleus. This is quite similar to the resonance excitation of optical spectrum lines. The existence of these excited states in N^{15} has been confirmed (12, 17) by measuring the energies of the γ rays that are emitted when one of these excited states is produced. A proposed energy-level scheme for N^{15} is shown in Fig. 5-10. These energy levels have also been produced by the N^{14} (d, p)

reaction. In this case one may determine the excitation energy of the residual N^{15} nucleus by measuring the energies of protons emitted in a specified direction (with respect to the bombarding beam direction) with a magnetic

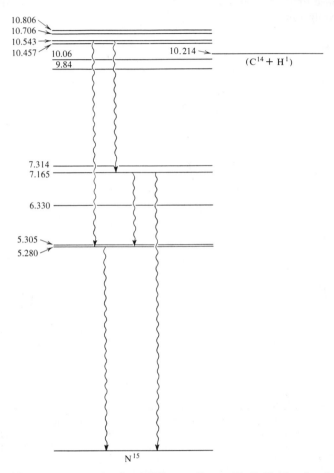

Fig. 5-10. Energy levels of N^{15} according to D. F. Hebbard and D. N. F. Dunbar, *Phys. Rev.*, **115**, 624 (1959). The mass energy of $(C^{14} + H^1)$ is given at the right for purposes of comparison. All energies given in Mev.

spectrometer. Such an energy spectrum is shown (34) in Fig. 5-11. The corresponding calculated energy levels of N^{15}, based on an assumed mass energy excess of $(N^{14} + H^2 - H^1)$ over N^{15} of 8.615 Mev, are given in Table 5-4. It is seen that these energy levels (which will have a systematic uncertainty equal to that of the 8.615-Mev ground state in addition to experimental

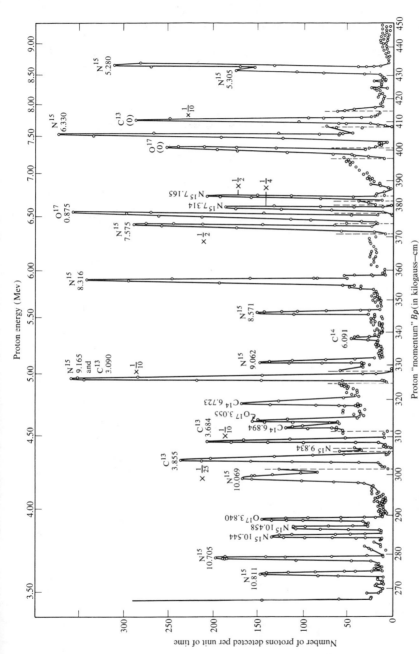

Fig. 5-11. Proton spectrum produced by proton bombardment of a nylon target mounted on a gold foil. The incident deuterons had an energy of 7.00 Mev. The protons observed were those emitted at an angle of 90° to the deuteron beam.

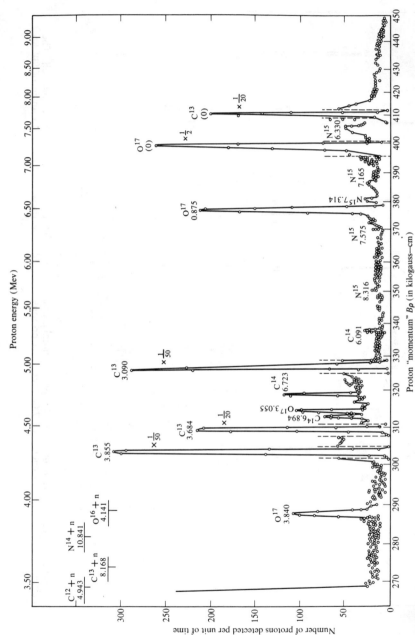

Fig. 5-12. Proton spectrum produced by proton bombardment of a Formvar target mounted on gold foil. Deuteron energy was 7.00 Mev. Protons were observed at 90°.

uncertainties in the proton energies) are in reasonably good agreement with the levels shown in Fig. 5-10.

Table 5-4 EXCITATION ENERGIES (IN MEV) OF N^{15} DEDUCED
FROM ENERGIES OF PROTONS EMITTED IN THE N^{14} (d, p)
REACTION

5.280	8.316	10.069
6.330	8.571	10.458
7.165	9.062	10.544
7.314	9.165	10.705
7.575	9.834	10.811

Beta decay will be discussed more thoroughly in Chap. 7, but we note here that maximum beta-decay energies and the energies of the subsequently emitted gamma rays again correspond to definite nuclear energy levels. An example of the energy levels resulting from β decay of Bi^{212} is shown in Fig. 5-8.

5-4 Gamma Radiation from Excited Nuclei

In Chap. 2 we noted the existence of magnetic dipole and electric quadrupole moments, and the absence of electric dipole moments in nuclei. At first it may seem strange that the nucleus can exhibit electric moments at all since it contains no negative charges. A nonspherical charge distribution, however, is equivalent to a spherical distribution (equivalent to a monopole) plus a distribution of positive and negative charges. This idea was illustrated in Fig. 2-21. A nucleus with an electric dipole moment would have to have an asymmetric charge distribution, perhaps somewhat egg-shaped. An ellipsoidal distribution would result in a quadrupole moment.

Even though a nucleus cannot have a permanent electric dipole moment, it is conceivable that it could be disturbed sufficiently to cause oscillations in its charge distribution that would be equivalent to an oscillating dipole. In other words it would exhibit a dipole moment whose strength varied with time in an oscillatory manner about a mean value of zero.

If the charges making up a dipole oscillate with respect to each other along the dipole axis, electromagnetic energy will be given off, according to classical theory, just as radio waves are radiated from an antenna in which there is an oscillating current. This radiation could be called *electric dipole radiation*. The electric and magnetic fields associated with such an oscillating dipole are shown in Fig. 5-13. If the two charges are moving toward each other as shown, each moving charge is equivalent to a current flowing in the negative *z*-direction. We see therefore that the oscillation of a positive charge (such as one would have to have in a nucleus) produces the same magnetic field as an oscillating dipole. A current element, $i\,dz$, produces a magnetic flux density at a distance r given by*

$$dB = \frac{i \sin \theta\, dz}{r^2},\qquad(5\text{-}16)$$

where θ is the angle between r and dz. Therefore, the magnetic flux density along the z-axis is zero. Since the rate of energy flow (Poynting vector) is proportional to $\mathbf{E} \times \mathbf{B}$ where $\mathbf{E}$ is the electric field intensity, it is clear that

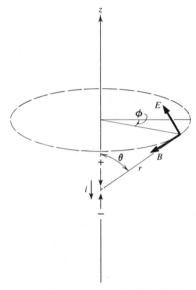

Fig. 5-13. Diagrammatic representation of electric and magnetic fields produced by an oscillating dipole at a time when the charges are moving toward each other. The fields are those at such a distance from the dipole that $r \gg \lambda$, where λ is the wavelength of the emitted radiation. It will be noticed that E is in almost the opposite direction to that expected *near* the dipole.

there is no radiant energy flow in this direction. A more exact analysis of the problem, taking account of the interplay of changing magnetic and electric fields as given by Maxwell's equations (33), shows that

$$B_r = B_\theta = 0,\qquad(5\text{-}17)$$

$$B_\phi = \frac{Y \sin \theta}{r}\left[\frac{4\pi^2\nu^2}{c^2}\cos 2\pi\nu\left(t-\frac{r}{c}\right) + \frac{2\pi\nu}{cr}\sin 2\pi\nu\left(t-\frac{r}{c}\right)\right],\qquad(5\text{-}18)$$

$$E_\phi = 0,\qquad(5\text{-}19)$$

* All units in this section are Gaussian.

$$E_r = \frac{2Y \cos \theta}{r^2} \left[\frac{1}{r} \cos 2\pi\nu \left(t - \frac{r}{c} \right) - \frac{2\pi\nu}{c} \sin 2\pi\nu \left(t - \frac{r}{c} \right) \right], \tag{5-20}$$

$$E_\theta = \frac{Y \sin \theta}{r} \left[\left(\frac{1}{r^2} - \frac{4\pi^2\nu^2}{c^2} \right) \cos 2\pi\nu \left(t - \frac{r}{c} \right) - \frac{2\pi\nu}{cr} \sin 2\pi\nu \left(t - \frac{r}{c} \right) \right], \tag{5-21}$$

where Y is the amplitude of the electric dipole moment oscillations (i.e., it has dimensions of an electric dipole moment), ν is the frequency of oscillation, t is time, and c is the velocity of light.

At appreciable distances, r, from the dipole, only the lowest powers of $1/r$ are important and the equations then simplify to

$$B_r = B_\theta = 0, \tag{5-22}$$

$$B_\phi \cong \frac{4\pi^2\nu^2 Y}{rc^2} \sin \theta \cos 2\pi\nu \left(t - \frac{r}{c} \right), \tag{5-23}$$

$$E_r \cong 0, \tag{5-24}$$

$$E_\theta \cong - \frac{4\pi^2\nu^2 Y}{rc^2} \sin \theta \cos 2\pi\nu \left(t - \frac{r}{c} \right). \tag{5-25}$$

In this case **E** and **B** are of equal magnitude, are in phase, and are perpendicular to each other and to r. The Poynting vector is then along r, so the radiation is radial with a maximum intensity at right angles to the axis of the dipole and decreasing to zero (as we saw before) in a direction parallel to the dipole axis. It is also evident that the radiation is plane polarized.

An oscillating magnetic dipole whose magnetic moment amplitude is μ gives the same sort of radiation field as an oscillating electric dipole (33) except that the roles of magnetic flux density and electric field intensity are reversed. In this case

$$B_\phi = 0, \tag{5-26}$$

$$B_r = \frac{2\mu \cos \theta}{cr^2} \left[\frac{1}{r} \cos 2\pi\nu \left(t - \frac{r}{c} \right) - \frac{2\pi\nu}{c} \sin 2\pi\nu \left(t - \frac{r}{c} \right) \right], \tag{5-27}$$

$$B_\theta = \frac{\mu \sin \theta}{cr} \left[\left(\frac{1}{r^2} - \frac{4\pi^2\nu^2}{c^2} \right) \cos 2\pi\nu \left(t - \frac{r}{c} \right) - \frac{2\pi\nu}{cr} \sin 2\pi\nu \left(t - \frac{r}{c} \right) \right]. \tag{5-28}$$

When r is large these reduce to

$$B_r = B_\phi = E_r = E_\theta = 0, \tag{5-29}$$

$$B_\theta = E_\phi = - \frac{\mu \, 4\pi^2\nu^2 \sin \theta}{c^3 r} \cos 2\pi\nu \left(t - \frac{r}{c} \right). \tag{5-30}$$

It will be observed that the plane of polarization (with respect to a plane containing the dipole axis and the radius vector from the dipole to the point in question) of magnetic dipole radiation is rotated 90° from that of electric dipole radiation. If two dipoles are placed end to end or side by side in such a way that the field of one dipole tends to cancel the field of the other dipole, then one has a quadrupole. Radiation from an oscillating electric quadrupole could be called *electric quadrupole radiation*. An oscillating magnetic quadrupole also gives off radiation, and this would be called *magnetic quadrupole radiation*. In general, one speaks of magnetic or electric 2^L pole radiation and these are read as follows:

$$2^1 = \text{dipole,}$$
$$2^2 = \text{quadrupole,}$$
$$2^3 = \text{octupole,}$$
$$2^4 = 16 \text{ pole, or simply 2 to the 4th pole.}$$

Electric dipole radiation is often spoken of as E1, magnetic dipole as M1, electric quadrupole as E2, magnetic quadrupole as M2, or in general, 2^L pole radiation as EL or ML.

Since it is not possible for the center of mass of a nucleus to undergo spontaneous oscillations, electric dipole radiation must be associated with oscillations of the center of charge. Ellipsoidal oscillations could produce electric quadrupole radiation, and more complicated oscillations of the nuclear surface could produce higher multipole electric radiation.

The radiation patterns of oscillating dipoles, quadrupoles, octupoles, etc., are each different. The wave mechanical counterpart of the radiation pattern is a probability pattern that is a function of the coordinates. If a large number of identical excited nuclei, with their dipole axes all parallel, emitted E1 photons of equal energy, the intensity of the observed gamma radiation would vary with the angle between the direction of emission and the dipole axis. Ordinarily the nuclei are oriented at random so that this directional characteristic is not observed, but if gamma emission is preceded by the emission of a particle or another gamma ray, the previously emitted particle's direction of emission may be used as a reference direction with respect to which the subsequent gamma propagation direction may be measured, provided that the intermediate state is not one of zero spin (in which case the intermediate nucleus itself has no reference direction) and provided also that the mean lifetime of the intermediate state is short enough that other disturbances do not disorient the intermediate nucleus before it emits a gamma ray. One then finds that the intensity of the gamma radiation is a function of the angle so defined. Again, the nuclei may be aligned magnetically, if they possess a magnetic moment, and it will then be possible to measure directional effects. If the nuclei are aligned (in the same direction, but not all in the same sense) the emitted gamma radiation may be linearly polarized but cannot show circular polarization. On the other hand, if the nuclei are polarized (same direction and same sense) then circular polarization of the emitted gamma radiation is possible. Figure 5-14 shows how a particular kind of classical quadrupole oscillation can produce circularly polarized waves.

An important aspect of the classification of types of gamma emission is that it gives information concerning the nuclear spin of the excited state. Heitler (14) has shown that a photon emitted in either electric or magnetic 2^L pole radiation carries away an amount of angular momentum equal to $L\hbar$.

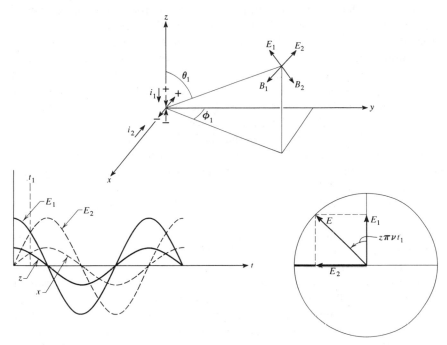

Fig. 5-14. Two identical electric dipoles with equal amplitudes of oscillation and 90° phase difference, when oriented as shown in the upper figure, produce circularly polarized radiation. The figure at the lower left shows how the electric field intensities at r, θ_1, ϕ_1 vary with time. E_1 and E_2 have been taken positive in the sense shown in the upper figure. This is to be contrasted with Eq. (5-25) where E_1 is taken positive in the direction of increasing θ. The figure at the lower right shows the electric field intensities at the end of the vector r as viewed from the origin. There is no significance in the fact that E_2 appears to be negative here. This is just the direction of E_2 corresponding to that in the figure above.

Since a photon has an intrinsic spin of $\hbar$ and since angular momentum must be conserved, our classical view would be that in those cases where $L > 1$, the photon is emitted noncentrally (i.e., its extended line of motion would not pass through the center of mass of the emitting nucleus). Let the excited nucleus have a (maximum observable) spin I', and let it decay to a state whose spin is I. Since angular momentum must be conserved, the vector sum of the angular momentum carried away by the photon and the spin of the nucleus in its lower energy state must equal the spin of the initial excited state. This means that L can have any integral value from $|I' - I|$ to $(I' + I)$, or, in symbols,

$$|I' - I| \leqslant L \leqslant (I' + I).$$

The absolute value signs on $|I' - I|$ are necessary because I' may be either greater or less than I. As an example, suppose the upper state has a spin of $\frac{7}{2}$ and the lower, a spin of $\frac{3}{2}$. Then L may have values from $\frac{7}{2} + \frac{3}{2}$ to $\frac{7}{2} - \frac{3}{2}$, or in other words, 5, 4, 3, 2. Transitions in which $L = 0$ are strictly forbidden (i.e., impossible) since this would require monopole radiation. Monopole radiation would have to be spherically symmetric (i.e., a function of r only) but this is not possible with the transverse electric fields characteristic of electromagnetic radiation, since the field lines have to point in some definite direction rather than in all directions at once.

The intrinsic spin of the photon may be looked upon as circular polarization of the electromagnetic waves. Right- and left-handed polarization then correspond to spin parallel or antiparallel to the direction of propagation. When it is said that E1 radiation is plane polarized, what is meant is that either parallel or antiparallel orientation of the intrinsic photon spin is equally likely.

Transitions are possible even when $I' = I$ provided that both I' and I are not zero. There are obviously no allowed single photon transitions in the latter case, since the only possible value of L is zero and one says that $0 \to 0$ transitions are "strictly forbidden." It should be possible to emit a pair of photons in a $0 \to 0$ transition, but no clear-cut case of such a transition has been found. The subject of multiple photon, multiple particle, or particle photon mixture transitions will be touched on again in Chap. 8. Since the number of nucleons is the same before and after a γ transition, gamma transitions always take place either between two half-integral spin states or between two integral spin states.

5-5 Parity

A quantum mechanical concept that has no classical counterpart is that of *parity*, which is a mathematical property of the wave function describing a particular system. If a particular wave function

$$\psi(x, y, z) = \psi(-x, -y, -z), \tag{5-31}$$

then that wave function is said to possess *even parity*. If, on the other hand,

$$\psi(x, y, z) = -\psi(-x, -y, -z), \tag{5-32}$$

then the function is said to possess *odd parity*. Even parity is often designated by + and odd parity by −. Thus a nucleus in a state in which it has a nuclear spin of $\frac{3}{2}$ and even parity is designated $\frac{3}{2}+$ or $3/2^+$. Now each nucleus is believed to possess a definite parity. Laporte's rule (20) for allowed and forbidden electronic transitions in the spectroscopic multiplets, which was proclaimed in 1924, was shown by Wigner (38) in 1927 to be explicable in terms of the invariance of the Hamiltonian of the system under spatial inversion. In modern terminology we would say that, in gamma transitions, the parity of the system must be conserved, that is, the parity of the gamma ray plus de-excited nucleus must be the same as that of the original excited nucleus.

It is fairly easy to show that the quantum mechanical calculation of γ-ray transition probabilities requires that the parity change be

$$(-1)^L \quad \text{for pure electric multipole transitions}$$

and $\quad -(-1)^L \quad$ for pure magnetic multipole transitions,

where −1 indicates a parity change and +1 no parity change. We see then that L must be consistent both with the spin change and with the parity change. The value of L can be determined (at least in principle) by studying the angular distribution of the emitted γ rays. In a gamma-gamma cascade (i.e., one gamma decay followed by a second in the same nucleus) as has been mentioned previously, the direction of emission of the first γ provides a preferred direction in space with respect to which the second gamma's direction of emission may be measured. In practice this is done by studying the γ-γ coincidence rate as a function of the angular separation of the detectors. Yang (39) has shown that the angular correlation function, $P(\theta)$, for the relative frequency of emission per unit solid angle, Ω, of the two gammas at an angular separation, θ, is given by

$$P(\theta)\, d\Omega = \sum_{n=0}^{n=L} C_{2n} P_{2n}(\cos \theta)\, d\Omega, \tag{5-33}$$

where the C_{2n} are coefficients that depend upon the values of L_1, L_2, and the spins of the three energy states involved for the two gamma rays, L is the smallest of L_1, L_2, and the spin of the intermediate state, and $P_{2n}(\cos \theta)$ is an even Legendre polynomial. This equation is only applicable where the magnetic sublevels of the initial level are equally populated, where all three of the levels concerned have well-defined angular momentum and parity, and where the emitted gammas are produced by pure (i.e., not mixed) multipole radiation transitions. Even with these restrictions the presently available measurement techniques are sufficiently imprecise that the method is only successful for low multipole orders.

The angular distribution is exactly the same for a given L whether the radiation be magnetic or electric 2^L pole. How then is one to determine the parity change? The answer lies in measuring the polarization of the radiation, for the polarization of EL is always different from that of ML radiation.

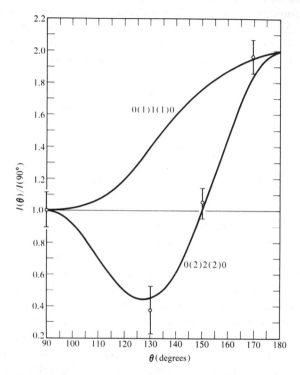

Fig. 5-15. Variation in relative number of $\gamma - \gamma$ coincidences as a function of the angle (θ) between the detectors. The data is from Bunker, Mize, and Starner, *Phys. Rev.*, **105**, 227 (1957). The upper solid curve labeled 0 (1) 1 (1) 0, is the theoretical value for a cascade from a spin-zero state to a spin-one state and then to a spin-zero state. L for each transition is one (1). The lower solid curve is for a 0 (2) 2 (2) 0 cascade. The equation of the upper curve is

$$I(\theta)/I(90°) = \tfrac{4}{3} [1 + \tfrac{1}{2} P_2 (\cos \theta)] = 1 + \cos^2 \theta$$

and that of the lower curve is

$$I(\theta)/I(90°) = \tfrac{5}{4} [1 + .357 P_2 (\cos \theta) + 1.143 P_4 (\cos \theta)]$$
$$= 1 - 3 \cos^2 \theta + 4 \cos^4 \theta$$

The coefficients [The C_{2n} of Eq. 5-33] were taken from Biedenharn and Rose, *Rev. Mod. Phys.*, **25**, 729 (1953).

Since such measurements measure only *changes* in parity rather than the parity of either the excited or de-excited state, one often speaks of the "relative parity" of one state with respect to another state.

Table 5-5 SELECTION RULES FOR RADIATIVE TRANSITIONS

Type of radiation	Designation	Observable spin change L (in units of $\hbar$)	Parity change
Electric dipole	E1	1	-1 (yes)
Magnetic dipole	M1	1	$+1$ (no)
Electric quadrupole	E2	2	$+1$ (no)
Magnetic quadrupole	M2	2	-1 (yes)
Electric octupole	E3	3	-1 (yes)
Magnetic octupole	M3	3	$+1$ (no)
Electric L-pole	EL	L	$(-1)^L$
Magnetic L-pole	ML	L	$-(-1)^L$

5-6 Lifetimes of Excited Nuclei

In contrast to charged-particle decay, where the mean lifetime, t_a, may be very long (e.g., U^{238} has a mean lifetime of 6.50×10^9 years), the lifetime of the majority of excited nuclei that decay by gamma emission is too short to be measured. A relatively large fraction of known gamma emitters, however, have lifetimes that, though relatively short for the most part, are long enough to be determined with reasonable accuracy. These are known as *isomeric nuclei*. Although the laws of electromagnetic interactions are well known it is not possible to calculate radiative transition probabilities with any exactitude because the nuclear wave functions are not known (i.e., we still do not have a satisfactory theory of nuclear forces). Weisskopf (37) has given expressions for approximate radiative transition probabilities for a nuclear model in which a single proton, moving about the rest of the nucleus, makes a transition from a higher to a lower energy state with a change in I of L. For the electric multipole case the formula is

$$\left(\frac{1}{t_a}\right)_{EL} = \lambda_{EL} = \frac{4.4 \times 10^{21}(L+1)}{L[(2L+1)!!]^2}\left(\frac{3}{L+3}\right)^2\left(\frac{W_\gamma}{197}\right)^{2L+1}(1.45 \times A^{1/3})^{2L}$$

(5-34)

and for the magnetic multipole transitions,

$$\left(\frac{1}{t_a}\right)_{ML} = \lambda_{ML} = \frac{1.9 \times 10^{21}(L+1)}{L[(2L+1)!!]^2}\left(\frac{3}{L+3}\right)^2\left(\frac{W_\gamma}{197}\right)^{2L+1}(1.45 \times A^{1/3})^{2L-2},$$

(5-35)

where t_a is the mean lifetime in seconds when no other process competes with radiative decay, W_γ is the energy of the emitted gamma ray in Mev, and A is the mass number of the emitting nucleus. The double factorial symbol (!!) means the product of the odd numbers only—for example $5!! = 5 \cdot 3 \cdot 1 = 15$. Some examples of data calculated from these formulae are given in Fig. 5-16.

A few isomeric nuclei with their experimentally determined mean lifetimes are given in Table 5-6. It will be noticed that the shortest lifetime listed is 1.4×10^{-10} second. This is because 10^{-10} second is about the limit of the ability of present-day equipment to directly measure time intervals. Shorter lifetimes may be inferred from "line widths," a matter which will be taken

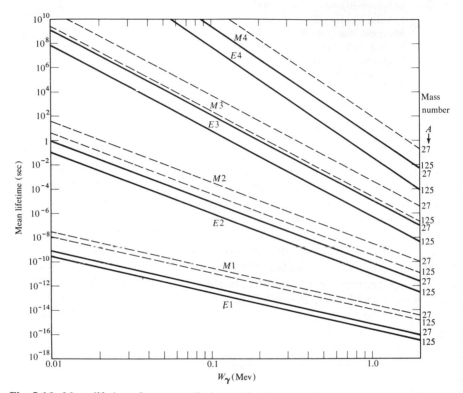

Fig. 5-16. Mean lifetimes for pure radiative multipole decay of excited nuclei, calculated from formulae given by Weisskopf [*Phys. Rev.*, **83**, 1073 (1951).] These give only rough estimates of actual lifetimes, but they frequently aid in identifying the type of transition being studied. The upper curve of each pair is for a mass number of 27, while the lower curve is for a mass number of 125. The upper E4 and lower M4 curve just happen to be so nearly coincident that they could not be shown as separate curves.

up in this chapter in a discussion of nuclear resonance absorption. Notations such as Ge^{72m} or Ge^{72*} are commonly used to denote isomeric states. A source of possible confusion to which the reader should be alerted is the custom of listing gamma rays under the parent substance rather than the actual gamma-emitting daughter in the case of non-isomeric nuclei.

It is possible to treat the radiation field in several different ways. For example, it could be broken down into a sum of plane waves, but this is not

Table 5-6

Nuclide	Energy of emitted γ ray (Mev)	Mean lifetime*	Spins Initial	Final†
V^{51}	0.323	1.4×10^{-10} s		$\frac{7}{2}$
Eu^{153}	0.069	2.02×10^{-10} s		$\frac{5}{2}$
Cm^{243}	0.278	1.59×10^{-9} s		
Sm^{152}	0.122	2.02×10^{-9} s		0
Am^{241}	0.0596	9.1×10^{-8} s		$\frac{5}{2}$
Fe^{57}	0.0144	1.4×10^{-7} s		$\frac{1}{2}$
Np^{239}	0.105	2.78×10^{-7} s		$\frac{1}{2}$
Rb^{85}	0.513	13×10^{-7} s		$\frac{5}{2}$
Zn^{87}	0.092	13.6×10^{-6} s		$\frac{5}{2}$
Y^{88}	0.40	5.3×10^{-4} s		
As^{75}	0.280	2.6×10^{-2} s		$\frac{5}{2}$
Pu^{237}	0.145	2.6×10^{-1} s		
Cl^{38}	0.66	1.4 s		2
Au^{197}	0.130	10.7 s		$\frac{3}{2}$
Kr^{81}	0.193	19 s		
Se^{77}	0.162	25.3 s		$\frac{1}{2}$
Ge^{75}	0.139	1.15 m		
Se^{79}	0.096	5.62 m		$\frac{7}{2}$
Br^{78}	0.108	9.2 m		
Co^{60}	0.0589	15.2 m		5
Rb^{84}	0.24	33 m		
Se^{81}	0.103	1.37 h		
Kr^{83}	0.0093	2.71 h		$\frac{9}{2}$
Sr^{87}	0.388	4.04 h		$\frac{9}{2}$
Cs^{134}	0.127	4.6 h	8	4
Os^{189}	0.0304	8.2 h	$\frac{9}{2}$ (?)	$\frac{3}{2}$
Co^{58}	0.025	13 h		2
Zn^{69}	0.436	19.9 h		
Sc^{44}	0.271	3.52 d		
Xe^{129}	0.196	12 d		$\frac{1}{2}$
Sn^{117}	0.159	14.0 d		$\frac{1}{2}$
Te^{129}	0.106	48 d		
Te^{123}	0.0885	150 d		$\frac{1}{2}$
Sn^{119}	0.024	1.09 y		$\frac{1}{2}$
Nb^{93}	0.030	~ 14 y		$\frac{9}{2}$
Cd^{113}	0.265	20 y	$\frac{11}{2}$ (?)	$\frac{1}{2}$

* s = second, m = minute, h = hour, d = day, y = year.

† These are actually ground state spins. The decay may be to a spin-favored intermediate state.

suitable because there is no unique angular momentum associated with a plane wave. The alternative of breaking the wave motion down into a sum of spherical waves each with a definite angular momentum is more suitable. Selection rules based on angular momentum and parity conservation rule out some of the possible spherical wave contributions, and of the remaining ones, those of larger L must usually be so small in amplitude, compared with the component of smallest possible L, that they may be ignored. The small contribution of these other possible modes to the total radiation field is what makes it possible in so many instances to treat the radiation as though it possessed a single multipolarity. This is not invariably the case, however, and several isomeric transitions are difficult to explain unless one assumes a mixture of multipolarities, such as M1 + E2.

5-7 Internal Conversion

The momentum spectrum of the electrons from a beta emitter usually consists of sharp spikes superposed on a continuous background as shown in Fig. 5-17. Ellis (6) was able to show convincingly in 1922 that the sharp spikes could easily be accounted for if one assumed that gamma rays emitted by the nucleus often eject electrons from the K, L, M, etc., shells of the emitting atoms. Somewhat later, the term "internal conversion" was applied to this process. With the discovery of isomeric states, it became possible to separate

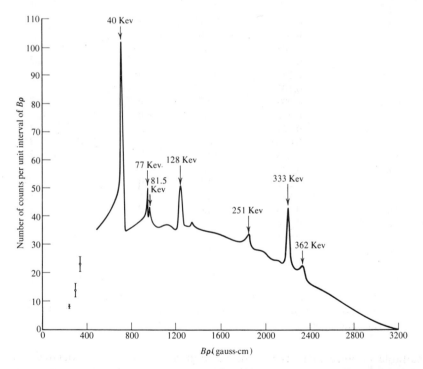

Fig. 5-17. Electron momentum spectrum of I^{131}. The peaks at 48, 77, and 81.5 Kev are believed to correspond to the K, L, and M internal conversion lines, respectively, of an 83 ± 2 Kev transition. Similarly, the 333 and 362 Kev peaks are ascribed to the K and L conversion lines of a 368 ± 7 Kev transition. [From G. E. Owen, D. Moe, and C. S. Cook, *Phys. Rev.*, **74**, 1879 (1948).]

the isomer and observe its conversion electrons free from the beta-decay electrons of the parent substance. The conversion electron momentum spectrum of such an isomer is shown in Fig. 5-18. If a K shell electron is ejected

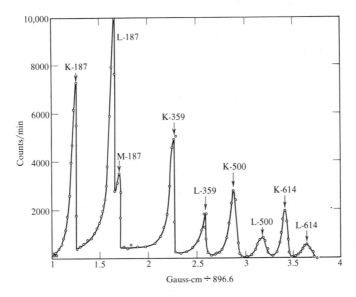

Gauss-cm ÷ 896.6

Fig. 5-18. Internal conversion electron spectrum of Os^{190m} above 65 Kev taken with intermediate image spectrometer at 1.6% resolution. The source thickness was 0.7 mg/ cm^2. The data have been corrected for decay of the 10-min activity and for counter background. [From G. Scharff-Goldhaber, D. E. Alburger, G. Harbottle, and M. McKeown, *Phys. Rev.*, **111**, 913 (1958.)]

one speaks of K conversion, if an L shell electron, of L conversion, etc. Conservation of energy then requires that the energy, W_e, of the ejected electron, be equal to the energy W_γ, of the gamma ray which is usually emitted, less the binding energy or ionization potential, W_i, of the ejected orbital electron, or, in equation form,

$$W_e = W_\gamma - W_i. \qquad (5\text{-}36)$$

Since W_i has different values for the K, L_I, L_{II}, L_{III}, etc., shells, electrons that are ejected from the various shells have different amounts of kinetic energy. This means that it is possible to identify the origins of the electrons by measuring their energies with a device, such as a β-ray spectrograph or scintillation spectrometer, that has the required energy resolution. If the transition energy is smaller than the binding energy of a particular orbital electron, then it is clear that that electron cannot be ejected. For example, if $W_{L_I} < W_\gamma < W_K$, then electrons can be ejected from the L_I shell but not from the K shell. The similarity between Eq. (5-36) and the Einstein photoelectric equation led Ellis to propose that monoergic gamma rays were emitted by the nucleus, in some cases escaping from the emitting atom and in other cases ejecting an electron from one of the electronic shells.

Smekal (32) pointed out that the fact that energy was conserved in the process in no way required that a gamma ray actually be emitted. Rosseland (28) went further and assumed that an excited nucleus could give up its excitation energy *either* by gamma emission *or* by ejecting an orbital electron. He admitted that it would not ordinarily be possible to distinguish between his and Ellis' hypotheses but said, "There will be a difference between the process considered by Ellis and that put forward by me only when β radiation can take place in a system in which the probability for electromagnetic radiation is zero."

If Ellis' conjecture were correct we should expect the fraction of gamma rays (of the same energy) that eject orbital electrons to vary slowly (if not near an absorption edge) from one element to another. We should also expect the probability of internal conversion to be about the same as that for external conversion (photoelectric ejection of electrons from other atoms of the same kind as the emitting atom). Neither of these expectations is borne out by experiment.

The existence of the internal conversion process implies that most observed gamma-decay lifetimes will be shorter than that which would be observed if decay took place in bare nuclei not surrounded by electrons. If one assigns decay constants λ_γ, λ_K, λ_L, etc. to the probabilities of decay per unit time by gamma emission, K conversion, L conversion, etc., then the total decay constant, λ, is

$$\lambda = \lambda_\gamma + \lambda_K + \lambda_L + \cdots, \tag{5-37}$$

and the mean lifetime, t_a, is

$$t_a = \frac{1}{\lambda} = \frac{1}{\lambda_\gamma + \lambda_K + \lambda_L + \cdots}, \tag{5-38}$$

which is certainly less than $t_{a\gamma} = 1/\lambda_\gamma$. Before one attempts to utilize the curves in Fig. 5-16 as a guide in classifying the type of gamma decay it is necessary to learn what fraction of all decaying nuclides decay by internal conversion. Once this is known, the formula given above may be used to solve for λ_γ and this can be used to compute $t_{a\gamma} = 1/\lambda_\gamma$ for comparison with the figure.

The "internal conversion coefficient," α, is defined* by

$$\alpha = \frac{\lambda_e}{\lambda_\gamma}, \tag{5-39}$$

* In older literature, the internal conversion coefficient is often defined as

$$\alpha' = \frac{\lambda_e}{\lambda_e + \lambda_\gamma}.$$

This older definition is the one used by Ellis and Fowler in the works cited here.

where $$\lambda_e = \lambda_K + \lambda_L + \lambda_M + \cdots. \qquad (5\text{-}40)$$

Equation (5-38) then becomes

$$t_a = \frac{1}{\lambda_\gamma + \lambda_e} = \frac{1}{\lambda_\gamma + \alpha\lambda_\gamma} = \frac{1}{(1 + \alpha)\lambda_\gamma} \qquad (5\text{-}41)$$

$$= \frac{t_{a\gamma}}{1 + \alpha}, \qquad (5\text{-}42)$$

or $$t_{a\gamma} = (1 + \alpha)t_a. \qquad (5\text{-}43)$$

Since the volume in which an orbital electron interacts with the multipole radiation field is usually very great compared with the nuclear volume itself, early calculations of conversion coefficients treated the nucleus as a point. The form of the electron wave function in the vicinity of the nucleus is significantly different for a nucleus of finite size and a point nucleus. More recent calculations of internal conversion coefficients by Rose (27) and by Sliv (31) take account of this effect of finite nuclear size but ignore interactions within the nuclear volume itself. These two authors differ in their methods of computing conversion coefficients, but one would expect their values to agree within a few per cent. Unfortunately, there are some unexplained differences of larger magnitude in their tabulations.

As long as the interaction occurs outside of the nuclear volume, the ratio of electron ejection to gamma-ray emission probabilities should be virtually independent of the details of nuclear structure. Where the absolute probability of either process is "normal," the contribution of interactions within the nuclear volume will be very small. On the other hand, when the probability of interaction outside the nucleus is much smaller than normal (an inhibited transition) the contribution of interactions within the nuclear volume will become important. The tabulations of Rose and Sliv are not applicable to the latter class of conversion process.

Where the tables of Rose or Sliv are applicable, determination of the internal conversion coefficient serves as a partial check on the multipolarity of the radiation as deduced from gamma-ray measurements. Unfortunately, it is difficult to make accurate measurements of the relative number of gamma rays and conversion electrons emitted. A simpler quantity to determine experimentally is the K/L conversion ratio, which is just the ratio of the number of electrons emitted with an energy corresponding to K-conversion to the number emitted with an energy consistent with L-conversion in the same length of time. The K/L conversion ratio may be defined in terms of the appropriate decay constants by

$$\frac{K}{L} = \frac{\lambda_K}{\lambda_L} = \frac{\lambda_K}{\lambda_{L_I} + \lambda_{L_{II}} + \lambda_{L_{III}}}, \qquad (5\text{-}44)$$

the L_I/L_{II} conversion ratio defined by

$$\frac{L_I}{L^{II}} = \frac{\lambda_{L_I}}{\lambda_{L_{II}}}, \text{ etc.} \tag{5-45}$$

The tables of conversion coefficients (27) give

$$\alpha_K = \frac{\lambda_K}{\lambda_\gamma} \tag{5-46}$$

and

$$\alpha_L = \frac{\lambda_L}{\lambda_\gamma} \tag{5-47}$$

so that

$$\frac{K}{L} = \frac{\alpha_K}{\alpha_L} \tag{5-48}$$

can easily be obtained from the tabulated values. The calculated internal conversion coefficients show that internal conversion competes most favorably with gamma emission at low energies (provided that the energy is greater than the electron binding energy), for large angular momentum changes, and for large atomic numbers. Under the most favorable conditions (large Z, small energy, large L), it becomes dominant and gamma-decay contributes very little to the total decay rate.

Thibaud (36) noticed in 1925 that, although there was a strong conversion line from Po^{214} corresponding to a transition energy of 1.4 Mev, there was no evidence of an externally converted gamma ray of this energy when the Po^{214} radiations were passed through sheets of various metals. Ellis and Aston (7) restudied the radiation of Po^{214} in 1930 and made an especially careful search for this "missing" gamma ray but could find no evidence for it, although they, too, found the strong 1.4-Mev conversion line. Fowler (8) then pointed out that an earlier attempt by Swirles (35) to predict internal conversion coefficients from classical theory gave values that disagreed with experiment in an erratic way but were about a factor of 10 too low on average. He was able to show from a quantum mechanical treatment of the problem that Swirles' neglect of interaction within the volume of the nucleus itself could not lead to any large errors in the calculated conversion coefficients *except in one case*, namely that in which both the initial and final nuclear spins were zero. Here interactions within the nuclear volume allow electron conversion even though gamma radiation is strictly forbidden in a $0 \rightarrow 0$ transition.

This is easy to understand if we remember that an oscillating monopole (an E0) would consist of a spherical charge distribution that expands and contracts. Now such a motion produces changes in neither the electric nor magnetic fields at points outside the nucleus, so there can be no electromagnetic radiation nor will there be electromagnetic fields with which orbital

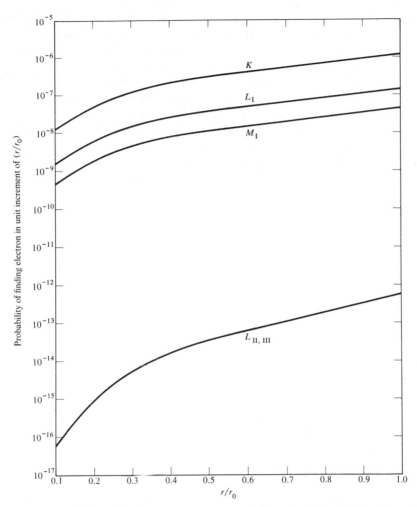

Fig. 5-19. Probability of finding an electron per unit interval of r/r_0 calculated from the hydrogenlike wave functions for a single electron (i.e., not taking account of the effect of the other orbital electrons) for a nuclide of atomic number 50 and mass number 120. No magnetic interactions are considered so there is no distinction between L_{II} and L_{III}. The nucleus is treated as a point charge in these calculations. Actually, the distribution of charge within the nucleus will change the electric field, and therefore the electron distribution, somewhat. It should also be noted that since there are 2 K, 2 L_I, 2 M_I, and 6 L_{II+III} electrons, the probabilities of conversion of electrons from these shells should be correspondingly greater than that shown in the figure. Radii are given as fractions of an approximate nuclear radius calculated from $r_0 = 1.45A^{1/3} \times 10^{-13}$ cm. It is clear from this figure why only K, L_I, and M_I conversion lines are observed in $0 \rightarrow 0$ transitions, where the interaction must take place within the nuclear volume. As a standard with which to compare these probability densities, the maximum probability of finding the K electron occurs at the classical Bohr orbit radius where the probability density has the value 3.63×10^{-3}.

For a more careful analysis of this problem, see Church and Weneser (4).

electrons can interact in the region outside the nuclear volume. (The explanation given earlier, that E0 radiation is inconsistent with the transverse nature of electromagnetic radiation, is just another way of looking at the same thing.) There will be varying electric fields *within* the nuclear volume, however, so that orbital electrons that move inside the nuclear volume may suffer conversion ejection. Classically, of course, orbital electrons would never come very near the nucleus, but quantum mechanics predicts a small but finite probability that orbital electrons will be found within the nucleus. Figure 5-19 shows the relative probability of finding orbital electrons from various shells within the nucleus as given by hydrogenlike wave functions. Figure 5-20, which shows a more recent conversion electron spectrum from the $0 \to 0$

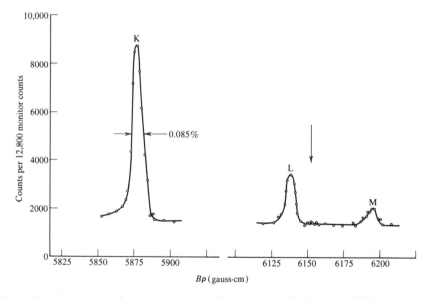

Fig. 5-20. K, L, and M internal conversion lines associated with the 1.4158-Mev zero–zero transition in Po^{214}. The arrow indicates the expected position of an L$_{III}$ component. [From D. E. Alburger and A. Hedgran, *Arkiv För Fysik*, **7**, 424 (1953–54).]

transition in Po^{214}, confirms the prediction one would make from Fig. 5-19: the K, L$_I$, and M$_I$ electrons should be ejected in measurable numbers but the number of L$_{II}$ and M$_{II}$ electrons ejected should be too small by comparison to be detectable.

Actually internal conversion, in which a single orbital electron is emitted, is forbidden in $0 \to 0$ transitions unless there is no change in parity. All observed cases of single internal conversion of this type are thus classed as "zero-zero, no" transitions. Other examples of such transitions are shown in Table 5-7 and Fig. 5-21.

Table 5-7 ZERO-ZERO INTERNAL CONVERSION ELECTRON
TRANSITIONS

Excited nuclide	Decay energy (Mev)	Half-life of excited state	Reference
$_{32}Ge^{70}$	1.215	$(3.0 \pm 0.5) \times 10^{-9}$ sec	2
$_{32}Ge^{72}$	0.7	$(2.9 \pm 0.6) \times 10^{-7}$ sec	3, 21
$_{40}Zr^{90}$	1.75	$(6.0 \pm 1.5) \times 10^{-8}$ sec	16, 2
$_{58}Ce^{140}$	1.902	~ 40 hr	5
$_{84}Po^{214}$	1.4158	$\sim 5 \times 10^{-10}$ sec	7, 1
$_{92}U^{234}$			1
$_{94}Pu^{238}$	0.935		25

It is clear that an E0 conversion transition can take place between any pair of states having equal spin and the same parity. Church and Weneser

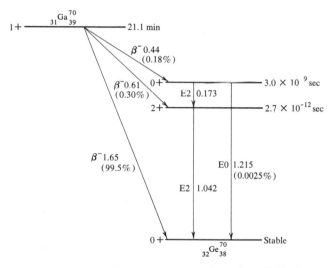

Fig. 5-21. Zero–zero internal conversion in excited Ge^{70}. Transition energies are given in Mev. The frequency with which this mode of de-excitation takes place is very small compared to the alternative two-step process in which successive E2 gamma rays are emitted. [From D. E. Alburger, *Phys. Rev.*, **109**, 1222 (1958).]

(4) have pointed out that this process may, under some circumstances, compete effectively with higher multipole transitions. The existence of total internal conversion is a compelling argument for the view that internal conversion is a primary process rather than a secondary interaction of a γ ray with an orbital electron.

5-8 Nuclear Resonance Fluorescence

The time that has elapsed between the emission of a beta particle and the subsequent emission of a gamma ray may be measured by delaying an electrical pulse produced by the beta-ray detector and then placing it in coincidence with the electrical pulse from the detector of the gamma ray. A sufficiently large output pulse from the coincidence circuit is produced when, and only when, the delayed beta pulse and the direct gamma pulse coincide in time. By measuring the number of coincidences in some convenient time interval for different beta-pulse delay times, it is possible to construct a curve of decays per unit time as a function of the time between beta decay and gamma emission and from this to determine the mean lifetime of the gamma-emitting excited state. As mentioned earlier, present delayed coincidence measurements are not capable of measuring lifetimes less than about 10^{-10} sec. Although it is not possible to measure shorter excited-state lifetimes by direct methods, they can be estimated from other information. According to the uncertainty principle, the product of the uncertainty in transition energy, ΔW, and the uncertainty* of the lifetime of the excited state, t_a is given by

$$\Delta W \cdot t_a \cong \hbar. \tag{5-49}$$

It is customary in nuclear theory to introduce a "level width," Γ, defined by

$$\Gamma = \frac{\hbar}{t_a}, \tag{5-50}$$

so that
$$\Gamma \cdot t_a = \hbar. \tag{5-51}$$

The level width associated with the excited state is therefore approximately equal to the uncertainty in the transition energy. It might be said that gamma photons (and it is equally true of the photons coming from atomic transitions) do not have a precisely defined energy. If one could measure this energy spread he could deduce the mean lifetime of the excited state from Eq. (5-51).

Since $\hbar = 6.59 \times 10^{-16}$ ev-sec, it is seen that a mean lifetime of 10^{-12} sec will result in a level width of

$$\Gamma = \frac{6.59 \times 10^{-16}}{10^{-12}} = 6.59 \times 10^{-4} \text{ ev.}$$

This is many orders of magnitude beyond the energy resolution of our customary detectors, but it turns out that the nucleus itself can be used for this fine discrimination.

* See Prob. 5-7.

When a gamma ray is emitted by a nucleus, conservation of momentum requires that the nucleus recoil. One may then write

$$Mv = \frac{W_\gamma}{c},$$ (5-52)

where M and v are the mass and recoil velocity, respectively, of the nucleus, W_γ is the energy of the emitted gamma ray, and c is the velocity of light. The energy carried away by the recoiling nucleus is then

$$W_n = \frac{1}{2} Mv^2 = \frac{1}{2} \frac{W_\gamma^2}{Mc^2},$$ (5-53)

so that the energy of the emitted gamma ray is less than the transition energy, W_{tr}, by an amount $\frac{1}{2}(W_\gamma^2/Mc^2)$, which is approximately $\frac{1}{2}(W_{tr}^2/Mc^2)$. When a gamma ray is *absorbed* by a nucleus its energy must *exceed* the transition energy by an amount equal to the recoil energy of the absorbing nucleus, or again approximately $\frac{1}{2}(W_{tr}^2/Mc^2)$. Thus an emitted gamma ray is off resonance by an amount

$$\Delta W = \frac{W_\gamma^2}{Mc^2}$$ (5-54)

as far as resonance absorption is concerned. Suppose the nucleus has a mass of 100 amu and emits an 0.5-Mev gamma ray. Then it will be off resonance by an amount

$$\Delta W = \frac{(0.5)^2}{100 \times 931} = 2.69 \times 10^{-6} \text{ Mev} = 2.69 \text{ ev}.$$

This is so much greater than the natural width of the excited level that no emitted photons will be absorbed by another identical nucleus. (In atomic spectra the natural width of the levels is *greater* than the recoil spread so that resonance absorption is perfectly possible.)

Kuhn (18) made an unsuccessful attempt in 1929 to observe nuclear resonance scattering. He pointed out that the emitted gamma ray would have less energy than the transition energy because of nuclear recoil, but apparently did not realize that extra gamma-ray energy would have to be available because of the recoil of the scattering nucleus. Heitler (13) gives the resonant scattering cross section, σ, as

$$\sigma = \frac{6 \times 10^{-10}}{W_{eff}^2} \frac{\Gamma^2}{(W_{eff} - W_{tr})^2 + \frac{1}{4}\Gamma^2},$$ (5-55)

where, in case both emitting and scattering nuclei are initially at rest,

$$W_{eff} \cong W_{tr} - \frac{W_{tr}^2}{Mc^2},$$ (5-56)

and where W_{tr}, W_{eff}, and Γ are expressed in ev, while σ is in cm². This formula omits statistical weights and is applicable only to a transition between the ground and first excited states. For over 20 years, following Kuhn's work, investigators attempted to observe resonance scattering, with the idea that even though the cross section for the process is small when $W_{eff} < W_{tr}$ it

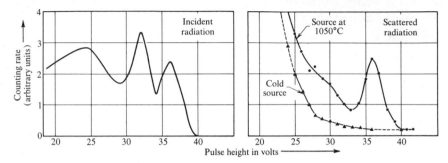

Fig. 5-22. Nuclear resonance scattering by a ring of solid Ni⁶⁰. The two peaks at the right in the upper plot are from the 1.17-Mev and 1.33-Mev gamma rays emitted by the excited Ni⁶⁰ resulting from beta decay of Co⁶⁰. The source consisted of CoCl₂ in the gaseous state. Although the recoil energy given the Ni⁶⁰ nucleus by emission of the beta particle and the 1.17-Mev gamma ray is sometimes sufficient to make resonance scattering possible, no effect is observed when the CoCl₂ is cold. The thermal Doppler broadening at 1050°C, on the other hand, produces a strong resonance scattering peak. The fact that only the 1.33-Mev gamma ray is resonantly scattered shows that it is emitted in a transition to the ground state. If the 1.17-Mev gamma ray is emitted before the 1.33-Mev gamma, a photon of about 2.50 Mev (1.33 + 1.17) would be required to show resonance scattering from the upper state. [From F. R. Metzger, *Phys. Rev.*, **103**, 983 (1956).]

might yet be detectable. In 1951 Moon (22) showed that one could observe resonant scattering if the source were moved toward the scatterer with a velocity such that the Doppler shift of the emitted gamma ray is approximately W_{tr}^2/Mc^2. Since the Doppler energy displacement is vW_y/c this requires that

$$\frac{vW_{tr}}{c} \cong \frac{W_{tr}^2}{Mc^2} \tag{5-57}$$

or

$$v = \left(\frac{W_{tr}}{Mc^2}\right)c \tag{5-58}$$

in order that the resonant scattering cross section be near its maximum value. He studied scattering by mercury of the 0.411-Mev gamma ray emitted by excited Hg¹⁹⁸. The velocity of the source in this case should be

$$v = \left(\frac{0.411}{198 \times 931}\right)3 \times 10^{10} = 6.6 \times 10^4 \text{ cm/sec.}$$

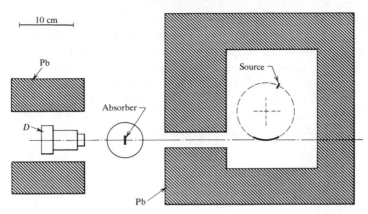

Fig. 5-23. Schematic diagram of experimental arrangement used by Mössbauer (23) to demonstrate recoil-free emission and absorption. The source was mounted on the periphery of a wheel which could be rotated in either direction to produce a Doppler shift to either higher or lower energies.

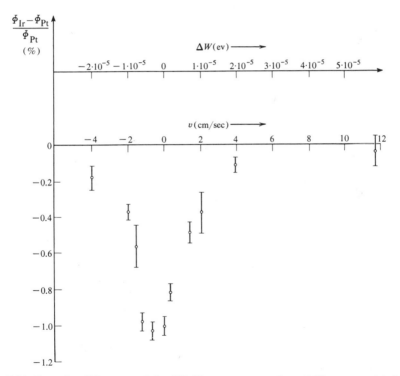

Fig. 5-24. Intensity differences of the 129-Kev gamma ray from Ir[191] measured behind an iridium resonance absorber and a comparison platinum absorber. The differences are plotted against the relative velocity of the source to the absorber with both at a temperature of 88°K. The upper scale gives the Doppler shift in energy, ΔW, of the emitted gamma ray corresponding to the source velocity, v, shown on the lower scale.

He obtained speeds up to about 6×10^4 cm/sec by placing the source on the tip of a centrifuge rotor. He obtained an increase in scattering of about (15 ± 6) per cent when the rotor was brought from rest up to full speed. From his crude determination of the scattering cross section he obtained a value for the level width, Γ, and from this a half-life of about 10^{-11} sec.

The "centrifuge method," as it is now called, has become a standard technique for studying resonance scattering of gamma rays. Ilakovac and Moon (15) showed in 1954 that thermal Doppler broadening of the emitted

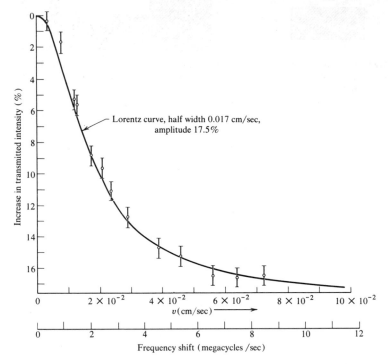

Fig. 5-25. The increase in intensity of the 14.4-Kev gamma ray from 0.1-μ sec Fe^{57m} transmitted through a Fe^{57} absorber as a function of the absolute velocity of the source. A velocity of 0.01 cm/sec corresponds to a frequency displacement of 1.16 megacycles/sec. [From R. V. Pound and G. A. Rebka, Jr., *Phys. Rev. Lett.*, **3**, 554 (1959).]

gamma-ray line, a process which had been discussed by Kuhn in 1929, could be made to yield resonance scattering. A nice example of this technique is shown in Fig. 5-22.

In 1958, Mössbauer (23) in studying nuclear resonance absorption, in which he measured the transmitted rather than the scattered radiation, made a most interesting discovery. Since thermal Doppler broadening should increase the resonant absorption, lowering the temperature would be expected to decrease the absorption. Mössbauer found, by contrast, that when he lowered the temperature of his absorber and source sufficiently, the resonant absorption became much *larger*. The reason, as Lamb (19) had shown theoretically in 1939, is that when the emitting atom is in a crystal lattice, the recoil momentum may go into many possible lattice vibrational modes including one in which the whole lattice (or a large section of it) moves together. In the latter case the mass is so great that the energy given to the crystal in the recoil process is negligible. The gamma ray is then emitted with essentially the full transition energy. Similarly, if the absorbing nucleus is part of a crystal it may absorb some gamma rays resonantly even though their energy is just equal to the excitation transition energy. Mössbauer was able to show

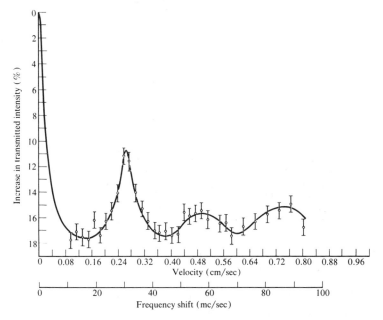

Fig. 5-26. The low-velocity part of this curve is the same as that of Fig. 5-25, but here the velocities have been increased to the point where hyperfine structure is evident. Pound and Rebka (26) believe the hyperfine structure is traceable to magnetic substates of the nucleus.

that he actually had such a resonance absorption by the centrifuge technique. In this case a Doppler shift toward either higher or lower energies led to a reduction in the absorption as shown in Fig. 5-24. Pound and Rebka (26) have obtained similar results for the much longer lived ($t_{1/2} = 0.1$ microsecond) excited state of Fe^{57} at 14.4 Kev. Their results are shown in Figs. 5-25 and 5-26. Note how very small the source velocities are here. This corresponds to the extremely narrow level width of this transition. They also found additional resonances interpreted as a magnetic hyperfine splitting of the excited level. If the excited level has a spin of $\frac{3}{2}$ while the ground state has a spin of $\frac{1}{2}$, then, as shown in Fig. 5-27, there would be 6 transitions allowed by the selection rule $\Delta m = 0, \pm 1$. If the spin $\frac{1}{2}$ level splitting is small

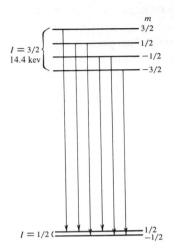

Fig. 5-27. Schematic diagram of possible energy levels in the 14.4-Kev excited state and in the ground state of Fe^{57}. The separation between levels of different m is grossly exaggerated. If we limit our consideration to the most probable transitions (i.e., those with the smallest value of L), then $L = \frac{3}{2} - \frac{1}{2} = 1$ and the only admissible values of Δm are $\Delta m = 0$ or $\Delta m = \pm 1$. There are 6 transitions that satisfy this selection rule, so we would expect 6 resonance peaks in Fig. 5-25. However, if the ground-state levels are very close together, transitions from a given excited level to the two ground states may not be resolvable.

compared with that of the $\frac{3}{2}$ level splitting, it would be difficult to resolve the resonances into more than 4 peaks.

5-9 Summary

In this chapter it has been shown that the nucleus is capable of existing in a ground state and in a number of excited states. When the excitation energy is not large, de-excitation usually occurs by gamma-ray emission, but under some conditions particle emission competes with or completely supplants gamma-ray emission. When an α or β particle is emitted by a radionuclide, the daughter nucleus is quite commonly left in an excited state which then decays to a lower energy state with the emission of a gamma ray. In the early days of nuclear physics it was not known whether the gamma rays were emitted before, simultaneously with, or after the associated particle was emitted. Many bits of evidence show that the gamma ray is emitted by the excited daughter nucleus. We may list some of these:

1. In the longer-lived (isomeric) nuclei the time between particle emission and gamma-ray emission has actually been measured.

2. Where internal conversion competes with gamma-ray emission, the deduced binding energies of the orbital electrons agree with the known binding energies of the daughter nucleus. Moreover, the x-rays that are emitted following internal conversion are characteristic of the daughter nucleus.

3. The ground-state nuclei that are capable of nuclear resonance scattering or absorption of gamma rays are of the same kind as the daughter nucleus that results from the process that emitted the gamma rays.

4. Excited states of nuclei of the same kind as the daughter can be produced by resonances in such reaction as (d, p) and (p, γ), or in resonant scattering of protons.

PROBLEMS

5-1 Estimate the half-life of an even-even radionuclide that emits 1-Mev alpha particles from the fact that Th^{232} has a half-life of 1.4×10^{10} years and emits alpha particles with an energy of 4 Mev, while Po^{212} has a half-life of 3×10^{-7} sec and emits 8.78-Mev alpha particles. [*Ans.* 5.79×10^{52} years.]

5-2 An automobile weighing 1.5 tons is going 2.5 miles per hour. What is the probability that it will cross a square bump in the road which is 3 inches high and 5 feet long? (Treat the automobile as a point mass.)
[*Ans.* Approximately $10^{-8.5 \times 10^{36}}$.]

5-3 Ra^{221} has a half-life of 31 seconds and emits a 6.7-Mev alpha particle. Estimate the "radius" of the Ra^{217} nucleus. [*Hint:* Make a plot of

$$\left(\cos^{-1} \sqrt{\frac{r_0}{b}} - \sqrt{\frac{r_0}{b} - \frac{r_0^2}{b^2}} \right) \quad vs. \quad \frac{r_0}{b}$$

and take τ to be 10^{-20} sec.] [*Ans.* 9.6×10^{-13} cm.]

5-4 Th^{227} gives off alpha particles with energies of 5.674, 5.719, 5.744, 5.766, 5.817, 5.870, 5.924, 5.968, 5.990, 6.019, 6.051 Mev and the excited Ra^{223} resulting from the decay emits gamma rays with energies of 27, 31, 48, 61, 80, 112, 127, 132, 149, 164, 173, 204, 220, 253, 273, 281, 304, 332, 377 Kev. Work out an energy-level diagram for Ra^{223}.

5-5 Derive a relationship between the bombardment energy, W (Mev), of a projectile of mass M (amu) and the excitation energy, W_e (Mev), of the resulting nucleus if the bombarding particle is absorbed by the target nucleus. Let the target nucleus be initially at rest and have a mass M_t (amu). The mass energy of the bombarding particle plus that of the target nucleus exceeds that of the unexcited product nucleus by Q Mev. [*Ans*. Eq. (5-59).]

$$W_e = Q + \frac{M_t W}{M + M_t}. \tag{5-59}$$

5-6 How far from the nucleus would a 1-Mev photon have to be formed so that, if emitted at right angles to a line from its point of origin to the center of the nucleus, it would carry away an amount of angular momentum $2\hbar$? Remember that a photon has an intrinsic spin of $\hbar$.

[*Ans*. 1.97×10^{-11} cm.]

5-7 One might question the use of t_a rather than Δt in the uncertainty relation [Eq. (5-49)]. Show that if one defines Δt as the standard deviation, σ, in t, where $\sigma^2 = \overline{t^2} - (\bar{t})^2$, then $\sigma = \bar{t}$. Remembering that $t_a \equiv \bar{t}$, one can write this equation as $\sigma = t_a$. The proof involves an integration by parts like that of Eq. (1-21).

5-8 Mössbauer found the width, at half of maximum absorption, of the Ir^{191} 129-Kev level, in terms of the velocity spread of the source, to be 1.51 cm/sec. (a) What is the level width in ev? (b) What is the half-life of the excited state? [*Ans*. (a) 6.5×10^{-6} ev, (b) 7.03×10^{-9} sec.]

5-9 Attempts have been made to detect a gravitational red shift of the 14.4-Kev gamma ray from excited Fe^{57} by measuring the Doppler shift required to restore resonance absorption or resonance scattering. If one treats the photon as though it had a mass M_γ, then the expected increase in energy caused by falling a distance of y cm from source to detector would be given by

$$\frac{\Delta W_\gamma}{W_\gamma} = \frac{M_\gamma g y}{M_\gamma c^2} \tag{5-60}$$

or

$$\Delta W_\gamma = \frac{g y}{c^2} W_\gamma. \tag{5-61}$$

How far would the source have to lie above the detector, in a uniform gravitational field, to give a gravitational red shift equal to 10 per cent of the line width of the 14.4-Kev line? [*Ans*. 291 m.]

REFERENCES

1. Alburger, D. E., and Hedgran, A., *Arkiv för Fysik*, **7**, 423 (1953–54).

2. Alburger, D. E., *Phys. Rev.*, **109**, 1222 (1958).

3. Bowe, J. C., Goldhaber, M., Hill, R. D., Meyerhof, W. E., and Sala, O., *Phys. Rev.*, **73**, 1219 (1948).

4. Church, E. L., and Weneser, J., *Phys. Rev.*, **103**, 1035 (1956); *Ann. Rev. Nuc. Sci.*, **10**, 193 (1960).

5. Dželepow, B. S., Kholnov, Yu. V., and Prikhodtseva, V. P., *Nuc. Phys.*, **9**, 665 (1958–59).

6. Ellis, C. D., *Z. Physik*, **10**, 303 (1922).

7. Ellis, C. D., and Aston, G. H., *Proc. Roy. Soc.*, **A129**, 180 (1930).

8. Fowler, R. H., *Proc. Roy. Soc.*, **A129**, 1 (1930).

9. Gamow, G., *Z. Physik*, **51**, 204 (1928).

10. Geiger, H., and Nuttall, J. M., *Phil. Mag.*, **22**, 613 (1911).

11. Gurney, R. W., and Condon, E. N., *Nature*, **122**, 439 (1928).

12. Hebbard, D. F., and Dunbar, D. N. F., *Phys. Rev.*, **115**, 624 (1959).

13. Heitler, W., *Quantum Theory of Radiation* (Oxford: Oxford University Press, 1936).

14. Heitler, W., *Proc. Camb. Phil. Soc.*, **32**, 112 (1936).

15. Ilakovac, K., and Moon, P. B., *Phys. Rev.*, **93**, 254 (1954).

16. Johnson, O. E., Johnson, R. G., and Langer, L. M., *Phys. Rev.*, **98**, 1517 (1955).

17. Kinsey, B. B., Bartholomew, G. A., and Walker, W. H., *Can. Jour. Phys.*, **29**, 1 (1951).

18. Kuhn, W., *Phil. Mag.*, **8**, 625 (1929).

19. Lamb, W. E., Jr., *Phys. Rev.*, **55**, 190 (1939).

20. Laporte, O., *Z. Physik*, **23**, 135 (1924).

21. McGowan, F. K., DeBenedetti, S., and Francis, J. E., Jr., *Phys. Rev.*, **75**, 1761 (1949).

22. Moon, P. B., *Proc. Phys. Soc.* (*London*), **A64**, 76 (1951).

23. Mössbauer, R. L., *Naturwiss.*, **45**, 538 (1958).

24. Perlman, I., Ghiorso, A., and Seaborg, G. T., *Phys. Rev.*, **77**, 26 (1950).

25. Perlman, I., and Asaro, F., in *Proceedings of the International Conference on Nuclear Structure, Rehovoth, Israel, September* 1957 (Amsterdam: North-Holland Publishing Co., 1958).

26. Pound, R. V., and Rebka, G. A., Jr., *Phys. Rev. Letters*, **3**, 554 (1959).

27. Rose, M. E., *Internal Conversion Coefficients* (New York: Interscience Publishers, Inc., 1958).

28. Rosseland, S., *Z. Physik*, **14**, 173 (1923).

29. Rutherford, E., *Phil. Mag.*, **13**, 110 (1907).

30. Rutherford, E., *Phil. Mag.*, **4**, 580 (1927).

31. Sliv, L. A., and Band, I. M., *Tables of Internal Conversion Coefficients of Gamma Radiation, Part I: K-Shell* (Moscow–Leningrad: USSR Academy of Sciences Publishing House, 1956).

32. Smekal, A., *Z. Physik*, **10**, 275 (1922).

33. Smythe, W. R., *Static and Dynamic Electricity*, first edition (New York: McGraw-Hill, 1939), pp. 466 *et seq.*

34. Sperduto, A., Buechner, W. W., Bockelman, C. K., and Browne, C. P., *Phys. Rev.*, **96**, 1316 (1954).

35. Swirles, B., *Proc. Roy. Soc.*, **A116**, 491 (1927); **A121**, 447 (1928).

36. Thibaud, Jean, *Thèse* (Paris: Masson, 1925).

37. Weisskopf, V. F., *Phys. Rev.*, **83**, 1073 (1951).

38. Wigner, E. P., *Z. Physik*, **43**, 624 (1927).

39. Yang, C. N., *Phys. Rev.*, **74**, 764 (1948).

6

THE NEUTRON

6-1 Historical Introduction

The discovery of artificially stimulated nuclear gamma-ray emission by Bothe and Becker (8) in 1930 induced Curie and Joliot (13, 39) to repeat these experiments using a 100-millicurie Po alpha-particle source in place of the much weaker source used by Bothe and Becker. They confirmed that when a number of light elements were bombarded with Po α particles they emitted a penetrating radiation. The effect was greatest when Be was the target material, and was moderately great with boron. It was thought that the penetrating rays were γ rays, and this is true in most cases, but when Curie measured the absorption by lead of the penetrating radiation from Be she found that it required 4.7 cm of Pb to reduce the intensity of the radiation to half of its initial value. A half-thickness of 4.7 cm Pb can also be expressed as 53 gm/cm² and yields a mass absorption coefficient* of 0.013 cm²/gm.

---

* If one assumes an absorption law for γ rays of

$$\Phi = \Phi_0 e^{-\mu x}, \qquad (6-1)$$

where Φ is the intensity of the beam, whose initial intensity was Φ_0, after passing through

165

Using the same apparatus, Joliot found the mass absorption coefficient for the Boron rays to be 0.02 cm^2/gm. From the Klein-Nishina formula for the Compton scattering of γ rays (which will be discussed in Chap. 8) they deduced gamma-ray energies of 15 to 20 Mev for the Be rays and about 11 Mev for the B rays. These energies are much greater than the energies of γ rays emitted by any naturally radioactive substance. In the case of B it seemed possible that the reaction B^{10} (α, γ) could yield γ rays of the required energy, but no nuclear reaction appeared to be able to explain the more energetic Be rays.

In 1932 Curie and Joliot (14) reported an interesting discovery concerning the Be and B rays. The penetrating radiations were first passed through 1.5 cm of Pb (enough to remove nearly all gamma rays emitted by naturally radioactive substances) and then into an ionization chamber. When thin sheets of C, Al, Cu, Ag, and Pb were then placed in the beam just between the thick Pb absorber and the ionization chamber, no noticeable effect was produced. On the other hand, sheets of material containing paraffin, water, and cellophane caused a marked increase in the ionization current. They found that 0.2 mm of Al completely absorbed the secondary radiation obtained from these substances. They concluded (correctly) that the secondary radiation consisted of protons for the following reasons:

1. The effect is observed only with substances containing hydrogen.
2. The secondary radiation could not be removed by applying a magnetic field. If the secondary radiation consisted of electrons, one would expect the electrons to be strongly deflected by the magnetic field.
3. The intensity of the secondary radiation is proportional to the intensity of the incident radiation.
4. The incident radiation is strongly absorbed by substances containing hydrogen, whereas the γ rays from Tl^{208} are not.

The range in air of the protons ejected by Be radiation is 26 cm, corresponding to an energy of 4.5 Mev, while that of B protons is 8 cm, corresponding to an energy of 2 Mev. They suggested that the protons might be Compton-type recoils from energetic γ-ray collisions. When they calculated the γ-ray energies needed to produce the observed proton energies they found Be rays were required to have an energy of 50 Mev while the B rays needed an energy of 35 Mev. These values are much larger than the values (15–20 Mev for Be and 11 Mev for B) deduced from the mass absorption coefficients, but Curie and Joliot felt that the differences lay within their experimental error.

These experiments were first taken up in the Cavendish Laboratories at

---

a thickness x of absorber (expressed in gm/cm^2), and μ is the "mass absorption coefficient," then

$$\mu = \frac{0.693}{x_{1/2}},\qquad(6\text{-}2)$$

where $x_{1/2}$ is the "half-thickness" of the absorber.

Cambridge University by Webster (72) in 1932. He essentially repeated what Bothe and Becker had done earlier and was able to confirm their results but found no evidence of "anomalous" γ rays. In summing up the results of his experiments, Webster says:

> The fact that reasonable and consistent values were obtained for the nuclear absorption coefficients is evidence against the suggestion that the ionization observed was produced not by electromagnetic radiations but by high-speed corpuscles, e.g., of a proton and an electron in very close combination. If this suggestion were correct it should be possible to detect the corpuscles by means of the expansion chamber. Mr. Champion has kindly taken 50 expansion chamber photographs, with the chamber adjusted for β-ray tracks, beryllium bombarded by polonium α particles being placed near the chamber. Only one track was observable, and the position of this showed that it could not possibly have been due to a corpuscle originating in the beryllium. Calculations showed that if the corpuscles produced 10 ions per centimeter of track, about 10 tracks altogether would have been expected in the photographs taken. Thus it is justifiable, for the present at any rate, to assume the secondary radiations to be electromagnetic in nature. This point is interesting in view of the suggestion that cosmic radiation may consist of protons, or neutrons, and the usefulness of the conception of neutrons* in accounting for astrophysical and nuclear phenomena.

Chadwick had suggested to Webster the investigation of the penetrating Be radiation, but when he learned of the discovery by Curie and Joliot of protons released by the Be radiation he decided to repeat their experiments and, if possible, to improve the accuracy of the measurements. He felt that their interpretation of the effect as a Compton-type process in which a proton recoils when struck by an energetic γ ray was implausible, not only because of the very high energies that had to be ascribed to the γ rays but also because

---

* He refers here to a paper entitled "The Neutron" by R. M. Langer and N. Rosen which appeared in the *Physical Review*, 37, 1579 (1931). The idea is much older than this, however. In his Bakerian lecture delivered in 1920, Rutherford (57) made the following statement. "In the other case, it involves the idea of the possible existence of an atom of mass 1 which has zero nucleus charge. Such an atomic structure seems by no means impossible. On present views, the neutral hydrogen atom is regarded as a nucleus of unit charge with an electron attached at a distance, and the spectrum of hydrogen is ascribed to the movements of this distant electron. Under some conditions, however, it may be possible for an electron to combine much more closely with the H nucleus, forming a kind of neutral doublet. Such an atom would have very novel properties. Its external field would be practically zero, except very close to the nucleus, and in consequence it should be able to move freely through matter. Its presence would probably be difficult to detect by the spectroscope, and it may be impossible to contain it in a sealed vessel. On the other hand, it should enter readily the structure of atoms, and may either unite with the nucleus or be disintegrated by its intense field, resulting possibly in the escape of a charged H atom or an electron or both."

the observed frequency of scattering of the γ rays by protons was several thousand times greater than that predicted by the Klein-Nishina formula.

6-2 Discovery of the Neutron

When Chadwick (11) repeated the experiments of Curie and Joliot he found that the maximum energy of a recoil proton from paraffin irradiated by a radium–beryllium source was 5.7 Mev. Since the maximum energy transferred by a photon, whose energy is $h\nu$, in a Compton collision with a particle of mass M is

$$W = \left(\frac{2}{2 + Mc^2/h\nu}\right) h\nu \qquad (6\text{-}3)$$

(see Prob. 6-2), it would require a 55-Mev γ ray to produce the observed effects. The maximum recoil energy of nitrogen nuclei was found to be about 1.2 Mev, which corresponds to production by a 90-Mev γ ray. In general, it was found that the more massive the recoil nucleus, the greater the required energy of the γ ray.

Chadwick showed that this inconsistency could be removed by assuming that the radiation consists not of γ rays but of neutral particles whose mass is approximately equal to that of a proton. Following Rutherford, he called this neutral particle a *neutron*.

Dee (18) soon found that a neutron produces no more than one ion pair, on average, in passing through 3 meters of air. He obtained this information by passing neutrons from a Po-Be source through a cloud chamber. His results explain the failure, reported by Webster, to find tracks of neutrons in a cloud chamber. On the other hand, numerous investigators (15, 54, 4) soon obtained cloud chamber photographs of proton recoils produced by passing neutrons through the chambers.

6-3 Methods for Producing Neutrons

Neutrons are produced in appreciable quantities by α-particle bombardment of Li and F, as well as Be, and B. The yields are so much smaller than from Be, however, that these substances are rarely used. Table 6-1 gives the neutron yields for a number of elements bombarded by particles from Po^{210}.

Neutrons may be produced by irradiating various elements with γ rays and, in fact, the National Bureau of Standards (67) has developed a radium-beryllium photo neutron source as a standard of neutron emission. Neutrons have also been produced by proton and deuteron bombardment. A typical reaction is

$$_3Li^7 + _1H^1 \rightarrow _4Be^7 + _0n^1,$$

which may be written more compactly as $Li^7(p, n)Be^7$. Other reactions are $Be^9(p, n)B^9$, $B^{10}(p, n)C^{10}$, and $H^2(d, n)He^3$, $Li^6(d, n)Be^7$, $Be^9(d, n)B^{10}$. Since tritium has become available, a popular source of very fast neutrons is the $H^3(d, n)He^4$ reaction. Taking advantage of the strong adsorption of tritium on zirconium, one usually uses a Zr target on which tritium has been adsorbed for the $H^3(d, n)$ reaction. Such a Zr target will yield about 10^8 neutrons per microcoulomb of deuterons. For purposes of comparison with the (α, n) yields shown in Table 6-1, this is about 16 neutrons per 10^6 incident deuterons. Not only is the $H^3(d, n)$ reaction strongly exoergic ($Q = 17.6$ Mev),* but it exhibits a resonance near 100 Kev so that copious neutron emission can be produced by a relatively low-voltage deuteron accelerator.

6-4 Artificial Disintegration by Neutrons

The first evidence for artificial disintegration by neutrons was obtained by N. Feather (20), who observed paired tracks produced in a cloud chamber through which neutrons were being passed. He was able to show that several of these could be caused by the recoiling He and B^{11} nuclei from an $N^{14}(n, \alpha)B^{11}$ reaction. Subsequently (n, γ), (n, p), and $(n, 2n)$ reactions were observed for a large number of elements.

Table 6-1   CORRECTED NEUTRON YIELDS FOR THICK TARGETS BOMBARDED WITH Po^{210} ALPHAS

Element	Yield (neutrons/10^6 alpha particles)
Li	2.6
Be	80
B	24
C	0.11
N	0.01
O	0.07
F	12
Na	1.5
Mg	1.4
Al	0.74
Si	0.16
Cl	0.11
A	0.38

SOURCE: J. H. Roberts, *M.D.D.C.* 731 (1944).

---

* The Q of a reaction is defined as the difference between the total mass energy of the reactants and that of the products of the reaction. In this example it would be given by $Q = 931(M_T + M_D - M_n - M_{He^4})$ Mev.

6-5 Artificial Radioactivity

Although artificial disintegration of nuclei by α-particle bombardment had been accomplished in 1919, the production of artificially radioactive nuclei was not observed until 1934. In this year Curie and Joliot (16) found that boron, magnesium, and aluminum were made β^+-active (see Chap. 7) by α-particle bombardment. When the α-particle source was removed, these elements continued to emit particles, the activity dying off exponentially in the manner of naturally radioactive substances.

With the bombardment energies available in 1934, the production of artificially radioactive nuclei by charged-particle bombardment was limited to the light elements, because of the huge coulomb repulsions of heavy nuclei. Fermi (22) therefore began a systematic bombardment of the heavier nuclei with neutrons from an 800-millicurie Rn-α-Be neutron source. Out of the first 68 elements bombarded, 47 were found to be radioactive after bombardment. Chemical separations showed that some of the active nuclei had the same atomic number as the bombarded substance. These were ascribed to (n, γ) reactions. Others were found to have an atomic number one less than the bombarded element. These were said to be due to (n, p) reactions. Still others were found to have an atomic number two less than the parent element and these were explained as (n, α) reactions. Regardless of which type of reaction occurred, the new nuclides resulting from the reactions were all negative electron emitters.

6-6 Fission

Fermi soon realized that an (n, γ) reaction with $_{92}$U might produce a β^--active uranium whose daughter product would be element 93. In collaboration with Rasetti and D'Agostino he made a study (23) of the activities induced in chemically purified uranium and thorium. In the case of thorium, the decay indicated a mixture of at least two half-lives, while uranium gave half-lives of (very roughly) 10 sec, 40 sec, 13 min, and at least two more of longer period. By a series of chemical precipitations they convinced themselves that the 13-minute activity could not be due to elements 82, 83, 86, 87, 88, 89, 90, 91, or 92. They felt it was reasonable to assume, therefore, that a *transuranic* element, number 93, had been formed. An interesting fact is that so many activities were produced. In elements consisting of many isotopes this is not unusual, but the abundance of U^{234} and U^{235} is quite small compared with U^{238}. For these isotopes to exhibit comparable activities, extraordinarily large capture cross sections would be required for the less abundant isotopes.

A large number of workers tried to identify more accurately the activities produced in uranium and thorium, and by 1937 Meitner, Hahn, and Strassmann (45) had concluded that the reactions were as follows:

(1) $_{92}U + n \longrightarrow {}_{92}U(10 \text{ sec}) \xrightarrow{\beta^-} {}_{93}EkaRe(2.2 \text{ min}) \xrightarrow{\beta^-} {}_{94}EkaOs(59 \text{ min})*$
$\xrightarrow{\beta^-} {}_{95}EkaIr(66 \text{ hr}) \xrightarrow{\beta^-} {}_{96}EkaPt(2.5 \text{ hr}) \xrightarrow{\beta^-} {}_{97}EkaAu(?),$

(2) $_{92}U + n \longrightarrow {}_{92}U(40 \text{ sec}) \xrightarrow{\beta^-} {}_{93}EkaRe(16 \text{ min}) \xrightarrow{\beta^-} {}_{94}EkaOs(5.7 \text{ hr})$
$\xrightarrow{\beta^-} {}_{95}EkaIr(?),$

(3) $_{92}U + n \longrightarrow {}_{92}U(23 \text{ min}) \xrightarrow{\beta^-} {}_{93}EkaRe(?).$

They also observed that the first two reactions occurred with either fast or slow neutrons, whereas the third occurred only with slow neutrons. The third reaction appeared to be a typical resonance capture with a maximum capture cross section for neutrons having an energy of 25 ± 10 ev. Although they felt fairly certain of their results, there were implausible aspects to the situation. For one thing, either U^{234} and U^{235} have extraordinarily large cross sections, or else U^{238} must exist in three isomeric forms which persist through several decay steps. In the second place, the emission of five β particles in succession had never been encountered before, and moreover, such decays would result in higher and higher atomic numbers, going far beyond the apparent limit of stability, 92.

Noddack (49) had pointed out in 1934, in criticizing Fermi's early report of transuranic elements, that the chemical procedures did not rule out the possibility that the uranium nucleus might have split up into rare-earth nuclei which would have chemical properties very similar to those expected of transuranic elements. This criticism apparently received little serious consideration.

Curie and Savitch (17) came very close to discovering fission when they separated out a 3.5-hour activity from neutron-bombarded uranium and found that it was indistinguishable from lanthanum. They assumed it to be a transuranic element but pointed out the difficulty of understanding a transuranic element with the chemical properties of lanthanum.

Since some of the reactions were suspected to be (n, α) reactions or to result in formation of α emitters, it was natural to search for such alphas. No positive evidence for their existence was obtained. Again there was a near miss in the discovery of fission. Von Droste (71) bombarded U and Th with fast and slow neutrons in a search for (n, α) reactions. A thin layer of U (or Th) preparation was placed just outside the thin foil wall of an ionization chamber. *The foils were chosen to be thick enough to absorb the α particles naturally emitted by U (or Th)*, but it was anticipated that the α particles from

* These names for the transuranic elements are of historical interest only.

any (n, α) reactions would be more energetic than the naturally emitted α particles because of the binding energy and kinetic energy of the neutrons, and would therefore be able to penetrate the foil and produce a pulse in the ionization chamber. No ionization bursts corresponding to energetic α particles were observed. The range of a fission fragment, with its large nuclear charge, is very much smaller than the thickness of the foils used in these experiments.

Hahn and Strassmann (29) next made a very careful separation, from neutron-bombarded uranium, of an activity that was coprecipitated with barium. Several substances with different half-lives were found, but by allowing the separated material to stand for several days to allow the short-half-life components to decay, then redissolving and reprecipitating, a purified long-half-life activity was obtained. Since coprecipitation with Ba is a standard method for separating radium isotopes, this activity was called " Ra IV." Various fractional crystallization techniques which were known to concentrate Ra failed to concentrate " Ra IV." When a mixture of purified " Ra IV " and Ra^{228} was coprecipitated with $BaCl_2$ and given the fractional crystallization treatment, the Ra^{228} was enriched as expected but the " Ra IV " was not. They concluded: " As chemists we must really say that the new bodies behave not as radium, but as barium."

They next subjected an activity coprecipitated with lanthanum oxalate and called " Ac II " to a similar test. A mixture of purified " Ac II " and Ac^{228} was coprecipitated with lanthanum oxalate and then fractionally crystallized. The Ac^{228} was concentrated as expected but the " Ac II " was not. They concluded that " Ac II " must actually be lanthanum, an expected daughter product of β-active Ba. Since the lanthanum was also β-active, its daughter product would be cerium.

They suggested that the "transuranics" might actually be their lower homologs Rh, Os, Ir, Pt which should be chemically similar to the transuranic elements. Further, they stated, "whether they are chemically the same as the still lower homologs, technetium,* ruthenium, rhodium, palladium, has not yet been tested. One could not even think of such things before now. The sum of the mass numbers of Ba + Tc, for example, 138 + 101, gives 239!"

In the following month, Hahn and Strassmann (30) reported additional fractional crystallization tests of the type mentioned above. In some of these tests the added Ra or Th isotope was enriched severalfold with no enrichment of the activity separated from the neutron irradiated U. These tests made them even more certain that they were dealing with radioisotopes of Ba and La. They pointed out that the β-active Ba, previously called " Ra III," has a half-life of 86 $\pm$ 6 min while a known β-active Ba isotope (19), Ba^{139}, has a half-life of 85 min. This suggested that their activity was Ba^{139} which would

* Called masurium at that time. The atomic number of Tc is 43.

then decay to stable La^{139}. They suggested that the daughter product of the β-active Ba isotope called "Ra IV" with a half-life of less than 40 hours, could be identified with La^{140}, whose half-life had been found to be 31–46 hours, which would mean that "Ra IV" was actually Ba^{140}.

They also made a search for Tc, Ru, Rh, Pd, their chemical homologs Re, Os, Ir, Pt, and for Mo and Ag, all with negative results. They also failed to find evidence for Ga, Ge, As, and Se. It was then realized that a breakup of U into two parts such that the mass is conserved would fail to conserve nuclear charge ($_{56}Ba + _{43}Tc = _{99}X$). On the other hand, if the U nucleus broke up in such a way that the nuclear charge was conserved, then one would expect something like $_{56}Ba + _{36}Kr = _{92}U$ with perhaps several neutrons released in the breakup. A long series of careful separations of material from neutron-irradiated U, which should leave only strontium, showed definite β activity. When this was allowed to stand and then subjected to a procedure which should separate any yttrium daughter products, it was found that the separated yttrium was also β-active. They then made an indirect test for Kr by passing air through a neutron-irradiated U solution and into an absorber solution. Any β-active Kr brought over with the air would then form Rb. Since natural Rb is slightly β-active it was not feasible to test for Rb, but if the daughter Rb were β-active also it would form Sr, so a chemical procedure for separating Sr was carried out. The separated Sr was again β-active.

It was recognized at once by many workers that the breakup of uranium into barium and krypton should release something like 200 Mev of energy. Frisch (27) and others observed ionization bursts corresponding to energies up to 100 Mev when thin films of uranium or thorium were irradiated with neutrons. Since only one of the fragment nuclei would leave the film of uranium in the direction of the ionization chamber gas, the smaller observed energy is to be expected.

Meitner and Frisch (46), who first applied the term "fission" to nuclear breakup into approximately equal fragments, collected the fission fragments on a water surface. Since simple absorption of a neutron with subsequent β decay would not release enough energy to expel a transuranic nucleus, the activities observed in this way should be due exclusively to fission nuclei. In this manner, they found nearly all the activities which had at one time been believed to be due to transuranic elements, thus making it very doubtful that any transuranic elements had been produced in detectable amounts. They also suggested the analogy between a heavy nucleus and a liquid drop. When the nucleus absorbs a neutron, according to this picture, the excitation may cause it to break up into two smaller droplets.

It should be noted that if the U^{239} nucleus breaks into a barium and krypton nucleus, each of these is likely to have a large neutron excess, so that several β decays would be necessary before stable nuclides would be formed.

Something of this sort would seem to be demonstrated by the results of Hahn and Strassmann. An alternative possibility is that a part of the neutron excess is taken care of by the release of free neutrons in uranium fission.

Tracks of fission fragments were observed by Joliot (40) in a cloud chamber and by Myssowsky and Zhdanoff (48) in photographic emulsions. The identification of the fission products by purely chemical means was soon confirmed by the x-rays emitted by some of the radioisotopes. Since the frequency of the K_α line from an element is proportional to $(Z - 1)^2$, [Eq. (2-5)], the frequency to be expected from $_{56}Ba$, for example, would be very different from that of a transuranic element $(Z > 92)$. Actually, fissions result in many different combinations of isotopes. The distribution of the fission products of U^{235}

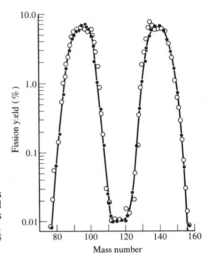

Fig. 6-1. Distribution of fission fragments as a function of mass number. The yield given is the number of fragments of mass number A per 100 fissioned U^{235} nuclei. [From H. W. Newson, *Phys. Rev.*, **122**, 1224 (1961).]

bombarded by thermal* neutrons as a function of mass number is shown in Fig. 6-1. If a uranium nucleus breaks into only two fragments and one of these has a mass greater than half the uranium nuclear mass, then the other must have a mass less than half the uranium mass. Fission in which the most

---

* Thermal neutrons are usually understood to possess an approximately Maxwellian velocity distribution, with a most probable neutron velocity of 2200 m/sec at 27°C (300°K) which corresponds to an energy of 0.026 ev. The Maxwellian distribution is given by the formula

$$\frac{dN}{dv} = \frac{4N_0}{\sqrt{\pi}} \left(\frac{M}{2k\,\Theta} \right)^{3/2} v^2 e^{-Mv^2/2k\Theta}, \tag{6-4}$$

where dN is the number of neutrons with velocities between v and $v + dv$, N_0 is the total number of neutrons, M is the neutron mass, k is Planck's constant, and Θ is the absolute temperature. The most probable velocity is then given by

$$v_p = (2k\,\Theta/M)^{1/2}. \tag{6-5}$$

probable masses of the fission fragments are unequal, as is the case in thermal fission of U^{235}, is called "asymmetric fission." Conversely, fission in which the most probable fission fragment masses were equal would be called "symmetric fission." The latter case would give a fission-fragment distribution (as a function of mass number) with a single peak rather than the double peak of Fig. 6-1.

It was pointed out previously that uranium has more neutrons than the stable isotopes into which it could be split on the basis of conservation of charge. Free neutrons resulting from fission were sought and found by many investigators. There are 2.45 $\pm$ 0.03 neutrons released (52), on the average, per thermal neutron fission of U^{235}.

It is now known that neutron fission is possible for all elements of atomic number 73 or greater. U^{235} is the only *naturally occurring* nuclide which has been found to undergo fission from thermal neutron bombardment, all others requiring higher-energy neutrons, generally of the order of 1 Mev. Fission has also been produced by gamma rays and by bombardment with high-energy charged particles such as protons, deuterons, and alphas. When Bi, Pb, Au, etc. are bombarded with α particles having an energy of about 350 Mev they undergo symmetrical fission rather than the asymmetric fission characteristic of the thermal neutron fission of U^{235}. When lighter elements are bombarded with protons they often undergo fission. For example, a Cu^{64} target contains Cl^{38} and Na^{24} after high-energy proton bombardment.

The occurrence of minute amounts of Pu^{239} in uranium ores is believed to be produced by the neutrons released in *spontaneous fission* of U^{238}. The disintegration constant for spontaneous fission of U^{238} corresponds to a half-life, for this process alone, of about 10^{16} years. While fission is generally understood to mean binary fission, fission into three or more particles has been observed.

A process much like fission, except that one or more fragments is much less massive than a typical fission fragment, is known as *spallation*. Both fission and spallation take place when targets are bombarded by high-energy particles, so that a target of uranium will contain nearly every element after bombardment with 350-Mev α particles.

6-7 Delayed Neutron Emission

In fission, most of the free neutrons are emitted at once, but a few are delayed. In the case of thermal fission of U^{235}, 0.76 per cent of the neutrons are delayed neutrons. These delayed neutrons are emitted by the offspring of some of the fission fragments. The actual neutron-emitting nuclides have an immeasurably short half-life, but since they depend for their existence on the β decay of parent nuclides they have apparent half-lives equal to the half-lives of the β-active parents. Not all the delayed neutron emitters have been identified, but two which are reasonably certain are Kr^{87} (precursor, Br^{87}), the decay scheme of which is shown in Fig. 6-2, and Xe^{137} (precursor, I^{137}). In 1948, the first example of neutron emission, by other than fission fragments, was reported by Knable, Lawrence, Leith, Moyer, and Thornton (41), who found delayed neutrons with a half-life of about 4 min coming from oxygen and a number of higher-atomic-number nuclei after bombardment with

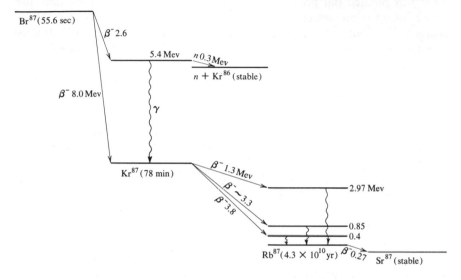

Fig. 6-2. Decay scheme of Br^{87}. When Br^{87} decays to the excited state of Kr^{87} the excited nucleus may emit either a gamma ray, thus falling to the ground state of Kr^{87}, or a neutron. In the latter case the residual nucleus is stable Kr^{86}.

175-Mev deuterons, or with energetic protons or neutrons. Alvarez (1) showed that the neutron emitter was O^{17} in an excited state resulting from β decay of N^{17}. Another reported delayed-neutron precursor is Li^{9} (28). The significance of delayed neutrons in connection with our ideas of nuclear structure is discussed in Chap. 9.

6-8 Chain Reactions

As soon as it was learned that more than two neutrons are released per U^{235} thermal fission, it was realized that·a chain reaction might possibly be made to take place, with the evolution of a vast amount of energy (see Prob. 6-6). Since no nuclear explosions had occurred in fission experiments, it was evident that special conditions were required for a chain reaction. The basic consideration is that more than one neutron, on the average, from each fission shall produce an additional fission. Since neutrons are lost by escape from

Fig. 6-3. The low-flux homogeneous reactor at the University of Oklahoma. This is a swimming-pool type of reactor, that is, one in which the reactor core is immersed in a tank of water. In the photograph, you are looking down through approximately five feet of water to the top of the core. The elements with light gray tops are blocks of graphite to scatter neutrons back into the core. The dark-topped elements have graphite reflector blocks at top and bottom and central blocks consisting of a uniform dispersion of powdered uranium oxide in polyethylene. The polyethylene acts as a moderator to slow the fast fission-neutrons down to thermal speeds. The uranium contains 20% U^{235}. The total uranium content is about 4 kg. The white-topped graphite block at the right corner contains a 10-mg Ra-Be neutron source. The two raised flat devices are safety rods. They are flat aluminum cans filled with boron carbide. The uppermost rod is like the safety rods but acts as a coarse control rod. The lowermost rod is a plate of stainless steel used as a fine control rod. The vertical cylinders between the cylindrical supports at the upper right contain a proportional counter and an ionization chamber for monitoring the radiation level, and hence the power output, of the reactor.

the uranium, and by nuclear capture which does not produce fission, these two forms of loss must be minimized if a chain reaction is to take place. Some of the detailed considerations involved in controlled nuclear chain reactions are discussed in Appendix B.

Nuclear reactors are of importance in research because they furnish thermal neutron fluxes and thermal neutron beams many orders of magnitude more intense than can be obtained in any other way.

6-9 Transuranic Elements

An actual transuranic element was first identified in 1940 by McMillan and Abelson (44), who found that neptunium ($_{93}Np^{239}$) was a β emitter whose chemical properties suggested that it was a member of a new rare-earthlike series. Seaborg, Kennedy, and Wahl (61) next isolated plutonium ($_{94}Pu^{238}$) and, in 1945, Seaborg discovered americium ($_{95}Am$) and curium ($_{96}Cm$). In 1950 the elements berkelium ($_{97}Bk$) and californium ($_{98}Cf$) were produced by α bombardment of $_{95}Am$ and $_{96}Cm$, respectively (68, 69). Einsteinium ($_{99}Es$) and fermium ($_{100}Fm$) were isolated from the debris of a thermonuclear explosion by Ghiorso *et al.* in 1952. Mendelevium ($_{101}Md$) was produced in 1955 by α-particle bombardment of Es^{253}. Nobelium ($_{102}No$) was produced (26) in 1957 by bombarding Cm^{244} with C^{13} ions. Ghiorso, Sikkeland, Larsh, and Latimer produced lawrencium ($_{103}Lw$) in 1961 by bombarding $_{98}Cf$ with 70-Mev $_5B$ nuclei.

6-10 Diffraction of Neutrons

By the time neutrons were discovered it was known that electrons, protons, and even neutral atoms exhibit that phenomenon characteristic of waves, diffraction. The de Broglie wavelength of a particle is given by

$$\lambda = \frac{h}{Mv} \qquad (6\text{-}6)$$

and, by good fortune, thermal neutrons have wavelengths comparable to the interatomic spacing in crystals, so that crystal diffraction of a thermal neutron beam should be observable, and should follow the Bragg equation

$$n\lambda = 2d \sin \theta, \qquad (6\text{-}7)$$

where n is an integer, d is the spacing between diffracting planes of atoms in the crystal, and θ is the *glancing angle* of incidence (which must be equal to the glancing angle of diffraction for a diffraction pattern maximum). Such diffraction was first observed in 1936 by Mitchell and Powers (47) and by Halban and Preiswerk (31). The experimental arrangement of Mitchell and Powers is shown in Fig. 6-4.

Although the interaction between neutrons and the atoms by which they are scattered is very different from the interaction between x-rays and electrons, they have many characteristics in common. Like x-rays and gamma rays, neutrons are scattered by stationary scatterers in three different ways:

1. Coherently scattered neutrons are scattered without loss of energy and with a constant phase change in the waves describing their propagation. It is thus possible to observe interference effects among the scattered neutrons.

2. Diffusely scattered neutrons lose no energy in the scattering process, but do suffer random phase changes. It follows that diffusely scattered neutrons do not show interference effects.

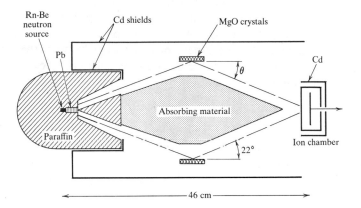

Fig. 6-4. Cross section of the apparatus used by Mitchell and Powers (47) to test for the wave properties of neutrons. The 16 MgO single crystals were placed in a ring about the absorber at such a radial distance that neutrons scattered into the ion chamber would satisfy the diffraction conditions for thermal neutrons having the most probable velocity. The ion chamber was filled with BF_3 on one run and was lined with B_4C on two other runs. Three sets of data were taken in each run. First, the background rate of fast neutrons was determined by covering the ion chamber face with a sheet of cadmium. Next, the rate was determined with the crystals oriented as shown. Finally the crystals were alternately tipped 25° one way and 25° the opposite way from the normal position. The reduction in the count rate with the crystals tipped showed that a true diffraction phenomenon was being observed when the crystals were in the normal position.

3. Inelastically scattered neutrons lose energy in the process. They then have different velocities and different de Broglie wavelengths after they have been scattered, and therefore cannot produce observable interference effects.

Diffraction effects are possible, then, only when the scattering is coherent, and it is with this type of scattering that we shall be primarily concerned in this section.

When x-rays are scattered by the electrons of an atom there is interference between the waves scattered by electrons in different parts of the atom. This gives a variation in the intensity of radiation scattered in different directions with respect to the incident beam. Thermal neutrons, by contrast, are usually scattered appreciably only by the nucleus of the atom, so that the scattering is the same in all directions. Scattering by the electrons of the atom has been observed, but is ordinarily negligibly small compared to nuclear scattering except in the case of magnetic scattering, which is discussed in Sec. 6-11. If the incident beam of thermal neutrons is represented by a plane wave of unit amplitude, then the scattered wave, if a spherical wave as we expect for nuclear scattering, will have an amplitude which is inversely proportional to the distance it has traveled from the scattering center. Its amplitude may then be written as $-a/r$, the negative sign being chosen because most nuclei scatter neutrons with a 180° change in phase. Remembering that the intensity of a wave is proportional to the square of its amplitude, the flux of incident neutrons may be taken to be $1 \cdot v$ neutrons/cm²-sec, where v is the velocity of the incident neutrons. The number of neutrons coherently scattered by one nucleus per second will then be

$$\sigma_{\text{coh}} \cdot (\text{number of neutrons incident per second}) = \sigma_{\text{coh}} v,$$

where σ_{coh} is the coherent scattering cross section. Since the coherently scattered neutrons have the same energy as the incident neutrons, they will move with the same speed. The current of neutrons coherently scattered through the surface of a sphere of radius r surrounding the scattering nucleus will be

$$\left(\frac{-a_{\text{coh}}}{r}\right)^2 4\pi r^2 v = \sigma_{\text{coh}} v. \tag{6-8}$$

From this, one obtains

$$\sigma_{\text{coh}} = 4\pi a_{\text{coh}}^2. \tag{6-9}$$

The amplitude coefficient, a_{coh}, is called the "coherent scattering amplitude" or the "scattering length." If one considers the neutron wave to be scattered by a "square" potential well, then when σ_{coh} is not a function of neutron energy, the radius of the square well is just a_{coh}. Such energy-independent scattering is known as "potential scattering." It is observed experimentally, however, that in some cases the coherent scattering cross section passes through a maximum value at some value of neutron kinetic energy. This type of energy dependence is characteristic of a resonance process. In analogy with the electromagnetic case [Eq. (5-55)], Breit and Wigner (9) in 1936 developed a theory of neutron scattering according to which the cross section for coherent scattering is given by

$$\sigma_{\text{coh}} = 4\pi \left| a_{\text{coh}} + \frac{b}{(W - W_{\text{res}}) + (i/2)(\Gamma_{\text{re}} + \Gamma_{\text{abs}})} \right|^2, \tag{6-10}$$

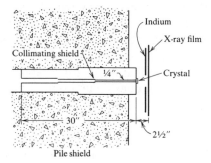

Fig. 6-5. Schematic diagram of apparatus used by Wollan, Shull, and Marney (73) to obtain Laue neutron diffraction patterns from crystals. A collimated beam of thermal neutrons is diffracted by the crystal onto the indium foil. The foil nuclei capture the neutrons and become beta-active. The beta rays emitted by the activated nuclei in the foil produce latent images in the photographic film.

Fig. 6-6. Laue diffraction pattern of NaCl. [Photo courtesy of E. O. Wollan and C. G. Shull.]

where b is a constant, W is the energy of the incident neutron, W_{res} is the energy which the neutron must have in order to produce resonance (i.e., the excitation energy of the neutron-nucleus system at resonance less the binding energy of the neutron), $i = \sqrt{-1}$, Γ_{re} is the "level width" for re-emission of the quasi-bound neutron (i.e., $\Gamma_{re} = \hbar/\tau_{re}$, where τ_{re} is the lifetime of the state against re-emission of the neutron), and Γ_{abs} is the level width for absorption of the neutron. Equation (6-10) is applicable only where the energy necessary to excite other quasi-bound states is far removed from W_{res}.

Table 6-2 COHERENT SCATTERING AMPLITUDES OF BOUND NUCLIDES

Nuclide	Coherent scattering amplitude, a_{coh} (10^{-12} cm)		Coherent scattering cross section $\sigma_{coh}(= 4\pi a_{coh}^2)$ (barns)	Total scattering cross section σ_t (barns)
H^1	-0.378 ± 0.02	(a)	1.80 ± 0.19	80
H^2	0.64	(b)	5.2	7.4
Li^6	0.7	(b)	6.0	
Li^7	-0.25	(b)	0.8	2
C^{12}	0.66	(c)	5.5	5.5
C^{13}	0.60 ± 0.04	(c)	4.5 ± 0.6	5.5 ± 1
Al^{27}	0.35	(b)	1.5	1.5
Ti^{48}	-0.58	(d)	4.23	6
V^{51}	-0.048 ± 0.010	(e)	0.029 ± 0.01	5
Ni^{58}	1.44	(f)	25.9	27.0
Ni^{60}	0.30	(f)	1.1	1
Ni^{62}	-0.87	(f)	9.5	9
Ag^{107}	0.83	(b)	8.7	10
Ag^{109}	0.43	(b)	2.3	6
Bi^{209}	0.89	(b)	10.1	10

(a) M. T. Burgy, G. R. Ringo, and D. J. Hughes, *Phys. Rev.*, **84**, 1160 (1951)
(b) C. G. Schull and E. O. Wollan, *Phys. Rev.*, **81**, 527 (1951)
(c) W. C. Koehler and E. O. Wollan, *Phys. Rev.*, **85**, 491 (1952)
(d) S. S. Sidhu, LeRoy Heaton, and M. H. Mueller, *J. Appl. Phys.*, **30**, 1323 (1959)
(e) S. W. Peterson and H. A. Levy, *Phys. Rev.*, **87**, 422 (1952)
(f) G. E. Bacon, *Neutron Diffraction* (Oxford: Clarendon Press, 1955).

With the advent of nuclear reactors, the much more intense thermal neutron beams made practical experiments that could not be performed with the weak beams from Ra-Be neutron sources. Neutron diffraction has been used to study the velocity distribution of the thermal neutrons issuing from a port in a nuclear reactor and has been extensively used in crystal structure studies (60, 73, 74). Such studies complement x-ray diffraction studies, for neutrons are found to be about as strongly scattered (coherently) by light nuclei as by heavy, whereas x-rays are most strongly scattered by atoms having many electrons (i.e., the heavy elements). Thus, while the location of light atoms in a crystal cannot always be determined by x-ray diffraction, their location can often be determined by neutron diffraction. It has also been possible to distinguish between elements of approximately the same Z and

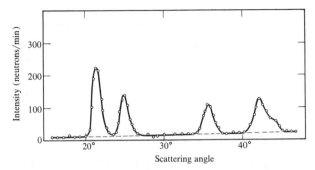

Fig. 6-7. Debye-Scherrer neutron diffraction pattern for powdered lead. [From C. G. Shull and E. O. Wollan, *Phys. Rev.*, **81**, 527 (1951).]

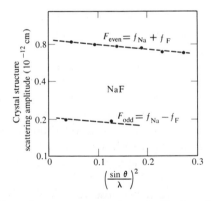

Fig. 6-8. Crystal structure scattering amplitudes of NaF determined from powder diffraction measurements. In this type crystal, the reflection amplitudes from Na and F atoms from planes having even Miller indices add, while for reflection from planes defined by odd Miller indices the scattering amplitude of F must be subtracted from that of Na. Hence, if amplitudes from Na and F have the same sign, the reflections from even planes will be stronger than those from odd planes. The opposite situation is encountered in LiF crystals. [From C. G. Shull and E. O. Wollan, *Phys. Rev.*, **81**, 527 (1951).]

even between isotopes of the same element where their coherent neutron scattering amplitudes happen to be quite different.

The experimental setup for obtaining Laue diffraction patterns of NaCl, quartz, calcite, LiF, and other crystals, is shown in Fig. 6-5. A Laue diffraction pattern of NaCl obtained by this method is shown in Fig. 6-6. Debye-Scherrer type diffraction has also been obtained using a monoergic beam (obtained from a heteroergic beam by crystal diffraction) and powdered scatterers. Figure 6-7 shows an intensity pattern obtained in this way. Table 6-2 gives a few of the observed coherent scattering amplitudes and cross sections as well as the total (coherent + incoherent) scattering cross sections. Powder diffraction studies do not yield the sign of the scattering amplitude, although they often give the sign of the scattering amplitude of one element relative to that of another (see Fig. 6-8). The sign is determined for certain reference elements by reflection studies (see Sec. 6-11).

6-11 Magnetic Moment of the Neutron

Since charged particles (electrons and protons) have magnetic moments which are of the proper order of magnitude to agree with that expected for a charged body rotating with the observed angular momentum $\hbar/2$, one would expect the neutron, being uncharged, to have no magnetic moment. In Table 2-2 the proton magnetic moment is given as 2.7935 nm (nuclear magnetons) while the deuteron magnetic moment is 0.85761 nm. If one assumes that the deuteron consists of a neutron with no magnetic moment and a proton in close combination, then it is difficult to explain the small magnetic moment of the deuteron on the basis of orbital motion of the proton. In Prob. 2-7 we saw that two protons revolving about their common center of mass with one unit of angular momentum ($\hbar$) would produce a magnetic dipole moment of 1 nm. Since the neutron bears no electrical charge, a neutron and proton revolving about their common center of mass with one unit of angular momentum would produce (neglecting a very small correction required by the difference in mass of neutron and proton) a dipole moment of only $\frac{1}{2}$ nm. The deuteron, then, would have to have a spin of almost 4, rather than the observed value of 1, to reduce the dipole moment from that of the proton alone to that of the deuteron. Moreover, the magnetic moment computed from such a model differs from the observed dipole moment by an amount considerably larger than the experimental error. An alternative explanation is that the nuclear particles have no orbital angular momentum, but that the neutron, like the proton, has a spin of $\frac{1}{2}$. The two particles together could then have a spin of 1, but this would require the neutron to possess a magnetic moment of -1.9359 nm.

Polarization of neutron beams. If neutrons have spin and magnetic moment, one should be able to differentiate between neutrons whose spin axes are differently oriented in space. Rutherford showed that when charged (α) particles are scattered by charged atomic nuclei, the scattering increases with the force exerted by the nucleus on the charged particle, and the scattering is the same whether the force be one of attraction or repulsion. Now if the force which the nucleus exerts on a scattered particle does not follow the inverse square law, the amount of scattering will be different, but qualitatively it will still be true that the scattering increases with the force exerted by the nucleus on the particle.

Suppose that a neutron moves close to a nucleus to which it is attracted by forces other than magnetic ones.* Then one would expect a certain amount of scattering due to this interaction, the scattering being greater the greater the attractive force. But if the neutron has a magnetic moment, there will be, in addition, a magnetic interaction force between the neutron and the magnetic moment of the scattering atom. Let the spin of the neutron be in the same direction and sense as the magnetic moment of the scattering atom. Then, if the neutron has a negative magnetic moment, its magnetic moment will be in the opposite sense to that of the atom. Since two parallel and oppositely directed dipoles, side by side, attract each other, it is evident that in such circumstances the atom exerts a force greater than that due to nonmagnetic nuclear forces alone and hence the scattering should be greater. Conversely, if the neutron spin is directed oppositely to the magnetic moment of the atom, the attractive force, and hence the scattering, will be reduced. Fairly satisfactory theories (5, 33, 34, 56, 58, 65, 70) have been developed which yield expressions for computing the magnitude of the expected magnetic interaction effects.

Suppose that a beam of unpolarized neutrons of assumed spin $\frac{1}{2}$ is passed through a slab of iron of thickness x which is magnetized in a direction normal to the axis of the neutron beam. If the iron is magnetized close to saturation, most of the atoms will be oriented with their magnetic moments in the direction of the magnetizing field. When an unpolarized neutron comes into this magnetic field it must assume a magnetic quantum state in which its observable spin is either $+\frac{1}{2}$ or $-\frac{1}{2}$ in the direction of the magnetic field. It has been suggested (5, 53, 58) that the scattering cross sections for slow neutrons scattered by magnetized iron may be written

$$\sigma_{+1/2} = \sigma_0(1 + \kappa), \qquad (6\text{-}11)$$

$$\sigma_{-1/2} = \sigma_0(1 - \kappa), \qquad (6\text{-}12)$$

where $\sigma_{+1/2}$ is the scattering cross section for neutrons whose spins are parallel to the magnetic field, $\sigma_{-1/2}$ is the scattering cross section for those aligned antiparallel to the magnetic field, σ_0 is the scattering cross section for

* Magnetic forces alone are insufficient to account for the binding energy of a neutron in a nucleus like that of deuterium.

unmagnetized iron, and κ is a fraction which is a measure of the magnetic interaction of the neutron and the magnetized iron.

The fractional number of neutrons transmitted through the magnetized slab then, remembering that, on the average, half of them have spins of $+\frac{1}{2}$ and half spins of $-\frac{1}{2}$, is given by

$$P_{\text{mag}} = \tfrac{1}{2}e^{-Nx\sigma_0(1+\kappa)} + \tfrac{1}{2}e^{-Nx\sigma_0(1-\kappa)} \qquad (6\text{-}13)$$

$$= e^{-Nx\sigma_0} \cosh (nx\sigma_0\kappa), \qquad (6\text{-}14)$$

where N is the number of iron atoms per cubic centimeter. The fractional transmission through the slab when it is unmagnetized is

$$P_{\text{unmag}} = e^{-Nx\sigma_0}. \qquad (6\text{-}15)$$

Since $\cosh Nx\sigma_0 P$ is always greater than one if $Nx\sigma_0 p$ is greater than zero, it follows that magnetizing the iron should *increase* its neutron transmission. In 1938 Powers obtained the results listed in Table 6-3 for single transmission

Table 6-3 DEPENDENCE OF MAGNETIC SCATTERING OF NEUTRONS ON NEUTRON ENERGY AND THICKNESS OF IRON

Effective neutron temp.	Iron thickness (cm)	No. neutrons/min transmitted[1]		Increase in no. transmitted	% Increase in transmission	κ	Effective cross section[2] (in barns)	
		Unmagnetized	Magnetized				Spin = $+\frac{1}{2}$ $\sigma_{+1/2} =$ $\sigma_0(1+\kappa)$	Spin = $-\frac{1}{2}$ $\sigma_{-1/2} =$ $\sigma_0(1-\kappa)$
300°K	0.80	719.5 ± 1.0	725.0 ± 1.0	5.5 ± 1.4	0.76 ± 0.19	0.150 ± 0.018	13.8	10.2
300°K	1.30	440.3 ± 0.6	448.2 ± 0.7	7.9 ± 0.9	1.78 ± 0.20	0.142 ± 0.008	13.7	10.3
300°K	1.95	221.08 ± 0.24	228.41 ± 0.25	7.33 ± 0.35	3.32 ± 0.16	0.130 ± 0.003	13.6	10.4
						Avg. 0.135 ± 0.008		
120°K	1.30	417.5 ± 1.2	429.2 ± 1.2	11.7 ± 1.6	2.8 ± 0.4	0.178 ± 0.012	14.1	9.9
120°K	1.95	209.3 ± 0.6	221.0 ± 0.6	11.7 ± 0.8	5.6 ± 0.4	0.158 ± 0.005	14.0	10.0
						Avg. 0.171 ± 0.008		

SOURCE: P. N. Powers, *Phys. Rev.*, **54**, 827 (1938).

[1] Absolute values at 300°K and 120°K not comparable.

[2] Total cross section (scattering + capture) for iron taken as 12.0 barns.

of slow neutrons through unannealed Armco Iron. Bloch, Hamermesh, and Staub (6) made similar experiments in which the effect of incomplete magnetic saturation of the iron was studied. Their results are reproduced in Table 6-4.

If the beam be passed through two slabs of iron of thicknesses x_1 and x_2, which may be magnetized to the same extent and such that their fields are

Table 6-4 DEPENDENCE OF SINGLE TRANSMISSION EFFECT
UPON MAGNETIC SATURATION

Thin sample (1.91 cm) % deviation from saturation	% Difference in transmission	Thick sample (3.81 cm) % deviation from saturation	% Difference in transmission
2.50	0.43 ± 0.13	2.56	0.80 ± 0.76
1.70	1.76 ± 0.25	2.01	−0.06 ± 0.72
1.16	1.08 ± 0.19	1.21	2.79 ± 0.69
0.63	1.65 ± 0.24	0.87	3.24 ± 0.76
0.41	2.78 ± 0.26	0.69	3.27 ± 0.77
0.25	3.33 ± 0.25	0.44	4.51 ± 0.69
0.17	3.27 ± 0.25	0.38	6.39 ± 0.71
0.12	3.67 ± 0.25	0.30	7.22 ± 0.75
		0.24	7.70 ± 0.69

SOURCE: F. Bloch, M. Hamermesh, and H. Staub, *Phys. Rev.*, **64**, 47 (1943).

parallel or antiparallel, then the fractions transmitted in these cases are given by

$$P_{\parallel} = e^{-N\sigma_0(x_1 + x_2)} \cosh \kappa N\sigma_0(x_1 + x_2), \tag{6-16}$$

$$P_{\text{anti}} = e^{-N\sigma_0(x_1 + x_2)} \cosh \kappa N\sigma_0(x_1 - x_2), \tag{6-17}$$

and

$$P_0 = e^{-N\sigma_0(x_1 + x_2)}. \tag{6-18}$$

In the special case where $x_1 = x_2 = x$ these equations become

$$P_{\parallel} = e^{-2N\sigma_0 x} \cosh 2\kappa N\sigma_0 x, \tag{6-19}$$

$$P_{\text{anti}} = e^{-2N\sigma_0 x}, \tag{6-20}$$

$$P_0 = e^{-2N\sigma_0 x}. \tag{6-21}$$

It is seen that for slabs of equal thickness, antiparallel magnetization should give the same transmission as is observed in the case where the iron slabs are demagnetized. Powers' results for this double transmission effect are shown in Table 6-5.

It will be noted that while the transmission is less for the antiparallel than for the parallel case, it still exceeds the transmission of demagnetized iron. This rather surprising result is attributable to depolarization of the beam between the slabs. When the two slabs are magnetized antiparallel, the neutron passes through a region between the plates in which the field reverses its direction. To the moving neutron this is tantamount to being in a rotating magnetic field and may result in a change in the space quantization of the neutron. In other words, its spin may change from $+\frac{1}{2}$ to $-\frac{1}{2}$ or vice versa, so that the degree of polarization of the beam is reduced by the time it reaches the second magnetized slab.

Table 6-5 OBSERVATION OF MAGNETIC SCATTERING OF
NEUTRONS THROUGH DOUBLE TRANSMISSION EXPERIMENTS
(I.E., POLARIZER-ANALYZER ACTION)[1]

Effective thickness of iron (cm)	Magnetization of iron plates	No. neutrons/min transmitted[2]	Difference in number transmitted	% Increase in transmission
1.30	parallel	358.0 ± 0.8	6.4 ± 1.1	1.8 ± 0.3
	antiparallel	354.8 ± 0.7	3.2 ± 1.0	0.9 ± 0.3
	zero	351.6 ± 0.7	0	0
1.95	parallel	181.11 ± 0.40	6.01 ± 0.56	3.44 ± 0.32
	antiparallel	178.82 ± 0.40	3.72 ± 0.56	2.12 ± 0.32
	zero	175.10 ± 0.39	0	0

SOURCE: P. N. Powers, *Phys. Rev.*, **54**, 827 (1938).

[1] Since no appreciable difference could be observed for normal and oblique incidence for the same effective thickness of iron, both results are averaged together here.

[2] The fast neutron background, obtained by interposing Cd in the beam, has been subtracted.

By introducing a pair of wires carrying currents of 90 amperes in the region between the slabs, Powers was able to produce a field in the space between the two slabs which varied in direction. In the moving frame of reference of the neutron this field would appear as a rotating field. When the current was in one direction it had very little effect on the transmission through plates magnetized parallel to each other, but when the current was in the opposite direction, there was an appreciable decrease in transmission indicative of nonadiabatic depolarization of the neutron beam between the plates. In the reference frame of the moving neutron, when the direction of rotation of the magnetic field is in the same sense as the precession of the neutron there is a measurable probability that the neutron will flip its spin from, say $+\frac{1}{2}$ to $-\frac{1}{2}$, whereas, when the field appears to be rotating in the opposite sense, the probability of inducing a spin flip becomes virtually zero. This is very closely akin to the molecular beam spin transitions discussed in Sec. 2-5. From an analysis of these rather crude results Powers was able to conclude that the magnetic moment of the neutron must be (-2 ± 1) nuclear magneton.

The general method used by Powers has been greatly refined by Bloch, Nicodemus, and Staub (7). Using the apparatus shown schematically in Fig. 6-9, they obtained a value of the ratio of neutron to proton magnetic moments of 0.685001 ± 0.00003. If one takes the proton magnetic moment to be 2.7935 nm, then the neutron has a magnetic moment of −1.9136 nuclear magnetons. This is very close to the value -1.9359 deduced above from the deuteron magnetic moment. The difference, however, is well beyond the experimental errors involved and must be assumed to be real.

One explanation which has been advanced for this difference is that the deuteron does not spend all of its time in the $^3S_1$ state (i.e., with no orbital angular momentum) but rather spends about 3.5 per cent of its time in a $^3D_1$ state (i.e., one in which the orbital angular momentum is 2, but total angular

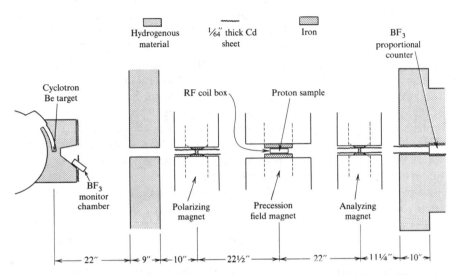

Fig. 6-9. Experimental arrangement used by Bloch, Nicodemus, and Staub (7) for the determination of the ratio of the neutron magnetic moment to the proton magnetic moment. This arrangement actually allows one to determine the Larmor precession frequencies of the neutron and proton in the field of the precession field magnet. Since this magnetic field is the same for both particles, no knowledge of the absolute magnetic field intensity is required; only the ratio of the precession frequencies need be known.

momentum is again 1). A nucleus in a pure S state is spherically symmetric and therefore cannot possess an electric quadrupole moment. The measured electric quadrupole moment of the deuteron is in reasonably good agreement with the 3.5 per cent admixture of D state necessary to explain the observed magnetic moment. It is by no means certain, however, that this is the correct explanation of the deuteron magnetic moment.

The high precision obtained in the experiment of Bloch, Nicodemus, and Staub is brought about primarily by comparing the frequency for nonadiabatic depolarization of the neutron beam with the frequency for nuclear induction of a proton sample in the same steady magnetic field. In this way it is not necessary to know the value of the steady magnetic field or the absolute frequencies involved, but only the ratios of the two frequencies.

Scattering of neutrons by hydrogen gas. It was mentioned in Sec. 2-5 that hydrogen molecules exist in two forms, orthohydrogen (proton spins parallel) and parahydrogen (proton spins antiparallel). In their ground states neither has an electronic magnetic moment and only orthohydrogen has a nuclear magnetic moment. If neutrons whose de Broglie wavelengths are long compared to the internuclear spacing of the protons in a hydrogen molecule are scattered by such a molecule, the waves (representing a neutron) that are scattered by the two protons will be essentially in phase and hence lead to constructive interference and a relatively large amount of scattering if the phase change associated with scattering at each proton is the same. On the other hand, if the scatterings at the two protons result in different phase changes, then the scattered waves may interfere destructively with a resultant smaller scattering cross section. If the force of interaction between neutron and proton is not spin-dependent (i.e., dependent on the relative orientation of the spin axes of neutron and proton) then there is no reason for expecting a phase change at one proton different from that at the other. On the other hand, if the interaction between neutron and proton is spin-dependent the waves scattered by the two protons in orthohydrogen should be in phase, but in parahydrogen could well differ in phase.

The deuteron is normally found in a triplet state (neutron and proton spins parallel) and we know that the binding energy in this case is positive since the nucleus is stable. It has been shown (59) that if the binding energy of the deuteron in a singlet state (neutron and proton spins anti-parallel) is also positive, the scattering cross section of parahydrogen should be little different from that of orthohydrogen. On the other hand, if the binding energy in a singlet state should be negative, then the phase change at the proton whose spin is parallel to the neutron should be quite different from that at the proton whose spin is antiparallel to that of the neutron. In this case it was predicted that for liquid air temperature neutrons, the scattering cross section for orthohydrogen in its ground state should be 300 times that of parahydrogen in its ground state. A more classical way of looking at the situation is that a bound state, such as the triplet state, bespeaks an attractive force while an unbound state (one with negative binding energy) implies a repulsive force. In orthohydrogen the forces exerted on the neutron by the two protons would be of the same sign, but in parahydrogen, if the singlet state has a negative binding energy, the force exerted by one proton would be repulsive while that exerted by the proton of oppositely oriented spin would be attractive. In such circumstances, the net force exerted by parahydrogen on a neutron would be smaller than that exerted by orthohydrogen and the scattering cross section would correspondingly be less for parahydrogen.

Alvarez and Pitzer (2) have attempted to check this experimentally. They maintained their H_2 at 20.4°K by jacketing the scattering chamber in liquid hydrogen boiling at atmospheric pressure. Neutrons whose energy corresponded to 20.2°K were selected by a rotating cadmium shutter velocity selector. Parahydrogen gas was prepared by allowing liquid hydrogen to remain in contact with activated charcoal for 36 hours to remove orthohydrogen, which is normally about 3 times as abundant as parahydrogen, then pouring off the liquid and allowing it to vaporize. This process should give 99.8 per cent pure parahydrogen. The cross section that they obtained for orthohydrogen is 100 ± 3 barns, and that for parahydrogen 5.2 ± 0.6 barns. Even though the ratio between these cross sections is 19, in contrast to the theoretical prediction of 300, it shows conclusively that the interaction of a neutron and a proton is spin-dependent, that the binding energy of the deuteron in the $^1S_1$ state is negative and explains why we do not find deuterons of zero spin.

Polarization by reflection. Since neutrons have wave properties, as evidenced in diffraction by crystals, Fermi (25) was led to expect that substances would have indices of refraction, n, for neutrons such that

$$n - 1 \cong \pm 10^{-6}.$$

(6-22)

He was led to this conclusion by a wave mechanical argument which is essentially the following. If thermal neutrons are incident normally on a slab of material, a very minute fraction of them suffer scattering through 180°. If a wave which is traveling in a medium whose refractive index is unity, is incident normally on a slab of transmitting material whose index of refraction is n, the amplitude of the reflected wave is

$$Y_{\text{refl}} = \left(\frac{1 - n}{1 + n}\right) Y_{\text{incident}}$$

(6-23)

and the intensity of the reflected beam, which is proportional to Y^2, is

$$\Phi_{\text{refl}} = \left(\frac{1 - n}{1 + n}\right)^2 \Phi_{\text{incident}}.$$

(6-24)

If one thinks in terms of the de Broglie waves which describe the motion of the neutrons, then, the index of refraction of the medium must either be smaller or greater than unity by a very small amount to account for the small fraction of neutrons which is "reflected." A similar situation is encountered in x-rays, where the refractive indices of various substances are always less than unity but only by an amount on the order of 10^{-6} to 10^{-5}. Snell's law, written in terms of the glancing angle of incidence, θ_1, and the glancing angle of refraction, θ_2, is

$$n_1 \cos \theta_1 = n_2 \cos \theta_2.$$

(6-25)

As in ordinary optics, when a wave front strikes an interface between media of different refractive index, part of the wave is reflected and part usually transmitted. If $n_1 > n_2$, however, (6-25) cannot be satisfied by any value of θ_2 when θ_1 is less than the "critical angle" given by

$$\cos \theta_c = \frac{n_2}{n_1}, \qquad (6\text{-}26)$$

in which case there can be no transmitted wave and one will get total reflection for all angles less than θ_c. When the indices are nearly equal, as they must be for neutrons, the reflection coefficient is very small for all incidence angles which are appreciably greater than θ_c, so that in cases where $n_2 > n_1$, the reflection is almost nil.

Using an experimental setup, shown schematically in Fig. 6-10, it was found that C (graphite), Al, Be, Cu, Zn, Ni, Fe, and glass all showed total

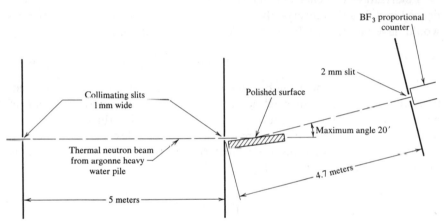

Fig. 6-10. Schematic diagram of arrangement used by Fermi and Zinn (25) to demonstrate specular reflection of neutron beams. The slit sizes and deviation of the beam are greatly exaggerated.

reflection, so that n is less than unity for these substances. Manganese, on the other hand, failed to exhibit total reflection and therefore presumably has an index greater than unity.

From (6-23) it is seen that the coherent scattering amplitude is negative if n is greater than unity and positive if n is less than unity. Shull and Wollan have found that not only Mn^{55} but also H^1, Li^7, Ti, and Ni^{62} have negative coherent scattering amplitudes and therefore refractive indices greater than unity.

Since the scattering of neutrons depends in part on the magnetic interaction between neutron and nucleus, or, especially in the case of ferromagnetic materials where the magnetic moment of the atom is much greater than that of the nucleus alone, between neutron and atomic dipole field, it was suggested (32, 35) that the index of refraction for neutrons whose magnetic moments are parallel to the field in a magnetized plate would be different than the index for neutrons whose magnetic moments are antiparallel to the magnetic field. A material whose nuclear coherent scattering amplitude is positive and greater than its magnetic scattering amplitude would have two positive scattering

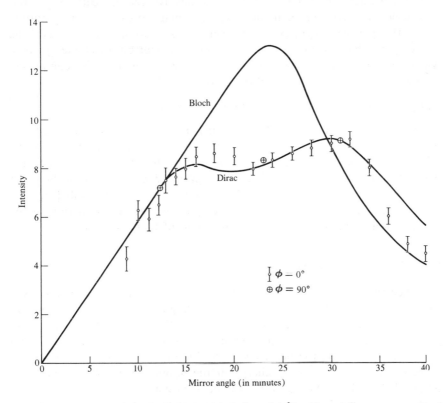

Fig. 6-11. Intensity of BeO filtered neutrons ($\lambda > 4.4$ Å) reflected from a magnetized iron mirror *vs.* the glancing angle of incidence of the neutron beam on the mirror (38). The curve marked "Bloch" is a theoretical curve which predicts that the magnetic interaction contribution to the coherent scattering amplitude is proportional to the magnetic intensity H. The curve marked "Dirac" is based on a theory which predicts that the magnetic contribution to the coherent scattering amplitude is proportional to the flux density B. The $\phi = 0$ data points are for a mirror magnetized in the direction (approximately) of the incident beam, while the $\phi = 90°$ points are for a mirror in which B is perpendicular to the beam. B is taken to be 22,500 gauss in the theoretical curve.

amplitudes corresponding to the two orientations of the neutron spin. Such a material is iron for which a_{nuclear} is 0.96×10^{-12} cm while the maximum value of a_{magnetic} is $\sim 0.6 \times 10^{-12}$ cm. Figure 6-11 shows a plot of reflected beam intensity *vs.* glancing angle of incidence of neutrons on an iron plate magnetized parallel to its reflecting surface. The fact that the curve has just two maxima shows that the index has two and only two values, corresponding to the two allowable orientations of a spin $\frac{1}{2}$ particle.

It is not possible to obtain completely polarized beams of neutrons from a material like iron if the beam is heteroergic since the scattering amplitudes are energy-dependent. A material which had a positive nuclear scattering amplitude which was smaller than the maximum magnetic scattering amplitude would then, when magnetized sufficiently closely to saturation, have one index greater than one and one less than one. All neutrons in an energy range where one state of polarization will be reflected will then be completely polarized by reflection. A 10-mil thick layer of cobalt

$$(a_{\text{nuclear}} = 0.28 \times 10^{-12} \text{ cm}, \qquad \text{maximum } a_{\text{magnetic}} \cong 0.46 \times 10^{-12} \text{ cm})$$

plated onto a smooth 5 in. $\times$ 10 in. copper backing plate has been used (38) to produce "completely" polarized beams of neutrons. As in double transmission experiments, a second cobalt mirror magnetized antiparallel to the first fails to give zero reflection because of partial depolarization of the beam in transit between the two mirrors. Reflection polarization not only furnishes polarized neutron beams but also makes possible the determination of the coherent scattering amplitude (including sign) of various nuclides (36).

6-12 Mass of the Neutron

When the neutron was first discovered it was thought that its mass was slightly less than that of a proton and that it might therefore be a proton and an electron in much closer combination than is the case in a hydrogen atom. By applying conservation of momentum and energy to the observed recoil proton and assuming the neutrons to be due to the Be^9 (α, n) reactions, in order to estimate the kinetic energy of the impinging neutrons, Chadwick obtained the value 1.0067 amu for the neutron mass.

Lauritsen and Crane (43), using the results of Oliphant (51) on the reactions

$$_3\text{Li}^7 + _1\text{H}^2 + W_d = 2\,_2\text{He}^4 + _0n^1 + W_1$$

and $\qquad\qquad _3\text{Li}^7 + _1\text{H}^1 + W_p = 2\,_2\text{He}^4 + W_2,$

pointed out that by subtracting one equation from the other (considered as energy equations), one obtains

$$_0n^1 = (_1\text{H}^2 - _1\text{H}^1) + (W_2 - W_1) + (W_d - W_p).$$

In Oliphant's work the bombarding energy was approximately constant at about 0.2 Mev, so that $W_d - W_p = 0$. The maximum range in air at NPT of an α particle in the case of deuteron bombardment corresponded to an energy of 8.3 Mev, while the maximum energy of an α particle in the case of proton bombardment was 8.75 Mev. In the second reaction, if the proton momentum is neglected, the energies of the two alphas must be equal, so that $W_2 = 2 \times 8.75 = 17.5$ Mev. Lauritsen and Crane assumed that maximum α range in the first reaction would occur when the neutron was given no kinetic energy. In this case, neglecting the deuteron momentum, the two alphas would again have equal energies, and one would obtain

$$W_1 = 2 \times 8.3 = 16.6 \text{ Mev,}$$

giving

$$W_2 - W_1 = 0.9 \text{ Mev} = 0.00096 \text{ amu.}$$

Taking $_1H^2 - _1H^1 = 1.00586$ (present-day value 1.00659), one then obtains for the mass of the neutron $1.00586 + 0.00096 = 1.0068$ amu. If one adopts the idea (42, 50)—discarded by Lauritsen and Crane as being statistically too improbable to be observed—that the maximum α range in the first reaction resulted when a neutron and one α particle moved off at the same speed in one direction while the other α particle moved off in the opposite direction, then the second α particle, again neglecting the deuteron momentum, would have received $\frac{5}{9}$* of the total energy. In this case, $W_1 = \frac{9}{5} \times 8.3 = 14.9$ Mev and

$$W_2 - W_1 = 2.6 \text{ Mev} = 0.00279 \text{ amu,}$$

so that the mass of the neutron would then be

$$1.00586 + 0.00279 = 1.0086 \text{ amu.}$$

If one assumes that the bombardment energy was 0.2 Mev for both reactions and takes account of the proton and deuteron momenta, the results are

$$W_1 = 13.6 \text{ Mev,} \qquad W_2 = 16.2 \text{ Mev,} \quad \text{and} \quad _0n^1 = 1.00865 \text{ amu.}$$

Chadwick and Goldhaber (12) arrived at the mass of the neutron through a study of the photodisintegration of the deuteron. This reaction may be written

$$_1H^2 + h\nu = _1H^1 + _0n^1 + W,$$

where $h\nu$ is the energy of the γ ray which produces the reaction and W is the combined kinetic energy of the proton and neutron. Using the γ rays of Tl^{208}, which have a quantum energy of 2.62 Mev, Chadwick and Goldhaber were able to produce disintegration, although it could not be produced by the less energetic (1.8-Mev) γ rays from Bi^{214}. On the basis of the sizes of ionization pulses which the protons produce in an ionization chamber, they estimated the energy of the protons to be 0.25 Mev, and since the mass of the neutron

---

* The reader should satisfy himself that the approximation made in using mass numbers rather than actual masses is justified.

and proton are approximately equal, the value of W would be (the momentum of the γ ray is so small that it may be neglected)

$$W \cong 2 \times 0.25 = 0.5 \text{ Mev} = \frac{0.5}{931} = 0.0054 \text{ amu},$$

so that

$$_0n^1 = (_1H^2 - _1H^1) + h\nu - W$$
$$= 1.0058 + 0.0028 - 0.0005 = 1.0081 \text{ amu}.$$

Since the accepted $_1H^1$ mass at that time was 1.0078 amu, this seemed to show that the mass of the neutron is greater than that of a hydrogen atom. Many other nuclear reactions as well as mass spectrometer measurements subsequently confirmed this result. Present-day values (66) are $_0n^1 = 1.008983$ amu, $_1H^1 = 1.008144$ amu.

6-13 Radioactive Decay of Free Neutrons

The fact that the neutron is heavier than the hydrogen atom immediately suggested the energetically possible radioactive decay of the neutron into a proton and an electron. Thus

$$_0n^1 \longrightarrow {}_1p^1 + {}_{-1}\beta^0 + 0.782 \text{ Mev}.$$

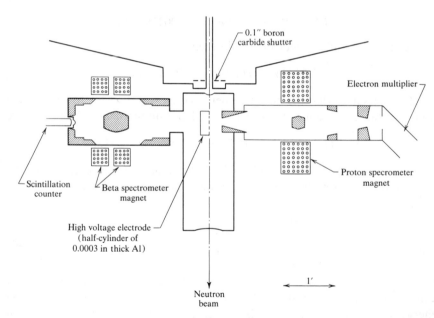

Fig. 6-12. Experimental arrangement employed by Robson (55) to detect and study radioactive decay of neutrons. The beam intensity was approximately 1.5×10^{10} thermal neutrons per second. Most of the lead and boron carbide shielding to decrease the background from gamma rays and neutrons that penetrate the pile shielding is not shown. The tank in which the neutrons decay is evacuated and has a 0.005-in. thick aluminum entrance window and a 0.018-in. thick exit window.

Attempts to observe this disintegration were fruitless before the advent of nuclear fission reactors as high neutron flux sources. The first evidence for such decay was obtained by Snell (62, 63), and beautifully confirmed by

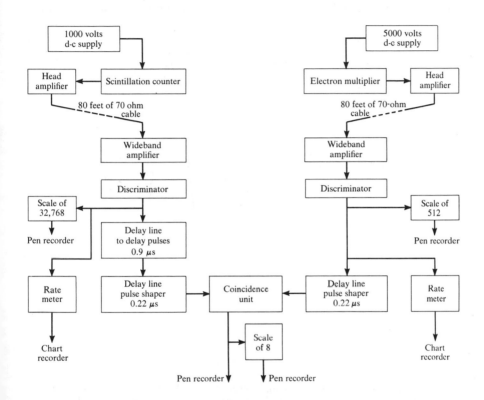

Fig. 6-13. Block diagram of the electronic equipment used, in conjunction with the apparatus shown in Fig. 6-11, to detect delayed coincidences between protons and electrons coming from the radioactive decay of free neutrons.

Robson (55). In one experiment by Robson the apparatus shown in Figs. 6-12 and 6-13 was used. The thermal neutron beam, with as many γ rays as possible removed by a 5-in. absorber, is passed through an evacuated chamber. Disintegration protons are accelerated at right angles to the beam by a 15-kv potential difference and are then passed through a thin magnetic-lens type mass spectrograph to an electron multiplier (similar to that used in the scintillation counter) which is inside the vacuum system. The peak of the curve shown in Fig. 6-14 is in the correct position to correspond to H^1 ions.

From the number of protons counted and a measurement of the thermal neutron flux, from which the density of neutrons in the beam can be calculated, it is possible to compute the half-life of the neutron. Robson finds the value to be 12.8 ± 2.5 minutes. A more recently reported (64) Russian result gives 12.0 ± 1.5 minutes.

Conservation of momentum shows that the proton energy, due to the β decay, is less than 500 ev, so that the proton energy is almost entirely

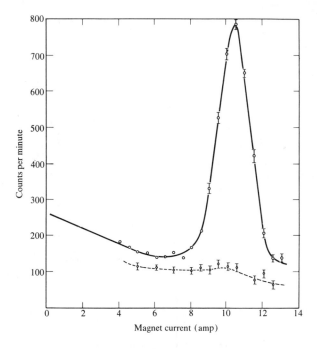

Fig. 6-14. Counting rate of the electron multiplier *vs.* current through the windings of the proton spectrometer magnet. The solid curve represents data taken with the shutter open, while the dotted curve represents data taken with the shutter closed, thereby removing the thermal neutrons from the beam. The peak is at the correct position for protons accelerated by the 13-kv electric deflecting field. The data are those of Robson (55).

determined by the 15-kv accelerating field. On the other hand, the electrons may be given a large part of the 0.782 Mev decay energy, so that their energy is not affected greatly by the deflecting field. If the positive electrode is close to the beam, while the negative electrode is some distance away, the electrons will be given only a fraction of the 15-kv potential difference. Since the figure shows this to be the case in Robson's experimental setup, the energy imparted by the electric field contributes relatively very little to the total observed energies of all but the slowest decay electrons. A thin magnetic-lens type β-ray spectrograph was placed opposite the proton spectrograph. The decay electrons (of a given energy for a given current in the magnetic-lens coils) pass through the spectrograph and are focused onto a scintillation counter. All counts are rejected except those in delayed coincidence with proton counts. The delay is introduced into the scintillation-counter circuit to allow for the time required for a 15-Kev proton to travel from the beam to the proton counter. This greatly reduces the background count, as shown

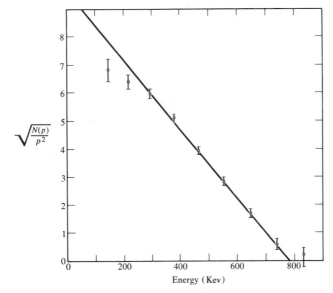

Fig. 6-15. A Kurie plot of the momentum distribution of the beta particles from decay of free neutrons. $N(p)$ is the number of particles observed in some small momentum interval, Δp, centered at p. The function plotted is usually $\sqrt{N(p)/Fp^2}$, where F is a calculated function. In this case, however, F is approximately one throughout the observed momentum spectrum, so it has been omitted. The data are those of Robson (55).

by the fact that there are now no coincidences when the boron shutter is placed in the neutron beam. By varying the current in the β-spectrograph coils, a β-energy spectrum is obtained which shows the maximum β energy to be 0.782 ± 0.013 Mev. A Kurie plot (discussed in Chap. 7) is shown in Fig. 6-15.

6-14 Theories of Nuclear Constitution

Prior to the discovery of the neutron, it was supposed that a nucleus consisted of protons (equal in number to the mass number of the nuclide) plus enough electrons to make the net nuclear charge equal to the atomic number times the charge on a single proton, but as pointed out in Chap. 2 there were facts which seemed incompatible with such a structure.

The discovery of the neutron suggested (37) the possibility that a nucleus might consist of protons (equal in number to the atomic number) plus enough neutrons to make the total number of nucleons (nuclear particles) equal to the mass number. In Sec. 2-5 it was pointed out that a nucleus consisting of half-integral spin particles equal in number to the mass number of the nuclide would give spins compatible with the observed nuclear spins if the nucleons were bound tightly enough that their spins had to be either parallel or anti-parallel. Thus the discovery of the neutron, together with the experimental establishment of the fact that it possesses a spin of $\frac{1}{2}$, resolved the previous difficulties of explaining the observed nuclear spins and nuclear magnetic moments.

An alternative hypothesis, suggested by Chadwick at the time he announced the discovery of the neutron, is that the nucleus consists of α particles, neutrons, and protons. For most purposes there is no basis for a decision as to which, if either, of these theories is correct. Both are in agreement with the observed spins and in qualitative agreement with the observed magnetic moments, and both avoid the difficulties entailed in attempting to explain the properties of nuclei on the assumption that they contain free electrons. The neutron-proton theory is the more widely held of the two because it is simpler.

In order to explain β decay under either of these theories, it is necessary to assume that a nuclear neutron can transform into a proton with emission of a β-particle. Such a transformation would conserve charge and leave the mass number of the nucleus unchanged. The ability of the neutron to dissociate was generally accepted as a necessary part of the neutron-proton or alpha-neutron-proton theory of the nucleus. The proof of the radioactive decay of the free neutron removed any lingering doubts about the immutability of this "elementary" particle. The theory of nuclear structure is discussed more fully in Chap. 9. It is easy to see why stable nuclides that are made radio-active by (n, p) reactions are always negatron emitters. The (n, p) reaction changes a nuclide $_N X^A$ to $_{N-1} Y^A$. This increases $(A - Z)$ by one and decreases Z by one, which is equivalent to increasing the number of neutrons by one and decreasing the number of protons by one. A glance at Fig. 2-9 shows that there are only three stable nuclides which could be changed to another stable nuclide by the (n, p) reaction. These are Te^{123}, La^{138}, and Ce^{138}. The product of La^{138} is Ba^{138}, a "magic number" nucleus (see Chap. 9). If we consider the trend of the data points of Fig. 2-9 to define a rough curve of neutron/proton stability ratios, then clearly most of the products of (n, p) reactions are on the excess-neutron side of the curve. The neutron/proton balance can be restored in these cases by β^- emission. In the case of the other nuclides, one can only say that β^- emission restores the nuclide to its original condition.

6-15 Selection of Neutrons in a Given Energy Range

It is often desired to study the effects of neutrons as a function of their energy. In other cases, one wishes to measure the energies of neutrons from a certain reaction. Since neutrons cannot be deflected in magnetic and electrostatic fields as charged particles are, nor accelerated by an electric field to a desired energy, other means have been devised for obtaining monoergic beams or for sorting out the effects in a narrow energy interval.

Filtering. There is a maximum value of λ for a particular crystal beyond which it is not possible to get a diffraction maximum (see Prob. 6-8). Thus if the neutron beam from a nuclear fission reactor is filtered through polycrystalline graphite, neutrons having wavelengths less than the critical wavelength will be diffracted out of the beam and the remaining neutrons will be subthermal neutrons. In this way Anderson, Fermi, and Marshall (3) observed neutrons whose energy was only about $18°K$.

Fission. Fast neutrons may be obtained from a nuclear reactor by placing some uranium in the thermal neutron beam and utilizing the fast neutrons released in the fission process.

Velocity selector. Another method for selecting neutrons of a given energy range from a heteroergic beam is to use a device somewhat like the Fizeau toothed wheel. Such a device is called a *velocity selector*. In its most elemental form it consists of two cadmium disks, separated from each other but mounted on a common shaft. Cadmium is used because of its unusually large absorption cross section for thermal neutrons (see Fig. 6-16), a fact which makes it possible to absorb a very large fraction of thermal neutrons with thin sheets of the metal. These disks have openings cut in them with the opening of the second offset angularly from the first, so that a neutron coming through the first opening would be stopped by the second cadmium disk if it were not turning. When both disks are rotating, only those neutrons whose velocity is such that they just travel the distance separating the disks in the time it takes for the second disk opening to rotate into the beam will be able to get past the second disk. If fast neutrons are present in the beam, paraffin may be placed between the two disks and a helical slot cut through the paraffin connecting the two openings. The paraffin slows down the fast neutrons so that they are unable to pass through the second cadmium disk. Since the slowed-down neutrons will be scattered and may pass through the second opening, it is better to make a cylinder of alternate layers of paraffin and cadmium, the layers being perpendicular to the axis of rotation, and cut a helical slot through the cylinder for the desired velocity group to follow.

Time-of-flight spectrometer. A somewhat different approach is the time-of-flight spectrometer. In this method a pulse of neutrons is created by

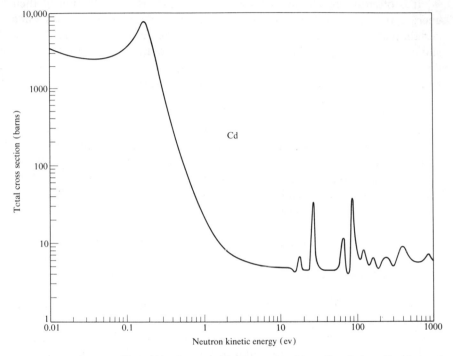

Fig. 6-16. This curve illustrates the very high cross sections of cadmium for thermal neutrons. The total cross section (scattering plus absorption) is given, but scattering contributes only 1% to the total cross section at 0.25 ev and even less at smaller energies. [Data taken from "Neutron Cross Sections," BNL 325 (1955).]

rotating a shutter in a neutron beam (10, 24) or by pulsing a particle accelerator so that a target is bombarded for only a short interval of time. The neutron detector is then connected to an electronic circuit which registers signals only during a short interval synchronized with the pulsing of the neutron beam. In this way neutrons of higher energy and of lower energy reach the counter either too soon or too late to be recorded. It is possible with this system and sufficient recording channels to study several velocity intervals all at the same time simply by altering the time during which each channel will register signals from the neutron detector.

Charged-particle reactions. Monoergic neutrons may be produced by certain bombardment reactions. In this way almost the entire energy spectrum can be obtained by bombarding thin targets with charged particles of continuously variable energy. The energy also depends, of course, on the angle which the path of the emitted neutron makes with the direction of the incident charged-particle beam. Figure 6-17 shows the variation in neutron

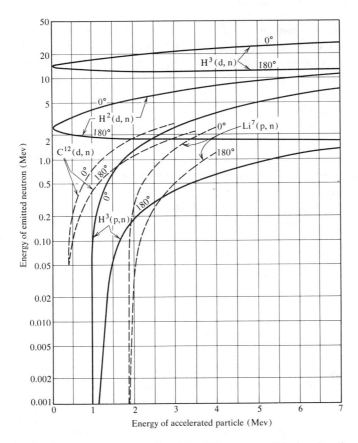

Fig. 6-17. Emitted neutron energy as a function of the energy of the bombarding particle for several reactions commonly employed to obtain neutrons for experimental work. For each reaction, the neutron energies which would be observed in the direction of the beam (0°) and at 180° to this direction are given. Intermediate energies may be obtained by observing the neutrons at some other angle. [From A. O. Hanson and R. F. Taschek, "Monoenergetic Neutrons from Charged Particle Reactions," Preliminary Report No. 4, Nuclear Science Series (Washington, D.C.: National Research Council).]

energies which may be obtained from various charged-particle reactions as a function of the energy of the impinging charged particle.

Threshold detector. It is sometimes possible to use the highest-energy neutrons from a heteroergic source if the threshold of the detector is at the lower limit of the high-energy group. Examples of such threshold detectors are Cu^{63}, which has a threshold of about 11 Mev for the Cu^{63} $(n, 2n)Cu^{62}$ reaction, the Cu^{62} having a half-life of 10 minutes, and a corresponding reaction in C which has a threshold of about 21 Mev and produces an activity with a half-life of 20.5 minutes.

Proportional counter. Feld (21) has suggested a somewhat different method of recording only those neutrons having a narrow velocity range. If a proportional counter is filled with a gas which suffers (n, p) reactions, such as $N^{14}(n, p)C^{14}$ or $Cl^{35}(n, p)S^{35}$, then the total energy released each time a neutron is absorbed is the sum of the Q value for the reaction and the kinetic energy of the neutron, so that the pulse amplitude from the proportional counter will be a linear function of the neutron energy. Electronic pulse-height discriminators, which will accept pulses only if they are within a given amplitude range, would enable one to record only those counts due to neutrons in the corresponding energy interval.

A proportional counter of this type, which has been rapidly developed since He^3 became more readily available, utilizes the $He^3(n, p)$ reaction. This reaction has a Q of 770 Kev. Unfortunately, the elastic scattering cross section for neutrons scattered by He^3 is roughly twice the cross section for the (n, p) reaction in the 0 to 2.5 Mev region. Since the maximum energy imparted to the recoiling He^3 in an elastic collision is three-fourths of the kinetic energy of the impinging neutron, elastic scattering does not interfere with measurements where only monoergic neutrons are concerned. Where the neutron beam is not monoergic or where there is a large neutron background, the (n, p) peaks may be masked or overlapped by the elastic recoil spectrum.

Although elastic collisions were spoken of as a disadvantage in the He^3 counter, they form the basis for hydrogen recoil counters. In these, the proportional counter is filled with hydrogen or a hydrogenous gas such as methane or propane. Since the energy imparted to the recoiling proton will vary from 0 (for those that recoil at 90° to the direction of motion of the incident neutron) up to 100 per cent (for those that recoil at 0°) of the incident neutron kinetic energy, the electrical pulses from the proportional counter will be of all sizes up to a maximum size corresponding to the full energy of the neutron. It is this high-energy cutoff which is used as a measure of the incident neutron energy.

PROBLEMS

[*Note:* In Probs. 6-1 and 6-2, use the relativity expressions for the momenta and energies. Remember that the momentum of a photon is $h\nu/c$.]

6-1 What would be the maximum possible energy of the emitted γ ray if the reaction

$$_4Be^9 + {}_2He^4 \longrightarrow {}_6C^{13} + \gamma$$

were possible, the α particle having a kinetic energy of 5 Mev?

[*Ans.* 14.3 Mev.]

6-2 (a) Show that the maximum energy which may be transferred from a γ ray whose energy is $h\nu$ to a proton of mass M_p in a Compton collision is

$$W = \left(\frac{2}{2 + M_p c^2 / h\nu}\right) h\nu.$$

(b) What is the maximum energy which a 10-Mev γ ray may impart to a proton at rest? [*Ans.* (b) 0.21 Mev.]

6-3 Li^7 is bombarded by 2-Mev protons, and a neutron is observed coming off at an angle of 90° to the path of the incident proton. What is its energy?

[*Ans.* 75 Kev.]

6-4 What would be the range in air at NTP of a 100-Mev Ba^{140} fission fragment nucleus, if it lost energy in the same manner as a lower-energy α particle? A 4.0-Mev α particle has a range, in air at NTP, of 2.55 cm. (This is actually not a valid assumption, but it gives a correct order of magnitude.)

[*Ans.* 0.68 mm.]

6-5 One might suppose the most probable mode of fission to be that in which a maximum amount of mass is transformed to energy. On this basis, what would be the most probable ratio of the masses of the two fragments in binary fission if one assumes that the isotopic masses can be computed from a packing fraction curve which is a linear function of the mass number, A, in the region concerned? [*Ans.* 1.]

6-6 Estimating the masses of the fission fragments from the packing fraction curve, what would be the amount of energy released in fission of U^{238} into approximately equal fragments by a fast neutron? [*Ans.* 250 Mev.]

6-7 At what glancing angle of incidence will 0.3-ev neutrons be diffracted in the first order by a crystal in which the reflecting planes are 1.5 Å apart?

[*Ans.* 10° 2′.]

6-8 What will be the maximum energy (in ev) of thermal neutrons filtered through a long polycrystalline plug of graphite in which the maximum spacing of the reflecting planes is 3.34 Å? [*Ans.* 0.0018 ev.]

6-9 With what energy must a deuteron strike a triton, which is initially at rest, to give a 20-Mev neutron in the forward direction? Compare your calculated answer with the value you obtain from Fig. 6-17.

6-10 Show that the threshold energy (minimum kinetic energy of the bombarding particle which can possibly cause the reaction when the struck nucleus is initially at rest) in an endoergic reaction is given by

$$W_{th} = \left(\frac{M_3 + M_4}{M_3 + M_4 - M_1}\right) Q,$$

where M_1 is the mass of the bombarding particle, M_3 and M_4 are the masses of the product particles, and Q is the difference between the mass energy of the product particles and the mass energy of the reactants.

6-11 What is the most probable speed of a neutron in thermal equilibrium with its surroundings at $18°K$? [Ans. 543 m/sec.]

6-12 (a) Calculate the magnetic force exerted by a proton at rest on a neutron at rest beside it if their spin axes are parallel and 3×10^{-13} cm apart. (b) The neutron and proton in a deuteron nucleus are bound together with an energy of 2.225 Mev. In other words, 2.225 Mev of work would have to be expended to separate a deuteron into its constituents. What fraction of this binding energy would be accounted for on the basis of the magnetic interaction assumed in (a)? [Ans. (a) 5.04×10^4 dynes; (b) 0.14%.]

6-13 Using Robson's data and the mass of H^1, what is the mass of the neutron? [Ans. 1.008983 amu.]

6-14 An evacuated container is placed in a reactor, operating at $27°C$, in which the average neutron "flux" is 10^{15} per sec-cm². Assuming that the neutrons travel with an average velocity of $(2/\pi) \times 2200$ m/sec, what will be the pressure of hydrogen gas in the container after 1 year of irradiation? The "flux" in a reactor is defined as $N\bar{v}$, where N is the number of free neutrons/cm³ and $\bar{v}$ is the average neutron velocity in cm/sec.

[Ans. 4.11 dynes/cm².]

6-15 According to Oliphant (Sec. 6-12), when Li^7 was bombarded by 0.2-Mev deuterons, α particles with a maximum energy of 8.3 Mev were observed. What does this give for the Q of the reaction? [Ans. $Q = 13.4$ Mev.]

6-16 The Q of the He^3 (n, p) reaction is reported to be 0.770 Mev. From this and the fact that the maximum energy of β particles emitted by tritium is 0.018 Mev, calculate the mass difference between the neutron and a hydrogen atom (H^1). [Ans. 0.000846 amu.]

6-17 How thick must a sheet of cadmium (density 8.65 gm/cm³) be in order to absorb 99.99% of normally incident 0.01-ev neutrons? [Ans. 0.283 mm.]

REFERENCES

1. Alvarez, L. W., *Phys. Rev.*, **74**, 1217 A (1948).

2. Alvarez, L. W., and Pitzer, K. S., *Phys. Rev.*, **55**, 596 (1939); **58**, 1003 (1940).

3. Anderson, H., Fermi, E., and Marshall, L., *Phys. Rev.*, **70**, 102 (1946).

4. Auger, P., *Compt. Rend.*, **194**, 877 (1932).

5. Bloch, F., *Phys. Rev.*, **50**, 259 (1936); **51**, 994 (1937).

6. Bloch, F., Hamermesh, M., and Staub, H., *Phys. Rev.*, **64**, 47 (1943).

7. Bloch, F., Nicodemus, D., and Staub, H., *Phys. Rev.*, **74**, 1025 (1948).

8. Bothe, W., and Becker, H., *Z. Physik*, **66**, 289 (1930).

9. Breit, G., and Wigner, E., *Phys. Rev.*, **49**, 519 (1936).

10. Brill, T., and Lichtenberger, H. V., *Phys. Rev.*, **72**, 585 (1947).

11. Chadwick, J., *Nature*, **129**, 312 (1932); *Proc. Roy. Soc.*, **A136**, 692 (1932).

12. Chadwick, J., and Goldhaber, M., *Nature*, **134**, 237 (1934).

13. Curie, Irène, *Compt. Rend.*, **193**, 1412 (1931).

14. Curie, I., and Joliot, F., *Compt. Rend.*, **194**, 273 (1932).

15. Curie, I., and Joliot, F., *Compt. Rend.*, **194**, 708, 876 (1932).

16. Curie, I., and Joliot, F., *Compt. Rend.*, **198**, 254 (1934).

17. Curie, I., and Savitch, P., *J. Phys. Radium*, **8**, 385 (1937); **9**, 355 (1938).

18. Dee, P. I., *Proc. Roy. Soc.*, **A136**, 727 (1932).

19. Diebner and Grassmann, *Kunstliche Radioactivität* (Leipzig: S. Hirzel, 1939).

20. Feather, N., *Proc. Roy. Soc.*, **A136**, 709 (1932).

21. Feld, B. T., *Phys. Rev.*, **70**, 429 (1946).

22. Fermi, E., *Nature*, **133**, 757 (1934).

23. Fermi, E., *Nature*, **133**, 898 (1934).

24. Fermi, E., Marshall, J., and Marshall, L., *Phys. Rev.*, **72**, 193 (1947).

25. Fermi, E., and Zinn, W. H., *Phys. Rev.*, **70**, 103 (1946).

26. Fields, P. R., Friedman, A. M., Milsted, J., Atterling, H., Forsling, W., Holm, L. W., and Aström, B., *Phys. Rev.*, **107**, 1460 (1957).

27. Frisch, O. R., *Nature*, **143**, 276 (1939).

28. Gardner, W. L., Knable, N., and Moyer, B. J., *Phys. Rev.*, **83**, 1054 (1951).

29. Hahn, O., and Strassmann, F., *Naturwissenschaften*, **27**, 11 (1939).

30. Hahn, O., and Strassmann, F., *Naturwissenschaften*, **27**, 89 (1939).

31. Halban, H., and Preiswerk, P., *Compt. Rend.*, **203**, 73 (1936).

32. Halpern, O., *Phys. Rev.*, **75**, 343 (1949).

33. Halpern, O., Hamermesh, M., and Johnson, M. H., *Phys. Rev.*, **59**, 981 (1941).

34. Halpern, O., and Johnson, M. H., *Phys. Rev.*, **55**, 898 (1939).

35. Hamermesh, M., *Phys. Rev.*, **75**, 1766 (1949).

36. Hamermesh, M., *Phys. Rev.*, **77**, 140 (1950).

37. Heisenberg, W., *Z. Physik*, **77**, 1 (1932).

38. Hughes, D. J., and Burgy, M. T., *Phys. Rev.*, **76**, 1413 (1949); **81**, 498 (1951).

39. Joliot, F., *Compt. Rend.*, **193**, 1415 (1931).

40. Joliot, F., *Compt. Rend.*, **208**, 647 (1939).

41. Knable, N., Lawrence, E. O., Leith, C. E., Moyer, B. J., and Thornton, R. L., *Phys. Rev.*, **74**, 1217 A (1948).

42. Ladenburg, R., *Phys. Rev.*, **45**, 224 (1934).

43. Lauritsen, C. C., and Crane, H. R., *Phys. Rev.*, **45**, 550 (1934).

44. McMillan, E., and Abelson, P. H., *Phys. Rev.*, **57**, 1185 (1940).

45. Meitner, L., Hahn, O., and Strassmann, F., *Z. Physik*, **106**, 249 (1937).

46. Meitner, L., and Frisch, O. R., *Nature*, **143**, 471 (1939).

47. Mitchell, D. P., and Powers, P. N., *Phys. Rev.*, **50**, 486 (1936).

48. Myssowsky, L., and Zhdanoff, A., *Nature*, **143**, 471 (1939).

49. Noddack, I., *Z. angew. Chem.*, **37**, 653 (1934).

50. Oliphant, M. L. E., *Int. Un. of Pure and Appl. Phys.* (Oct. 24, 1934).

51. Oliphant, M. L. E., Kinsey, B. B., and Rutherford, E., *Proc. Roy. Soc.*, **A141**, 722 (1933).

52. *Physics of Nuclear Fission* (New York: Pergamon Press, 1958). Article by P. G. Erozolimskii, p. 75.

53. Powers, P. N., *Phys. Rev.*, **54**, 827 (1938).

54. Rasetti, F., *Naturwissenschaften*, **20**, 252 (1932).

55. Robson, J. M., *Phys. Rev.*, **78**, 311 (1950); **81**, 297 (1951); **83**, 349 (1951).

56. Ruderman, I. W., *Phys. Rev.*, **76**, 1572 (1949).

57. Rutherford, E., *Proc. Roy. Soc.*, **97**, 374 (1920).

58. Schwinger, J. S., *Phys. Rev.*, **51**, 544 (1937).

59. Schwinger, J. S., and Teller, E., *Phys. Rev.*, **51**, 775 (1937).

60. Shull, C. G., Wollan, E. O., Morton, G. A., and Davidson, W. L., *Phys. Rev.*, **73**, 842 (1948).

61. Smyth, H. D., *Atomic Energy for Military Purposes* (Princeton, N.J.: Princeton University Press, 1946).

62. Snell, A. H., and Miller, L. C., *Phys. Rev.*, **74**, 1217 (1948).

63. Snell, A. H., Pleasonton, F., and McCord, R. V., *Phys. Rev.*, **78**, 310 (1950).

64. Sosnovskii, A. N., Spivak, P. E., Prokof'ev, Iu. A., Kutikov, I. E., and Dobrynin, Iu. P., *J. Exptl. Theoret. Phys. (USSR)*, **35**, 1059 (1958).

65. Steinberger, J., and Wick, G. C., *Phys. Rev.*, **76**, 994 (1949).

66. Strominger, D., Hollander, J. M., and Seaborg, G. T., *Revs. Modern Phys.*, **30**, 585 (1958).

67. *Technical News Bulletin*, National Bureau of Standards, Washington, D.C., January, 1950.

68. Thompson, S. G., Ghiorso, A., and Seaborg, G. T., *Phys. Rev.*, **77**, 838 (1950).

69. Thompson, S. G., Street, K. Jr., Ghiorso, A., and Seaborg, G. T., *Phys. Rev.*, **78**, 298 (1950).

70. Van Vleck, J. H., *Phys. Rev.*, **55**, 924 (1939).

71. Von Droste, G., *Z. Physik*, **110**, 84 (1938).

72. Webster, H. C., *Proc. Roy. Soc.*, **A136**, 428 (1932).

73. Wollan, E. O., Shull, C. G., and Marney, M. C., *Phys. Rev.*, **73**, 527 (1948).

74. Wollan, E. O., and Shull, C. G., *Phys. Rev.*, **73**, 830 (1948).

GENERAL REFERENCES

1. Bacon, G. E., *Neutron Diffraction* (Oxford: Clarendon Press, 1955).

2. Marion, J. B., and Fowler, J. L., *Fast Neutron Physics*, Part I (New York: Interscience Publishers, Inc., 1960).

BETA DECAY

7-1 Dirac's Hole Theory

The relativistic expression for the total energy (including rest energy), W, of a particle whose momentum is p, and whose rest mass is M_0, is

$$W^2 = p^2c^2 + M_0^2c^4 \qquad (7\text{-}1)$$

so that

$$W = \pm\sqrt{p^2c^2 + M_0^2c^4}. \qquad (7\text{-}2)$$

One is tempted merely to discard the negative root as being one without physical significance. If one were to accept this equation with both roots, then he would expect to find particles with positive energies ranging from M_0c^2 to infinity and other particles with energies ranging from $-M_0c^2$ to negative infinity, but no particles of the same kind with energies between $-M_0c^2$ and $+M_0c^2$. The situation as applied to electrons is depicted schematically in Fig. 7-1. A moving particle, in a negative energy state, has even less energy than when it is at rest. If it were moving slowly we could say its kinetic energy was $-M_0v^2/2$. This result and the rest energy of $-M_0c^2$

are both consistent with the idea that the particle behaves as though it had a mass of $-M_0$.

Dirac (18), in 1930, encountered these same negative energy solutions in developing the relativistic wave mechanical treatment of the electron and

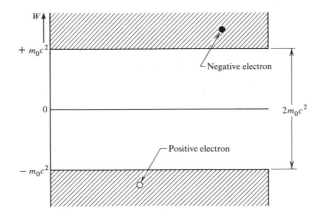

Fig. 7-1. Possible energy states of an electron according to Dirac's theory. It is necessary to assume that all possible negative energy states are normally filled. The circle labeled "positive electron" represents a temporarily vacant negative energy state.

pointed out difficulties in merely excluding such solutions as not being consistent with reality. On the other hand, if such negative energy states are allowed, the results do not seem to correspond to observed phenomena. For example, an electron in a negative energy state, acted on by the "repulsive" force of an electron in a positive energy state, would, because of its effectively negative mass, move *toward* the normal negative electron. Such motion is what one would expect of a positively charged particle. The current, magnetic field, and momentum, by contrast, correspond to a particle of positive charge and mass moving *away* from the normal electron.

If negative energy states were available, one would expect transitions from the positive energy states which would soon remove almost all "normal" electrons.

To avoid these difficulties, Dirac proposed that all, or nearly all, negative energy states, from $-m_0c^2$ to $-\infty$, be considered as filled with electrons. This requires that there be an infinite number of electrons per unit of volume of actual space, but because each electron is uniformly surrounded by electrons there will be no net force acting on an electron due to this "electron sea." Hence electrons in negative energy states are unobservable. If, now, a γ-ray photon gives up its energy to an electron in a negative energy state and raises it to a positive energy state, the vacancy or hole in the electron sea exhibits the properties of a positively charged electron.* This may be illustrated by reference to Fig. 7-2. The hole acts like a positive charge when at rest because it represents a disturbance to the uniformity of the normal negative charge density. When a neighboring electron moves into the vacant energy state, the hole moves in a direction opposite to that of the motion of the electron. Since there is no distinction between the current and the electromagnetic field of a negative charge moving in one direction and that of a positive charge

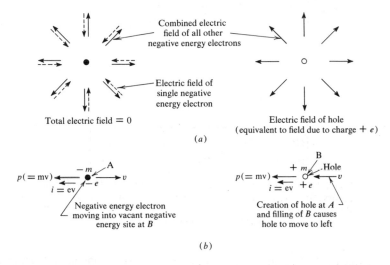

(a)

(b)

Fig. 7-2. Diagrams illustrating the properties of holes. In (a), the unobservability of the negative energy electron requires that its own field be canceled by the fields of all the other negative energy electrons. Therefore, when it is removed, only the field of the other negative energy electrons remains and this field is identical with the field of a positive electron. Diagrams (b) show that the motion of a negative energy electron into a vacant site results in motion of the hole such that the hole appears to be a particle of positive mass and charge.

moving in the opposite direction, the motion of the hole corresponds to the motion of a positive charge in the direction of motion of the hole. While the velocity of the electron is opposite in direction to that of the hole, the momentum of the electron, by virtue of its negative mass, is in the same direction as the velocity of the hole. Therefore the hole acts in all respects like an electron with positive charge and positive mass.

7-2 The Positron

In 1932 Anderson (2), who was studying cosmic ray particles by means of the cloud chamber technique, observed a track which was inconsistent

---

* Dirac originally considered the holes to be protons since these were the only positively charged elementary particles known at that time, but in the 1931 paper (18) he pointed out that they must correspond to positively charged electrons.

with that which would have been produced by any known particle. In his experiment, the cloud chamber was placed in a magnetic field of 15,000 gauss. A 6-mm thick lead plate was placed across the center of the chamber as shown in Fig. 7-3. In this particular event, a track of small curvature extends from the bottom of the chamber to the lower side of the lead plate; another track, of greater curvature, extends from the upper side of the lead plate to the side wall of the chamber. The positions and orientations of the two tracks are

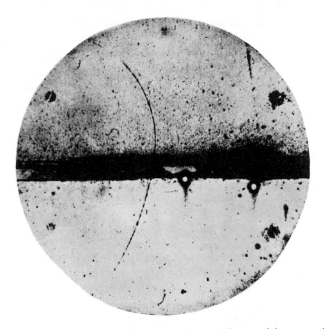

Fig. 7-3. Anderson's (2) positron discovery picture. The particle entered the cloud chamber from below, passed through the lead plate and into the upper half of the chamber with reduced energy (indicated by smaller radius of curvature). A magnetic field perpendicular to and into the page deflected the particle to the left. The direction of the magnetic field shows that the particle must have been positively charged. The positron entered with an energy of 63 Mev ($B\rho = 2.1 \times 10^5$ gauss-cm) and, after passing through the lead plate, had an energy of 23 Mev ($B\rho = 7.5 \times 10^4$ gauss-cm). [From *Phys. Rev.*, **43**, 491 (1933).]

such that they could be parts of the trajectory of a single particle. The fact that the upper track has the greater curvature, and therefore the smaller momentum, is consistent with the view that the particle entered the chamber from below at high speed and lost energy in traversing the lead plate. The *direction* of the particle's motion is thus established. The known direction of the magnetic field showed that the particle must be positively charged. If the particle is assumed to be a proton, then the curvature of its path gives its momentum and hence its energy. The curvature of the path, after traversal of the lead plate, corresponds to an energy of 300 Kev, but a 300-Kev proton has a range in air of only 5 mm whereas the observed range here is greater than 5 cm. If the particle were slowing down appreciably, the curvature of its track would become greater toward the end of its range. The total range would be much greater than the observed 5 cm, therefore, since there is no observable increase in curvature along the track. From this it follows that the particle must be considerably less massive than the proton. Anderson concluded that the particle must be a positive electron and gave to it the name "positron." Anderson (3) also observed, shortly after his discovery of the positron, that pairs of positrons and negatrons often issued from a common point of the lead plate when a collimated beam of gamma radiation was allowed to fall on it. The gamma-ray source in this case was Th^{228} and its products. Such a source yields a large number of 2.6-Mev gamma rays. He found that the combined kinetic energies of the partners in a pair ranged from 1 to 1.8 Mev with only one pair, out of 23 observed, having a kinetic energy greater than 1.6 Mev. This lent some weight to a suggestion of Blackett and Occhialini (6) that a gamma ray might *create* a positron-negatron pair. Conservation of energy would then give (neglecting a small amount of energy associated with momentum conservation),

$$W_{e^+} + W_{e^-} = W_\gamma - 2m_0c^2$$
$$= 2.6 - 2 \times 0.51 \cong 1.6 \text{ Mev.} \tag{7-3}$$

While the experimental proof of the existence of the positron stands on its own merits, it is seen that it is in perfect agreement with the Dirac theory. The observance of positron-electron pairs is an especially strong confirmation of the theory, because the lifting of an electron from a negative to a positive energy state not only makes observable an electron that was not observable before, but also produces a hole that will be detected as a positron.

7-3 Annihilation Radiation

Gray and Tarrant (24), in a 1932 study of the scattering of energetic gamma rays, found two bands of what appeared to be fluorescence radiation at about 0.5 and 0.9 Mev. Blackett and Occhialini pointed out that this might be due to the simultaneous annihilation of a positron and a negatron, and showed that this was in keeping with the Dirac hole theory. Since the energy difference between an electron at rest in a positive and a negative energy state is about 1 Mev, the hole theory predicts that there is a high probability that a normal electron will fall into a hole with the emission of about 1 Mev of radiant energy. The hole, or positron, would be expected to have an extremely short existence, which is probably one of the reasons why positrons were not discovered many years sooner. The probability of combination of a positron and an electron is greater when they have a small relative velocity. Conservation of momentum demands that when the two particles, both of which are moving slowly, combine and are converted to energy, at least two photons be produced.* This two-photon process has been verified by placing a positron emitter such as Cu^{64} between two Geiger counters, as shown in Fig. 7-4. When the positrons combine with electrons, the resulting γ rays move off in opposite directions and some fraction will pass through the two counters. Since they pass through the two counters at the same time, they give rise to a coincidence count, whereas random discharges in the two Geiger tubes will only rarely coincide. The observance of a high coincidence rate when the

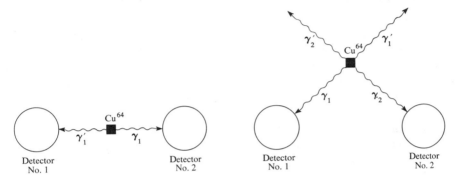

Fig. 7-4. Schematic diagram of arrangement for detecting coincident gamma-ray pairs produced in the annihilation of positrons. If both positron and negatron are virtually at rest when they combine, then conservation of momentum demands that the two gamma rays be collinear. In the upper diagram, coincident gamma rays γ_1 and γ_1 enter both detectors. If both gamma rays are detected, the coincidence circuit will record one event. In the lower diagram, when one gamma ray of a pair (γ_1 or γ_2) enters one detector, the other member of the pair (γ_1' or γ_2') always escapes detection and no coincidences are recorded.

Cu^{64} is between the counters, compared with a small coincidence rate when the Cu^{64} is above the plane of the counters, establishes the existence of the pairs of γ rays. The γ rays produced by the complete conversion of a positive and negative electron to radiant energy are known as *annihilation* radiation. This is the first phenomenon observed in which matter is completely converted to radiant energy.

It cannot readily be proven in the laboratory, but it is generally believed that the positron is a stable particle. The hole theory would predict that if no positive energy electrons were available there would be nothing to fill the vacant negative energy site and that it would persist indefinitely. The relatively great abundance of normal electrons in any piece of laboratory

---

* Infrequently, single-photon annihilation occurs. In this case a third body which can carry away the requisite momentum must be involved. As one would expect, this usually occurs when a K-shell electron is annihilated.

equipment makes it inevitable* that a positron involved in a laboratory experiment will suffer annihilation in a very short time.

As suggested by Mohorovićić (39) in 1934, positrons and negatrons can form a hydrogenlike "atom" in which the two particles move about the center of mass of the system. Ruark (46) called this substance "positronium." Positronium, like the hydrogen molecule, can exist, in its ground state, in two forms. The state in which the spins are parallel, the triplet state, is called "orthopositronium," and the state in which the spins are antiparallel, the singlet state, is called "parapositronium." It is perhaps not quite accurate to refer to these as ground states since there is a still lower energy state, the annihilation state. When one recalls that a hydrogen atom in its ground state has no "orbital" angular momentum, then it is seen that parapositronium has a total angular momentum, including electron spin, of zero. In the process of annihilation, then, since the intrinsic angular momentum of a photon is $\hbar$, two photons of opposite spin, or more than two photons with a total angular momentum of zero, must be emitted. Annihilation in orthopositronium, with a total angular momentum of $\hbar$, must take place with the emission of at least three photons, if angular momentum is to be conserved. Dirac's (19) expression for the annihilation rate of slowly moving holes, written in 1930, before positrons were discovered, is

$$\lambda = C_s \psi_s^2 + C_t \psi_t^2, \tag{7-4}$$

where ψ_s^2 and ψ_t^2 are the electron densities of antiparallel spin and parallel spin electrons, respectively, at the average position of the positron. The interaction rate parameters are given (40) by

$$C_s = 4\pi c \left(\frac{e^2}{mc^2}\right)^2 = 3 \times 10^{-14} \text{ cm}^3/\text{sec} \tag{7-5}$$

and

$$C_t = 4\pi c \left(\frac{e^2}{mc^2}\right)^2 \frac{4\alpha}{9\pi} (\pi^2 - 9)$$

$$= \frac{C_s}{1120} = 2.7 \times 10^{-17} \text{ cm}^3/\text{sec}. \tag{7-6}$$

For a positron in the singlet state, $\psi_t^2 = 0$ and ψ_s^2 may be expressed in terms of the Bohr radius for positronium, which, since the reduced mass is $m/2$, will be

$$a = \frac{2\hbar^2}{me^2}$$

so that

$$\psi_s^2 = \frac{1}{\pi a^3} = \frac{m^3 e^6}{8\pi\hbar^6}.$$

* This difficulty has been partially circumvented by containing positrons in a magnetic "mirror machine." [G. Gibon, W. C. Jordan, and E. J. Lauer, *Phys. Rev. Letters*, **5**, 141 (1960)]. The observed rate at which positrons leak from the containment region is consistent with loss by scattering from residual gas atoms, but if the observed rate of decrease of leakage with time were ascribed wholly to a hypothetical positron decay, the mean life of the positron would have to be at least 5 sec.

The mean lifetime of the singlet state is then

$$t_a = \frac{1}{\lambda} = 1.24 \times 10^{-10} \text{ sec.}$$

An experimentally determined value for two-photon annihilation in Al (4) is

$$(1.5 \pm 0.3) \times 10^{-10} \text{ sec.}$$

For a positron in the triplet state, $\psi_s^2 = 0$ and $\psi_t^2 = 1/\pi a^3$ so that

$$t_a = 1.39 \times 10^{-7} \text{ sec.}$$

Lifetimes of the order 10^{-7} sec have been obtained by Deutsch (16) who showed that the gamma rays in this case form a continuous spectrum as expected for three-photon annihilation. Three-photon decay has been more directly established (15) by triple-coincidence experiments. Positronium decay has turned out to be a rather complex subject and the measured lifetimes are

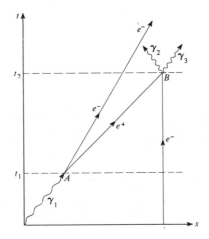

Fig. 7-5. Here, events are shown conventionally. A gamma ray strikes a target at A producing a positron-negatron pair. The positron meets a negatron at rest at B and they undergo mutual annihilation with emission of gamma rays γ_2 and γ_3.

quite variable. A number of interesting experiments have been done on such effects as Zeeman splitting. It has also been used (38) as a means of measuring the electron density in different parts of a molecule in the liquid state. In general, these experiments are in the field of atomic rather than nuclear physics, but the intensity of the optical spectral lines from positronium (because of its extraordinarily low concentrations) is too small to be measured by present-day techniques. What one actually measures is the annihilation radiation using the methods and techniques of nuclear physics.

Although Dirac's hole theory has been spectacularly successful, many physicists are dissatisfied with the *concept* of a space densely filled with negative energy electrons. An alternative hypothesis which agrees equally well with experiment has been put forward by Stueckelberg (50) and developed in detail by Feynman (22). According to this theory, a positron is an electron moving *backward in time*. The idea is most easily illustrated with an *x-t*

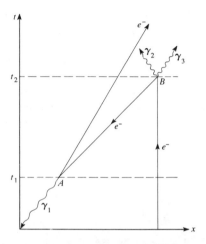

Fig. 7-6. The event shown conventionally in Fig. 7-5 is shown now as the motion of a single electron. An electron, initially at rest, is scattered backward in time at *B* toward *A* with the emission of two "bremsstrahlung" rays, γ_2 and γ_3. At *A* the electron is again scattered, this time forward in time with the emission of a bremsstrahlung gamma ray, γ_1, which travels backward in time from *A* toward the origin. Both schemes conserve charge and the particles appear at the same place at the same time in each representation. Note, however, in this figure that a single electron, at times between t_1 and t_2, exists simultaneously at three different places.

diagram as shown in Figs. 7-5 and 7-6. The concept of a single electron moving backward and forward in time leads to simpler mathematical formulations of electron interactions than does the hole theory. Since either view is consistent with experiment the reader may choose that one which he finds most appealing esthetically.

7-4 Orbital Electron Capture

We have already mentioned the doubly remarkable discovery of induced radioactivity. This phenomenon had been sought in many laboratories over a period of years but had not been found, perhaps because detection equipment was used which was sensitive to the expected protons rather than the positrons which were actually emitted. It is remarkable also in that what was finally discovered was a new type of decay, positron emission. Other investigators had all the equipment and materials at hand necessary to confirm Curie and Joliot's discovery and did so immediately* when they knew what to look for.

Positron decay may be represented as follows:

$$Z^A \longrightarrow (Z - 1)^A + e^+ + e^-, \qquad (7\text{-}7)$$

the e^- being a spare orbital electron which is not needed by the product atom. Since the isotopic masses given in tables are the masses of *neutral* atoms, the mass of Z^A must exceed that of $(Z - 1)^A$ by the equivalent of at least 1.02 Mev ($2m_0c^2$). An energetically more favorable process would be one in which the nucleus absorbs one of its own orbital electrons. In this case there is no spare orbital electron after the process is finished, and the mass of Z^A need exceed the mass of $(Z - 1)^A$ only by an infinitesimal amount.

How would one detect such a decay process? The first thing which suggests itself is that the residual nucleus might be left in an excited state which would emit detectable gamma rays. If the residual nucleus were left in its ground state, this method would fail. The capture of an orbital electron would leave a vacancy, the filling of which would cause the atom to emit x-rays or Auger electrons. The x-rays would be those characteristic of the *residual* atom rather than of the parent atom. Alvarez (1), in 1937, first observed such x-rays and was able to identify them by their absorption coefficients. Electron capture occurs most often from the K shell and is then referred to as K capture. Less frequently, L, M, etc. electrons are captured. If one assumes that the interaction between electron and nucleus involves a short-range nuclear force, then the interaction volume will be comparable to the volume occupied by the nucleus itself. In this case the situation would be very similar to that encountered in total internal conversion where the probability of internal conversion is dependent on the probability of finding an electron within the

---

* Livingston (35) relates the following story. "I recall the day early in 1934 (February 24) when Lawrence came racing into the lab waving a copy of the *Comptes Rendus* and excitedly told us of the discovery of induced radioactivity by Curie and Joliot in Paris, using natural alpha particles on boron and other light elements. They predicted that the same activities could be produced by deuterons on other targets, such as carbon. Now it just so happened that we had a wheel of targets inside the cyclotron which could be turned into the beam by a greased joint, and a thin mica window on a re-entrant seal through which we had been observing the long-range alpha particles from deuteron bombardment. We also had a geiger point counter and counting circuits at hand. We had been making 1-minute runs on alpha particles, with the counter switch connected to one terminal of a double-pole knife-switch used to turn the oscillator on and off. We quickly disconnected this counter switch, turned the target wheel to carbon, adjusted the counter circuits, and then bombarded the target for 5 minutes. When the oscillator switch was opened this time, the counter was turned on, and click–click—click——click——click. We were observing induced radioactivity within less than a half-hour after hearing of the Curie-Joliot results."

nuclear volume. It was seen in Fig. 5-18 that the probability of finding a K-shell electron within the nuclear volume is greater than that of finding an L_I electron, which in turn is more probable than finding an M_I electron and very much more probable than finding an L_{II} electron. As the atomic number, Z, increases, the electrons move closer to the nucleus so one would expect the probability of electron capture to increase with increasing Z. All of these expectations are in agreement with experimental observations. As in internal conversion, there are cases where capture of an L, M, etc. electron is energetically possible but where there is insufficient energy to allow K capture. In such cases, obviously, it will no longer be true that K capture predominates since no K electrons are captured. Examples of nuclides, presumably of this kind, in which only the L x-rays have been observed (44) are $_{78}Pt^{193}$ and $_{82}Pb^{205}$. As pointed out earlier, electron capture is often energetically possible where positron decay is not. $_4Be^7$, $_{24}Cr^{51}$, $_{31}Ga^{67}$, and $_{49}In^{111}$ are examples of nuclei that decay exclusively by electron capture.

7-5 Energy Spectrum of Beta Rays

It will be remembered that in the magnetic deflection experiments of des Coudres (Fig. 1-4) the deflected β rays were spread out over a considerable portion of the photographic plate, while the α rays, which were deflected by a much stronger magnetic field, formed a sharp line on the plate. It was thought at first that the spreading of the β rays was due to a variation in velocity caused by scattering and slowing down in passing out of the radioactive material. Experiments with thin films of β emitters subsequently showed that there was a variation in β-ray energy even when scattering and slowing down could not have taken place.

Internal conversion peaks. A typical β spectrum has been shown in Fig. 5-16. It will be noticed that it consists of sharp peaks of intensity for certain discrete energies superposed on a continuous spectrum of β-ray energies. The peaks are due to internal conversion electrons ejected in the de-excitation of nuclei left in an excited state by prior beta decay.

The continuous beta-ray spectrum. Since the peaks on the β-ray spectrum are due to internal conversion electrons, let us concentrate our attention on the primary beta-ray spectrum. It is found that the difference in mass of the parent and daughter nuclides in a β decay corresponds to the maximum energy of the observed β rays, but since very few β rays have this maximum energy, where does the remaining energy go when a β ray of smaller energy is emitted from the nucleus? It could possibly be given to the recoiling nucleus, but if the parent nucleus were initially at rest, then there is only one proportion in which the energy could divide between the electron and recoil nucleus if momentum is conserved. It might be supposed that in such cases the daughter nucleus was left in an excited state and that it then emitted the remaining energy as a γ ray. β emitters do not emit a *continuous spectrum* of γ rays of the required energies although they do emit a continuous spectrum of much lower energy. Calorimetric experiments (19, 36) to determine the total energy given off in the β decay of Bi^{210} show that the energy is just what would be expected from integrating the area under the β-ray energy-spectrum curve. It would almost seem that the law of conservation of energy just does not apply to the process of β emission.

Conservation of energy is not the only difficulty raised by the process of β decay. If a nuclide of even mass number (and therefore having an integral nuclear spin quantum number) undergoes β decay, it emits an electron with spin $\frac{1}{2}$ and becomes another nuclide of even mass number and integral nuclear spin, so that the whole system, electron plus daughter nucleus, now has an odd half-integral spin where before it had integral spin. (Since the orbital electrons are only loosely bound to the nucleus, we may consider the disintegration of the nucleus to be independent of them.) Hence the angular momentum of the system would *appear* not to be conserved in β decay. When β decay occurs, one would expect the residual nucleus to recoil in order that linear momentum be conserved. The great mass of the nucleus, relative to the electron mass, leads to a small recoil energy so that it is difficult to measure the nuclear recoil momentum. In cloud chamber photographs (11), for example, the track made by the recoiling nucleus is a mere "blob." A satisfactory experimental test to find whether linear momentum is conserved in β decay did not occur for many years.

7-6 The Neutrino

Conservation of energy and momentum require that the particles emitted in a two-body decay be monoergic—as observed, for example, in the case of alpha decay. By contrast, a three-body decay would allow the electrons to be emitted with a continuous energy spectrum extending from zero to a definite maximum value. Pauli (41) suggested, in 1933, that β decay was such a three-body process, the three bodies being the electron, the residual nucleus, and a new hypothetical particle to which he gave the name "neutrino." Some of the necessary characteristics of the neutrino, if it were to be compatible with known facts, could be specified at once. Since charge is already conserved in β decay without introducing the neutrino, the latter must be a neutral particle. The fact that the maximum energy of beta-decay electrons is, within experimental uncertainty, equal to the difference between the mass energy of the parent and daughter atoms, means the mass energy and hence the mass of the neutrino must be considerably less than that of an electron. Its spin must be $\frac{1}{2}$ or some larger half-integral value in order that angular momentum be conserved in beta decay. If it has a magnetic moment it must be very small, since the calorimetric experiments failed to detect any measurable energy corresponding to the absorption or slowing down of such particles.

In beta decay, the neutrino energy spectrum should be continuous, extending, like the electron energy spectrum, from zero up to approximately the same maximum energy as that of the electron spectrum.* In K capture, on the other hand, as long as the residual nucleus is left in the same energy state, the neutrinos would have to be monoergic, as this would be a two-body decay, the two bodies being the neutrino and the recoiling product nucleus.

It is possible that just as the positron is the antiparticle to the negatron, an antineutrino exists which is the antiparticle of the neutrino. If one adopts the hypothesis that a particle cannot be created without the simultaneous creation of an antiparticle, then the particle accompanying negatron decay would be called an antineutrino. This would correspond to the conversion of a neutron into a proton according to the scheme

$$n^0 \longrightarrow p^+ + e^- + \bar{\nu}, \tag{7-8}$$

while positron decay would be represented by

$$p^+ \longrightarrow n^0 + e^+ + \nu, \tag{7-9}$$

where ν represents a neutrino and $\bar{\nu}$ an antineutrino. The meanings attached to these names are sometimes interchanged, partly because the neutrino was originally conceived of in connection with negatron decay. In a later section of this chapter we shall look into the question as to whether there is any distinction between a neutrino and an antineutrino.

An early attempt to test the neutrino hypothesis was made by Leipunski (34) in 1936. He studied the velocity spectrum of the positive recoil ions resulting from positron decay of C^{11}. The C^{11}, in the form of carbon monoxide or carbon dioxide, was adsorbed on a plate. Recoil positive ions ejected outward from the plate were decelerated by an electrical field established between this plate and a grid. Those particles with kinetic energies greater than the electrical work done in moving from plate to grid (i.e., qU) passed through the grid, were accelerated by a 5000-volt potential difference, and struck a metallic plate which then emitted secondary electrons. The secondary electrons were detected by a Geiger counter. The velocity distribution obtained showed more high-velocity recoils than would have been expected for two-body beta decay (where low-energy electrons would have been associated with low-velocity recoil ions). The results, although not conclusive, were at least consistent with the neutrino hypothesis.

A more definitive experiment was carried out by Sherwin (48) in 1948.

---

* The maximum neutrino energy and maximum electron energy would be exactly equal if it were not for the fact that the energies imparted to the recoiling particles, though very small fractions of the total decay energy, are different in the two cases.

A schematic diagram of the apparatus which he used is shown in Fig. 7-7. His results are shown in Fig. 7-8. In this case the recoil ions from beta decay of P^{32} were studied. Again, it seems necessary to admit the emission of a neutrino if one is to understand the recoil ion energy spectrum.

Davis (13) has measured the positive ion recoil energy spectrum of Be^7. Since Be^7 decays by orbital electron capture, the recoil ions should be monoergic. His results, shown in Fig. 7-9, exhibit a single peak near the high-energy end of the spectrum. This is evidence for the emission of a single

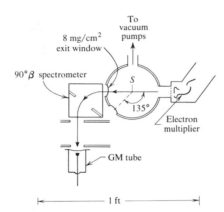

Fig. 7-7. Schematic diagram of apparatus used by Sherwin (48) to test for apparent conservation of momentum in beta decay. The source S is a thin layer of P^{32} vaporized onto a blown glass film (0.4 mg/cm²). The layer of P^{32} faces the electron multiplier, so that the recoil S^{32} ions can reach the multiplier with a minimum loss of energy. Those beta particles emitted in a direction opposite the electron multiplier lose only a small amount of energy in traversing the glass film. The vacuum in the source chamber is maintained at about 10^{-7} mm Hg. The beta particles leave the source chamber, pass through a 90° spectrometer, and are detected by a GM tube with a thin end window. A Kurie plot of the beta spectrum is straight above $B\rho = 3600$ gauss-cm. which shows that the effect of passing through the thin windows and the air between the source chamber and GM tube is unimportant for momenta greater than that corresponding to $B\rho = 3600$. The pulse produced by the GM tube initiates a 17-microsecond sweep on a cathode ray tube. The arrival of a recoil S^{32} ion produces another electrical pulse which intensifies the beam of the cathode ray tube and produces a dot. These dots are recorded on a moving photographic film. The displacement of a dot is a measure of the time of flight and hence of the momentum of a recoil S^{32} ion. The momentum of the beta particle is determined by the setting of the 90° spectrometer.

neutrino rather than several neutrinos in a single electron capture decay. Since one can detect the recoil of the positive ion, he is almost forced to assume that an undetected particle (neutrino) is emitted in the capture process.

A number of more recent experiments of the so-called "neutrino-recoil" type have been made, but these are no longer made with the idea of testing for the existence of neutrinos. Rather, they are concerned with angular correlation of the electron and recoil ion. These studies are directed at testing aspects of beta-decay theory.

Beginning in 1953, Reines and Cowan (42) and their collaborators at Los Alamos began to obtain more direct evidence for the reality of the

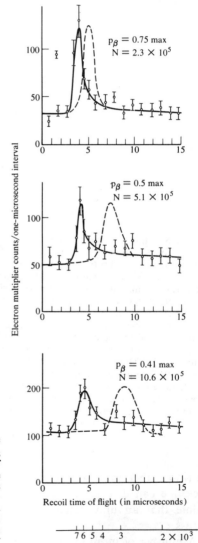

Fig. 7-8. Momentum spectra of recoil S^{32} ions observed by Sherwin (48) for various beta momenta. N is the total number of betas detected in obtaining each curve, while p_β is the momentum of the beta particles passed through the 90° spectrometer, expressed as a fraction of the maximum beta momentum of P^{32} electrons. The dotted curve in each case gives the momentum spectrum anticipated if the apparent linear momentum were conserved.

neutrino. They looked for a reaction which is essentially a reversal of the neutron decay reaction. Thus

$$p^+ + \bar{\nu} \longrightarrow n^0 + \beta^+$$

would be a reaction conserving energy, momentum, spin, particles, and anti-particles. The reaction is clearly closely akin to orbital electron capture which may be represented as $p^+ + \beta^- \longrightarrow n^0 + \nu$. The fission fragments

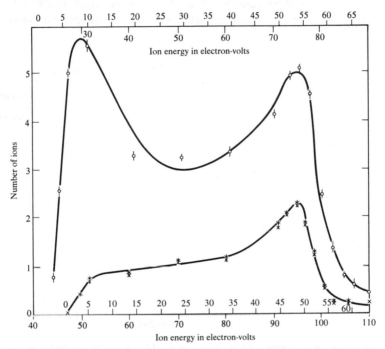

Fig. 7-9. Recoil ion spectrum resulting from electron capture in Be[7]. The upper curve gives the raw data, while the lower curve is a plot of corrected values. Single neutrino emission should result in monoergic recoil ions. The single peak in the observed spectrum near the upper energy limit has been interpreted by Davis (13) as evidence in favor of single neutrino emission. The ions in this case were accelerated by a 46-volt potential difference so that, if singly charged, their total energies are 46 ev greater than their recoil energies. The numbers given just above the ion energies are presumed, on this basis, to be the recoil energies. The scales at the top of the figure refer to the upper curve, those at the bottom to the lower curve.

produced in a nuclear reactor are all negatron emitters so a nuclear reactor produces a large flux of antineutrinos.

The calorimetric experiments show that the cross section for the $p(\bar{\nu}, \beta^+)$ reaction must be very small, so that one would not expect many events of this type per unit time. Since one always has background effects due to radio-active contamination of equipment, cosmic rays, and reactor leakage neutrons and gamma rays, the experimental problem becomes one primarily of distinguishing neutrino-induced events from background. A schematic diagram of the apparatus used by Reines and Cowan is shown in Fig. 7-10. Five large flat tanks were used, the outer ones and the central one being liquid scintillators, the other two reaction tanks containing water with a small amount of dissolved cadmium chloride. If an antineutrino from the reactor converts one of the protons in a water molecule to a neutron plus a positron, then the positron will be quickly slowed down in the water and will undergo annihilation with an electron, producing, in most cases, two oppositely

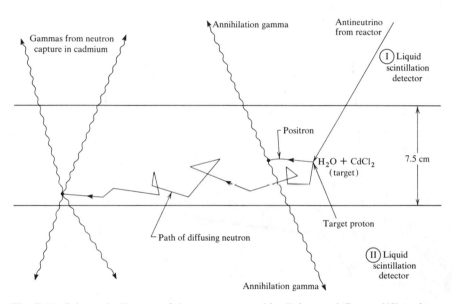

Fig. 7-10. Schematic diagram of the apparatus used by Reines and Cowan (42) to detect the free antineutrino. The central part represents one of the two target tanks. There was another one below the scintillation tank number 2 and another scintillation tank below the second target tank. Scintillation tank number 2 served in common as part of both the upper and lower triads. The target tanks were 1.9 m × 1.3 m × 0.075 m and were filled with water containing a small amount of dissolved $CdCl_2$. The scintillation tanks were each 1.9 m × 1.3 m × 0.61 m thick and were filled with triethylbenzene containing terphenyl and a wavelength shifter, POPOP.

directed 0.51-Mev gamma rays. The neutron loses energy by scattering and diffuses through the water until captured by a cadmium nucleus, which then emits a cascade of gamma rays with a total energy of 9.1 Mev. Acceptable events are those in which coincident scintillations of magnitude expected from 0.51-Mev gamma rays are observed in the upper and lower scintillation tanks, followed, within 0.75 to 25.75 microseconds, by a coincident pair of scintillations corresponding to a total gamma-ray energy of 3 to 10 Mev. An acceptable sequence of such pulses, as seen on an oscilloscope, is shown in Fig. 7-11. Of course, not all neutrino events would be detected in this setup. For example, if the annihilation gammas were emitted at such an angle that they did not pass into the scintillator tanks, or if the neutron leaked out of the target tank before being captured by a cadmium nucleus, then the event would not be counted. The sizes of the tanks were chosen such as to reduce the number of neutrino events not counted to the extent that this was possible without an undue increase in the number of background events recorded. The target tanks used were 1.9 m × 1.3 m × 0.075 m thick while

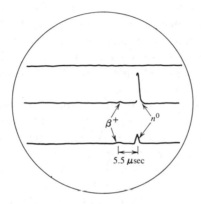

Fig. 7-11. Typical oscilloscope traces as observed by Reines and Cowan (42). The center trace records scintillations from the central scintillation tank and the outer traces those from the outer scintillation tanks. Here the pulses from the annihilation gammas are followed after an interval of 5.5 microseconds by pulses from the neutron capture gammas. Since the latter are much larger than the former, an amplifier gain suitable for the neutron capture gammas gives quite small annihilation gamma pulses. A second oscilloscope with a higher-gain amplifier was used to obtain a more certain indication of the annihilation signals. Had the neutrino capture taken place in the other target tank, the pulses would have appeared on the upper pair of traces.

the scintillation tanks were 1.9 m × 1.3 m × 0.61 m thick. The scintillation liquid consisted of terphenyl and POPOP (a wavelength shifter) dissolved in triethylbenzene. Each scintillator tank was viewed from the ends by 110 Dumont 5-in. photomultiplier tubes. The entire tank assembly was shielded by lead and paraffin and located deep underground near one of the Savannah River reactors.

After 1371 hours of operation, part of the time with the reactor running and part of the time with the reactor off, a reactor-dependent signal of 2.88 ± 0.22 counts/hour was obtained. The ratio of signal to reactor-independent background was 3:1 while the ratio of signal to reactor-associated accidental background was better than 20:1. This is a marked improvement over the 1953 experiment which yielded a count rate of 0.4 ± 0.2 counts per minute with a signal to background ratio of 1:20.

Because the proton in a deuterium nucleus is bound to the neutron with a binding energy of about 2.2 Mev, the threshold for the $d(\bar{\nu}, \beta^+)$ reaction should be higher than that for the $p(\bar{\nu}, \beta^+)$ reaction. It was expected that this would reduce the effective cross section of the $d(\bar{\nu}, \beta^+)$ reaction by more than a factor of 10. The principal effect of substituting heavy water for some of the ordinary water would accordingly be to reduce the density of unbound protons. When the free proton density was thus reduced to one-half its former value, the reactor-associated count rate was also reduced by a factor of two. The efficiency of detection of neutrons from a polonium-beryllium source was unchanged by the dilution, thus increasing one's confidence in the interpretation that the reactor-associated signal is truly connected with an antineutrino-induced reaction.

A second such test consisted in substituting pure water for the cadmium chloride solution in the target tanks. When this was done the reactor-associated count rate became zero. When a strong americium-beryllium neutron source was placed near the tanks, very few acceptable delayed coincidences were observed. When extra shielding in the form of bags of wet sawdust with an attenuation factor of at least 10 for reactor neutrons and gamma rays was placed between the tanks and the reactor, no change in reactor-associated count rate greater than normal statistical fluctuations was observed. All of these things give us considerable confidence that neutrinos not only exist, as was so long expected, but that they also interact weakly with matter. The mean cross section for the $p(\bar{\nu}, \beta^+)$ reaction using fission reactor antineutrinos is $(11 \pm 2.6) \times 10^{-44}$ cm^2.

7-7 Theory of Beta Decay

It is not possible to do complete justice to this subject here, since the theory involves relativistic wave mechanics which is beyond the scope of the book. We must accordingly be content with a description of the theory and a comparison of some of its predictions with experimental results.

In Dirac theory, a system is described by a set of four wave functions instead of a single wave function as in Schrödinger theory. This leads not only to more complex equations but also to a greater number of possible types of interaction between particles, so that even today we are not absolutely sure of which type or combination of types is the correct one, although the situation has been clarified a great deal since about 1956. The most general relativistically invariant Hamiltonian density which conserves leptons (the meaning of lepton conservation will be explained in due course) and which does not contain derivatives of the fermion field is given by

$$H = C_S(\bar{\psi}_p\psi_n)(\bar{\psi}_e\psi_\nu) + C_V(\bar{\psi}_p\gamma_\mu\psi_n)(\bar{\psi}_e\gamma_\mu\psi_\nu)$$
$$+ \tfrac{1}{2}C_T(\bar{\psi}_p\sigma_{\lambda\mu}\psi_n)(\bar{\psi}_e\sigma_{\lambda\mu}\psi_\nu) - C_A(\bar{\psi}_p\gamma_\mu\gamma_5\psi_n)(\bar{\psi}_e\gamma_\mu\gamma_5\psi_\nu)$$
$$+ C_P(\bar{\psi}_p\gamma_5\psi_n)(\bar{\psi}_e\gamma_5\psi_\nu) + [\text{hermitian conjugates of these}], \qquad (7\text{-}10)$$

where, in the context of quantum field theory, the $\bar{\psi}_p$, $\bar{\psi}_n$, $\bar{\psi}_e$, and $\bar{\psi}_\nu$ are creation operators for the proton, neutron, electron, and neutrino respectively, while the ψ_p, ψ_n, ψ_e, and ψ_ν are the annihilation operators. The destruction of a neutrino is considered to be equivalent to the creation of an antineutrino. Each term in Eq. (7-10) thus represents the annihilation of a proton and the creation of a neutron, an electron, and an antineutrino. The ψ are each column matrices consisting of four functions and the $\bar{\psi}$ are their hermitian conjugates. The γ_μ, γ_5, and $\sigma_{\lambda\mu}$ are 4×4 matrices. The C_S, C_V, C_T, C_A, and C_P are called the *coupling constants* and bear the following names and symbols:

$$S = \text{scalar},$$
$$V = \text{vector},$$
$$T = \text{tensor},$$
$$A = \text{axial vector},$$
$$P = \text{pseudoscalar}.$$

These names describe the quantities such as $(\bar{\psi}_p\gamma_\mu\psi_n)$ and their transformation properties. The products $(\bar{\psi}_p\psi_n)$ and $(\bar{\psi}_p\gamma_5\psi_n)$ are both single functions but differ in that the second changes sign under a spacial inversion while the first does not. Since they involve single functions they are called *scalar* $(\bar{\psi}_p\psi_n)$ and *pseudoscalar* $(\bar{\psi}_p\gamma_5\psi_n)$. Each of the products $(\bar{\psi}_p\gamma_\mu\psi_n)$ and $(\bar{\psi}_p\gamma_\mu\gamma_5\psi_n)$ consists of a set of four functions, one for each value of the index μ. The four functions making up a set may be looked upon as the components of a vector in four-space. The second again changes sign under a spacial inversion while the first does not, so $(\bar{\psi}_p\gamma_\mu\psi_n)$ is called *vector* and $(\bar{\psi}_p\gamma_\mu\gamma_5\psi_n)$ is called *axial vector*. The product $(\bar{\psi}_p\sigma_{\lambda\mu}\psi_n)$ consists of 16 functions, one for each value of the index $\lambda\mu$. It may be looked upon as a tensor of the second rank, hence the name *tensor*.

The inversion properties of these functions can be illustrated by some simple examples. An inversion consists of replacing the x-, y-, and z-axes of a coordinate system by a set of axes along the negative x-, negative y-, and negative z-directions. This is equivalent to replacing the x-axis by one along the negative x-axis and then rotating the y,z-plane about the x-axis through an angle of 180°. When, as is often the case, the 180° rotation is not important, it is more convenient to look upon the inversion in this way. Any situation, looked at from the coordinate system with the x-axis inverted, will look like the image of the system as seen in a mirror in the y,z-plane. A scalar quantity, such as the length of a vector, will be the same after inversion as before. A vector, however, has its sense reversed by the operation [see Fig. 7-12(a)] so that a vector function changes sign under inversion. An axial vector, such as angular momentum [Fig. 7-12(b)], unlike a true vector, does not change sign under inversion. A pseudoscalar, such as the dot (scalar) product of a vector,

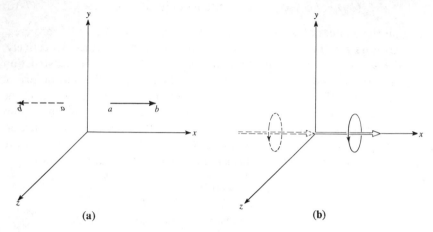

Fig. 7-12. (a) A vector in the x-direction has its sense reversed by reflection in the y,z-plane. This is equivalent to an inversion, in a particular coordinate system in which the x-axis is parallel to the vector.

(b) The sense of an axial vector remains the same after a reflection in the y,z-plane. If the axial vector represents the angular momentum of a spinning body, it is clear that the image will spin in the same direction as the object itself, so the angular momentum "vector" would be unchanged.

r, and an angular momentum, **ω**, unlike a true scalar, changes sign under inversion since the **r** becomes $(-\mathbf{r})$ while **ω** remains unchanged.

Electromagnetic coupling was known to be of the vector type, so Fermi (21) guessed in his 1933 paper that beta decay could also be represented by vector-type interaction. Fermi's result applies only to "allowed" transitions, that is, those in which there is no change in nuclear spin or parity. The other interactions have selection rules for allowed transitions as shown in Table 7-1.

Table 7-1

Fermi transitions $\Delta I = 0$ No change in nuclear parity		Gamow-Teller transitions $\Delta I = 0, \pm 1$ (not $0 \to 0$) No change in nuclear parity	
S	V	T	A

It has since been shown that, to a high degree of approximation, all five forms of allowed interaction lead to the same energy spectrum.

The principal factor in determining the shape of allowed beta spectra is the so-called *statistical weight*, which is the density of possible states available in momentum space. If the electron is ejected with momentum between p and $p + dp$ while the neutrino is given a momentum between p_ν and $p_\nu + dp_\nu$, then the total number of states available to the electron is proportional to the volume of a spherical shell in momentum space of radius p and thickness dp, that is,

$$4\pi p^2 dp.$$

The actual number of states will be determined, within a finite multiplicative constant, by the Heisenberg uncertainty principle, since the position and momentum of a particle cannot be specified to an extent greater than

$$(\Delta x\, \Delta p_x)(\Delta y\, \Delta p_y)(\Delta z\, \Delta p_z) \cong h^3. \tag{7-11}$$

If one considers the interaction to take place in some volume u, then

$$\Delta p_x\, \Delta p_y\, \Delta p_z \cong \frac{h^3}{u} = \epsilon^3 \tag{7-12}$$

where $\epsilon = h/u^{1/3}$. If the spherical shell of thickness dp is divided up into cubical cells of volume ϵ^3, then the total number of states available in phase space to an electron with momentum between p and $p + dp$ will be

$$dn_e = \frac{4\pi p^2\, dp}{\epsilon^3}. \tag{7-13}$$

Similarly, the total number of states available in phase space to a neutrino with momentum between p_ν and $p_\nu + dp_\nu$ will be,

$$dn_\nu = \frac{4\pi p_\nu^2\, dp_\nu}{\epsilon^3}. \tag{7-14}$$

If the momentum distributions of electrons and neutrinos were independent, the probability of finding an electron in the momentum interval p to $p + dp$ and of simultaneously finding a neutrino in the momentum interval p_ν to $p_\nu + dp_\nu$ would be

$$P\, dp\, dp_\nu = \frac{p^2\, dp \cdot p_\nu^2\, dp_\nu}{\int_0^{p_{\max}} \int_0^{p_{\nu\max}} p^2\, dp\, p_\nu^2\, dp_\nu}. \tag{7-15}$$

The momenta of electrons and neutrinos are not independent, however, as they are related through the energy equation

$$W_0 = W_e + W_\nu + \bar{W}_n \tag{7-16}$$

where W_0 is the total energy released in the decay plus the mass energy of an electron, W_e is the total energy of the emitted electron including its mass energy, W_v is the total energy of the emitted neutrino, and $\bar{W}_n$ is the kinetic energy of the recoiling nucleus. If one neglects $\bar{W}_n$ and assumes that the neutrino has no rest mass, then

$$W_0 \cong W_e + p_v c \qquad (7\text{-}17)$$

so that
$$p_v = \frac{W_0 - W_e}{c}. \qquad (7\text{-}18)$$

If W_0 could be specified precisely, then for each electron momentum there would be a precisely known neutrino momentum. Thus, if W_e is expressed in terms of p, Eq. (7-18) represents a curve on a p,p_v-plane and the interpretation of $dp\, dp_v$ as an area in this plane, as implied in (7-15), loses its meaning. On the other hand, if W_0 is uncertain* by an amount $\pm\Delta W_0$, then there will

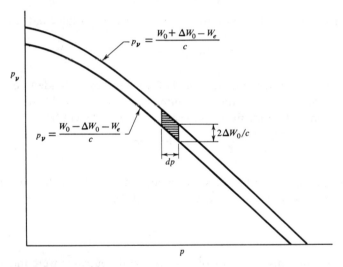

Fig. 7-13. A plot of the neutrino momentum, p_v, versus the electron momentum, p, for the two limiting cases of "conservation of energy," $p_{v-} = (W_0 - \Delta W_0 - W_e)/c$ and $p_{v+} = (W_0 + \Delta W_0 - W_e)/c$. For a given electron momentum, p, the simultaneously emitted neutrino must have a momentum lying between the upper and lower curves at that value of p. For electron momenta which lie between p and $p + dp$, the associated neutrino and electron momenta will be points lying within the crosshatched area.

* The uncertainty ΔW_0 as introduced here is a mathematical artifice, since the final result is independent of the magnitude of ΔW_0. In wave mechanical perturbation theory, on the other hand, the energy of the decaying nucleus must be uncertain by some amount in order that the probability of decay not be zero. The Heisenberg uncertainty principle also requires that $\Delta W_0 \tau \cong h$, where τ is the mean lifetime of the decaying nucleus.

be two bounding curves in the p,p_v-plane, as shown in Fig. 7-13, one corresponding to

$$p_v = \frac{W_0 + \Delta W_0 - W_e}{c}$$

and the other to

$$p_v = \frac{W_0 - \Delta W_0 - W_e}{c}$$

so that the electron and neutrino momenta may lie anywhere in the area between these two bounding curves. Equation (7-15) can then be revised to give the probability of finding an electron with momentum between p and $p + dp$. The result is

$$P' \, dp = \frac{p^2 \, p_v^2 (2\Delta W_0 c) \, dp}{\int_0^{p_{\max}} p^2 p_v^2 \, (2\,\Delta W_0/c) \, dp}$$

$$= \frac{p^2 p_v^2 \, dp}{\int_0^{p_{\max}} p^2 p_v^2 \, dp},$$

$$P' \, dp = Gp^2(W_0 - W_e)^2 \, dp, \tag{7-19}$$

where

$$G^{-1} = c^2 \int_0^{p_{\max}} p^2 p_v^2 \, dp = \int_0^{p_{\max}} p^2(W_0 - W_e)^2 \, dp, \tag{7-20}$$

is a constant which depends only on W_0. Since $W_e^2 = p^2 c^2 + m^2 c^4$,

$$p \, dp = \frac{W_e \, dW_e}{c^2}$$

so that (7-19) may also be written as

$$P'' \, dW_e = G'p W_e(W_0 - W_e)^2 \, dW_e, \tag{7-21}$$

where $G' = G/c^2$.

There is no a priori reason to believe that only one neutrino is emitted in beta decay, but if one assumes that more than one is emitted then the statistical weight is changed in such a way that the theory does not agree well with experimental spectra. Conservation of angular momentum in neutron decay requires that the neutrino have a spin of $\frac{1}{2}$ or $\frac{3}{2}$. If it had a spin of $\frac{3}{2}$ the statistical weight would be proportional to

$$p^2(W_0 - W)^4 \, dp,$$

which again is in disagreement with experiment. Thus the shape of the beta momentum spectrum shows, without reference to any exact theory of the interaction involved, that beta decay consists of the emission of a single neutrino of spin $\frac{1}{2}$.

In a typical momentum spectrum, such as that shown in Fig. 5-16, the curve approaches the momentum axis parabolically at the high-momentum end of the spectrum. Since the spectrum is very weak in this region, the statistical accuracy of the measurements is inherently low. As a result, it is difficult from such a plot to determine the maximum decay energy with satisfactory precision.

The original form of the theoretical momentum distribution obtained by Fermi has been recast by Kurie, Richardson, and Paxton (29) into a form which, if the Fermi theory is correct, allows experimental data for allowed transitions to be fitted by a straight line. The Kurie plot is advantageous not only because it is easier to fit data to a straight line than to a curve, but also because the intersection of this straight line with the energy axis gives the total decay energy W_0 or $W_0 - mc^2$, depending on whether the data is plotted against W or $W - mc^2$. It should be remembered, however, that the rest mass of the neutrino was assumed to be zero in this formulation, so that the decay energy is uncertain by an amount equal to the rest energy of the neutrino. In most cases this uncertainty is less than the other experimental uncertainties.

The Kurie forms of the beta energy distribution are

$$\frac{N(p)\, dp}{F(Z, W)p^2} = K(W_0 - W)^2\, dp \tag{7-22}$$

or

$$\frac{N(W)\, dW}{F(Z, W)pW} = K'(W_0 - W)^2\, dW, \tag{7-23}$$

where the subscript has now been dropped from W_e, $N(p)$ is the fraction of beta particles per unit momentum interval having momenta near p, $N(W)$ is the fraction per unit energy interval having energies near W, K and K' are constants, and the "Fermi function," $F(Z, W)$, which takes account of the coulomb field of the nucleus, is given by

$$F(Z, W) = \frac{2(2pr)^{2s-2}e^{\pi\alpha ZW/p}|\Gamma(s + i\alpha ZW/p)|^2(1 + s)}{[\Gamma(2s + 1)]^2}, \tag{7-24}$$

where r is the nuclear radius,

$$s = (1 - \alpha^2 Z^2)^{1/2}, \tag{7-25}$$

$\alpha(=\frac{1}{137})$ is the fine structure constant, and $\Gamma(\ )$ is a gamma function. Z is the atomic number of the residual nucleus in the case of negatron emitters. For positron emitters Z is the negative of the atomic number. Figure 7-14 gives $mcpF/W$ as a function of p/mc for several values of Z. The effect of the orbital electrons on the spectrum is not included in Fermi's theory but has been treated by others (36, 43, 45). The effects are important only at the low-energy end of the spectrum. To use these equations, one simply plots*

$$\left[\frac{N(p)}{F(Z, W)p^2}\right]^{1/2} \quad \text{or} \quad \left[\frac{N(W)}{F(Z, W)pW}\right]^{1/2}$$

against W.

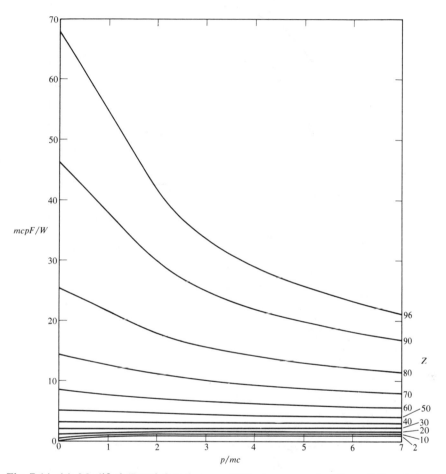

Fig. 7-14. (a) Modified Fermi function $mcpF/W$ given as a function of the electron momentum p/mc. The numbers given at the right are the atomic numbers of the product nuclei. Applies to negatron emitters only.

* In the literature it is common to plot a quantity containing a term N without defining what is meant by N. If a beta scintillation counter with constant channel width is used, the number of counts per channel is proportional to $pN(p)/W$, or in other words to $N(W)$. When a magnetic spectrometer is used in which the magnetic field is varied, the number of counts, N', is proportional to $pN(p)$, so that one then plots $[N'/p^3F]^{1/2}$. One may also encounter $[N(p)/f]^{1/2}$. For a given nuclide, this differs from $[N(p)/p^2F]^{1/2}$ only by a constant.

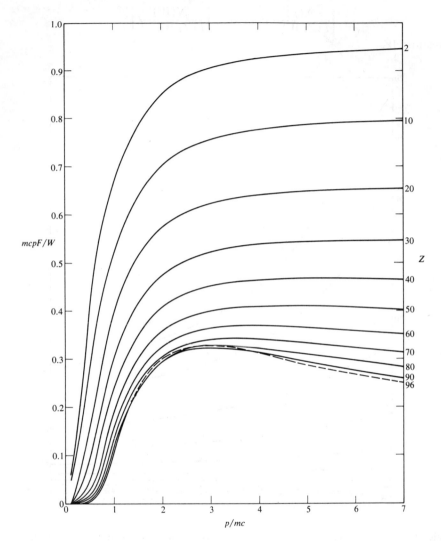

Fig. 7-14. (b) Modified Fermi function for positron emitters. [Data taken from Rose, M. E., Dismuke, N. M., Perry, C. L., and Bell, P. R., Oak Ridge National Laboratory Report No. 1222.]

For many years experimental results from beta spectra gave results which often conflicted with each other or with theory. These difficulties were caused by energy losses suffered by the electrons in traversing sources of finite thickness. They were cleared away beginning in 1939 with the work of Lawson and Cork (31) on In^{114}. The effect of even very thin sources on the observed spectrum is nicely demonstrated by Fig. 7-15.

Since the half-lives of beta-active nuclei are very sensitive to the decay energy, the half-lives themselves are not a good indication of whether a

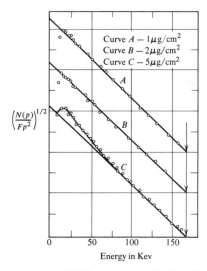

Fig. 7-15. Beta spectra of S^{35} obtained by R. D. Albert and C. S. Wu [*Phys. Rev.*, **74**, 847 (1948)] using a solenoidal magnetic spectrometer. The thickest source used (Curve C) is still very thin but already shows the effects of scattering of the low-energy electrons suffered in passing through the source material itself. The vertical scales have been displaced for ease of comparison. The energy axis of Curve B is on the second line and that of Curve C on the third line.

particular decay is allowed or forbidden. (The terms *allowed* and *forbidden*, whose meanings will become clearer as the discussion progresses, are defined by the selection rules of Table 7-3.) A much better quantity is the so-called "comparative half-life." This quantity, which is almost universally designated as ft, is the product of

$$f(Z, W_0) = \frac{(mc^2)^5}{c} \int_{mc^2}^{W_0} F(Z, W) \, pW(W_0 - W)^2 \, dW \qquad (7\text{-}26)$$

and the half-life $t \equiv t_{1/2}$. Graphs of $f(Z, W_0)$ are given by Rose (49). It is found that the ft values for allowed transitions fall into two groups, the first of which may be called the *normal allowed* group and the second the *superallowed* group. For the normal allowed group

$$\log ft = \begin{cases} 4.0 \text{ to } 5.7 \text{ for } A \text{ even.} \\ 4.5 \text{ to } 6.0 \text{ for } A \text{ odd.} \end{cases}$$

The superallowed transitions have $\log ft$ values close to $\log ft = 3.5$.

Table 7-2 VALUES OF ft

A. Superallowed Transitions Between Mirror Nuclei

Z	Nuclide	Mode of decay	$t_{1/2}$	Energy (Mev)	$Log_{10} ft$
0	n^1	β^-	12 ± 1.5 m	0.780	3.11
1	H^3	β^-	12.26 y	0.0185	3.05
6	C^{11}	β^+	20.4 m	0.98	3.59
7	N^{13}	β^+	10.13 m	1.24	3.67
8	O^{15}	β^+	118 s	1.68	3.57
9	F^{17}	β^+	66 s	1.75	3.44
10	Ne^{19}	β^+	19 s	2.2	3.26
11	Na^{21}	β^+	23 s	2.5	3.58
12	Mg^{23}	β^+	11 s	2.95	3.53
14	Si^{27}	β^+	4.9 s	3.8	3.62
16	S^{31}	β^+	2.6 s	4.42	3.52
18	A^{35}	β^+	1.83 s	5.0	3.67
22	Ti^{43}	β^+	0.58 s	(5.4?)	3.40

B. Superallowed Transitions of Type $N = Z \leftrightarrow N = Z \pm 2$

2	He^6	β^-	0.82 s	3.5	2.89
5	B^{12}	β^-	0.022 s	13.43	3.84
6	C^{10}	β^+	19.1 s	1.9	3.10
8	O^{14}	β^+	74 s	1.83	3.52
9	F^{18}	β^+	1.87 h	0.65	3.58
13	$Al^{26}*$	β^+	6.6 s	3.2	3.51
19	$K^{38}*$	β^+	0.95 s	5.1	3.59

C. Other Transitions (Allowed and Forbidden)

3	Li^8	β^-	0.86 s	13	5.6
4	Be^{10}	β^-	2.5×10^6 y	0.557	13.65
6	C^{14}	β^-	5.6×10^3 y	0.156	9.02
7	N^{17}	β^-	4.14 s	3.7	3.78
10	Ne^{23}	β^-	40.2 s	4.40	5.11
15	P^{32}	β^-	14.3 d	1.71	7.90
20	Ca^{45}	β^-	164 d	0.254	6.01
30	Zn^{69}	β^-	52 m	0.90	4.41
43	Tc^{99}	β^-	2×10^5 y	0.29	12.34
55	Cs^{135}	β^-	2.0×10^6 y	0.21	13.07
55	Cs^{138}	β^-	32 m	3.4	7.13

In the half-lives given above, s = second, m = minute, h = hour, d = day, y = year.

These transitions take place between mirror nuclei (i.e., $N = Z \pm 1 \longrightarrow N = Z \mp 1$, where N is the neutron number, the upper sign applying to negatron, the lower to positron decay) or between nuclei either of which has $N = Z$ while the other has $N = Z \pm 2$. Values of ft for a number of beta-emitting nuclides are given in Table 7-2.

Prior to 1949, the spectrum of Bi^{210} (RaE) was the only one found that was not of the "allowed" shape (i.e., the only one that did not give a straight-line Kurie plot). Not all of the observed transitions were allowed, but those that were not allowed were first forbidden transitions in which $\Delta I = 0$ or 1, and these still may give spectra of the "allowed" shape. The advent of high-flux nuclear reactors permitted the production of high specific activities of substances decaying via more highly forbidden transitions, and it was soon found that many of these did not exhibit the "allowed" shape.

A particularly interesting type of forbidden spectrum is the so-called "unique forbidden" spectrum. This type of spectrum is obtained whenever $\Delta I = n + 1$, where n is the order of forbiddenness. The selection rules for interactions of different degrees of forbiddenness are given in Table 7-3.

Table 7-3 SELECTION RULES FOR BETA DECAY

	Fermi Transitions			Gamow-Teller Transitions		
	Matrix elements	ΔI	Parity change	Matrix elements	ΔI	Parity change
Allowed	$\left\|\int 1\right\|$	0	no	$\left\|\int \sigma\right\|$	0, ± 1 (No $0 \rightarrow 0$)	no
First forbidden	$\left\|\int r\right\|, \left\|\int \alpha\right\|$	0, ± 1 (No $0 \rightarrow 0$)	yes	$\left\|\int \sigma \cdot r\right\|$	0	yes
				$\left\|\int \sigma \times r\right\|, \left\|\int \alpha\right\|$	0, ± 1 (No $0 \rightarrow 0$)	yes
				B_{ij}	0, ± 1, ± 2 (No $0 \rightarrow 0$, $1 \longleftrightarrow 0$, $\frac{1}{2} \rightarrow \frac{1}{2}$)	yes
Second forbidden	R_{ij}, A_{ij}	± 1, ± 2 (No $1 \longleftrightarrow 0$)	no	T_{ij}, A_{ij}	± 2	no
	$\left\|\int \alpha \times r\right\|$	± 1	no	S_{ijk}	± 2, ± 3 (No $0 \longleftrightarrow 2$)	no
				$\left\|\int \alpha \cdot r\right\|$	$0 \rightarrow 0$	no

SOURCE: Konopinski (28).

It will be seen at once that not only changes in nuclear spin and parity are involved but also matrix elements. It is, accordingly, frequently impossible to tell from the spin and parity changes, even when known, what the degree of forbiddenness is, although the ft value may be of help in some cases.

One may define a "shape factor" for a beta spectrum as that function, $w(W)$, which results in a straight-line Kurie type plot when

$$\left[\frac{N(W)}{w(W)\,F(Z,\,W)\,pW}\right]^{1/2}$$

is plotted against W. If one ignores the nuclear coulomb effects, which amounts to letting $Z = 0$ so that $F(Z,\,W)$ is a constant, then the shape factors for unique spectra are:

First forbidden:

$$w_1 = (W^2 - 1) + (W_0 - W)^2; \tag{7-27}$$

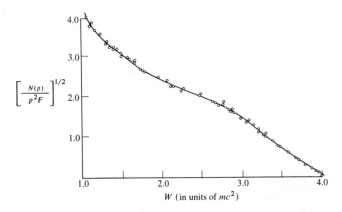

Fig. 7-16. (a) A Kurie plot of the Y^{91} beta spectrum. It departs quite appreciably from the straight line expected for an allowed transition.

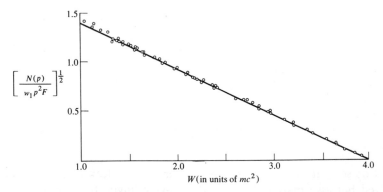

(b) The same data as shown in (a) but now plotted using the unique first forbidden shape factor w_1. [From L. M. Langer and H. C. Price, *Phys. Rev.*, **75**, 1109 (1949).]

Second forbidden:

$$w_2 = (W^2 - 1)^2 + (W_0 - W)^4 + \tfrac{10}{3}(W^2 - 1)(W_0 - W)^2; \qquad (7\text{-}28)$$

Third forbidden:

$$w_3 = (W^2 - 1)^3 + (W_0 - W)^6 + \\ 7(W^2 - 1)(W_0 - W)^2[(W^2 - 1) + (W_0 - W)^2]; \qquad (7\text{-}29)$$

where W and W_0 are now expressed in units of mc^2. A Kurie plot of the spectrum of Y^{91} is shown in Fig. 7-16. It is seen that the shape factor w_1 gives a good straight-line plot, so it is assumed that this is a unique first forbidden transition. Figure 7-17 shows the unique second forbidden spectrum of Be^{10},

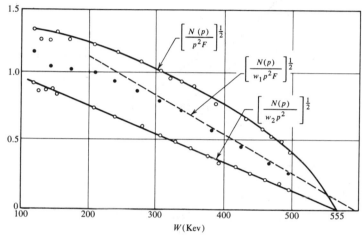

Fig. 7-17. Beta spectrum of Be^{10} obtained by Wu and Feldman [*Rev. Mod. Phys.*, **22**, 386 (1950)]. The standard Kurie plot is far from a straight line. Application of the unique first forbidden shape factor gives a better but not satisfactory fit, while the unique second forbidden shape factor gives an almost perfect straight line.

a case where the nuclear spin changes by 3 ($\Delta I = 3$) with no change in parity. The unique third forbidden spectrum of K^{40}, a case in which $\Delta I = 4$ and the parity changes, is shown in Fig. 7-18. Unlike the allowed spectra, whose shapes are determined principally by the statistical weight and which therefore do not provide a sensitive test of the Fermi theory, the forbidden spectra give strong confirmation of the Fermi theory and additionally provide information on the types of coupling involved.

7-8 Helicity of Electrons and Neutrinos

If one ignores pseudoscalar coupling (P), which should be unimportant as long as the nuclear recoil velocity is small compared with the velocity of light and for which there is no experimental evidence, then one sees from Table 7-1 that it might be possible to use a combination of S and T or one of V and A which would work for both Fermi and Gamow-Teller allowed transitions. A great deal of experimentation has been carried out over the years in an effort to find whether such a combination of interactions exists, but up

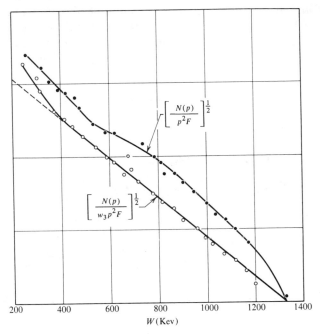

Fig. 7-18. The beta spectrum of K^{40} as obtained by Feldman and Wu [*Rev. Mod. Phys.*, **22**, 386 (1950)]. In this case the unique third forbidden shape factor yields the most nearly rectilinear plot.

until 1956 the answer had not been found. Up until that time, theorists had been convinced that parity was conserved in beta decay. Parity here refers to the whole system, which, after the transition, consists of a beta particle, a neutrino, and the residual nucleus.

In 1956 Lee and Yang (32) showed that the beta-decay experiments that had been performed up to that time were incapable of determining whether parity was or was not conserved. They suggested several experiments that would differentiate between parity-conserving and nonparity-conserving interactions. One of these was a study of the angular distribution of decay electrons from oriented nuclei. It was shown that the general form of the intensity distribution is

$$\Phi(\theta)\, d\theta = \text{const}\, (1 + \kappa \cos\theta) \sin\theta\, d\theta, \tag{7-30}$$

where θ is the angle between the nuclear spin axis of the oriented nuclei and the direction of emission of the beta particle. If parity is conserved, κ must be zero. Wu *et al.* (51) observed the beta decay of Co^{60} which was grown as a thin layer (about 0.002 in. thick) of cerium magnesium (cobalt) nitrate on the upper surface of a good single crystal of pure cerium magnesium nitrate. This crystal was placed in a cryostat as shown in Fig. 7-19. A solenoid around the outside of the cryostat could be raised to magnetize the crystal and thus align the Co^{60} nuclei with their spins pointing up or down as desired. The beta particles were detected by a $\frac{3}{8}$-in. diameter by $\frac{1}{16}$-in. thick anthracene scintillation crystal, the scintillations being conducted out of the cryostat to an external photomultiplier tube by a long Lucite light pipe, as shown. The degree of orientation of the nuclei was monitored by observing the asymmetry between gamma-ray emission at 90° and as near 0° as was mechanically possible. It is evident from Eq. (7-30) that the integrated intensity of beta rays received in a cone of half-angle θ from a point source, when the nuclear spins are pointing upward, is

$$\int_0^\theta \Phi(\theta) \, d\theta = \text{const} \left[1 - \left(\cos\theta - \frac{\kappa}{2} \sin^2\theta \right) \right], \qquad (7\text{-}31)$$

while that with the nuclear spins pointing downward is

$$\int_{\pi-\theta}^\pi \Phi(\theta) \, d\theta = \text{const} \left[1 + \left(\cos\theta - \frac{\kappa}{2} \sin^2\theta \right) \right]. \qquad (7\text{-}32)$$

The observed asymmetry is shown in Fig. 7-20. As the crystal warms up the degree of nuclear orientation decreases, as indicated by the decrease in gamma-ray asymmetry, and the beta asymmetry gradually disappears. These results not only demonstrate that parity is not conserved in beta decay, but indicate that parity violation is large, perhaps maximal. As of 1960, the experimental evidence was in favor of *V-A* coupling in allowed beta decay. Some of the evidence that supports this conclusion is given in the discussion that follows, and still further support from the field of high energy physics is given in Chap. 11. It is seen from Table 7-1 that this choice is capable of accommodating both Fermi and Gamow-Teller allowed transitions. The situation regarding forbidden beta transitions is less certain.

It was pointed out by several investigators (12, 27, 30, 33) in 1957 that parity violation should lead to the emission of beta particles by unaligned nuclei that are longitudinally polarized. By "longitudinally polarized" one means that the electron spin is parallel to its direction of motion. A number of terms including *handedness, chirality, screw-sense,* and *spirality* have been used to describe the longitudinal polarization of particles with spin, but the term that has been used most widely is *helicity.* Helicity is defined as the cosine of the angle between the spin vector and the linear momentum vector. The helicity is $+1$ if the forward motion and spin of the particle are those of a right-hand screw.

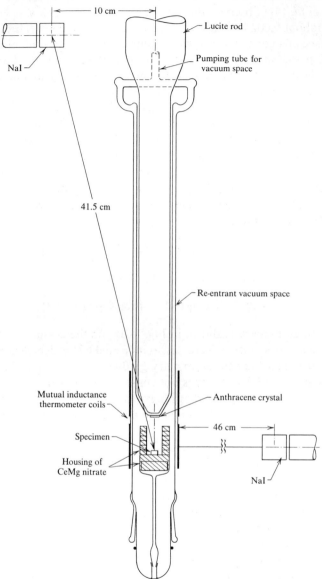

Fig. 7-19. Diagram of the lower part of the cryostat used by Wu *et al.* (51) to search for asymmetry in the beta decay of oriented nuclei.

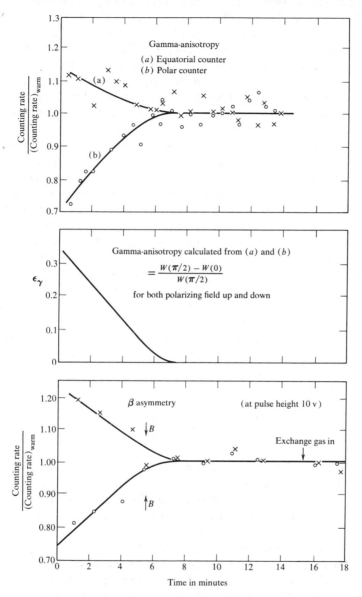

Fig. 7-20. Asymmetry in beta-decay counting rate between the cases where the magnetizing field was up or down. The degree of polarization is indicated by the anisotropy of the gamma emission. As the sample warms up, the degree of polarization decreases and both gamma anisotropy and beta asymmetry decrease.

Cox *et al.* (10) in 1928 scattered beta rays from radium through 90° using a Au or Pb scatterer. The particles were then scattered a second time through 90° in a direction perpendicular to the plane determined by the incident and scattered beam of the first scattering. They found a slight asymmetry between the number of particles scattered to the right and to the left of this plane. Chase (9), a student of Cox, refined this experiment and found a smaller asymmetry (about 3 parts in 100). In Cox's analysis of the experiment he said ". . . it should be remarked of several of these suggested explanations of the observations that their acceptance would offer greater difficulties in accounting for the discrepancies among the different results than would the acceptance of the hypothesis that we have here a true polarization due to the double scattering of asymmetrical electrons. This latter hypothesis seems the most tenable at the present time. It is necessary to suppose further that the polarization is also selective, the effect being manifest only in the faster beta particles." Critics of this work objected to (1) the use of thick scatterers which could produce plural and multiple scattering, (2) the lack of precise collimation of the beam, which allowed scattering from the walls with resulant poor definition of the scattering angles, and (3) the fact that the velocities of the electrons were determined only from absorption measurements. Workers who followed Cox tried to avoid these difficulties by using thin scatterers, well-collimated beams, and *high-voltage electron accelerators as sources* of electrons with well-defined energies. They found no asymmetry, of course, since it is not the electrons that are asymmetric but the beta-decay process.

Curtis and Lewis (12), in their 1957 paper, showed that the helicity of electrons emitted in allowed transitions should be given by

$$\mathcal{H} = \pm\left(\frac{v}{c}\right)\frac{d}{1 + b/W}, \qquad (7\text{-}33)$$

where v and W are the velocity and total energy, respectively, of the electron and d and b are quantities involving the coupling constants. The maximum possible value of d is 1 and the minimum possible value of b is zero. Thus the greatest possible value of $\mathcal{H}$ under any possible choice of coupling constants is $\pm v/c$.

There are several methods for determining the helicity of electrons. Transversely polarized electrons show an asymmetry in scattering (Mott scattering) to the left and to the right. Experiments employing this method must first turn the direction of polarization of the electron through 90° as by passing through a cylindrical electrostatic analyzer (which leaves the spin axis of the electron unchanged but changes the direction of motion by 90°). Longitudinally polarized electrons show an asymmetry when scattered twice in an experiment essentially like that of Cox. Polarized electrons also show asymmetry when scattered by a magnetized foil (Møller scattering). As in neutron scattering, the fringing magnetic fields may produce some depolarization of the beam in this latter method.

Co^{60}, which undergoes a pure G-T transition ($5^+ \longrightarrow 4^+$), has been found to give a polarization ratio (37)

$$\frac{\mathscr{H}}{v/c} = -0.994 \pm 0.057$$

and similar values have been reported by others (5, 8). Sc^{46}, which undergoes a mixed ($F + G$-T) transition ($4+ \longrightarrow 4+$) shows a polarization ratio (17) of -1 ± 0.015. Forbidden transitions show the same helicity as allowed transitions within experimental error. Positrons show a helicity whose magnitude is approximately v/c but the sign is positive. These experiments show that within the accuracy of the experimental data, the helicity is maximum so that $d = 1$ and $b = 0$.

Since the neutrino does not interact appreciably with matter it is almost impossible to make a direct measurement of its helicity. Goldhaber, Grodzins, and Sunyar (23) measured its helicity in a very clever way. They used Eu^{152m} (0^-) which undergoes K capture to a 961-Kev level of Sm^{152} (1^-), which then emits a gamma ray in passing to its ground state (0^+). Before K capture the system of interest has a total angular momentum [0 (nucleus) + $\frac{1}{2}$ (K electron)] of $\frac{1}{2}$. After K capture this system must still have a total angular momentum of $\frac{1}{2}$ [1 (nucleus) + ($-\frac{1}{2}$) neutrino]. Conservation of linear momentum requires the nucleus to recoil in the opposite direction to that of neutrino emission, and since the helicity is the cosine of the angle between the spin vector and linear momentum vector it is seen that the helicity of the recoiling nucleus is exactly the same as that of the emitted neutrino. Since the subsequent gamma emission proceeds via a 1 $\longrightarrow$ 0 transition, the gamma ray will be circularly polarized if emitted in the direction of the nuclear spin, or, more generally, its helicity will be equal to the cosine of the angle between the nucleus spin vector and the direction of gamma emission. If the observed gamma ray is emitted in the direction opposite to that of the neutrino, its helicity will then be identical with that of the neutrino. Measurement of the gamma-ray helicity is straightforward, but how is one to know in what direction the neutrino was emitted? Nuclear resonance fluorescence was used for this purpose. When the neutrino is emitted, the nucleus recoils with a velocity determined by conservation of momentum.

$$Mv = \frac{W_\nu}{c} \tag{7-34}$$

or

$$\frac{v}{c} = \frac{W_\nu}{Mc^2}, \tag{7-35}$$

where M is the mass of the recoiling nucleus, v is its velocity, and W_ν is the energy of the neutrino. The energy of the emitted gamma ray, if its direction of propagation makes an angle θ with the direction of motion of the emitting nucleus, is (see Chap. 5)

$$W_\gamma = W_0\left(1 + \frac{v}{c}\cos\theta\right) - \frac{W_0^2}{2Mc^2}, \tag{7-36}$$

where W_0 is the excitation energy of the nucleus. The energy required of a gamma ray to excite an identical ground state nucleus at rest is

$$W_\gamma' = W_0 + \frac{W_0^2}{2Mc^2}. \tag{7-37}$$

Resonance scattering will then be possible if

$$W_\gamma' = W_\gamma$$

or

$$W_0 = W_\nu \cos\theta. \tag{7-38}$$

If one can find a situation where $W_0 = W_\nu$, then resonance scattering can take place only when the gamma ray is emitted in a direction exactly opposite to that of the neutrino. Eu comes quite close to satisfying this requirement

since $\qquad W_\nu = 900 \pm 10\ \text{Kev}, \qquad W_0 = 961\ \text{Kev}.$

The gamma-ray polarization measurements showed that the neutrino emitted in K capture has negative helicity.

The experimental evidence for the helicity of the antineutrino is not as conclusive but the work of Burgy et al. (7) on the decay of polarized neutrons and that of Herrmannsfeldt et al. (26) on the recoil ion spectrum of the negatron emitter He[6] indicate that its helicity is positive.

In Dirac theory a moving free electron may be represented by a plane wave. This requires the usual four wave functions, although the amplitudes of these are related in pairs. If the electron has a helicity of $+1$ or -1, however, it requires only two of the four functions to specify it. Lee and Yang (33) and others as well (30, 47) have proposed a two-component neutrino theory. This at once requires that all neutrinos be emitted with helicity of ± 1. This in turn suggests that neutrinos have helicity -1 while antineutrinos have helicity $+1$. Lee and Yang also postulate lepton conservation. Leptons are the light particles, electron, neutrino, and muon (see Chap. 11). Lepton conservation means that the total number of leptons minus the number of antileptons must be a constant. In neutron decay, for example, a lepton is created (the electron) so an antilepton (the antineutrino) must also be created. In K capture, on the other hand, a lepton (electron) is destroyed so a lepton (neutrino) must be created to replace it. In positron emission an antilepton (positron) is created, so a lepton (neutrino) must also be created.

If there is a real distinction between neutrinos and antineutrinos it should be impossible to promote the reaction

$$n + \nu \longrightarrow p + \beta^-$$

by subjecting matter to the antineutrino flux from a fission reactor. Davis (14) tried, unsuccessfully, to observe the latter reaction by placing 1000 gallons of carbon tetrachloride near a fission reactor and searching for radioactive A^{37} produced in the reaction

$$Cl^{37} + \nu \longrightarrow A^{37} + \beta^-.$$

In principle, double beta decay should be a crucial test of the distinguishability of neutrinos and antineutrinos. If they are distinguishable particles then the emission of two electrons must be accompanied by the emission of two neutrinos. If they are identical, then a neutrino created with one electron can be absorbed as an antineutrino in the creation of the second electron, with

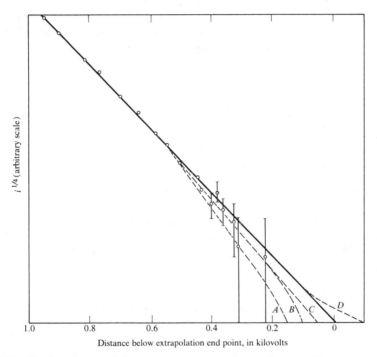

Fig. 7-21. The fourth root of the electron current collected from a tritium source at the center of a spherical electrostatic analyzer is plotted against the retarding voltage which is applied between the source and a concentric spherical grid. All electrons with an energy greater than that corresponding to the retarding voltage contribute to the current, thus giving an integral rather than differential spectrum. It is shown by the authors that $i^{1/4}$ should be proportional to $(W_0 - W)$ for a zero rest-mass neutrino. Curve A gives the expected shape of the curve for a neutrino mass of 250 ev (F) or 350 ev (M). Curve B is for a neutrino mass of 150 ev (F) or 200 ev (M). Curve C is for a neutrino mass of 500 ev (D). Curve D is for a neutrino mass of 0 ev (F, M, or D). F, M, and D stand for Fermi, Majorana, and Dirac types of interaction, respectively. [From Hamilton *et al.* (25).]

the end result that two electrons but *no* neutrinos are emitted. The probability of the latter process is much greater than that of the former. The probability of either process is so small that it is difficult to make reliable measurements on this type of decay. The data favor distinguishable particles, but a definitive experiment remains to be performed.

It has been assumed in most of the preceding discussions that the rest mass of the neutrino is zero. If the two-component neutrino theory is correct then the rest mass must be zero, for if it were not, an observer traveling at a speed greater than that of a neutrino could overtake the neutrino, and when he did so its apparent helicity would reverse, thus causing it to appear as an antineutrino.

Fermi showed that the high-energy end of the beta spectrum is quite sensitive to the neutrino rest mass. This fact has been used by a number of investigators to obtain an upper limit on the neutrino rest mass. The results of such an experiment by Hamilton, Alford, and Gross (25) are shown in Fig. 7-21. It seems certain that the rest energy is less than 500 ev.

PROBLEMS

7-1 Describe the path followed by an electron in a thin magnetic lens spectrograph (i.e., a thin circular coil of wire concentric with the line joining the source of electrons and the electron detector).

7-2 In a hypothetical monatomic gas of beta-emitting atoms of mass 20 amu, all of which have the most probable thermal velocity at 27°C, what spread in the observed beta energy would result from the thermal motion of the atoms if the laws of conservation of energy and momentum were assumed to hold in beta decay without neutrino emission? The energy released in the decay is 50 Kev.   [*Ans.* ~0.08 ev.]

7-3 How much energy must be expended in just separating a positron-negatron pair, considering only coulomb forces, if they are created with an initial separation of 1.5×10^{-13} cm (about one proton radius)?
[*Ans.* 0.94 Mev.]

7-4 In a semicircular beta spectrograph, the particles enter a narrow slit and pass into a region between two large plane magnet pole faces a small distance apart, are deflected through an angle of approximately 180°, and strike, say, a photographic plate. Show that there is approximate focusing of a slightly divergent monoergic beam and calculate the uncertainty in position of the slit image as a ratio of slit image width to mean distance between slit and image. Take the slit to be a geometric line. Calculate for beam divergence half-angles of 2.5° and 8°. (See illustration on page 251.)
[*Ans.* ±0.1% for $\theta = \pm 2.5°$; ±1.0% for $\theta = \pm 8°$.]

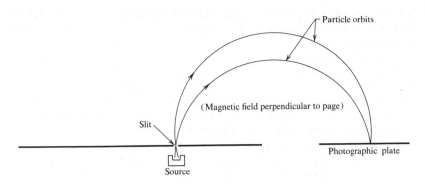

Slit

(Magnetic field perpendicular to page)

Particle orbits

Photographic plate

Source

7-5 R. L. Walker and B. D. McDaniel, *Phys. Rev.*, **74**, 315 (1948) have described a method used by them to measure the energy of energetic γ rays. The γ rays are allowed to fall on a thin foil and produce pairs. The positron and negatron are bent in opposite directions by a magnetic field (see Prob. 7-4). Under what conditions is it true that the sum of the two radii of curvature is a constant for a given γ ray energy?

7-6 Calculate the wavelengths of the first four lines of the Lyman series of the positronium "atom" on the basis of the simple Bohr theory.

[*Ans.* 2430, 2050, 1944, 1898 Å.]

7-7 The difference in mass energies of C^{13} and N^{13} is about 2.23 Mev. The maximum energy of the positrons emitted by N^{13} is given as 1.24 Mev. No γ rays are given off. Explain the apparent discrepancy of about 1 Mev.

7-8 When Cl^{36} undergoes K capture to the ground state of S^{36}, what velocity is imparted to the product nucleus, assuming the neutrino rest mass to be zero? [*Ans.* 7×10^5 cm/sec.]

7-9 The following beta-ray momentum distribution for Cu^{64} positrons is taken from a curve by C. S. Wu and R. D. Albert, *Phys. Rev.*, **75**, 315 (1949). Assume that the decay corresponds to an allowed transition, and make a Kurie plot of the spectrum. Find the maximum kinetic energy from the extrapolated curve.

No. of positrons per unit interval of $B\rho$	Momentum, $B\rho$, in gauss-cm	No. of positrons per unit interval of $B\rho$	Momentum, $B\rho$, in gauss-cm
25	800	155	2000
50	940	150	2200
75	1120	112	2600
100	1300	63	1930
125	1500	38	2100
150	1800	15	2260

[*Ans.* 657 Kev.]

7-10 Assume that 5% of the energy radiated by the sun is in the form of neutrinos and antineutrinos, that the effective cross section for interaction of an antineutrino with a proton is 10^{-43} cm^2, that the effective cross section for interaction of a neutrino with a neutron is likewise 10^{-43} cm^2, and that the mean neutron-to-proton ratio of the constituents of the earth is unity. The mass of the earth is 6×10^{24} kg and the measurable energy flux density from the sun at the mean distance of the earth's orbit is 0.033 cal/cm^2-sec.

(a) How much energy is given to the earth per day by absorption of neutrinos and antineutrinos coming to us from the sun?

(b) If the mean specific heat of the earth is 0.12 cal/gm°C, what daily increase in temperature of the earth would this cause, neglecting heat losses?

[*Ans.* (a) 1.14×10^9 joules/day; (b) 3.78×10^{-19} °C/day.]

7-11 In 1933 Sargent [*Proc. Roy. Soc.*, **139**, 659 (1933)] found the following empirical relationship between maximum beta-decay energies, W_0, and half-lives, $t_{1/2}$,

$$t_{1/2} W_0^5 = \text{const.}$$

Show that this relationship follows from the Fermi distribution of β-decay momenta if one treats $F(Z, W)$ as a constant.

7-12 The maximum recoil ion energy found by Davis (13) in Be^7 electron capture was 55.0 ev. Assuming that the neutrino has zero mass, what is the energy given to it? [*Ans.* 0.855 Mev.]

REFERENCES

1. Alvarez, L. W., *Phys. Rev.*, **52**, 134 (1937); **53**, 606 (1938); **54**, 486 (1938).

2. Anderson, C. D., *Science*, **76**, 238 (1932).

3. Anderson, C. D., *Phys. Rev.*, **43**, 1034 L (1933).

4. Bell, E. R., in *Beta and Gamma Ray Spectroscopy* (New York: Interscience Publishers, Inc., 1955).

5. Bienlein, H., Fleischmann, R., and Wegener, H., *Z. Physik*, **150**, 80 (1957).

6. Blackett, P. M. S., and Occhialini, G. P. S., *Proc. Roy. Soc.*, **A139**, 699 (1933).

7. Burgy, M. T., Krohn, V. E., Novey, T. B., Ringo, G. R., and Telegdi, V. A., *Phys. Rev.*, **110**, 1214 (1958).

8. Cavanagh, P. E., Turner, J. F., Coleman, C. F., Gard, G. A., and Ridley, B. W., *Phil. Mag.*, **21**, 1105 (1957).

9. Chase, C. T., *Phys. Rev.*, **34**, 1069 (1929); **36**, 894 (1930); **36**, 1060 (1930).

10. Cox, R. T., McIlwraith, C. G., and Kurrelmeyer, B., *Proc. Nat. Acad. Sci. Wash.*, **14**, 544 (1928).

11. Crane, H. R., and Halpern, J., *Phys. Rev.*, **56**, 232 (1939).

12. Curtis, R. B., and Lewis, R. R., *Phys. Rev.*, **107**, 543 (1957).

13. Davis, R. Jr., *Phys. Rev.*, **86**, 976 (1952).

14. Davis, R. Jr., *Bull. Am. Phys. Soc.*, ser. II, **1**, 219 (1956).

15. DeBenedetti, S., and Siegel, R., *Phys. Rev.*, **85**, 371 (1952); **87**, 335 (1952).

16. Deutsch, M., *Phys. Rev.*, **82**, 455 (1951); **83**, 866 (1951).

17. De Waard, H., and Poppema, O. J., *Physica*, **23**, 597 (1957).

18. Dirac, P. A. M., *Proc. Roy. Soc.*, **126**, 360 (1930); *Proc. Roy. Soc.*, **133**, 61 (1931); *Proc. Camb. Phil. Soc.*, **30**, 150 (1933–34).

19. Dirac, P. A. M., *Proc. Camb. Phil. Soc.*, **26**, 361 (1930).

20. Ellis, C. D., and Wooster, W. A., *Proc. Roy. Soc.*, **A117**, 109 (1927–28).

21. Fermi, E., *La Ricerca Scientifica*, **12** (1933); *Z. Physik*, **88**, 161 (1934).

22. Feynman, R. P., *Phys. Rev.*, **76**, 749 (1949).

23. Goldhaber, M., Grodzins, L., and Sunyar, A. W., *Phys. Rev.*, **109**, 1015 (1958).

24. Gray, L. H., and Tarrant, G. T. P., *Proc. Roy. Soc.*, **A136**, 662 (1932).

25. Hamilton, D. R., Alford, W. P., and Gross, L., *Phys. Rev.*, **92**, 1521 (1953).

26 Herrmannsfeldt, W. B., Burman, R. L., Stähelin, P., Allen, J. S., and Braid, T. H., *Phys. Rev. Letters*, **1**, 61 (1958).

27. Jackson, J. D., Treiman, S. B., and Wyld, II. W. Jr., *Phys. Rev.*, **106**, 517 (1957).

28. Konopinski, E. J., *Rev. Mod. Phys.*, **15**, 209 (1943).

29. Kurie, F. N. D., Richardson, J. R., and Paxton, H. C., *Phys. Rev.*, **49**, 368 (1936).

30. Landau, L., *Nuc. Phys.*, **3**, 127 (1957).

31. Lawson, J. L., and Cork, J. M., *Phys. Rev.*, **57**, 982 (1940).

32. Lee, T. D., and Yang, C. N., *Phys. Rev.*, **104**, 254 (1956).

33. Lee, T. D., and Yang, C. N., *Phys. Rev.*, **105**, 1671 (1957).

34. Leipunski, A. I., *Proc. Camb. Phil. Soc.*, **32**, 301 (1936).

35. Livingston, M. S., *Physics Today*, **12**, 18 (Oct. 1959).

36. Longmire, C., and Brown, H., *Phys. Rev.*, **75**, 264 (1949).

37. Malone, D. P., Greenberg, J. S., Gluckstern, R. L., and Hughes, V. W., *Bull. Amer. Phys. Soc.*, **4**, 76 (1959); *Phys. Rev.*, **120**, 1393 (1960).

38. Millett, W. E., *Bull. Amer. Phys. Soc.*, **5**, 106 (1960).

39. Mohorovičić, S., *Astronom. Nachr.*, **253**, 94 (1934).

40. Ore, A., and Powell, J. L., *Phys. Rev.*, **75**, 1696 (1949).

41. Pauli, W., *Rapp. Septième Conseil Phys.*, *Solvay, Brussels* (Paris: Gautier-Villars, 1934) (1933).

42. Reines, F., and Cowan, C. L. Jr., *Phys. Rev.*, **90**, 492 (1953); *Nature*, **178**, 446 (1956); *Phys. Rev.*, **113**, 273 (1959).

43. Reitz, J. R., *Phys. Rev.*, **77**, 10 (1950).

44. Robinson, B. L., and Fink, R. W., *Rev. Mod. Phys.*, **32**, 117 (1960).

45. Rose, M. E., *Phys. Rev.*, **49**, 727 (1946).

46. Ruark, E., *Phys. Rev.*, **68**, 278 (1945).

47. Salam, A., *Nuovo Cimento*, **5**, 299 (1957).

48. Sherwin, C. W., *Phys. Rev.*, **73**, 216, 1173 (1948); **75**, 1799 (1949); **82**, 52 (1951).

49. Siegbahn, K., *Beta and Gamma Ray Spectroscopy* (New York: Interscience Publishers, Inc., 1955).

50. Stueckelberg, E. C. G., *Helv. Phys. Acta.*, **14**, 588 (1941); **15**, 23 (1942).

51. Wu, C. S., Ambler, E., Hayward, R. W., Hoppes, D. D., and Hudson, R. P., *Phys. Rev.*, **105**, 1413 (1957).

GENERAL REFERENCES

1. Siegbahn, K., *Beta and Gamma Ray Spectroscopy* (New York: Interscience Publishers, Inc., 1955). Contains a wealth of detailed information on beta-ray spectroscopy.

2. Allen, J. S., *The Neutrino* (Princeton, N.J.: Princeton University Press, 1958). The title is a bit misleading, but this book contains a very fine account of the many recoil ion experiments.

3. Frisch, O. R., ed., *Progress in Nuclear Physics*, vol. 7 (New York: Pergamon Press, 1959). The article on "Measurement of Helicity" by Lee Grodzins gives a rather complete status report on helicity as of the date of publication.

8

ELECTROMAGNETIC RADIATION

8-1 Introduction

The origin of nuclear gamma radiation arising out of de-excitation of nuclear energy levels lying above the ground state has been discussed in Chap. 5. The process of internal conversion in which nuclear excitation energy, which commonly would be given off as gamma radiation, ejects an orbital electron from the atom instead was also discussed there. A rather rare variant of this process, called the *internal Compton effect*, has been observed by Siegbahn *et al.* (29) in the decay of Ba^{137m}. In this phenomenon, an orbital electron is ejected from the atom, and a gamma ray with the residue of the transition energy is emitted at the same time. They find 1.86×10^{-5} photons in the energy range of 97 to 120 Kev for every conversion electron that is detected coming off at an angle of 90° to the direction of gamma emission. These results seem to fit the predictions of Spruch and Goertzel (32).

Total internal conversion, which can take place in E0 (no) transitions where single gamma emission is strictly forbidden, was also discussed.

Another type of E0 (no) transition is described in the next section. In the remainder of the chapter the production of gamma rays by machines rather than by nuclei, the absorption and scattering of gamma rays, and the determination of gamma-ray energies will be taken up.

8-2 Internal Pair Creation

Curie and Joliot showed (6) in 1933 that the gamma rays from the Be^9 (α, n) reaction not only could produce conversion pairs (positrons + electrons) in an external radiator (a thin sheet of metal) but could also emit pairs without the presence of an external radiator. They concluded that the gamma ray was being converted, within the emitting nucleus, to an electron-positron pair. In analogy with the process of internal conversion they called this *internal materialization*. A commonly used alternative name is *internal pair conversion*. This process is obviously impossible unless the transition energy exceeds that necessary to create a pair ($2mc^2 = 1.02$ Mev). The existence of internal pair creation has since been firmly established. Jaeger and Hulme (19) have worked out the theory for the positron spectrum to be expected in pair creation and find that the number of positrons per unit energy interval should increase as the positron energy increases and then cut off sharply at the maximum possible energy. The theoretical predictions are supported by the work of Latyshev (21) as shown in Fig. 8-1, by Slätis and Siegbahn (30),

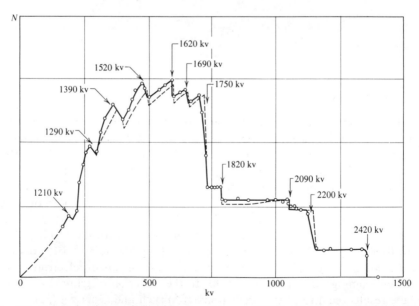

Fig. 8-1. Internal pair creation positron spectrum of Bi^{214} obtained by Latyshev (21). The dotted line is the theoretically predicted spectrum. The values adjacent to the sudden drops in intensity give the energies of the corresponding gamma-ray lines.

and by others. In contrast to internal conversion, the internal pair creation coefficient not only increases with the transition energy, but decreases with the change in angular momentum, L. It is not very sensitive to atomic number, decreasing slowly with increasing Z. More recently, some use has been made of angular correlation measurements in internal pair creation as a means of determining the multipolarity of the transition and from this, as in

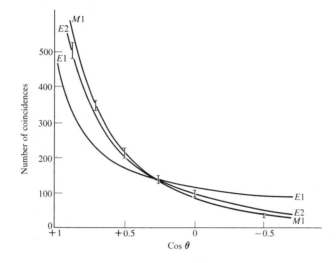

Fig. 8-2. Angular correlation of internal creation pairs from the 2.86-Mev transition in B^{10}. The three theoretical curves show that the transition is most likely an E2 or M1. The transition is believed to take place from a $2+$ state at 3.58 Mev to a $1+$ state at 0.72 Mev. [From Gorodetzky, S., Chevallier, P., Armbruster, R., and Sutter, G., *Nuc. Phys.*, **12**, 354 (1959).]

internal conversion and gamma ray studies, to determine the probable spins of excited states. Figure 8-2 shows angular correlation data obtained by Gorodetzky *et al.* (13) on the internally created pairs from the 2.86-Mev transition of B^{10}. The angle θ shown in the figure is the angle between the directions of emission of positron and electron.

As in total internal conversion, one may have total internal pair conversion when the excited and final states have the same spins and same parity. As a matter of fact, when the transition energy exceeds the threshold energy for pair creation ($2mc^2 = 1.02$ Mev), total internal pair creation may compete very effectively with total internal conversion. The first example of internal pair creation with no corresponding gamma ray was observed by Fowler and Lauritsen (11) in 1939 in a study of the $F^{19}(p, \alpha)O^{16m}$ reaction. In 500 cloud chamber photographs they found 29 definite pairs when the bombardment energy of the protons was 0.82 Mev. The radiation produced at this resonance energy was predominantly in the form of pairs, whereas other resonance energies led predominantly to gamma radiation. Figure 8-3, which compares the pair excitation function with the α and γ excitation functions for the F^{19} (p, α) reaction, shows rather nicely the absence of gamma rays when the pair-emitting level is preferentially excited. The work (33) shown in Fig. 8-3

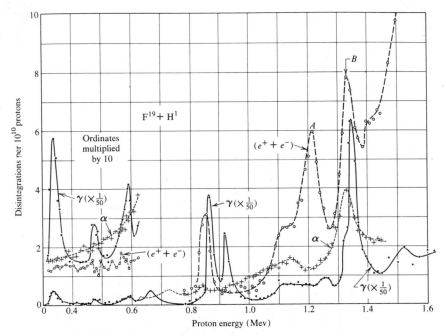

Fig. 8-3. Excitation curve obtained by Streib, Fowler, and Lauritsen (33) for the reaction $F^{19} + H^1 \rightarrow O^{16m} + He^4$. The $0 \rightarrow 0$ internal pair conversion at A is to be contrasted with the usual pair conversion peak associated with a gamma ray as shown at B. Presumably the resonantly excited level at B can decay by gamma emission or by pair conversion whereas the excited level at A can decay only by pair conversion.

together with that of numerous other investigators (1, 8) has now firmly established the existence of a 0^+ state of O^{16} at 6.06 Mev which decays to the ground state of O^{16} almost wholly by pair emission. The known cases of monopole transitions that give rise to pair emission are listed in Table 8-1.

Ordinarily, in nuclear pair emission, the electron is constrained to go into the electron continuum since the available low-energy states are already filled with orbital electrons. In the somewhat unlikely case that an orbital electron is missing, it should be possible for the electron to go into the vacancy. Under these circumstances the positron would have a definite energy, W_{e^+}, given by

$$W_{e^+} = W_{\text{transition}} - 2mc^2 + W_{\text{orbital}}, \tag{8-1}$$

Table 8-1 MONOPOLE PAIR-CONVERSION TRANSITIONS

Excited nuclide	Transition energy (Mev)	Comments	References
$_6C^{12}$	7.6	Believed to be second excited state	16
$_8O^{16}$	6.06	Believed to be lowest excited state	8
$_{20}Ca^{40}$	3.4	Believed to be lowest excited state	3, 12
$_{40}Zr^{90}$	1.75	Believed to be lowest excited state $\dfrac{\text{Int. pair emission}}{\text{Int. conversion}} = \dfrac{1}{4.4}$	2, 20

where $W_{\text{transition}}$ is the transition energy between the more excited and the less excited state of the nucleus, and W_{orbital} is the binding energy of the electron in its orbital state. In 1948 Latyshev (22) reported sharp positron lines in the conversion spectrum of Po^{214}. Sliv (31) suggested that these were due to the process discussed above and calculated the probability of such transitions. More recently Brunner (4) has found an example of such a transition in excited Pb^{206} resulting from electron capture in Bi^{206}. The electron capture

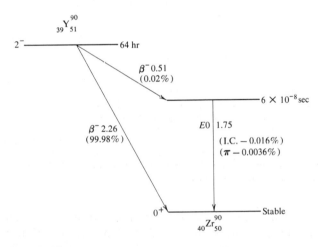

Fig. 8-4. Decay scheme of Y^{90}. An internal conversion (I.C.) electron is emitted in 0.016% of all beta decays of Y^{90}, while internal pairs (π) are emitted in 0.0036% of such decays. Transition energies are given in Mev.

event provides an orbital vacancy suitable for this type of transition. If the pair creation takes place in the short time interval before the vacancy is filled by normal orbital electron transitions, then the created electron may be captured in the orbital vacancy. The observed monoergic positron line is shown in Fig. 8-5.

In principle, one should find double gamma decay (14) competing with total internal conversion and pair emission in monopole transitions. No definite evidence for such a process has been found, but the reason may be that the gamma rays from such a process would have a continuous energy

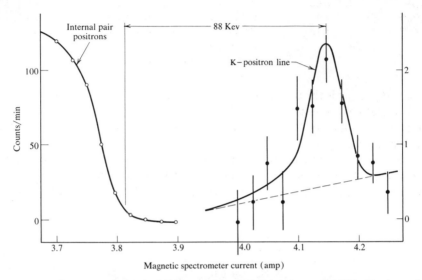

Fig. 8-5. Positron spectrum of Pb²⁰⁶ formed in electron capture of Bi²⁰⁶. The intensity is plotted against the magnetic spectrometer current which is a measure of the momenta, and hence of the energies, of the emitted positrons. The intensity scale for internal pair positrons is given at the left. The intensity of the K-positron line is given at the right. Bi²⁰⁵ and Bi²⁰⁶ also decay by the competing process of positron emission. The positron contribution from the latter, which is about ten times the maximum rate shown for the K-positron line, has already been subtracted from the measured rates. The separation between the pair spectrum cutoff and the K-positron peak is in good agreement with that expected for the process discussed in the text.

spectrum which would be difficult to differentiate from background gammas which are usually present. Estimates (25, 27) of the probability of simultaneous emission of a gamma ray and an electron-positron pair indicate that such a process is about 10^4 times less probable than straight pair conversion.

8-3 Production of Gamma Rays

Since gamma rays are a form of electromagnetic radiation similar in properties to x-rays but generally more penetrating, there can be no sharp boundary between the highest-energy x-ray and the lowest-energy gamma ray. Generally one calls photons whose energies are less than about 0.2-Mev x-rays and those of higher quantum energy gamma rays. The use of the words in practice is often conditioned by the origin or mode of production of the radiation. Photons emitted by nuclei are usually called gamma rays no matter how small their energies may be. On the other hand, radiation produced artificially in an x-ray generator is often designated as x-radiation even when the quantum energies are very large.

When energetic electrons strike a target they not only excite the characteristic x-ray line spectrum mentioned in Chap. 2, but also, by a process known as *bremsstrahlung*,* a continuous x-ray spectrum. It is well known from classical electrodynamics that a charged particle radiates electromagnetic waves when it is accelerated or decelerated. As the electron is slowed down in an absorber, therefore, radiation is produced, and this is the explanation usually given for the origin of the continuous part of the x-ray spectrum from a bombarded target. In the case of very energetic electrons, the deceleration produced by ionization energy-loss is quite small so that bremsstrahlung produced in this manner will be of very low quantum energy. On the other hand, if such a swiftly moving electron passes very close to a nucleus it may suffer a sudden change in direction with consequent production of a high-energy photon. It is apparent that while other charged particles, protons, deuterons, etc., can be used to produce x-rays, they are less effective than electrons because the forces acting on their larger masses produce smaller accelerations.

The betatron is now widely used to produce gamma rays with energies up to a little over 300 Mev. Linear accelerators, or "linacs" as they are often called, can produce up to about 700-Mev gammas. Electron synchrotrons produce gamma rays with energies as high as 1.2 Bev. Each of these devices produces, in the first instance, high-energy electrons. The gamma rays are created when the energetic electrons are allowed to impinge on targets of high-atomic-number materials. Still higher-energy linacs and electron synchrotrons are being designed or are already under construction, while cosmic rays produce even more energetic gamma rays in very small numbers.

Naturally radioactive nuclides and a much larger number of artificially created radionuclides emit gamma rays. These rays have the virtue of being monoergic or at least of possessing a line spectrum with a relatively small number of discrete energies. The quantum energy is usually not great, 10 Mev being about the upper limit. Except for the long-lived isomers and those nuclei which decay exclusively by electron capture, gamma emitters also emit beta rays, which are undesirable in some applications. Gamma rays may also be produced in nuclear reactions such as (n, γ), (p, γ), (d, γ), etc., the upper energy limit in this case being about 20 Mev. Positron emitters are often used as a source of the 0.51-Mev monoergic annihilation radiation.

---

* Bremsstrahlung comes from the German words *bremsen* (to put on the brakes) plus *strahlung* (radiation). Knowledge of the origin of the word may help the reader to avoid the common error of spelling it with a single *s*.

8-4 Absorption of Electromagnetic Radiation

A gamma-ray beam loses intensity as it passes through matter by elastic scattering of the photons, by the Compton effect, the photoelectric effect, pair production, nuclear absorption, and in other processes that do not set in until one reaches very high quantum energies. Each of these processes is most important in a particular energy region for a given absorber, the energy of the region increasing roughly in the order the effects are listed above. Discussion of the very high energy region will be deferred until Chap. 11.

Gamma rays may be scattered elastically by nuclei (Thomson scattering) and by atomic electrons (Rayleigh scattering). Nuclear scattering is quite negligible except in the case of resonance scattering which, as was seen in Chap. 5, takes place only under very specially contrived circumstances. Rayleigh scattering is appreciable, but small compared to the total attenuation, at low energies and the scattering angle tends to be small, as seen in Table 8-2, with the result that the scattered photons will still reach the detector in most experimental arrangements and therefore are not effective in attenuating the beam.

Table 8-2 ANGLE IN DEGREES, THROUGH WHICH 60 TO 70 PER CENT OF GAMMA RAYS ARE SCATTERED IN RAYLEIGH SCATTERING

Scatterer	Energy of gamma rays (Mev)		
	0.1	1	10
Al	15	2	0.5
Fe	20	3	0.8
Pb	30	4	1

SOURCE: (9). Adapted from Nucleonics, Vol. 11, No. 8, p. 11. Copyright 1953, McGraw-Hill Publishing Company, Inc. Used by permission.

Photoelectric effect. In this process the gamma ray gives up its entire energy to an atom. Conservation of momentum precludes the possibility of a gamma ray's giving all its energy to a free electron, so the transfer of its energy to a bound electron requires that momentum be given to the residual ion. The energy given to the ion is so small, however, that it may be neglected. The electron kinetic energy is then given by

$$W_e = W_\gamma - W_B, \tag{8-2}$$

where W_e is the kinetic energy of the ejected electron, $W_\gamma = h\nu$ is the energy of the photon, and W_B is the binding energy of the orbital electron which the gamma ray ejects. This might lead one to suspect that the electrons would be emitted nearly isotropically, but this is not the case. Actually they are ejected preferentially in the direction of the electric vector of the incident gamma rays as shown in Fig. 8-6. Photoelectric absorption varies roughly as W_γ^{-3} and

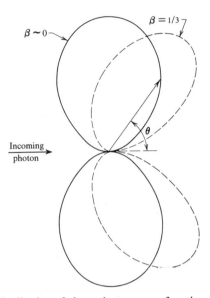

Fig. 8-6. Distribution of photo electrons as a function of direction of emission with respect to the path of the incident photon. The probability of an electron being emitted in any direction, θ, is proportional to the length of the line from the origin to the curve. The solid curve is for electrons ejected with a very small velocity. The dotted curve is for electrons ejected with a velocity one-third that of light. If the electric vector of the incident photon is considered to lie in the plane of the paper, then the loops in other planes would be smaller in proportion to $\cos^2 \phi$, where ϕ is the angle between the other plane and the plane of the page, so that in a plane normal to the page the emission probability is zero for all θ. The equation from which these curves were calculated is good only if the frequency of the incident photon is not near an x-ray absorption edge of the atom. The $\beta = \frac{1}{3}$ curve is not drawn to the same scale as the other curve.

suffers sudden changes at photon energies equal to the binding energies of orbital electrons as shown in Fig. 8-7. The energies at which these sudden changes in absorption coefficient occur are called *absorption edges*. Where W_B is known, Eq. (8-2) makes it possible to compute the gamma-ray energy from the energy of the photoelectron as measured, say, in a beta-ray spectrograph. McVoy (24), using the plane wave approximation and assuming a photon energy much larger than the binding energy of a K electron, finds that the K electrons photoelectrically ejected by circularly polarized photons ($\mathscr{H}_\gamma = \pm 1$) tend to have the same helicities as the photons. A plot of the expectation value of the helicity of the electrons relative to that of the incident photons is given in Fig. 8-8 as a function of the photon energy.

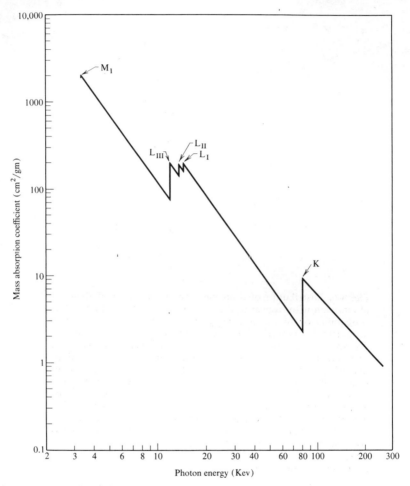

Fig. 8-7. Mass absorption coefficient of $_{79}$Au, showing the K, L_I, K_{II}, L_{III}, and M_I absorption edges. When the quantum energy becomes less than the binding energy of a K electron, K electrons can no longer be ejected from the atom and the absorption suddenly drops. From the rate at which the absorption coefficient decreases with increasing photon energy, it is evident that photoelectric absorption will not be appreciable for energetic γ rays.

Compton effect. Strictly speaking, the Compton effect is concerned with the scattering of photons by free electrons. In this event the photon loses

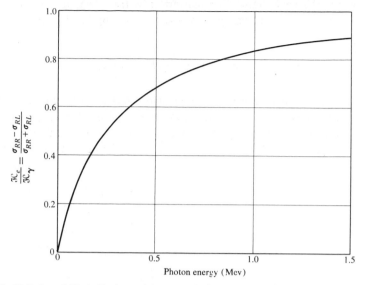

Fig. 8-8. Helicity of K-shell photoelectrons relative to the helicity of incident photons. These results were calculated by McVoy (24), who used the plane wave approximation and assumed the photon energy to be large compared to the binding energy of a K electron. σ_{RL} is the total cross section for production of a left-handed ($\mathscr{H} = -1$) electron by a right-handed ($\mathscr{H} = +1$) photon.

energy in the encounter and is scattered as a photon of lower frequency than the incident photon while the electron recoils with an energy equal to that lost by the photon. It is customary, nevertheless, to include such scattering by bound electrons under the designation of Compton effect. The reason is that, for high-energy gamma rays, the difference between true Compton scattering

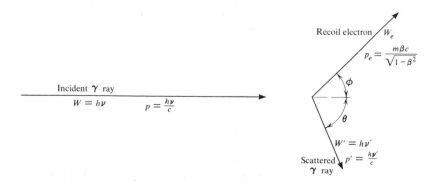

Fig. 8-9. Diagram of Compton collision.

by a free electron and this modified Compton scattering by a relatively loosely bound electron is very slight. For scattering by free electrons at rest, conservation of momentum and energy gives for the change in wavelength of the photon

$$\Delta\lambda = \lambda' - \lambda = \frac{h}{mc}(1 - \cos\theta), \qquad (8\text{-}3)$$

where h is Planck's constant, m is the electron mass, c is the velocity of light in free space, and θ is the angle between the direction of propagation of the scattered photon and the extended path of the incident radiation. Figure 8-10 shows the observed distribution in wavelengths of x-radiation scattered

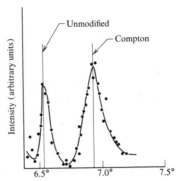

Fig. 8-10. Distribution in wavelengths of Mo K_α radiation after scattering by graphite. The glancing angles are given, but the wavelengths can be calculated from these by use of the Bragg equation and the known interplanar spacings in a calcite crystal.

by graphite at an angle of 135° as observed by Compton in 1923. The smaller peak has the same wavelength as the incident radiation while the larger peak has a mean wavelength predicted by the Compton formula. The quantity $h/mc = 2.426 \times 10^{-10}$ cm is called the "Compton wavelength."

The total cross section per electron for Compton scattering is given by the Klein-Nishina formula (17),

$$\sigma_c = \frac{2\pi e^4}{m^2 c^4}\left\{\frac{1+W}{W^3}\left[\frac{2W(1+W)}{1+2W} - \ln(1+2W)\right]\right.$$

$$\left. + \frac{1}{2W}\ln(1+2W) - \frac{1+3W}{(1+2W)^2}\right\}, \qquad (8\text{-}4)$$

where $W = h\nu/mc^2$ is the incident photon energy.

In contrast to the photoelectric effect, Compton recoil electrons are most intense in a direction at right angles to the plane of the electric vector of plane polarized photons. If circularly polarized ($\mathscr{H} = 1$) photons are Compton scattered by unpolarized electrons, then the recoil electrons show a degree of helicity which increases with incident gamma-ray energy and with scattering angle. This effect is illustrated in Fig. 8-11. Compton scattering, being strongly spin dependent, is appreciably different for right and left circularly

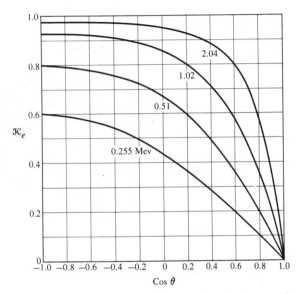

Fig. 8-11. Helicity of Compton electrons ejected from unpolarized material by circularly polarized ($\mathscr{H} = +1$) photons as a function of the angle θ through which the photon is scattered. [From Tolhoek (34).]

polarized photons in iron magnetized parallel to the direction of propagation of the incident photons. Transmission of unpolarized gamma rays through iron is increased by magnetization of the iron in exactly the same manner (mathematically speaking) that the transmission of unpolarized neutrons through iron is increased by magnetizing the iron. This effect was first demonstrated in 1953 by Gunst and Page (15).

The differential scattering cross section per unit solid angle, $d\sigma_e/d\Omega$ (i.e., the cross section for scattering a photon through an angle near θ per unit solid angle), is shown in Fig. 8-12. Since the solid angle between two cones of angle θ and $\theta + d\theta$ increases as θ goes from $0°$ to $90°$, the cross section per unit angle, $d\sigma_e/d\theta$, looks quite different from $d\sigma_e/d\Omega$ as seen by an inspection of Fig. 8-13.

When gamma rays are detected by a device such as a proportional counter or a scintillation counter, the electrical output pulse is a function of the energy given to an electron. In a single Compton collision, therefore, the energy indicated by the pulse is less than the energy of the incident gamma ray.

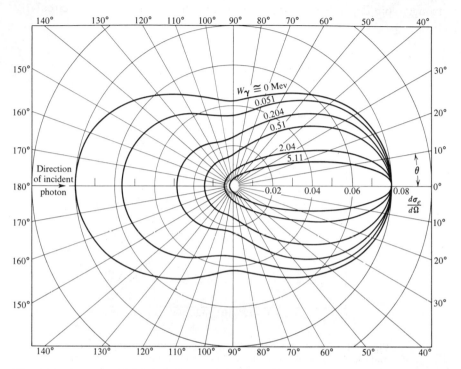

Fig. 8-12. Average differential cross section per unit solid angle, $d\sigma_e/d\Omega$, (in barns per electron per steradian) for the Compton scattering of unpolarized photons through an angle near θ. σ_e is the cross section per electron. This plot is applicable in the detection of scattered radiation where the detector usually subtends a relatively small solid angle. [From Davisson and Evans (7).]

Figure 8-14 demonstrates the variation in differential cross section with energy of the Compton electron, $d\sigma_e/dW_e$, for 3 gamma-ray energies.

Heitler and Nordheim (18), in 1934, predicted the occurrence of Compton-type collisions in which two or more photons were emitted. It is expected that such higher-order processes should occur roughly $(\frac{1}{137})^{n-1}$ as often as the normal Compton effect. Cavanagh (5) reported on a search for this phenomenon in 1952. In his experiments the background coincidence rate was about four times the coincidence rate attributed to the multiple Compton effect so no statistically accurate results could be obtained, but the results were consistent with theoretical predictions.

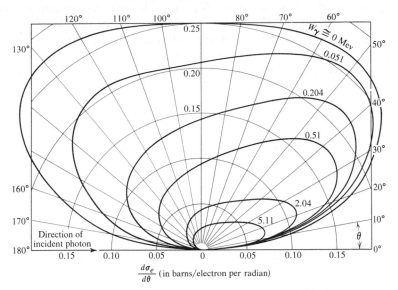

Fig. 8-13. Average differential cross section per unit angle, $d\sigma_e/d\theta$ in barns per electron per radian, for Compton scattering of unpolarized photons. σ_e is the cross section per electron. Note the great difference between this plot and that in Fig. 8-12, which displays essentially the same information in a different way. [From Davisson and Evans (7).]

Pair production. The discovery of pair production was discussed in Sec. 7-2. It is evident that the threshold energy for the creation of such a positron-negatron pair is slightly greater than the combined rest-mass energies of the two particles, which is 1.02 Mev. Hence pair production cannot contribute to the absorption of gamma rays of energy less than 1.02 Mev. If a gamma ray of energy $hv = W_\gamma$ were to give up its entire energy in the creation of a pair, then since

$$W_\gamma^2 = p^2c^2 + (2mc^2)^2, \tag{8-5}$$

where p is the momentum of the pair as a system, W_γ is the total energy of the system, and $2m$ is the rest mass of the two particles, the momentum of the system is

$$p = \frac{\sqrt{W_\gamma^2 - 4m^2c^4}}{c}. \tag{8-6}$$

The momentum of the photon, on the other hand, was

$$p_\gamma = \frac{W_\gamma}{c}. \tag{8-7}$$

It is seen at once that the pair can never carry away sufficient momentum to satisfy the conservation condition. We conclude that some massive body—specifically a nucleus—must be involved in the interaction. Because of its relatively great mass it can take up the additional momentum with very little energy so the energy of the pair will be nearly equal to that of the gamma photon. The necessity for the presence of matter in pair creation is attested

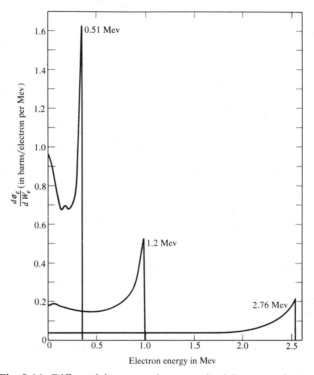

Fig. 8-14. Differential cross section per unit of Compton electron energy, $d\sigma_e/dW_e$, for the production of Compton recoils by gamma rays of various energies. This curve is important in energy-sensitive detectors where the probability of a Compton-scattered photon undergoing a collision is small. [From Davisson and Evans (7).]

to by the fact that very few pairs are formed in the gas of a cloud chamber but are formed in much greater numbers within absorbing plates of heavy elements such as lead.

Actually the third body need not be as massive as a nucleus. Perrin (28) has shown that when the third body is an electron the threshold for pair production is $4mc^2$ which means that the process cannot be effective for gamma photons of energy less than 2.04 Mev. This process is not of much importance in the energy range of nuclear gamma rays but becomes very important at higher energies.

Figure 8-15 shows the differential cross section for positron production per unit positron energy as a function of the fractional total kinetic energy of the pair given to the positron.

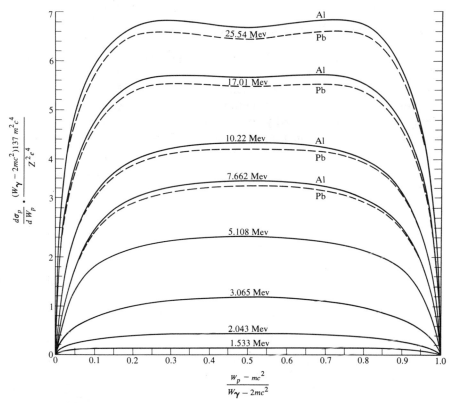

Fig. 8-15. Differential cross section per unit positron energy for production of positrons in pair production. W_γ, the incident photon energy, is shown at the center of each curve. W_p is the positron energy. Z is the atomic number of the absorber. [From Davisson and Evans (7).]

The contributions of the photoelectric effect, Compton effect, and pair production, together with their combined absorption cross section per atom of lead as a function of incident photon frequency, are shown in Fig. 8-16. Total absorption cross sections per atom for a number of elements are compared in Fig. 8-17.

Nuclear absorption. Absorption of photons by nuclei is important in nuclear physics as we saw in Chap. 6 when we discussed photodisintegration of the deuteron. The cross sections for nuclear absorption are so small, however, that this process contributes only a negligible amount to the total absorption cross section. This is true even for the so-called "giant resonances" which are characteristic of light nuclei at relatively high energy. For example, Ferguson *et al.* (10) found a (γ, n) giant resonance in Ne^{20} at 21.5 Mev with a width of 6.6 Mev and a peak cross section of 7.3 millibarns.

8-5 Determination of Gamma-Ray Quantum Energy

The available methods may be roughly categorized as absorption, crystal diffraction, magnetic methods, and other methods including scintillation and proportional counter techniques. Each is discussed in turn below.

Absorption. About the oldest method, and one of the quickest, for determining the energy of γ rays is by absorption. Since the absorption coefficient for a given material is a function of the energy of the photons, this method is

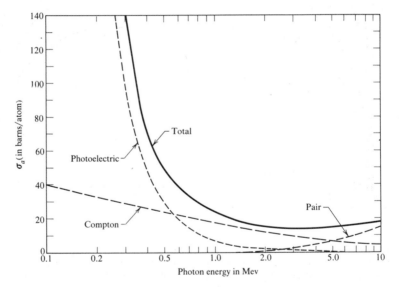

Fig. 8-16. Absorption cross sections per atom of lead as a function of incident photon energy. The solid curve is the total absorption cross section per atom for all three processes combined.

applicable essentially in determining the energy of a monoergic beam. If two or more components of comparable intensity and considerably different energies are present, the individual energies can be determined from the absorption curve in a manner entirely analogous to that used in separately identifying different half-life components in a mixture. The accuracy of the method is not great. Sometimes the energy can be bracketed between the absorption edges of two absorbers of different atomic number, as was done by Alvarez and Pitzer in proving that K x-rays were coming from the product nucleus of a K-capture decay. This method depends upon the fact that the mass absorption coefficients of two elements which differ by one unit in

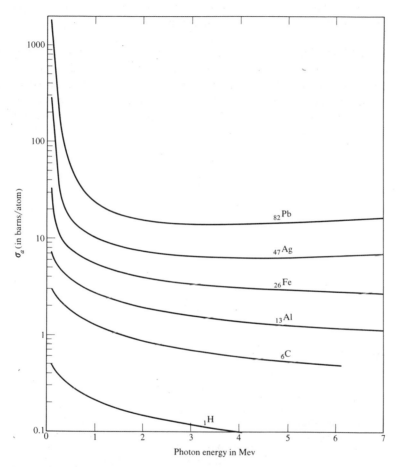

Fig. 8-17. Total absorption cross sections per atom as a function of incident photon energy for several elements.

atomic number are very nearly equal except near the absorption edge. The mass absorption coefficient of $_{79}$Au is plotted as a function of photon energy in Fig. 8-7. The corresponding plot for $_{78}$Pt would lie very slightly below the gold curve at the right side of the figure but would continue to rise as the photon energy decreases beyond the K absorption edge of gold at 81.2 Kev.

At 78.8 Kev, the K absorption edge of platinum, the mass absorption coefficient would suddenly drop and for smaller values of photon energy would again lie just below the gold curve. If one measured the mass absorption coefficient of radiation of unknown quantum energy and found a value of about 9 cm²/gm with a platinum absorber, but only about 2.4 cm²/gm with a gold absorber, he would conclude that the photon energy lay between 78.8 and 81.2 Kev. Absorption methods have now been almost completely supplanted by the use of more modern equipment.

Crystal diffraction. This is a rather precise method of measuring the wavelengths and hence the quantum energies of x-rays and gamma rays. DuMond and coworkers (26) have used this method for the accurate determination of a number of gamma-ray lines. An interesting example is that of Cs^{137} for which they find $h\nu = 0.66160 \pm 0.00014$ Mev. By comparison, a

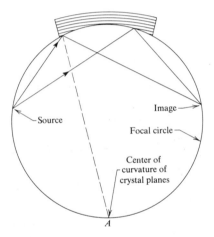

Fig. 8-18. Schematic diagram of a curved crystal spectrograph. Bending the crystal so that the center of curvature of the crystal planes is at A satisfies the Bragg condition for constructive interference, while grinding the surface of the crystal to fit the focal curve satisfies the condition for focusing. Rays reflected from deeper layers in the crystal do not quite focus at the point shown, however. For a very interesting discussion of both reflection and transmission types of bent crystal spectrographs, see J. W. M. DuMond, *Rev. Sci. Instr.*, **18**, 626 (1947).

magnetic spectrometer value (23) is $h\nu = 0.66165 \pm 0.00015$ Mev. There is little promise of extending the method above 2 Mev because of the very small diffraction angle, the small scattering cross section of the crystal atoms, and difficulties in collimating the beam. A curved crystal reflection spectrograph is shown diagrammatically in Fig. 8-18. A diagram of a curved crystal transmission spectrograph is given in Fig. 8-19. Crystal diffraction methods have served primarily as a means of accurately determining the energies of certain lines to be used as reference or calibration lines for other techniques.

Magnetic methods. The bulk of actual gamma-ray quantum energy determinations involve measurement of the energies of secondary electrons released by the photons. One group of techniques may be classed as magnetic

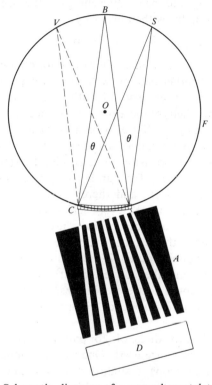

Fig. 8-19. Schematic diagram of a curved crystal transmission spectrograph. The source is placed at *S*. The center of curvature of the crystal is at *B*. Rays from the source which are diffracted by the crystal, *C*, pass through the collimator, *A*, as though they came from a virtual source at *V*, and are detected by the detector, *D*.

methods since they use standard magnetic beta-ray spectrographs or adaptations thereof to measure the electron energies. The procedure is to allow gamma rays to fall on a material, usually of high atomic number, which is called a *radiator* or a *converter*, and to observe the momenta of the ejected electrons or electron-positron pairs. Both thick and thin converters are used.

Thin converters have the advantage that the ejected electrons suffer minimum energy degradation in making their way out of the converter. On the other hand, a much greater number of electrons will be emitted by a thick converter, a consideration which may be crucial in the case of weak sources. When thick converters are used one must employ some extrapolation procedure to deduce the maximum (undegraded) energy of the released electrons.

Most commonly it is the photoelectrons which are measured. In this case one does not obtain the photon energy directly but rather the difference between the photon energy and the binding energy of the ejected orbital electron. According to Eq. (8-2), W_γ is then given by

$$W_\gamma = W_e + W_B.$$

Two significant facts emerge at once. One does not obtain a single monoergic group of electrons but rather one for each ionization potential of the converter atoms, and it becomes necessary to identify the observed electron groups with the K, L_I, L_{II}, etc. shells of the atom. W_γ is uncertain not only because of limitations in determining W_e but also because of uncertainties in the value of W_B. The ionization potentials of a number of elements, fortunately, are known with considerable precision as a result of extensive x-ray studies. Moreover, the very existence of a number of groups of electrons (usually called *lines*) overdetermines W_γ and thereby reduces the uncertainty in its value. The natural width of the K level itself is only about 80 ev even in the heaviest elements. This is much smaller than the experimental errors involved. The recoil energy given to the residual ion in the photoelectric effect is wholly negligible. The background caused by Compton electrons can almost be eliminated by surrounding the converter with high-efficiency scintillation detectors to detect Compton-scattered photons. Scintillation pulses from the latter are fed into an anticoincidence circuit* to suppress counts due to Compton electrons.

At energies exceeding the threshold for pair production (1.02 Mev) various forms of pair spectrometers are used. One was mentioned in Prob. 7-5.

Use of Compton electrons is slightly more complicated because of the dependence of electron energy on the angle of emission. If both the incident beam and the ejected electrons are carefully collimated then there is a one-to-one correspondence between the measured Compton electron energy and the incident photon energy, given by

$$W_e - mc^2 = \frac{2mc^2 \cos^2 \phi}{(1 + mc^2/W_\gamma)^2 - \cos^2 \phi}, \qquad (8\text{-}8)$$

* In an anticoincidence circuit, an electrical pulse from detector A produces a count in the absence of a simultaneous pulse from detector B. A simultaneous pulse from detector B, on the other hand, nullifies the pulse from detector A with the result that this type of event is not counted. In the above example, the electron detector is "detector A," while the Compton photon scintillation detectors constitute "detector B."

where $(W_e - mc^2)$ is the kinetic energy of the Compton electron ejected at an angle ϕ (see Fig. 8-9).

Other methods. Where high sensitivity is a necessity, as with weak sources, the thin converters which are usually used with magnetic spectrometers are not suitable. If the quantum energy of the photons is less than about 50 Kev, high-pressure ionization chambers or proportional counters may be used. Above 50 Kev, liquid or solid ionization chambers or scintillators are used. In these devices, the output electrical pulses are proportional to or nearly proportional to the energy expended in the device. In the case of photoelectrons, not only the primary photoelectron but also the Auger electron or secondary photoelectron from the atomic x-rays which are emitted immediately after the primary photoelectric encounter contribute to the output pulse. It is seen then that these devices measure the *total* photon energy rather than $W_\gamma - W_B$.

Compton electrons, in spite of their continuous spread of energies, will produce an energy spectrum with something of a peak followed by a sharp fall-off in intensity (see Fig. 8-14) as one approaches the maximum possible electron energy (given by setting $\cos \phi = 1$ in Eq. (8-8)). The peak is known as the *Compton peak* and the sharp fall-off as the *Compton edge*. They serve to give a rough value for W_γ. To obtain more precision, coincidence techniques must be used. The kinetic energy given to a Compton electron when the photon is scattered through an angle θ is

$$W_e - mc^2 = \frac{W_\gamma^2(1 - \cos \theta)}{mc^2 + W_\gamma(1 - \cos \theta)}. \tag{8-9}$$

Out of all the Compton electron pulses one selects only those which are in coincidence with a scattered photon detected at an angle θ with respect to the incident beam. The accuracy of a Compton scintillation coincidence spectrometer is comparable to that achieved with magnetic spectrometers.

It is also possible to use very large scintillators in which the Compton-scattered photon is almost certain to be absorbed. In this case the output pulses will almost all correspond to W_γ. In any such device there are always electrons which escape from the scintillator before being brought to rest. Some scattered photons also escape. If the background of random-sized pulses produced by these escape events is small in the region of the strong peak of full-energy pulses, their effect is not serious.

Scintillators can also be used as pair spectrometers. If the charged particles are brought to rest but the annihilation gammas from the stopped positron escape, then the electrical output pulse will be a measure of $W_\gamma - 2mc^2$. If the scintillator is large enough to absorb the annihilation radiation, the output pulses will be related to the full photon energy, W_γ. Sometimes, in order to reduce background effects, two other scintillators are used in addition to the converter-scintillator. Only those pulses from the latter which are in coincidence with annihilation gamma pulses in the other two scintillators are counted.

Photonuclear reactions are sometimes used to detect gamma rays, especially moderate-energy gammas in the presence of intense low-energy gammas. The thresholds for these reactions, such as $Be^9(\gamma, n2\alpha)$ at 1.66 Mev and $D^2(\gamma, pn)$ at 2.23 Mev, make detectors based upon their use insensitive to gammas below the threshold energy. The reactions have been detected with neutron counters, cloud chambers, and nuclear emulsions. The accuracy of energy determination by these methods is generally low.

PROBLEMS

8-1 It is said that, in operation, the water just outside the reactor area of the hull of a nuclear-powered submarine glows with a bluish light. What minimum energy must a gamma ray have to excite Čerenkov radiation in sea water if the index of refraction of sea water is taken to be 1.34?

[*Ans.* 0.256 Mev.]

8-2 A sheet of lead 0.58 cm thick reduces the transmitted intensity of a monoergic gamma-ray beam to one-half of the intensity of the incident beam.

(a) How thick a sheet of lead is needed to reduce the transmitted intensity to 1.0% of the incident intensity?

(b) From Fig. 8-16, what is the energy of the gamma rays?

[*Ans.* (a) 3.85 cm; (b) 0.63 Mev.]

8-3 A "point source" of gamma rays is located at the center of a large solid metal sphere. The linear absorption coefficient of the metal for the gamma rays given off by the source is $\mu(cm^{-1})$. Find the intensity at the outer surface of the sphere as a function of the sphere radius.

8-4 When sheets of lead of the following thicknesses are inserted between a source of gamma radiation and a scintillation counter, the following numbers of counts per minute (above background) are observed.

Thickness of lead sheet (cm)	Counts per minute	Thickness of lead sheet (cm)	Counts per minute
0	600	1.4	223
0.2	508	1.8	178
0.4	435	2.2	142
0.6	377	2.8	103
0.8	328	4.0	55
1.0	288	5.0	34

From Fig. 8-16, what are the energies of the gamma rays?

[*Ans.* 0.57 Mev and 2.27 Mev.]

8-5 Show that the energy of a photon, W'_γ, after a Compton collision, is related to the photon energy before collision, W_γ, by the equation

$$W'_\gamma = \frac{W_\gamma mc^2}{mc^2 + (1 - \cos\theta)W_\gamma},$$

where θ is the angle through which the photon is scattered, and from this derive Eq. (8-9).

8-6 A well-collimated beam of annihilation radiation is passed through a lead absorber 0.4 cm thick. What fraction of the incident photons suffer at least one Compton collision in passing through the lead? (Use the Klein-Nishina formula for your calculation.) [Ans. 99.43%.]

8-7 Show that the maximum momentum (for a given energy) will be carried away by a newly created pair when the momenta of the two particles are equal.

8-8 Derive Eq. (8-8).

8-9 In a betatron, the acceleration is provided by the changing magnetic field. This is most easily looked upon from the standpoint of an electro-motive force around the circular orbit produced by a changing flux through the area enclosed by the electron's orbit. The orbit radius is determined by the magnetic flux density component perpendicular to the plane of the orbit at the position of the orbit. Computation of the orbit radius is standard, but one must remember to use the relativistic momentum expression for the electron. Show that the condition for constant radius throughout the acceleration process (assuming that the electron is injected into the desired orbit with some initial velocity) is

$$\frac{d\Phi}{dt} = 2\pi\rho^2 \frac{dB}{dt},$$

where Φ is the total magnetic flux through the orbit, B is the perpendicular component of the magnetic flux density at the orbit, ρ is the orbit radius, and t is time. Any system of units in which B has the dimensions of Φ/ρ^2 is obviously acceptable.

REFERENCES

1. Ajzenberg, F., and Lauritsen, T., *Rev. Mod. Phys.*, **27**, 77 (1955).

2. Alburger, D. E., *Phys. Rev.*, **109**, 1222 (1958).

3. Bent, R. D., Bonner, T. W., and McCrary, J. H., *Phys. Rev.*, **98**, 1325 (1955).

4. Brunner, J. H., Leisi, H. J., Perdrisat, C. F., and Scherrer, P., *Phys. Rev. Letters*, **2**, 207 (1959).

5. Cavanagh, P. E., *Phys. Rev.*, **87**, 1131 (1952).

6. Curie, I., and Joliot, F., *J. Phys. Rad.*, **4**, 494 (1933). See also Chadwick, J., Blackett, P. M. S., and Occhialini, G. P. S., *Proc. Roy. Soc.*, **A144**, 235 (1934).

7. Davisson, C. M., and Evans, R. D., *Rev. Mod. Phys.*, **24**, 79 (1952).

8. Devons, S., Goldring, G., and Lindsey, G. R., *Proc. Phys. Soc.* (*London*), **67-A**, 134 (1954).

9. Fano, U., *Nucleonics*, **11**:8, 8 (1953).

10. Ferguson, G. A., Halpern, J., Nathans, R., and Yergin, P. F., *Phys. Rev.*, **95**, 776 (1954).

11. Fowler, W. A., and Lauritsen, C. C., *Phys. Rev.*, **56**, 840 (1939).

12. Gorodetzky, S., Chevallier, P., Armbruster, R., Gallman, A., and Sutter, G., *Nuc. Phys.*, **7**, 672 (1958).

13. Gorodetzky, S., Chevallier, P., Armbruster, R., and Sutter, G., *Nuc. Phys.*, **12**, 349 (1959).

14. Grechukin, D. P., *Zhur. Éksp. i Teoret. Fiz.*, **32**, 1036 (1957).

15. Gunst, S. B., and Page, L. A., *Phys. Rev.*, **92**, 970 (1953).

16. Harries, G., *Proc. Phys. Soc.* (*London*), **67-A**, 153 (1954).

17. Heitler, W., *The Quantum Theory of Radiation* (Oxford: Oxford University Press, 1936).

18. Heitler, W., and Nordheim, L., *Physica*, **1**, 1059 (1934).

19. Jaeger, J. G., and Hulme, H., *Proc. Roy. Soc.*, **A148**, 708 (1935).

20. Johnson, O. E., Johnson, R. G., and Langer, L. M., *Phys. Rev.*, **98**, 1517 (1955).

21. Latyshev, G. D., *Rev. Mod. Phys.*, **19**, 132 (1947).

22. Latyshev, G. D., Gei, V. V., Bashilov, A. A., and Barchuk, I. F., *Doklady Akad. Nauk. S.S.S.R.*, **63**, 511 (1948).

23. Lindström, G., Siegbahn, K., and Wapstra, A. H., *Proc. Phys. Soc.* (*London*), **66B**, 54 (1953).

24. McVoy, K. W., *Phys. Rev.*, **108**, 365 (1957).

25. Melikian, E. G., *Zhur. Éksp. i Teoret. Fiz.*, **32**, 384 (1957).

26. Muller, D. E., Hoyt, H. C., Klein, D. J., and DuMond, J. W. M., *Phys. Rev.*, **88**, 775 (1952).

27. Orlov, Iu. V., *Zhur. Éksp. i Teoret. Fiz.*, **31**, 1103 (1956).

28. Perrin, F., *Compt. Rend.*, **197**, 1100 (1933). See also Watson, K. M., *Phys. Rev.*, **72**, 1060 (1947).

29. Siegbahn, K., Lindquist, T., and Pettersson, B., in H. J. Lipkin, ed., *Proceedings of the Rehovoth Conference on Nuclear Structure, September 1957*, (New York: Interscience Publishers, Inc., 1958), p. 255.

30. Slätis, H., and Siegbahn, K., *Arkiv. Fysik*, **4**, 485 (1952).

31. Sliv, L. A., *Jour. Exptl. Theor. Phys. U.S.S.R.*, **25**, 7 (1953); *J. Phys. Rad.*, **16**, 589 (1955).

32. Spruch, L., and Goertzel, G., *Phys. Rev.*, **94**, 1671 (1954).

33. Streib, J. F., Fowler, W. A., and Lauritsen, C. C., *Phys. Rev.*, **59**, 253 (1941).

34. Tolhoek, H. A., *Rev. Mod. Phys.*, **28**, 277 (1956).

9

NUCLEAR STRUCTURE

9-1 Introduction

Since we do not as yet have a satisfactory theory of nuclear forces, several nuclear "models" have been espoused as devices for making predictions about nuclei and nuclear reactions. One also encounters such models in atomic physics, but there the force laws are known, making it possible to justify the models and to specify their limitations. The situation is somewhat different in the case of nuclear models. It is known in advance that none of them are accurate representations, but their limitations can only be judged by recourse to experiment. In spite of their shortcomings, they perform two very valuable services. They serve, just as firmly established physical "laws" do, to correlate a vast amount of experimental observation, and their predictive value, though limited, is extremely helpful in the process of planning new experiments.

In this chapter a number of lines of evidence will be discussed which form the background and the guidelines for the construction of the various models. More importantly, any accurate theory of nuclear forces will also have to be able to explain these facts.

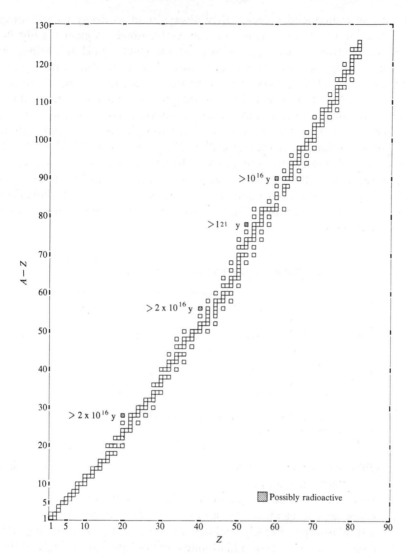

Fig. 9-1. Neutron *vs.* proton plot of all known stable nuclides. Four naturally occurring nuclides are included which may be radioactive. In each case, the half-life is greater than 10^{16} years. This same figure appears in Chap. 2, but is given again here because it is so pertinent to the discussion.

9-2 Nuclear Systematics

It was pointed out in an earlier chapter that the stable nuclei tend to have a fairly small range of neutron-to-proton ratios. Out of nearly 900 artificially produced nuclides which do not already exist naturally, *not one* is stable.

When these radionuclides decay, they always tend to decay to an isotope whose neutron-to-proton ratio is nearer the stable range. A glance at Fig. 9-1, which is a neutron-versus-proton plot of all the stable* nuclides, brings this out more vividly. A rough "curve of stability" could be drawn through the center of gravity of the points. This curve starts out with a slope of one (i.e., the number of protons is equal to the number of neutrons) and gradually increases in slope as the nuclides become heavier. There is also a certain imperfect regularity in the succession of neutron-plus-proton combinations. This is most pronounced in the regions $5 \leqslant Z \leqslant 7$, $8 \leqslant Z \leqslant 15$, $23 \leqslant Z \leqslant 27$, but if a relatively few points were removed there would be several other regions of equal regularity. This regularity suggests some sort of nuclear architecture.

The importance of even numbers in nuclei was noted by Harkins (9) in 1917. This is illustrated by Table 9-1 and by some pertinent observations enumerated below:

Table 9-1 DISTRIBUTION OF NUCLIDES

Z	Even	Even	Odd	Odd
$A - Z$	Even	Odd	Even	Odd
Number of nuclides	160*	53	49	4

* Includes 4 nuclides which may possibly be radioactive, but with extremely long half-lives.

1. Only one element with an even atomic number, $_4\text{Be}^9$, fails to have more than one isotope.
2. No element of odd atomic number has more than two isotopes.
3. There are two elements, both of odd atomic number, which have no natural isotopes, namely, technetium ($_{43}\text{Tc}$) and prometheum ($_{61}\text{Pm}$).
4. Twenty-six elements of odd atomic number have only a single isotope.
5. Only four of the above 26 isotopes have both an odd atomic number (Z) and an odd isotonic (neutron) number ($A - Z$). These are $_1\text{H}^2$, $_3\text{Li}^6$, $_5\text{B}^{10}$, and $_7\text{N}^{14}$. There are, in addition, two long-lived radionuclides, $_{23}\text{V}^{50}$ ($t_{1/2} = 4.8 \times 10^{14}$ yr) and $_{57}\text{La}^{138}$ ($t_{1/2} = 1.1 \times 10^{11}$ yr).

* The discussion in this section is concerned primarily with *stable* nuclides. Unless a statement is made to the contrary, the reader should assume that "stable nuclide" is meant when the words *nuclide, isobar, isotope, isotone, element*, etc. are used without qualification.

6. There are ten isotonic numbers, all odd, below 126 for which there is no natural nuclide. These are 19, 21, 35, 39, 45, 61, 71, 89, 115, and 123.

7. There are 51 isotonic numbers, all but three of which are odd, for each of which there exists but one nuclide.

8. There are no more than two isotones for *any* odd neutron number.

9. In the case of each element of even atomic number greater than 6, the lightest and heaviest isotope has an even number of neutrons. Where odd neutron numbers occur, they are always found near the center (i.e., near the mean neutron number) of the group of isotopes.

10. There are no proven cases in which there is more than one nuclide of any given *odd* mass number. There are five pairs of odd-mass-number isobars (nuclides with the same mass number, A) in which there is one stable and one long-lived radioactive isobar. These are listed in Table 9-2.

Table 9-2 ISOBARS OF ODD MASS NUMBER

A	Stable nuclide	Unstable nuclide	Half-life of unstable nuclide
87	$_{38}Sr_{49}$*	$_{37}Rb_{50}$	5×10^{10} yr
113	$_{49}In_{64}$	$_{48}Cd_{65}$	$> 10^{15}$ yr
115	$_{50}Sn_{65}$	$_{49}In_{66}$	6×10^{14} yr
123	$_{51}Sb_{72}$	$_{52}Te_{71}$	$> 10^{14}$ yr
187	$_{76}Os_{111}$	$_{75}Re_{112}$	5×10^{10} yr

* The right-hand subscript is the neutron number of the nuclide.

11. It follows from item 10 that all isobar groups consist wholly of even-A nuclides, and from item 5 that none contains an odd-Z member. Hence, the members of any one group have atomic numbers differing by 2^n.

The greater inherent stability of nuclides with an even number of protons or neutrons is shown more strikingly in Figs. 9-2 and 9-3, which portray the estimated (1) relative abundance of atoms as a function of atomic number and isotonic number respectively. Arsenic and bromine are the only violations of the rule that elements of even atomic number are more abundant than adjoining elements of odd atomic number.

There are no exceptions to the rule that atoms of even isotonic number have greater abundances than adjoining odd isotones. The even-odd alternation of abundances suggests the operation of the Pauli exclusion principle, which allows two identical particles of opposite spin in each (otherwise identical) state. Generally speaking, the heavy elements are much less

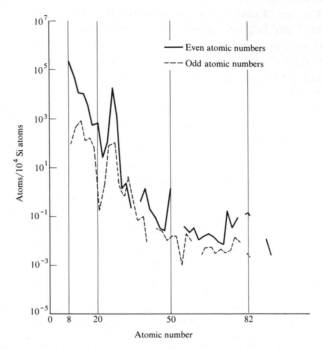

Fig. 9-2. Estimated abundance (1) of atoms, having the same atomic number, as a function of the atomic number.

abundant than the light elements, which indicates that the binding energy of an additional particle generally becomes smaller as more and more particles are added to the nucleus. There are several places on each figure where the abundance takes a sudden drop. Such drops occur on both curves as soon as the number of identical particles exceeds 20, 50, or 82. The special properties of 50 and 82 neutrons were noted by Guggenheimer (8) in 1934, and in the same year Elsasser (4) theorized, on the basis of abundance and stability, that atomic numbers 50 and 82 and neutron numbers 50, 82, and 126 are associated with increased nuclear stability. The peak at 126 neutrons is the maximum number of neutrons found in any stable nuclide, while there is a major drop in abundance from atomic number 28 to 29 and 30. The binding energy of the last neutron* is shown for the isotopes (including several radio-

* This quantity is often called the "neutron separation energy."

isotopes in this case) of several elements as a function of the neutron number in Fig. 9-4. This plot demonstrates again the strong preference for even numbers of neutrons. It also shows how loosely bound the third, ninth, and twenty-first neutrons are, thus demonstrating the unique properties of 2, 8, and 20 neutrons. The numbers 2, 8, 20, 50, 82, and 126 seem to possess a

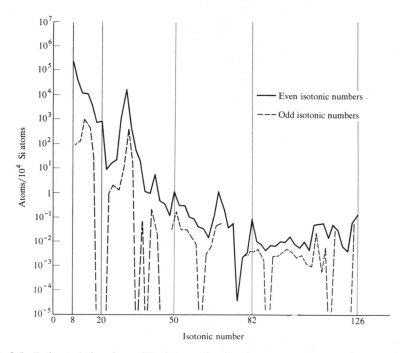

Fig. 9-3. Estimated abundance (1) of atoms, having the same neutron number, as a function of the neutron number. The isotonic number 78 appears to be an exception to the odd-even rule, but the abundance figure here does not include Te^{130} or Xe^{132}, the abundances of which are not known.

special significance and have acquired the name "magic numbers." Listed below are a number of other bits of evidence (5, 12) which confirm their importance in nuclear structure.

(a) Table 9-3 lists all nuclides which have an even atomic number greater than 32, and an isotopic abundance* of over 60 per cent. Each of these exceptional isotopes has a magic number of neutrons.

(b) Table 9-4 lists all the elements of even atomic number greater than 32 whose lightest isotopes have an isotopic abundance greater than 2 per cent.

* Isotopic abundance may be defined as the ratio, in a representative sample, of the number of atoms of a particular isotope to the total number of atoms of the element in question.

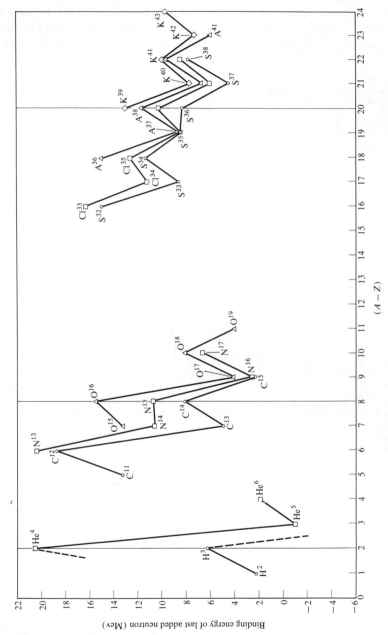

Fig. 9-4. Binding energy of last added neutron. This quantity, which is also called the "neutron separation energy" is calculated from the formula

$$W_n = 931.141[M(Z, N-1) + M_N - M(Z, N)].$$

Table 9-3 ABUNDANT EVEN-Z NUCLIDES WITH $Z > 32$

Element	Relative isotopic abundance (in per cent)	No. of neutrons
Sr^{88}	82.6	50
Ba^{138}	71.7	82
Ce^{140}	88.5	82

All of these except Ru^{96} have a magic number of neutrons. While the abundance of Sm^{144} is fairly small, the importance of its 82 neutrons is made evident by the complete absence of the next heavier even isotope, Sm^{146}.

Table 9-4 ABUNDANT LIGHTEST ISOTOPES OF EVEN-Z NUCLIDES WITH $Z > 32$

Element	Relative isotopic abundance (in per cent)	No. of neutrons
Zr^{90}	51.5	50
Mo^{92}	15.9	50
Ru^{96}	5.5	52
Nd^{142}	27.1	82
Sm^{144}	3.2	82

(c) Table 9-5 gives the frequency of occurrence of the more numerous isotones.

Table 9-5 THE MORE NUMEROUS ISOTONES

No. of isotones	No. of neutrons $(A - Z)$
7	82
6[a]	50
5[b]	20
5[b]	28
5	58
5[b]	74
5[c]	78
2[d]	126

[a] One of the six, Rb^{87}, is actually radioactive, but its half-life is 6×10^{10} years.

[b] These isotonic groups each contain one member with a magic number of protons.

[c] Includes Te^{130} which is radioactive but whose half-life is greater than 10^{21} years.

[d] Included because there are no stable isotones with more than 126 neutrons. One of these two is Bi^{209} which is radioactive, but with a half-life greater than 2×10^{18} years.

(d) Table 9-6 shows the frequency of occurrence of the more numerous isotopes. Tin ($Z = 50$) is outstanding in several ways. It has one of the largest spreads in neutron numbers, the greatest total number of isotopes, and is the only element with as many as three odd-A isotopes. The lightest element having as many as 6 isotopes is $_{20}$Ca. Its lightest isotope, Ca^{40}, contains a magic number (20) of neutrons and its heaviest, Ca^{48}, a semimagic number (28) of neutrons. Ca^{48} is probably weakly radioactive. Only one element of atomic number less than that of calcium has as many as four isotopes. One of the most notable features of the table is the fact that seven of the more numerous isotope groups contain isotopes having magic numbers of neutrons.

Table 9-6 THE MORE NUMEROUS ISOTOPES

No. of isotopes	Spread in neutron numbers	No. of protons (Z)
10	12	50
9	12	54[a]
8	10	48[d]
8	10	52[e]
7	8	42[b]
7	8	44
7	8	56[a]
7[f]	9	60[a]
7	8	66
7	8	64
7	8	70
7	8	76
7	8	80
6	10	62[a]
6[g]	8	20[c]
6	8	34
6	8	36[b]
6	8	46
6	8	68
6	6	72

[a] One isotope contains 82 neutrons.
[b] One isotope contains 50 neutrons.
[c] One isotope contains 20 neutrons.
[d] Includes Cd^{113} ($t_{1/2} > 10^{15}$ yr).
[e] Includes Te^{123} ($t_{1/2} > 10^{14}$ yr) and Te^{130} ($t_{1/2} > 10^{21}$ yr).
[f] Includes Nd^{144} ($t_{1/2} \sim 2 \times 10^{15}$ yr) and Nd^{150} ($t_{1/2} > 10^{16}$ yr).
[g] Includes Ca^{48} ($t_{1/2} > 2 \times 10^{16}$ yr).

(e) Twice in the periodic series the lightest isotopes of neighboring elements of even atomic number have the same number of neutrons. These pairs are $_{40}Zr^{90}$, $_{42}Mo^{92}$, both with 50 neutrons, and $_{60}Nd^{142}$, $_{62}Sm^{144}$, each possessing 82 neutrons.

(f) Three times in the periodic series the heaviest isotopes of neighboring elements of even atomic number have the same number of neutrons. These pairs are $_{20}Ca^{48}$,* $_{22}Ti^{50}$, with 28 neutrons, $_{36}Kr^{86}$, $_{38}Sr^{88}$, with 50 neutrons, and $_{54}Xe^{136}$, $_{56}Ba^{138}$, with 82 neutrons.

(g) Table 9-7 lists all of the nuclides of odd atomic number which have the same number of neutrons. The isotones La^{139} and Pr^{141} are especially remarkable as each has an isotopic abundance of 100 per cent.

Table 9-7 ELEMENTS OF ODD ATOMIC NUMBER POSSESSING THE SAME NUMBER OF NEUTRONS

Elements		No. of neutrons
$_{17}Cl^{37}$	$_{19}K^{39}$	20
$_{37}Rb^{87}$	$_{39}Y^{89}$	50*
$_{57}La^{139}$	$_{59}Pr^{141}$	82

* Rb^{87} is radioactive with a half-life of 6×10^{10} years.

(h) Figure 6-1 shows the asymmetric distribution in mass numbers of the fission fragments resulting from fission of U^{235} by slow neutrons. The greater probability of a fission into fragments of unequal mass may be connected with the low energy and extra stability of atoms having 50 and 82 neutrons.

(i) Delayed neutron emission takes place, as explained in Chap. 6 and Fig. 6-2, in those rare instances where neutron emission can compete effectively with radiative de-excitation. In the three well-established cases of neutron decay, the product of the decay contains a magic number of neutrons, O^{16} with 8, Kr^{86} with 50, and Xe^{136} with 82. In the less certain case of Li^{9m}, neutron emission would yield Be^{8}, which is unstable and breaks up immediately into two alpha particles. The result then is to form two magic-number nuclides, each with two neutrons. The inference is that the binding energy of the last neutron in the case of Kr^{87}, Xe^{137}, O^{17}, and Be^{9} is so small, even in the ground state, that when these nuclei are left in an excited state by beta emission, neutron emission becomes energetically very favorable.

(j) A few nuclides have extraordinarily large thermal neutron absorption cross sections. These are listed in Table 9-8. The largest cross section is that of Xe^{135}, in which case the addition of a neutron brings the total number of neutrons to 82. The addition of a neutron to V^{50} brings its total number of neutrons to 28.

Figure 9-5 is a plot of thermal neutron activation cross sections of nuclides of even neutron number. The largest cross sections show minima in the

* Ca^{48} is probably radioactive. If so, its half-life is greater than 2×10^{16} years.

Table 9-8 Nuclides with Large Thermal Neutron
Absorption Cross Sections

Nuclide	Cross section (in barns)
$_{23}V^{50}_{27}$	$\sim 2.5 \times 10^2$
$_{48}Cd^{113}_{65}$	2.1×10^4
$_{62}Sm^{149}_{87}$	5.3×10^4
$_{54}Xe^{135}_{81}$	2.6×10^6

vicinity of 20, 50, 82, and 126 neutrons, and certain nuclides such as $_{20}Ca^{40}$ with 20 neutrons and 20 protons, $_{38}Sr^{88}$ with 50 neutrons, $_{56}Ba^{138}$ with 82 neutrons, and $_{82}Pb^{208}$ with 82 protons and 126 neutrons have lower cross sections than neighboring nuclei. It is significant that the "doubly magic" isotopes Ca^{40} and Pb^{208} have extraordinarily low cross sections. The same sort of behavior is shown somewhat better by the fast neutron activation cross sections plotted against neutron number, as in Fig. 9-6.

Rather surprisingly, considering the large excitation energies, the half widths of the giant (γ, n) resonances also show a correlation with the magic numbers (13).

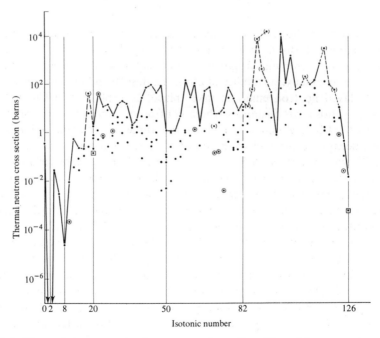

Fig. 9-5. Thermal neutron activation cross sections of nuclides with even neutron numbers. ⊙ indicates that the nuclide has a magic number of protons. ⊡ indicates a doubly magic nuclide. ($\cdot$) indicates a doubtful value, a poor approximation, or an average pile neutron value. Maximum values for each isotonic number are connected by solid or dashed lines.

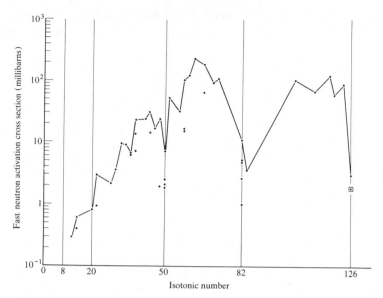

Fig. 9-6. Fast neutron activation cross section of nuclides with even neutron numbers. The fast neutrons were obtained from fission of U^{235} enriched uranium by thermal neutrons from a nuclear reactor. They have an average energy of about 1 Mev. [From D. J. Hughes and D. Sherman, *Phys. Rev.*, **78**, 632 (1950).]

(k) The two long-lived odd-odd radionuclides mentioned previously in item 5, namely $_{23}V^{50}$ with 27 neutrons, and $_{57}La^{138}$ with 81 neutrons, each has just one less neutron than a semimagic or a magic number. Since this is as close to a magic number as an odd-odd nucleus can get, the occurrence of these two unusual nuclides is probably significant.

9-3 Nuclear Shell Models

In 1934 Gamow (6), on the basis of a plot of $(A - Z)/A$ against A, suggested that the observed quasi-periodicities might be connected with a nuclear shell structure. Elsasser (4) showed that the numbers, which are now called magic, whose special nature he had pointed out, could be correlated with closed shells in a system in which the individual nucleons do not interact with each other but move in a common potential which he took to be of the wine-bottle* type. The spectacular early successes of the resonance formalism and the compound nucleus concept in explaining nuclear reactions caused the shell theory to go into eclipse for a number of years until it was revived by Mayer (11) in 1948. Her model has been so successful that we shall

* A wine-bottle potential differs from other potential wells in that the potential rises again at very small values of the radial distance from the origin.

not deal with the alternative (5, 14) shell structures which have been proposed even though they give better agreement with experiment in certain special cases.

Shell models are based on the fiction that the "orbital" particles do not interact with each other but rather each moves in a force field which can be described by a potential function which is a function only of radial distance from the center of the system. The artificiality of this picture becomes apparent when one remembers that the potential function exists only by virtue of the presence of all the particles other than the one under consideration. The Hartree-Fock model of the electronic structure of the atom is just of this kind. Assuming that any given particle fills only the lowest energy level available to it, then the potential function can be chosen so that the next higher energy level takes account of a *filled* lower energy level. Now it usually turns out that many of the energy levels computed on such a model are degenerate, that is, there are several combinations of quantum numbers which give the same energy. The actual interaction, which we have ignored in the model, will act to cause a small splitting of such energy levels so that each of the now separated levels can be occupied, according to the Pauli exclusion principle, by two particles with intrinsic spin $\frac{1}{2}$, one with its spin in one direction and one with its spin antiparallel to the first. In the atomic case we find shells which become filled when there are 2 electrons present (the K shell), 10 (K and L shells), 18 (K, L, and M shells), 36, 54, and 86 electrons. When a shell is filled, the last electron is very tightly bound (i.e., has a large ionization potential) which makes it difficult for the atom to share an electron with another atom and thus form a molecule. As a result, these filled-shell atoms, the rare gases, are monatomic and chemically inert. There is a comparatively large increase in energy to the next allowed energy state, so the next atom in the periodic series has its last electron very loosely bound. These are the alkali metals, which are very active chemically.

As long as one deals with potential functions which are functions of radial distance only, the quantum numbers are always the same regardless of the exact shape of the potential function, so they will be the same for the nuclear shell model as they are for the electronic shells of atoms.

The quantum numbers are usually designated by

> n, the radial quantum number, which increases as the orbital radius increases,
>
> l, the orbital angular momentum quantum number,
>
> s, the spin quantum number, which is always $+\frac{1}{2}$ or $-\frac{1}{2}$,
>
> j, the total angular momentum quantum number, $l + s$, or in other words $l \pm \frac{1}{2}$, and
>
> m_j, the magnetic quantum number, which is the projection of the vector **j** on some reference axis.

The quantum conditions require, as stated above, that $j = l + \frac{1}{2}$ or $j = l - \frac{1}{2}$. The $j = l + \frac{1}{2}$ case is usually referred to as the "parallel" configuration (i.e., orbital and spin angular momenta parallel) and the $j = l - \frac{1}{2}$ case as the "antiparallel" configuration. This is a loose usage of the words since the vectors have magnitudes given by

$$(\mathbf{l})^2 = l(l + 1),$$

$$(\mathbf{s})^2 = s(s + 1),$$

$$(\mathbf{j})^2 = j(j + 1),$$

but the nomenclature is standard and no ambiguity will arise through its application. The quantum number m_j may have any integral value from $-j$ to $+j$. The orbital angular momentum states, following the custom of atomic spectroscopy, are designated as s, p, d, f, g, h, i, etc., corresponding to the quantum values of l of 0, 1, 2, 3, 4, 5, 6, etc., respectively. A state in which the radial quantum number is 2 and the orbital angular momentum quantum number is 1 is then called a $2p$ state. The fact that the particles have intrinsic spin then requires that j be $1 + \frac{1}{2} = \frac{3}{2}$ or $1 - \frac{1}{2} = \frac{1}{2}$. These substates are then designated as $2p_{3/2}$ and $2p_{1/2}$. In the $p_{1/2}$ substate, m_j can have values of $+\frac{1}{2}$ or $-\frac{1}{2}$, while in the $p_{3/2}$ state, m_j can have the values $\frac{3}{2}$, $\frac{1}{2}$, $-\frac{1}{2}$, $-\frac{3}{2}$. Since the Pauli exclusion principle allows but one identical particle for each set of quantum numbers, a total of six identical particles can be placed in substates of the $2p$ state. In general there will be a total of $2(2l + 1)$ identical particles in the substates of the state whose orbital angular momentum quantum number is l. In the atomic case, the orbital particles are all electrons so they are all identical, but in the nuclear case there are both protons and neutrons to be added. Since these particles are different, the Pauli principle allows a complete set of states for the protons and another complete set with the same quantum numbers for the neutrons. The potential functions for the two kinds of particles will be different if for no other reason than the absence of the coulomb interaction between neutrons, so the energy levels and orbit radii will be different for protons and neutrons with the same quantum numbers, but the ordering of the levels may turn out to be the same if the potential functions are not too dissimilar. Henceforth, in this section, it is to be understood, unless stated to the contrary, that the word "particles" implies "identical particles."

Although the quantum numbers are the same, the energy of a level described by a given set of quantum numbers depends very sensitively on the potential function shape, and the relative spacing of the energy levels determines when a shell is "filled," since the criterion for a filled shell is that the next available state is one of considerably higher energy. It is no surprise that the coulomb interactions that determine the potential function in the atomic case fail to give the magic numbers revealed by nuclear data. Since the force laws for nucleon interactions are not yet formulated, one cannot write down a potential function at once but must adopt the expedient of trying various potential functions with the hope of finding one which predicts effects in accord with observations. We do know that nuclear forces are short range (see Sec. 9-4) since the binding energy per nucleon stays relatively constant as the mass number increases rather than increasing rapidly with mass number as it would if the range of nuclear forces were great enough that each nucleon interacted appreciably with every other nucleon in a given nucleus. This suggests a rather steep rise in the potential function at the nuclear radius and a practically constant potential at distances greater than the nuclear

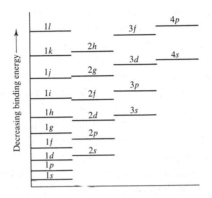

Fig. 9-7. Energy levels in an infinite three-dimensional square well. One would expect the levels of lower energy (greater binding energy) to fill first. Thus, if the nuclear potential function were of this very simple form, the levels would be filled in the order $1s$, $1p$, $1d$, $2s$, $1f$, $2p$, $1g$, $2d$, etc. [Adapted from H. A. Bethe and R. F. Bacher, *Rev. Mod. Phys.*, **8**, 82 (1936).]

radius. A nucleon outside the nucleus then experiences no force, but inside the nucleus is subjected to large forces. The simplest potential of this sort is the so-called square-well potential. The potential is given in this case by

$$U = \begin{cases} -U_0 & \text{for } r < r_0, \\ 0 & \text{for } r > r_0. \end{cases}$$

It is easier to obtain a mathematical solution if a "square well with infinite walls" is used, in which case

$$U = \begin{cases} -U_0 & \text{for } r < r_0, \\ \infty & \text{for } r > r_0. \end{cases}$$

The ordering of the levels is not changed by this approximation and the spacing of the lower energy levels is changed only slightly. The calculated energy levels are shown in Fig. 9-7 and at the right in Fig. 9-8. This potential function leads correctly to the magic numbers 2, 8, and 20 but not to any of the larger magic numbers.

A potential function which leads to even simpler solutions is the "three-dimensional isotropic oscillator." This formidable label describes the motion typified classically by a mass point constrained by a spring to move in three dimensions about a fixed point. The potential function is

$$U = -U_0[1 - (r/r_0)^2].$$

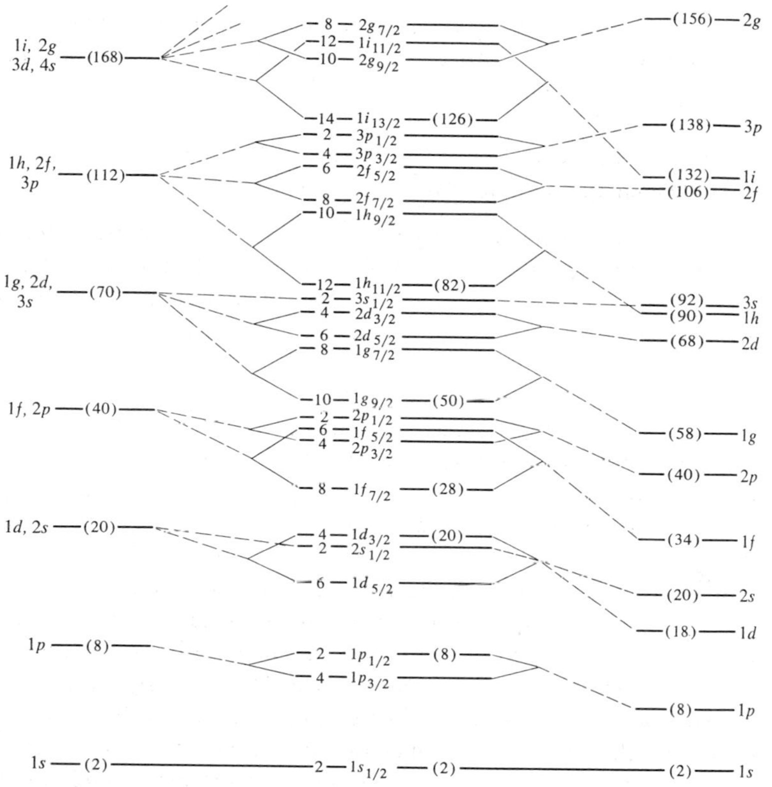

Three-dimensional isotropic oscillator levels (left):

- $1i, 2g, 3d, 4s$ —(168)—
- $1h, 2f, 3p$ —(112)—
- $1g, 2d, 3s$ —(70)—
- $1f, 2p$ —(40)—
- $1d, 2s$ —(20)—
- $1p$ —(8)—
- $1s$ —(2)—

Center levels proposed by Mayer (number of particles — spectroscopic designation — total):

- 8 — $2g_{7/2}$
- 12 — $1i_{11/2}$
- 10 — $2g_{9/2}$
- 14 — $1i_{13/2}$ —(126)—
- 2 — $3p_{1/2}$
- 4 — $3p_{3/2}$
- 6 — $2f_{5/2}$
- 8 — $2f_{7/2}$
- 10 — $1h_{9/2}$
- 12 — $1h_{11/2}$ —(82)—
- 2 — $3s_{1/2}$
- 4 — $2d_{3/2}$
- 6 — $2d_{5/2}$
- 8 — $1g_{7/2}$
- 10 — $1g_{9/2}$ —(50)—
- 2 — $2p_{1/2}$
- 6 — $1f_{5/2}$
- 4 — $2p_{3/2}$
- 8 — $1f_{7/2}$ —(28)—
- 4 — $1d_{3/2}$ —(20)—
- 2 — $2s_{1/2}$
- 6 — $1d_{5/2}$
- 2 — $1p_{1/2}$ —(8)—
- 4 — $1p_{3/2}$
- 2 — $1s_{1/2}$ —(2)—

Three-dimensional square well levels (right):

- —(156)— $2g$
- —(138)— $3p$
- —(132)— $1i$
- —(106)— $2f$
- —(92)— $3s$
- —(90)— $1h$
- —(68)— $2d$
- —(58)— $1g$
- —(40)— $2p$
- —(34)— $1f$
- —(20)— $2s$
- —(18)— $1d$
- —(8)— $1p$
- —(2)— $1s$

Fig. 9-8. The energy levels of a three-dimensional isotropic oscillator are shown at the left. At the far left, the spectroscopic designations of the levels are given. Slightly to the right of these are numbers in parentheses which are the total numbers of particles when those particular levels and all lower energy levels are filled. The energy levels in a three-dimensional square well with infinitely high walls are shown at the right and the spectroscopic designations of the levels are given at the far right. The numbers in parentheses slightly to the left of these have the same significance as before. In the center are the levels proposed by Mayer. The number of particles in each sublevel is shown on the left of the central part, then the spectroscopic designations are given, and total number of particles in that level and all lower energy levels where a so-called shell is formed.

The energy levels of the isotropic oscillator are shown at the left of Fig. 9-8. They are highly degenerate except for the two lowest states, and are equally spaced. This potential function also gives the magic numbers 2, 8, and 20, but again fails to give any of the larger magic numbers. The fact that two such different potential functions both yield the three lower magic numbers but not the higher ones led many early experimenters with shell models to the conclusion that the partial success was purely fortuitous and that the shell model was incapable of explaining the magic numbers.

The new hypotheses which have caused the more recent shell models to meet with success are:

1. There is strong spin orbit coupling in nuclei (i.e., there is a large energy dependence on the relative orientations of spin and orbital angular momenta).

2. The spin-orbit doublets are inverted; that is, in contrast to electronic energy levels, the levels of higher total angular momentum ($j = l + \frac{1}{2}$) have less energy than the levels corresponding to $j = l - \frac{1}{2}$.

The model discussed here uses a potential intermediate in shape between the isotropic oscillator and the square well. The energy levels associated with this intermediate potential are shown at the center of Fig. 9-8 with dotted lines connecting to the corresponding levels in the isotropic oscillator (at the left) and the square well (at the right). There is a large gap between the $1s_{1/2}$ and the $1p_{3/2}$ levels, so the first shell is closed when there are two identical particles with oppositely oriented spins in the $1s_{1/2}$ state. A second large energy gap occurs between the $1p_{1/2}$ and the $1d_{5/2}$ states, giving a closed shell at $1p_{1/2}$ with a total of 8 particles, 2 in the $1s_{1/2}$, 4 in the $1p_{3/2}$, and 2 in the $1p_{1/2}$ states. Another gap occurs between $1d_{3/2}$ and $1f_{7/2}$ which causes the third shell to be closed at $1d_{3/2}$ with a total of 20 particles. Thus far, there is not much improvement over the older models, but from here on the increasingly great splitting of the high angular momentum states causes the energy gaps which determine closed shells to occur in different places than they did in older models. The relatively large gap between $1f_{7/2}$ and $2p_{3/2}$ gives rise to a filled subshell with a semimagic number of 28 particles. It will be seen that it is possible with this model to obtain all of the magic numbers.

The model does not make any allowance for the extra binding energy associated with pairing of particles, a phenomenon which is strikingly evident in Fig. 9-4. The reason, of course, lies in the fact that the model ignores interactions between individual nucleons. If, as seems reasonable, the pairing energy increases for large angular momentum states, then it is quite possible that the large angular momentum states will be filled only in pairs, odd particles going into what appear in Fig. 9-8 to be higher energy levels of lower angular momenta. This idea is borne out by the observation that no ground state nucleus has a spin as great as $\frac{11}{2}$.

In 1937 Schmidt (16) pointed out that nuclear properties could be understood qualitatively by assuming that they are due entirely to the last added nucleon. This is known as the "extreme one-particle theory." In Table 9-1 it was seen that 160 stable nuclides belong to the even-even category, and it will be remembered that these have neither spin nor magnetic moment. Of the remaining stable nuclides, only four are not included in the class having an even number of protons and an odd number of neutrons or an even number of neutrons and an odd number of protons, so that a one-particle theory can be the basis for prediction of most of the observable spins and magnetic moments. All but the odd particle are assumed to be paired off and to contribute neither spin nor magnetic moment under this theory. The odd particle is then assumed, just as in shell theory, to move in an average potential created by the remainder of the nucleons. It is further assumed that the intrinsic magnetic moments of proton and neutron are the same when bound to a nucleus as they are in the free nucleons. The orbital motion contributes to the total magnetic moment only in the case of an odd proton, as the neutron has no charge. If the odd particle is in one of the two states $j = l + \frac{1}{2}$ or $j = l - \frac{1}{2}$, the total magnetic moment, $\mu_{l+(1/2)}$ or $\mu_{l-(1/2)}$ respectively, can be computed from the formulas (15)

$$\mu_{l+(1/2)} = lg_l + \tfrac{1}{2}g_s \tag{9-1}$$

and

$$\mu_{l-(1/2)} = \frac{(l+1)(l-\frac{1}{2})}{(l+\frac{1}{2})} g_l - \frac{1}{2}\frac{l-\frac{1}{2}}{l+\frac{1}{2}} g_s, \tag{9-2}$$

where $g_s = 2\mu_p$ for a proton and $2\mu_n$ for a neutron, $g_l = 1$ for a proton and zero for a neutron, and $\mu_{l\pm(1/2)}$ is in nuclear magnetons.* The magnetic moment of the free proton, μ_p, is 2.7935 nm, and that of the free neutron, μ_n, is -1.9136 nm. The magnetic moments calculated from these formulas are known as the "Schmidt limits." Actually, the particle may be in a mixed state, corresponding to a linear combination of solutions to the wave equation, in which case the magnetic moment should lie somewhere between the two Schmidt limits. Figure 9-9 is a plot of observed magnetic moments against spin for nuclei having an even number of neutrons but an odd number of protons. The Schmidt limits are also shown. Figure 9-10 gives the Schmidt limits and measured magnetic moments as a function of the spins for nuclei having an even number of protons and an odd number of neutrons. The extreme one-particle theory requires that the nuclear spin, I, be equal to the odd-particle spin, j. In Figures 9-9 and 9-10, μ is therefore plotted against the measured nuclear spin, I.

* With the values of g_l given here, no account is taken of the motion of the bulk of the nucleus about the center of mass of the system. The correction can easily be made, but is not large enough to account for the difference between calculated and measured magnetic moments.

Table 9-9 shows how one would expect the lighter nuclei to be built up on the basis of this shell model. For those nuclei having only one odd particle the predicted spin is given by the subscript to the term designation of the odd particle, as H^3, which has two $1s_{1/2}$ neutrons, a single $1s_{1/2}$ proton, and a

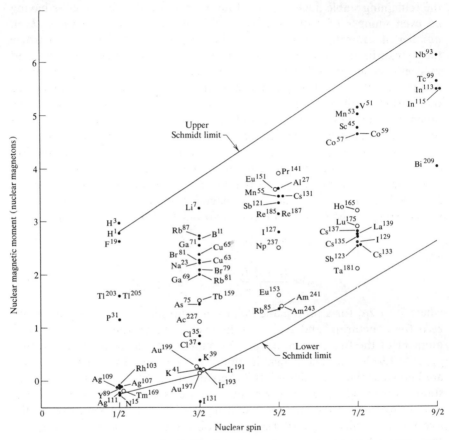

Fig. 9-9. Magnetic moments of nuclei having an even neutron number and an odd proton number. The open circles represent less accurately known data. The data points for a given spin value, such as $\frac{1}{2}$, have been spread sideward slightly, where crowded, for convenience in plotting. [Data from H. Kopfermann, *Nuclear Moments* (New York: Academic Press, 1958).]

predicted spin of $\frac{1}{2}$. In the case of odd-odd nuclides, the relative spin orientations of the two odd particles cannot be predicted. Where parallel or antiparallel orientation gives the observed spin, this information is used to calculate the "predicted magnetic moments" from the formulas given earlier. Since the observed magnetic moments do not all lie on the Schmidt limit lines, it is obvious that the predicted and observed magnetic moments will not exactly agree. Most measured values of spin, and to a lesser extent of magnetic moment, agree with the predictions of the shell model. There are several discrepancies, however, which should be mentioned. $_9F^{19}$ would be expected to have an odd $1d_{5/2}$ proton, but its measured spin is $\frac{1}{2}$. If one assumes that the odd proton goes into the $2s_{1/2}$ state, then the measured and calculated

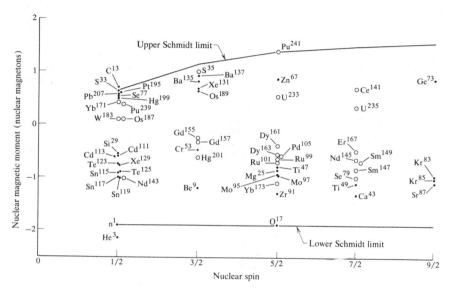

Fig. 9-10. Magnetic moments of nuclei having an even proton number and an odd neutron number. The open circles represent less accurately known data. [Data from H. Kopfermann, *Nuclear Moments* (New York: Academic Press, 1958).]

magnetic moments are in good agreement. It is also possible that the two $1d_{5/2}$ neutrons and a $1d_{5/2}$ proton couple together to give a total spin of $\frac{1}{2}$. This also gives good agreement as far as magnetic moment is concerned.

$_{11}Na^{23}$, as shown in Table 9-9, is expected to have three $1d_{5/2}$ protons and therefore a spin of $\frac{5}{2}$, but its measured spin is $\frac{3}{2}$. This obviously cannot be explained by saying the odd particle went into the next higher energy state of lower momentum, for that is a $2s_{1/2}$ state. It appears that the best explanation is a coupling of the three $1d_{5/2}$ protons to give a total spin of $\frac{3}{2}$. $_{22}Ti^{47}$, which should have five $1f_{7/2}$ neutrons, and $_{25}Mn^{55}$, which should have five $1f_{7/2}$ protons, both have spins of $\frac{5}{2}$ rather than the expected $\frac{7}{2}$. Again, the best explanation seems to lie in an unusual spin coupling of the odd particles to give the lower spin. $_{63}Eu^{153}$ should have an odd proton in a $2d_{5/2}$ state, but the magnetic moment is quite far from the predicted value; in fact it is

Table 9-9 POSTULATED NUCLEON STATES OF SEVERAL NUCLIDES

Nuclide	Postulated neutron states	Postulated proton states	Observed total nuclear angular momentum, I	Magnetic moment (in nm) Predicted	Observed
$_1H^1$			$\frac{1}{2}$		2.7935
$_0n^1$	$1s_{1/2}$	$1s_{1/2}$	$\frac{1}{2}$		-1.9136
*$_1H^2$	$1s_{1/2}$	$1s_{1/2}$	1	0.8799	0.85761
$_1H^3$	$(1s_{1/2})^2$	$1s_{1/2}$	$\frac{1}{2}$	2.7935	2.9795
$_2He^3$	$1s_{1/2}$	$(1s_{1/2})^2$	$\frac{1}{2}$	-1.9136	-2.1280
$_2He^4$	$(1s_{1/2})^2$	$(1s_{1/2})^2$	0	0	0
*$_3Li^6$	$(1s_{1/2})^2(1p_{3/2})$	$(1s_{1/2})^2(1p_{3/2})$	1	‡	0.82210
$_3Li^7$	$(1s_{1/2})^2(1p_{3/2})^2$	$(1s_{1/2})^2(1p_{3/2})$	$\frac{3}{2}$	3.7935	3.2567
$_4Be^9$	$(1s_{1/2})^2(1p_{3/2})^3$	$(1s_{1/2})^2(1p_{3/2})^2$	$\frac{3}{2}$	-1.9136	-1.1776
*$_5B^{10}$	$(1s_{1/2})^2(1p_{3/2})^3$	$(1s_{1/2})^2(1p_{3/2})^3$	3	1.8799	1.801
$_5B^{11}$	$(1s_{1/2})^2(1p_{3/2})^4$	$(1s_{1/2})^2(1p_{3/2})^3$	$\frac{3}{2}$	3.7935	2.6886
$_6C^{12}$	$(1s_{1/2})^2(1p_{3/2})^4$	$(1s_{1/2})^2(1p_{3/2})^4$	0	0	0
$_6C^{13}$	$(1s_{1/2})^2(1p_{3/2})^4(1p_{1/2})$	$(1s_{1/2})^2(1p_{3/2})^4$	$\frac{1}{2}$	0.6379	0.7023
$_6C^{14}$	$(1s_{1/2})^2(1p_{3/2})^4(1p_{1/2})^2$	$(1s_{1/2})^2(1p_{3/2})^4$	0	0	0
*$_7N^{14}$	$(1s_{1/2})^2(1p_{3/2})^4(1p_{1/2})$	$(1s_{1/2})^2(1p_{3/2})^4(1p_{1/2})$	1	0.3734	0.403
†$_{11}Na^{23}$	$(1s_{1/2})^2(1p_{3/2})^4(1p_{1/2})^2$ $(1d_{5/2})^4$	$(1s_{1/2})^2(1p_{3/2})^4(1p_{1/2})^2$ $(1d_{5/2})^3$	$\frac{3}{2}$		2.218
†$_{25}Mn^{55}$	$(1s_{1/2})^2(1p_{3/2})^4(1p_{1/2})^2$ $(1d_{5/2})^6(1d_{3/2})^4(2s_{1/2})^2$ $(1f_{7/2})^8(2p_{3/2})^2$	$(1s_{1/2})^2(1p_{3/2})^4(1p_{1/2})^2$ $(1d_{5/2})^6(1d_{3/2})^4(2s_{1/2})^2$ $(1f_{7/2})^5$	$\frac{5}{2}$		3.468

* Odd-odd nuclei.

† Postulated states leading to angular momentum values in disagreement with experiment.

‡ Since the observed value of I is neither 0 nor 3, corresponding to parallel or antiparallel spins respectively, no magnetic moment has been predicted.

characteristic of an $f_{5/2}$ state. No satisfactory explanation has been offered for this exception. There are a few other less serious cases where the order of filling of the subshells appears to be exceptional.

It will be recalled from Chap. 5 that when a nucleus is in an excited or isomeric state, the probability that it will drop to the ground state with emission of a γ ray is usually so great that the lifetime, or more accurately the half-life, of the isomer is almost immeasurably short, so that the known isomers are mostly those which have an unusually small transition probability and a correspondingly long half-life. Factors which make for small transition probabilities are (a) small energy difference between excited state and all lower states (usually the ground state), and (b) large differences in I between excited and ground states (18). The filling of states of large j in pairs makes for just such a condition. For example, a nucleus which normally has its odd particle in a $3s_{1/2}$ state with an even number of particles in $1h_{11/2}$ states (because of the large pairing energy of particles in high spin states mentioned previously) might be formed in an excited state with the odd particle in a $1h_{11/2}$ state. This would probably be a "low-lying state," or one in which the

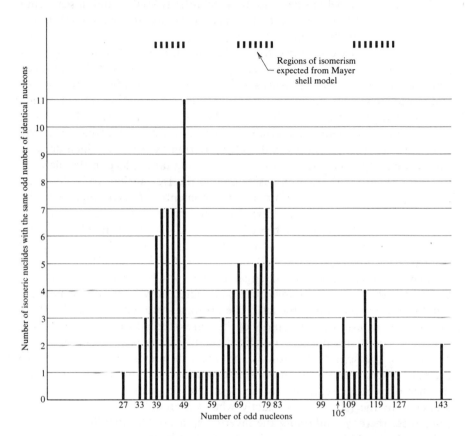

Regions of isomerism
expected from Mayer
shell model

Fig. 9-11. Distribution of odd-mass-number isomeric nuclides as a function of the number of odd nucleons. At the 49-nucleon peak, for example, there are 6 nuclides with an odd number of protons and 5 nuclides with an odd number of neutrons. The drop in number of isomers just beyond the closed shells at 50 and 82 identical nucleons is quite pronounced. Of the 236 known isomers, 137 have an odd mass number. Only 4 of the isomers counted in this plot have half-lives less than 10^{-8} sec, the shortest of these being 1.4×10^{-10} sec.

energy is only a little greater than that in the ground state. Transition to the ground state would then satisfy both (a) and (b) above, ΔI being 5. The distribution of isotopes of odd mass number which possess isomers against the number of odd particles of a given kind is shown in Fig. 9-11. From the arguments given above, one would expect isomers of odd nuclides to predominate from 39 to 49 and 69 to 71 neutrons or protons and perhaps from 111 to 125 neutrons. The absence of isomers just beyond the closed shells at 50 and 82 is striking.

In addition to predicting the correct ground states of most even-odd nuclei, the shell model has been useful in beta-decay studies and in scattering experiments. A number of scattering experiments have tended to confirm the basic premise of inverted-spin doublets.

When protons are scattered from $_2\text{He}^4$ nuclei, resonance scattering takes place when the excitation energy is equal to that of an excited (unbound) state of $_3\text{Li}^5$. Two such resonances are found, one at 2.4-Mev proton energy and one at a considerably higher energy. Angular distribution measurements indicate that the excited state is one in which $j = l \pm \frac{1}{2}$, specifically, $\frac{1}{2}$ or $\frac{3}{2}$, but it is difficult to determine certainly which spin state is involved. Heusinkveld and Frier (10) performed a double scattering experiment which decided this very clearly. Imagine that the first scattering takes place in the plane of this page. Then, as the proton passes around the He^4 nucleus to be deflected to the right, it will have a certain angular momentum l perpendicular to the page, and l will be pointing down. Another proton will pass around the opposite side of the nucleus to be deflected to the left and its angular momentum vector will point upward. Now let us suppose that the lower energy resonance, as predicted by the shell theory, is the $l + \frac{1}{2}$ state. If the impinging protons are initially unpolarized, equal numbers will be scattered to right and to left, but those with spin down will be preferentially scattered to the right and those with spins up to the left. The protons scattered to the right, then, are partially polarized, that is, more of them are oriented with spin down than with spin up. If this partially polarized beam is scattered a second time by He^4 nuclei, the spin-down protons will again be preferentially scattered to the right, and since there are more spin-down than spin-up protons, the total number of protons scattered to the right will be greater than the number scattered to the left. This is exactly what was found at the lower energy resonance, thereby confirming the inverted-spin doublet hypothesis, for Li^5 at least. It should be noted that since the proton loses energy to the recoiling He^4 nucleus when it is scattered, it cannot have the correct energy for maximum resonance scattering at both scatterings.

9-4 Liquid Drop Model

In Chap. 2 we utilized the concept of "packing fraction" introduced by Aston many years before the discovery of the neutron. A closely related, but more satisfactory, concept is that of "binding energy." If, as we now believe, nuclei are composed of protons and neutrons, then the mass of the nucleus should be equal to the mass of its protons plus the mass of its neutrons less the work required to separate the nucleus into its constituent nucleons against the attractive forces which hold the nucleons together. In practice, atomic rather than nuclear masses are used, so one uses the mass of Z hydrogen atoms rather than Z protons. This is not quite exact, as it takes no account of the binding of the orbital electrons, but this is usually a smaller quantity than the uncertainty in present-day mass determinations. In equation form, this may be written

$$M = ZM_H + (A - Z)M_n - W_B, \qquad (9\text{-}3)$$

where M is the atomic mass of the nuclide, M_H is the mass of a hydrogen atom, M_n is the mass of a neutron, and W_B is the binding energy. Making use of the mass energy equivalence, one expresses the masses and W_B in the same units, most commonly Mev or amu. If one divides Eq. (9-3) through by A and rearranges, he obtains the "binding energy per nucleon,"

$$\frac{W_B}{A} = \frac{ZM_H + (A - Z)M_n - M}{A}, \qquad (9\text{-}4)$$

a plot of which is shown in Fig. 9-12. A number of things are immediately evident from an inspection of this figure.

1. Although there are small wiggles or discontinuities in the plot, some of which are caused by experimental error, but most of which are real, the points lie surprisingly close to a smooth curve.
2. This curve rises very rapidly for small mass numbers.
3. The binding energy per nucleon is very nearly constant for mass number greater than 30.
4. The binding energy per nucleon decreases slowly as the mass number increases beyond about 60.

The smoothness of the binding energy curve is rather surprising in view of the success of the shell model, and evidently the small irregularities in the curve require something like the shell model for their explanation. The smoothness of the curve offers hope that a structureless model of the nucleus can explain many nuclear phenomena that do not depend on the detailed structure as approximated by the shell model. This section deals with just such a model.

Items 2 and 3 indicate that while the forces between nucleons are large, they are short range, so that nucleons essentially interact with their immediate neighbors but not with more distant nucleons. This phenomenon is known as "saturation." For the very light nuclides, the number of interactions increases rapidly with each additional nucleon—for example, in H^2 the proton and neutron interact with a single interaction; in He^3 the protons interact with each other and each interacts with the neutron, making three interactions; in He^4 there are six interactions, and in Li^6 there are 15. One therefore expects the binding energy curve to rise rapidly at first, but once the nucleus becomes large enough that an additional nucleon no longer interacts with all the nucleons present but only with those in its immediate vicinity, the binding energy per nucleon should cease rising steeply and become practically constant. The fact that the nuclear volume is roughly proportional to the number of nucleons, A, is in accord with this concept also, since nucleons

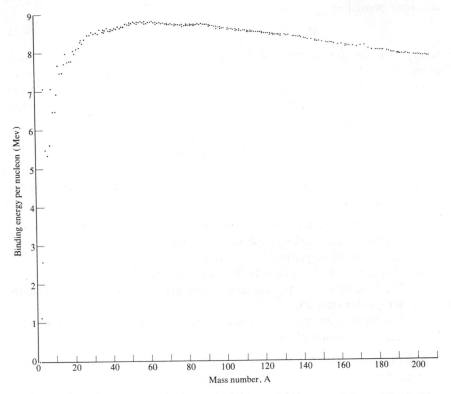

Fig. 9-12. Binding energy per nucleon, as defined by Eq. (9-4), of the stable nuclides.

in heavy nuclei would be subjected to the same forces as those in lighter nuclei and therefore one would not anticipate a greater compression, or higher nuclear density, in heavy nuclides. It has been known, of course, since the experiments on α-particle scattering by Geiger and Marsden that the coulomb field of the nucleus extends inward almost to the nucleus itself. On the other hand, the stability of nuclei requires that there be attractive forces between the nucleons great enough to more than offset the coulomb forces. These attractive forces must become insignificantly small compared with the coulomb forces a very short distance away from the nucleus, again testifying to the short-range character of nuclear forces.

There are just such short-range forces acting between the molecules of a liquid, and their existence prevents the thermal motion of the molecules from causing disintegration of the liquid. In a drop of liquid the thermal motions of the molecules causes a certain number of molecules in the surface at any instant to be moving away from the drop. Most of these may have insufficient velocity to escape under the short-range attractive forces of neighboring molecules. There will always be a few molecules which do have a sufficient velocity to escape, and the loss of these molecules constitutes evaporation from the drop. As the temperature of the liquid in the drop is raised, the number of molecules acquiring the necessary escape velocity increases and the rate of evaporation is augmented.

Surface tension is one manifestation of the short-range intermolecular forces. If one thinks in terms of surface energy, then the surface energy is a positive correction term in the expression for the total energy of the drop. Since the short-range forces are attractive, the energy of the molecules is less when they are close together than when separated from each other. Since the forces are short range, the reduction in energy of a molecule is influenced only by the molecules in its immediate neighborhood. Thus the energy loss is the same for each completely surrounded molecule and the energy loss for N such molecules is some positive constant k times N. Molecules at the surface, on the other hand, are not surrounded on all sides by other molecules, and in consequence their energy is lowered to a lesser degree. The energy loss, or what one might call the binding energy, of the drop may be written, then, as

$$W_d = kN - 4\pi r^2 \gamma, \tag{9-5}$$

and the binding energy per molecule as

$$\frac{W_d}{N} = k - \frac{4\pi r^2 \gamma}{N} = k - bN^{-1/3} \tag{9-6}$$

where r is the radius of the drop, γ is the surface tension, or better, the surface energy per unit area of surface, and b is a positive constant. Equation (9-6) shows that the binding energy per molecule is virtually constant for large values of N, but drops steeply as N becomes small. This is very much like the nuclear binding energy per nucleon curve.

In 1936, Bohr (2) drew attention to this analogy between a nucleus and a liquid drop. Since the laws governing a liquid are statistical in nature, it is necessary that a very large number of particles be involved. In the case of nuclei, less than 250 particles are involved at most, so that one should not expect predictions based upon this picture to be exact. Nevertheless, it does give a good qualitative understanding of many aspects of nuclear structure and therefore merits our attention. The presence of protons in the nucleus makes the nucleus more like the charged water droplets formed in cloud chambers than like ordinary, uncharged liquid drops. If one makes the assumption that the binding energy, aside from the effect of coulomb forces, is the same for proton-proton (pp), neutron-neutron (nn) and neutron-proton (np) interactions, and further, that these interactions are not spin dependent (which is in direct contradiction to shell theory), then one may rewrite Eq. (9-6) for nucleons as

$$\frac{W_s}{A} = k_1 - k_2 A^{-1/3}. \tag{9-7}$$

Each of the Z protons will interact with the other $(Z - 1)$ protons, so there are $\frac{1}{2}Z(Z - 1)$ interactions.* An estimate of the coulomb contribution to the binding energy can be obtained by assuming that the Z protons are spread uniformly throughout the volume of the nucleus. The electrostatic energy of such a uniform spherical charge distribution is

$$W_q = \int_0^{r_0} \frac{(\frac{4}{3}\pi r^3 D)(4\pi r^2 D \, dr)}{r}, \tag{9-8}$$

where r_0 is the radius of the nucleus, r is the radial distance from the center of the nucleus, and D is the charge density. Upon integration, (9-8) becomes

$$W_q = \frac{16\pi^2 D^2 r_0^5}{15}. \tag{9-9}$$

The charge density is related to the total nuclear charge, Ze, by

$$\frac{4}{3}\pi r_0^3 D = Ze, \tag{9-10}$$

or

$$D = \frac{3Ze}{4\pi r_0^3}. \tag{9-11}$$

When this value of D is substituted into (9-9), one obtains

$$W_q = \frac{3}{5}\frac{Z^2 e^2}{r_0}. \tag{9-12}$$

Equation (9-12) includes a fictitious self-energy of each proton as though the proton were spread throughout the volume of the nucleus and interacted with itself. The fictitious self-energy of one such proton is evidently, from Eq. (9-12), equal to $\frac{3}{5}(e^2/r_0)$. An amount $Z \cdot \frac{3}{5}(e^2/r_0)$ must, therefore, be subtracted from (9-12). This gives

$$W_q' = \frac{3}{5}\frac{e^2}{r_0} Z(Z - 1). \tag{9-13}$$

* The factor $\frac{1}{2}$ arises because each interaction gets counted twice.

If we now assume that

$$r_0 \cong 1.5 \times 10^{-13} A^{1/3} \text{ cm},$$

then

$$W_q' \cong \frac{3}{5} \frac{e^2 \times 10^{13} A^{-1/3} Z(Z-1)}{1.5}, \tag{9-14}$$

$$W_q' \cong 0.58 Z(Z-1) A^{-1/3} \text{ Mev}. \tag{9-15}$$

The binding energy per nucleon associated with coulomb repulsion may then be written

$$\frac{W_c}{A} = -k_3 Z(Z-1) A^{-4/3}, \tag{9-16}$$

where k_3 is a positive constant which depends both on the distribution of protons in the nucleus and on the nuclear radius, but whose value should be in the neighborhood of 0.6 Mev. The combination of Eqs. (9-7) and (9-16) gives

$$\frac{W_s + W_c}{A} = k_1 - k_2 A^{-1/3} - k_3 Z(Z-1) A^{-4/3}, \tag{9-17}$$

which has all the qualitative features of the binding energy per nucleon curve, namely, a steep rise at small A, a flattening off at somewhat larger A, and a gradual drop at very large A because of the increased coulomb energy associated with the large Z of large-A nuclides, but no choice of k_1, k_2, k_3 can be found which simultaneously fits both the small-A and large-A parts of the curve well. Equation (9-17) has another, more serious, deficiency. For a given A, it predicts that the binding energy will be a maximum when $Z = 0$, whereas we know that there is a very narrow range of Z values for a given A which yields stable nuclei and that artificially produced nuclei have smaller binding energies per nucleon than stable nuclei.

The fact that the light stable nuclei, in which coulomb effects are very small, tend to have equal numbers of neutrons and protons shows that the (pn) interactions must be somewhat stronger than (nn) interactions. In the heavy nuclei the extra energy of the (pn) interactions is offset by the coulomb repulsion with the result that heavy stable nuclei have somewhat more neutrons than protons. When neutrons in excess of the number of protons are present, their binding energy will be less than that of the Z protons plus Z neutrons. We evidently should add a negative term, involving the neutron excess $(A - 2Z)$, to the binding energy equation. The same argument would apply to a nucleus with an excess of protons, the proton excess being then $(2Z - A)$ or just the negative of the expression for the neutron excess. If the (pp) and (nn) interactions are assumed to be equal, the correction term should involve the quantity $|(A - 2Z)|$. Empirically, it has been found that $-(A - 2Z)^2/A$ gives the best agreement with observation. This form of the correction can also be derived analytically if one is willing to make sufficient assumptions. The binding energy per nucleon now becomes

$$\frac{W_s + W_c + W_{ez}}{A} = k_1 - k_2 A^{-1/3} - k_3 Z(Z-1)A^{-4/3} - k_4(A-2Z)^2 A^{-2}.$$

(9-18)

This is a big improvement over Eq. (9-17) as it predicts that value of Z which will give maximum binding energy per nucleon and hence, presumably,

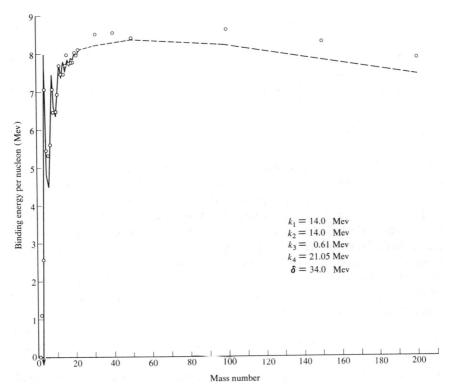

$k_1 = 14.0$ Mev
$k_2 = 14.0$ Mev
$k_3 = 0.61$ Mev
$k_4 = 21.05$ Mev
$\delta = 34.0$ Mev

Fig. 9-13. (a) Comparison of experimental binding energies per nucleon (circled points) with values for the same nuclides computed from Eq. (9-19). The constants used in the text were used here. The fit is best at small mass numbers.

maximum stability for a given value of A. The relationship between Z and A for maximum binding energy per nucleon can then be substituted into (9-18) and the value of A found which gives a maximum. This should coincide with the maximum in the experimental binding-energy-per-nucleon curve if the coefficients k_1, k_2, k_3, k_4 have been properly chosen.

At the very outset, it was stated that the interactions were to be assumed spin independent. If the shell-model concept that nucleons are paired off with opposite spins is correct, the assumption of spin-independent binding energies should only affect unpaired nucleons. This defect can be remedied by adding a term to our equation which takes specific account of whether the nucleus is even-even, even-odd, odd-even, or odd-odd. The result is Weizsäcker's (17)

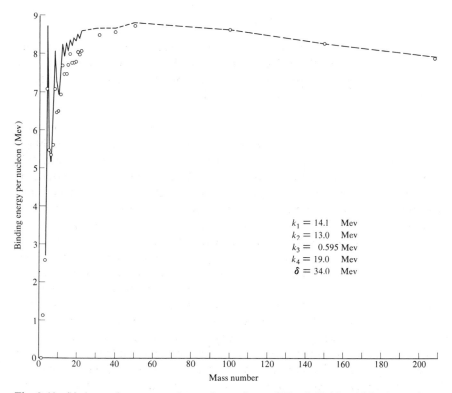

$$k_1 = 14.1 \quad \text{Mev}$$
$$k_2 = 13.0 \quad \text{Mev}$$
$$k_3 = \ 0.595 \ \text{Mev}$$
$$k_4 = 19.0 \quad \text{Mev}$$
$$\delta = 34.0 \quad \text{Mev}$$

Fig. 9-13. (b) A set of constants, alternative to those of Fig. 9-13 (a), which gives a better fit for large mass numbers but a poorer fit at small mass numbers.

semi-empirical mass formula, with the W_B term of Eq. (9-3) given by A times the binding-energy-per-nucleon expression

$$\frac{W_B}{A} = k_1 - k_2 A^{-1/3} - k_3 Z(Z-1)A^{-4/3} - k_4(A-2Z)^2 A^{-2}$$

$$+ A \times {}^{-7/4} \begin{cases} \delta \text{ for even-even nuclei,} \\ 0 \text{ for even-odd or odd-even,} \\ -\delta \text{ for odd-odd nuclei.} \end{cases} \quad (9\text{-}19)$$

This gives amazingly good agreement with all known nuclear masses (except those near closed shells) when

$$k_1 = 14.0 \ \text{Mev},$$
$$k_2 = 14.0 \ \text{Mev},$$
$$k_3 = 0.61 \ \text{Mev},$$
$$k_4 = 21.05 \ \text{Mev},$$

and
$$\delta = 34.0 \ \text{Mev}.$$

At closed shells the binding energy of the last neutron may be as much as 2 Mev different from the value predicted by Eq. (9-19). Comparisons of experimental values of binding energy per nucleon and values computed from (9-19) are shown in Figs. 9-13(a) and 9-13(b).

Fission. The explanation of fission is an outstanding success of the liquid drop model. When a neutron is captured by a nucleus the nuclear assemblage is given not only the kinetic energy of the captured neutron but also—and this is the significant fact in the capture of a thermal neutron—an amount of energy equal to the binding energy of the added neutron. It is assumed that this energy, with the exception of that part associated with translation of the center of mass, manifests itself in oscillations of the droplike assemblage, the alternating stretchings and contractions causing it finally to break into two more or less equal pieces and perhaps a spray of excess neutrons (3). If the nucleus is originally spherical, any deformation will increase its surface and therefore the surface energy. This increase in energy bespeaks a restoring force tending to return the nucleus to its original spherical shape. On the other hand, the coulomb energy is reduced as the protons are given a greater separation by the distortion. This decrease in coulomb energy corresponds to a force (the repulsive force between protons) acting in the opposite sense to the restoring force stemming from the short-range forces between nucleons. If the droplet is stretched far enough along one axis, its surface area will eventually become greater than the area of two smaller droplets of the same total volume. The surface energy of the droplet will then be greater than the surface energy of the two smaller equivalent droplets, leading one to expect, on the basis of surface-energy considerations alone, that the deformed droplet would break up into two smaller droplets. The repulsive forces between the protons make it energetically possible for the droplet to break up for smaller deformations than would be required on the basis of surface effects only. If the coulomb forces and surface forces are nearly equal, small distortions are sufficient to produce fission.

Since the coulomb energy increases relative to the surface energy as A increases, it is evident that conditions are most favorable for fission in the very heavy nuclei. In the case of U^{235} and U^{238}, Eq. (9-19) shows that, except for the last term, the increase in binding energy in going from U^{235} to U^{236} should be only 0.32 Mev greater than that in going from U^{238} to U^{239}. The last term *increases* by 0.56 Mev in going from U^{235} to U^{236} and *decreases* by about the same amount in going from U^{238} to U^{239}. As a result, U^{236} should have 1.44 Mev more excitation energy than does U^{239} when each has absorbed a thermal neutron. It is not surprising, therefore, that thermal neutrons cause fission of U^{235} but not of U^{238}. Significantly, the threshold neutron energy for fission of U^{238} is about 0.9 Mev.

9-5 Compound Nucleus

The concept of nuclear reactions taking place in two steps has been a very fruitful one in the region of excitation energies comparable to the binding energy of a nucleon and even up to 40 Mev. According to this idea, when a nucleus is excited, as for example by bombarding it with a proton, a compound nucleus is formed containing the target nucleons and the proton in some excited configuration which may involve excited states of one or several nucleons. This excitation energy or a part thereof is soon transferred to a nucleon which is ejected from the atom, or is given up in the form of a photon.

If the compound nucleus concept is correct, then the way in which the excited nucleus breaks down should be dependent only on its excitation and not on the manner in which it was formed. This has been beautifully demonstrated by Goshal (7) in the case of compound $_{30}Zn^{64}$ nuclei. He formed excited $_{30}Zn^{64}$ by bombarding $_{28}Ni^{60}$ with α particles and $_{29}Cu^{63}$ with protons. The Zn^{64} decays by emitting one neutron, two neutrons, or a proton and neutron simultaneously. It was found that the ratio of the number of excited nuclei decaying by each of these three competing processes was the same, for a given excitation energy, whether the Zn^{64} was formed from Ni^{60} or from Cu^{63}. The cross sections as functions of bombardment energy are compared in Fig. 9-14.

When the bombarding particle has an energy much higher than the binding energy of a nucleon, it is most likely to transfer enough energy to a single nucleon to drive it out of the nucleus without imparting appreciable energy to the remainder of the nucleus. In some instances, because of the dense packing of nucleons within the nucleus, the energy of the bombarding particle will be readily interchanged among nucleons and many of them will be raised to excited states. (This is in sharp contrast to electronic excitation of an atom, where the electronic atmosphere is very rare and exchange of energy between orbital electrons is uncommon.) In the usual case, where the excitation energy is rather large compared with the energy level differences, the number of energy states is large enough so that the problem may be treated statistically. Going back to the liquid drop analog, the situation is comparable to that in which a liquid drop is given additional thermal energy, with a resultant increase in rate of evaporation. Likewise, sufficient energy will occasionally be concentrated on a single nucleon (or group of nucleons such as an α particle) to allow it to escape. Most low-energy nuclear reactions are looked upon, then, as taking place in two steps: first, the creation of a "compound" or excited intermediate nucleus, and, second, the emission of particles or photons. At greater excitation energies, by analogy with a liquid drop, one

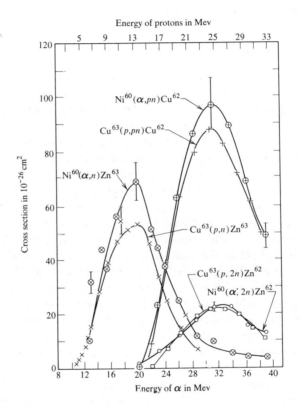

Fig. 9-14. A comparison of the cross sections, as functions of bombardment energy, for the α on Ni^{60} and p on Cu^{63} reactions. These reactions should lead to the same compound nucleus, if such exists. If this compound nucleus is in the same state of excitation in both cases, the competing processes of breakdown should have the same relative probability regardless of how the compound nucleus was created. The good agreement between the two sets of curves is a good confirmation of the compound nucleus hypothesis.

speaks of "evaporation" of nuclear particles, or says that the nucleus "boils off" particles. Cases which are thought to exemplify this process have been observed in the form of multiple-prong stars produced by energetic cosmic ray particles in cloud chambers and in nuclear emulsions.

9-6 Charge Symmetry and Independence

As mentioned earlier, there is considerable evidence that if one properly discounts the coulomb interaction between nucleons, the specifically nuclear interactions are all approximately the same whether the nucleons be protons or neutrons. One aspect of this situation is "charge symmetry," which means that the interaction between protons (other than coulomb interaction) is of the same magnitude as that between neutrons. The best evidence for this comes from the binding energies of mirror nuclei. Consider the mirror nuclei H^3 and He^3, both of which have nuclear spins of $\frac{1}{2}$. According to the shell model, H^3 has two $s_{1/2}$ neutrons and one $p_{1/2}$ proton, with the $s_{1/2}$ neutron spins antiparallel. If spin-spin interaction is strong, then the proton spin should be parallel to one of the neutron spins and antiparallel to the other. The specifically nuclear interactions in H^3 may then be listed as $^3(pn) + {}^1(pn) + {}^1(nn)$, where the superscript 3 means a triplet state (i.e., spins parallel) and the superscript 1 means a singlet state (i.e., spins antiparallel). Similarly, the specifically nuclear interactions in He^3 are $^3(pn) + {}^1(pn) + {}^1(pp)$. The excess binding energy of H^3 over He^3 then should be given by

$$\Delta W_B = {}^1(nn) - {}^1(pp) - W_c, \qquad (9\text{-}20)$$

where W_c is the coulomb energy of He^3 (the coulomb energy of H^3 is zero). W_c may be computed with the aid of Eq. (9-15). This yields

$$W_c = 0.58Z(Z-1)A^{-1/3} = \frac{0.58 \times 2 \times 1}{3^{1/3}} = 0.80 \text{ Mev},$$

which is to be compared with the observed binding energy difference of 0.76 Mev. Since the calculated coulomb energy depends on an assumed nuclear radius, it is quite possible that W_c is actually 0.76 Mev and that $^1(nn) = {}^1(pp)$.

The spin configurations of the other light mirror nuclei are less certain, but if the differences between triplet and singlet interactions are simply ignored a good case can again be made for charge symmetry. Suppose that we examine mirror isobars in which one has an atomic number Z and the other $Z + 1$.

If spin dependence is ignored, we may picture each nucleus as consisting of a central core of Z protons and Z neutrons interacting with the one odd particle. The binding energy of the nuclide with atomic number $Z + 1$ would then be written

$$W_B(Z + 1, A) = W_B(Zp, Zn) + W_B(p, Zp) + W_B(p, Zn) + W_c(Z + 1), \qquad (9\text{-}21)$$

where the first term on the right represents the interaction energy of the Z protons in the core with the Z neutrons in the core, the second term represents the specifically nuclear interaction energy of the odd proton with the Z core protons, the third term represents the interaction energy of the odd proton with the Z core neutrons and the fourth term the coulomb energy. Similarly, the binding energy of the nuclide with atomic number Z would be written

$$W_B(Z, A) = W_B(Zp, Zn) + W_B(n, Zp) + W_B(n, Zn) + W_c(Z). \qquad (9\text{-}22)$$

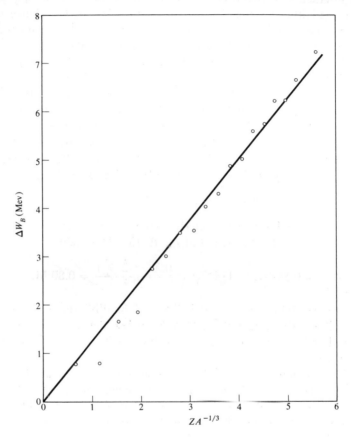

Fig. 9-15. A plot of the difference in binding energy between a nuclide $(Z + 1, A)$ and its mirror (Z, A), where $A = 2Z + 1$, as a function of $ZA^{-1/3}$. If charge independence of nuclear forces is a valid concept, the points should lie on a straight line through the origin. A best fit to these points would clearly intersect the ΔW_B axis at a small negative value. The deviation of the points from the line is probably no worse than one should expect in view of the simplifying assumptions made (for example, that the coulomb energy varies as $A^{-1/3}$).

Since the force which a neutron exerts on a proton is of the same magnitude as the force which a proton exerts on a neutron, we conclude that

$$W_B(p, Zn) = W_B(n, Zp). \qquad (9\text{-}23)$$

Therefore, the difference ΔW_B in the binding energies of the two nuclides is

$$\Delta W_B(A) = W_B(p, Zp) - W_B(n, Zn) + W_c(Z + 1) - W_c(Z).$$

Now $$W_c(Z + 1) - W_c(Z) = \frac{-Ze^2}{r} = -KZA^{-1/3}, \qquad (9\text{-}24)$$

where K is a constant. Then

$$\Delta W_B(A) = W_B(p, Zp) - W_B(n, Zn) + KZA^{-1/3}. \qquad (9\text{-}25)$$

If nuclear forces are charge independent, the first two terms on the right should be equal, in which case $\Delta W_B(A)$ should be equal to $KZA^{-1/3}$. If ΔW_B is plotted against $ZA^{-1/3}$, the points should fall on a straight line which passes through the origin. As can be seen from Fig. 9-15, the plotted points do lie fairly close to such a straight line.

Charge symmetry is a special case of what seems to be a more fundamental property of nucleons known as "charge independence." According to this hypothesis, all specifically nuclear, singlet interactions between nucleons are of the same magnitude. Thus

$${}^1(np) = {}^1(nn) = {}^1(pp). \qquad (9\text{-}26)$$

The triplet ${}^3(np)$ interaction, on the other hand, appears to be stronger than the singlet interactions. This is evidenced by the fact that H^2 has a spin of 1 and therefore appears to have a proton and neutron in $1s_{1/2}$ states with parallel spins. As far as is now known, there is no stable nuclide He^2, which would involve a ${}^1(pp)$ interaction, nor is there any evidence for the existence of a dineutron (a stably bound pair of neutrons) which would involve a ${}^1(nn)$ interaction. Moreover, of the four stable odd-odd nuclides, three $({}_1H^2, {}_5B^{10}, {}_7N^{14})$ appear from the shell theory and their measured spins to be in triplet states, indicating that the extra binding of the triplet state is what makes it possible for this unfavored combination of nucleons to exist.

9-7 Isobaric Spin*

If specifically nuclear forces are charge independent, then it becomes natural to look upon the neutron and proton as two different charge states of a nucleon. The Pauli principle allows two nucleons to occupy states with the same usual quantum numbers, provided that one is in the neutron state and

---

* This is the preferred name, but "isotopic spin" is an older name and one which is used just as frequently as isobaric spin in the literature. The incorporation of the word *spin* into the name of this quantity is rather unfortunate since it has nothing to do with angular momentum. The origin of the word is connected with the formal mathematical method in which this new quantum number is introduced into nuclear theory. Since the formalism is essentially the same as that used for electron spin, this new quantum number was called isotopic spin.

one in the proton state. This is the same situation that originally suggested the introduction of electron spin. The electron is endowed with a spin quantum number of $\frac{1}{2}$ and can have two orientations in space of $+\frac{1}{2}$ (often spoken of as "spin up") or $-\frac{1}{2}$ ("spin down"). Two electrons with different spin orientations can then occupy states with the same usual quantum numbers.

If the nucleon is given an isobaric spin quantum number of $\frac{1}{2}$, then it can have two orientations along some ζ-axis in isobaric spin space. When the projection of the isobaric spin along ζ is $+\frac{1}{2}$, the nucleon is a neutron; when it is $-\frac{1}{2}$, the nucleon is a proton. This idea can now be extended to nuclei. The projection of the total isobaric spin, T, along ζ is now called T_ζ and is *defined* to be given by

$$T_\zeta = \tfrac{1}{2}(A - 2Z); \tag{9-27}$$

that is, it is half of the neutron excess. The mirror nuclei $_3\mathrm{Li}^7$ and $_4\mathrm{Be}^7$ then constitute an isobaric spin doublet in which $T = \frac{1}{2}$ and $T_\zeta = +\frac{1}{2}$ for Li^7 and $-\frac{1}{2}$ for Be^7.

The total isobaric spin of a nucleus clearly must not be less than its projection T_ζ. If the nucleus is stable against positron decay and electron capture, then its total isobaric spin cannot be greater than T_ζ for, if it were, an isobaric multiplet with $T'_\zeta > T_\zeta$ should exist whose lowest charge state would have an electrostatic energy less than that of the state T_ζ. This would allow β^+ decay or electron capture in contradiction to the original stipulation that the nucleus was stable against such decay. Nuclides stable against positron decay and electron capture then have $T = T_\zeta$. This is a useful rule because, while it is easy to specify T_ζ for any given nucleus, it is much more difficult to find what T is.

Although T_ζ must evidently be the same for an excited nucleus as it is for the ground state, this is not necessarily true of T. For example, T_ζ for a given nucleus might be zero. If the nucleus is stable against positron decay and electron capture, then in the ground state, $T = 0$ also. On the other hand, an excited state of this nucleus may be a member of an isobaric spin triplet in which $T = 1$, this excited nucleus being, of the three possible isobars with T_ζ equal to $+1, 0, -1$, the one with $T_\zeta = 0$. If isobaric spin is a good quantum number, electromagnetic radiation can take place only if $\varDelta T = 0$ or ± 1, with $0 \longrightarrow 0$ forbidden for dipole radiation. Obviously $\varDelta T_\zeta = 0$ in electromagnetic transitions. In beta decay $\varDelta T = \pm 1$ and $\varDelta T_\zeta = \pm 1$. Wilkinson (19) reports a number of gamma-ray transitions in which the "strength" of the transition is enough lower than the strength of the majority of similar transitions that they are believed to be forbidden by the isobaric spin selection rules.

PROBLEMS

9-1 (a) Calculate the radius of the Po^{207} nucleus from the constant density formula.

(b) Calculate the radius of the K-orbit electron for this atom neglecting shielding. Do these numbers provide any insight into the fact that Po^{207} decays more than 99% of the time by electron capture?

[*Ans.* (a) 8.88×10^{-13} cm; (b) 7.51×10^{-13} cm.]

9-2 (a) On the basis of the shell model, what should be the ground-state configuration, spin, and magnetic moment of Pt^{195}?

(b) The measured spin of Pt^{195} is $\frac{1}{2}$ and its measured magnetic moment is 0.606 nm. What is the most likely actual configuration?

[*Ans.* (a) spin $\frac{13}{2}$; $\mu = 1.6402$ nm; (b) $3p_{1/2}$.]

9-3 Te^{123} has a 104-day isomeric state which decays in what is believed to be an M4 transition to an intermediate state, which in turn decays by an M1 transition to the ground state whose measured spin is $\frac{1}{2}$. From the shell model, what are the probable excited states?

[*Ans.* Upper, $1h_{11/2}$; lower, $2d_{3/2}$.]

9-4 By means of the Weizsäcker semi-empirical mass formula, find the most stable isobar of mass 201.

[*Ans.* $Z = 80.58$ gives $_{81}Tl^{201}$. Actually, the stable isotope is $_{80}Hg^{201}$.]

9-5 According to the Weizsäcker formula, which isotope of $_{27}Co$ should be most stable? [*Ans.* $_{27}Co^{59}$.]

9-6 Make a plot of $[M(Z, A) - AM_n]$ against Z, where $M(Z, A)$ is the mass of a nuclide with atomic number Z and mass number A, and M_n is the mass of a neutron. Use $A = 54$ and Z from 23 to 27 inclusive. Draw a smooth curve through the odd-odd points and another (more or less equidistant) curve through the even-even points. Show, by connecting points with arrow-tipped straight lines, where β decay will take place. Which nuclides would you expect to be stable? [*Hint:* First calculate W_B/A and then obtain $M(Z, A) - AM_n$ from this.] [*Ans.* Fe^{54} and Cr^{54} are stable.]

9-7 The following mirror nuclei decay by emitting positrons whose maximum energy is shown in the table below.

Emitting nuclide	Maximum β^+ energy (Mev)	Emitting nuclide	Maximum β^+ energy (Mev)
$_6C^{11}$	0.98	$_{14}Si^{27}$	3.8
$_7N^{13}$	1.24	$_{15}P^{29}$	3.94
$_8O^{15}$	1.68	$_{16}S^{31}$	4.42
$_9F^{17}$	1.748	$_{17}Cl^{33}$	4.2
$_{10}Ne^{19}$	2.2	$_{18}A^{35}$	4.96
$_{11}Na^{21}$	2.50	$_{19}K^{37}$	5.1
$_{12}Mg^{23}$	2.95	$_{20}Ca^{39}$	5.49
$_{13}Al^{25}$	3.24	$_{21}Sc^{41}$	4.94

Make a plot of maximum β^+ energy against $A^{2/3}$ and show that this confirms charge symmetry.

REFERENCES

1. Brown, H., *Rev. Mod. Phys.*, **21**, 625 (1949).

2. Bohr, N., *Nature*, **137**, 344 (1936).

3. Bohr, N., and Wheeler, J. A., *Phys. Rev.*, **56**, 426 (1939).

4. Elsasser, W., *J. Phys. Rad.*, **5**, 625 (1934).

5. Feenberg, E., *Shell Theory of the Nucleus* (Princeton: Princeton University Press, 1955).

6. Gamow, G., *Z. Physik*, **89**, 572 (1934).

7. Goshal, S. H., *Phys. Rev.*, **80**, 939 (1950).

8. Guggenheimer, K., *J. Phys. Rad.*, **5**, 253 (1934).

9. Harkins, W. D., *J. Amer. Chem. Soc.*, **39**, 856 (1917).

10. Heusinkveld, M., and Frier, G., *Phys. Rev.*, **85**, 80 (1952).

11. Mayer, M. G., *Phys. Rev.*, **74**, 235 (1948); **75**, 1969 (1949); **78**, 16 and 22 (1950). These papers list a large part of the earlier literature on shell structure.

12. Mayer, M. G., and Jensen, J. H. D., *Elementary Theory of Nuclear Shell Structure* (New York: John Wiley & Sons, 1955).

13. Nathans, R., and Halpern, J., *Phys. Rev.*, **92**, 207 (1953).

14. Nordheim, L. W., *Phys. Rev.*, **75**, 1894 (1949).

15. Rosenfeld, L., *Nuclear Forces II* (New York: Interscience Publishing Co., 1949).

16. Schmidt, T., *Z. Physik*, **106**, 358 (1937). See also Landé, A., *Phys. Rev.*, **43**, 620 (1933).

17. Von Weizsäcker, C. F., *Z. Physik*, **96**, 431 (1935).

18. Von Weizsäcker, C. F., *Naturwiss.*, **24**, 813 (1936).

19. Wilkinson, D. H., in *Proceedings of the Rehovoth Conference on Nuclear Structure* (New York: Interscience Publishing Co., 1958), p. 175.

GENERAL REFERENCES

1. Mayer, M. G., and Jensen, J. H. D., *Elementary Theory of Nuclear Shell Structure* (New York: John Wiley & Sons, 1955). This easily readable

book by two of the principal architects of present-day shell theory gives much more detailed information than could be given in this chapter This is especially true of the chapters on beta decay and nuclear quadrupole moments.

2. Feenberg, E., *Shell Theory of the Nucleus* (Princeton: Princeton University Press, 1955). This book is more mathematical than the previous one.

COLLISION DYNAMICS

10-1 Introduction

Since most nuclear reactions are produced by bombarding nuclei with particles such as protons and deuterons, a familiarity with the dynamics of collisions is very advantageous. It would perhaps be more accurate to call a nucleus a "system" rather than a particle, but we shall follow convention and refer to it by the latter name. Ordinarily only one particle at a time will be striking another particle, so restricting the discussion to one impinging particle and one struck, as we shall do here, loses us very little. A more restrictive limitation which will be imposed is that not more than two particles shall emanate from the point of collision (more accurately, from the interaction volume). From a practical standpoint, even this limitation is not a serious one. When only one particle results from the reaction, its energy and momentum are uniquely determined by the initial conditions. When two particles result, the energies and momenta can be calculated if one specifies sufficiently* the directions of motions of these particles. Put in another way, there are

* What is meant by "sufficiently" will be amplified subsequently.

four unknowns (for example, the speeds and directions of motion of each of the two product particles) but only three equations available in the two-particle case, so that one additional datum is required before the unknowns can be determined. When three particles result from the reaction there are nine unknowns and only four equations, so that five additional data must be supplied before the energies and momenta become determinate. Thus a large number of measurements are usually required before any inferences can be drawn concerning reactions in which more than two particles are evolved.

An unnecessary but convenient restriction which is imposed here is that the colliding particles move along the same straight line.

The collision process will first be treated nonrelativistically, and then in a rigorous relativistic manner. This may appear to be a waste of time since the relativistic treatment includes the nonrelativistic as a special case, but it is believed that this procedure will emphasize both the similarities and the differences between the two approaches.

10-2 Nonrelativistic Collisions

It is extremely helpful in gaining a qualitative understanding of a collision process to imagine that we are viewing it from a coordinate system or frame of reference which is moving with the center of mass of the system. This

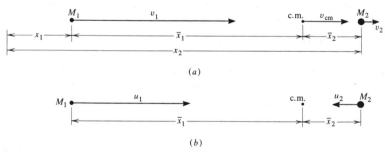

Fig. 10-1. Two particles, of masses M_1 and M_2, before collision. (a) As seen from the laboratory frame of reference. (b) As seen from the center-of-mass frame.

coordinate system will be referred to as the "center-of-mass frame" or simply the "c.m. frame." In actual experiments, of course, one's measuring devices ordinarily do not move with the c.m. Any frame of reference which does not move with the c.m. is therefore referred to as the "laboratory frame" or "lab frame." Figures 10-1(a) and (b) depict the situation of two particles of mass M_1 and M_2, which shall be referred to hereafter simply as M_1 and M_2, before collision in the lab and c.m. frame respectively. From the definition of center of mass, one can write

$$M_1 \bar{x}_1 = M_2 \bar{x}_2. \tag{10-1}$$

Since $\bar{x}_1/\bar{x}_2 = M_2/M_1$ is a constant, the ratio remains the same as the particles move toward the c.m. For example, when particle 1 has moved to a point half as far away from the c.m. as its initial displacement, particle 2 will also have moved a distance toward the c.m. equal to half its initial displacement. It is clear then that the particles will finally collide at the c.m. If the origin of coordinates of the c.m. frame is taken at the c.m., then the two particles will ultimately collide at the origin of coordinates.

If one differentiates both sides of Eq. (10-1) with respect to time, he obtains

$$M_1 \dot{\bar{x}}_1 = M_2 \dot{\bar{x}}_2 \tag{10-2}$$

or

$$M_1 u_1 = M_2 u_2, \tag{10-3}$$

since

$$u_1 = -\dot{\bar{x}}_1 \quad \text{and} \quad u_2 = -\dot{\bar{x}}_2. \tag{10-4}$$

From (10-3) we at once perceive one of the important features of the c.m. frame, namely that the total momentum of the system in the c.m. frame is zero. Another way of saying the same thing is that the momentum vectors of the two particles in the c.m. system are equal in magnitude and oppositely directed.

Since the equality of the c.m. momenta follows directly from the definition of center of mass, it is clear that the c.m. momentum vectors of the product particles, M_3 and M_4, must also be equal in magnitude and oppositely directed. The new center of mass (of M_3 and M_4) may move with a different velocity than did the c.m. of M_1 and M_2 and it is this question which will be investigated next.

If two particles have components of velocity along the x-axis in the lab frame given by v_{1x} and v_{2x}, then the component of the total momentum of the system along the x-axis, p_x, is given by

$$p_x = M_1 v_{1x} + M_2 v_{2x}. \tag{10-5}$$

If the velocity components of the particles along the positive x-axis in the c.m. frame are u_{1x} and u_{2x} and the c.m. frame is moving with a component of velocity v_{cmx} along the x-axis with respect to the laboratory frame, then

$$v_{1x} = u_{1x} + v_{cmx} \tag{10-6}$$

and

$$v_{2x} = u_{2x} + v_{cmx}. \tag{10-7}$$

When these identities are substituted into (10-5), one obtains

$$p_x = M_1(u_{1x} + v_{cmx}) + M_2(u_{2x} + v_{cmx}) \tag{10-8}$$

$$p_x = (M_1 u_{1x} + M_2 u_{2x}) + (M_1 + M_2)v_{cmx}. \tag{10-9}$$

But we have already shown that the definition of center of mass requires, since

$$u_{1x} = u_1 \tag{10-10}$$

and

$$u_{2x} = -u_2, \tag{10-11}$$

that

$$M_1 u_{1x} + M_2 u_{2x} = 0, \tag{10-12}$$

so that

$$p_x = (M_1 + M_2)v_{\mathrm{cm}x}. \tag{10-13}$$

Conservation of momentum requires that the total momentum of the system after a collision be the same as the total momentum before collision.

Fig. 10-2. Two particles, of masses M_3 and M_4, resulting from the collision of M_1 and M_2 which was imminent in Fig. 10-1. **(a)** As seen from the laboratory frame. **(b)** As seen from the center of mass frame.

This can be restated to read "the vector sum of $\mathbf{p}_3$ and $\mathbf{p}_4$ must be equal to a vector $\mathbf{p}_{\mathrm{initial}}$." The vectors $\mathbf{p}_3$ and $\mathbf{p}_4$ then always determine a plane which contains the x-axis of our coordinate system. Purely as a matter of convenience, we choose the y and y' axes to lie in the plane determined by $\mathbf{p}_3$ and $\mathbf{p}_4$. In these coordinate systems the momentum components after collision are

$$p'_x = (M_3 + M_4)v'_{\mathrm{cm}x} \tag{10-14}$$

and

$$p'_y = (M_3 + M_4)v'_{\mathrm{cm}y}. \tag{10-15}$$

The momentum components before collision are

$$p_x = (M_1 + M_2)v_{\mathrm{cm}x} \tag{10-16}$$

and

$$p_y = 0. \tag{10-17}$$

Momentum conservation requires that

$$p'_x = p_x \tag{10-18}$$

and
$$p'_y = p_y. \tag{10-19}$$

We deduce that

$$v'_{cmx} = \left(\frac{M_1 + M_2}{M_3 + M_4}\right)v_{cmx} \tag{10-20}$$

and
$$v'_{cmy} = 0. \tag{10-21}$$

Thus the new c.m. frame continues to move along the x-axis just as the old one did, but its speed is changed if $M_3 + M_4 \neq M_1 + M_2$. In low-energy nuclear reactions $(M_3 + M_4)$ is so near to equality with $(M_1 + M_2)$ that v'_{cm} may be taken, without serious error, to be equal to v_{cm}.

Application of the principle of conservation of energy gives

$$\tfrac{1}{2}M_1v_1^2 + \tfrac{1}{2}M_2v_2^2 + Q = \tfrac{1}{2}M_3v_3^2 + \tfrac{1}{2}M_4v_4^2, \tag{10-22}$$

where Q is the energy released in the reaction.

Substituting for v_1 and v_2 from (10-6) and (10-7) and making similar substitutions for v_3 and v_4, (10-22) becomes

$$\tfrac{1}{2}M_1(u_1 + v_{cm})^2 + \tfrac{1}{2}M_2(-u_2 + v_{cm})^2 + Q$$
$$= \tfrac{1}{2}M_3[(u_{3x} + v'_{cm})^2 + u_{3y}^2] + \tfrac{1}{2}M_4[(u_{4x} + v'_{cm})^2 + u_{4y}^2], \tag{10-23}$$

$$\tfrac{1}{2}M_1(u_1^2 + v_{cm}^2 + 2u_1v_{cm}) + \tfrac{1}{2}M_2(u_2^2 + v_{cm}^2 - 2u_2v_{cm}) + Q$$
$$= \tfrac{1}{2}M_3[u_{3x}^2 + u_{3y}^2 + v_{cm}'^2 + 2u_{3x}v'_{cm}] + \tfrac{1}{2}M_4[u_{4x}^2 + u_{4y}^2 + v_{cm}'^2 + 2u_{4x}v'_{cm}], \tag{10-24}$$

$$\tfrac{1}{2}M_1u_1^2 + \tfrac{1}{2}M_2u_2^2 + Q + \tfrac{1}{2}(M_1 + M_2)v_{cm}^2$$
$$= \tfrac{1}{2}M_3u_3^2 + \tfrac{1}{2}M_4u_4^2 + \tfrac{1}{2}(M_3 + M_4)v_{cm}'^2 + (M_3u_{3x} + M_4u_{4x})v'_{cm}, \tag{10-25}$$

or, since we have already shown that

$$M_3u_{3x} + M_4u_{4x} = 0, \tag{10-26}$$

for the same reason that Eq. (10-12) holds,

$$\tfrac{1}{2}M_1u_1^2 + \tfrac{1}{2}M_2u_2^2 + Q + \tfrac{1}{2}(M_1 + M_2)v_{cm}^2$$
$$= \tfrac{1}{2}M_3u_3^2 + \tfrac{1}{2}M_4u_4^2 + \tfrac{1}{2}(M_3 + M_4)v_{cm}'^2. \tag{10-27}$$

If one now substitutes from (10-20), he obtains

$$\tfrac{1}{2}M_1u_1^2 + \tfrac{1}{2}M_2u_2^2 + Q + \tfrac{1}{2}(M_1 + M_2)v_{cm}^2$$
$$= \tfrac{1}{2}M_3u_3^2 + \tfrac{1}{2}M_4u_4^2 + \left(\frac{M_1 + M_2}{M_3 + M_4}\right)\tfrac{1}{2}(M_1 + M_2)v_{cm}^2, \tag{10-28}$$

so that in those reactions where $(M_1 + M_2)$ equals $(M_3 + M_4)$, the conservation-of-energy equations may be applied in the c.m. frame. Again, in low energy nuclear reactions, where $(M_1 + M_2)/(M_3 + M_4) \cong 1$ we may write

$$\tfrac{1}{2}M_1u_1^2 + \tfrac{1}{2}M_2u_2^2 + Q \cong \tfrac{1}{2}M_3u_3^2 + \tfrac{1}{2}M_4u_4^2.$$

Use of the relativity mass-energy relation to obtain Q, gives

$$Q = (M_1 + M_2 - M_3 - M_4)c^2 \tag{10-29}$$

which implies that $M_1 + M_2 \neq M_3 + M_4$ in any interaction in which Q is not zero. The logical inconsistency of introducing the relativistic expression (10-29) into nonrelativistic mechanics can be avoided only by going to equations of mechanics which are relativistically invariant as we shall do in Sec. 10-3.

The following graphical method makes it easy to visualize a two-particle collision. In the c.m. frame the locus of the ends of all possible pairs of momentum vectors will be a circle whose radius p', can be calculated (with a little algebraic manipulation) by equating the left side of Eq. (10-22) to the right side of Eq. (10-28). Since

$$p' = M_3u_3 = M_4u_4, \tag{10-30}$$

the velocities of the two particles in the c.m. frame are

$$u_3 = \frac{p'}{M_3} \tag{10-31}$$

and $$u_4 = \frac{p'}{M_4}. \tag{10-32}$$

The lab velocity of either particle is the vector sum of its velocity in the c.m. frame and the velocity of the c.m. In Fig. 10-3 the loci of u_3 and u_4 are shown as semicircles. The loci are actually circles, but the omitted situations can be obtained from the ones shown by rotating the figure through $180°$ about the x-axis. Since the velocities u_3 and u_4 must be oppositely directed in the c.m. frame, choice of direction for one immediately determines the other. As shown, the vector sum of $\mathbf{u}_3$ and $\mathbf{v}_{cm}$ gives the lab velocity $\mathbf{v}_3$ while $\mathbf{v}_4$ gives the velocity of the associated particle, M_4. Tangents to the upper and lower semicircle, drawn from O, show at once the maximum lab angle at which M_3 and M_4 respectively can be emitted.

In general O may be located at almost any distance from the center of the semicircles, depending on the conditions of the problem. For example, if Q is large compared to the kinetic energies of the colliding particles, O will lie close to the center of the semicircles.

A special case of some interest is that of elastic collision, in which case $M_3 = M_1$, $M_4 = M_2$, $u_3 = u_1$, and $u_4 = u_2$. Let us further restrict the problem to the elastic collision of a moving particle, M_1, with a less massive particle, M_2, which is at rest in the lab frame. Then

$$u_2 = v_{cm} = \left(\frac{M_1}{M_1 + M_2}\right)v_1. \qquad (10\text{-}33)$$

Since u_1 and u_2 are inversely proportional to their masses, $u_1 < u_2$. This situation is depicted in Fig. 10-4. The point O now lies at the edge of the lower semicircle. One sees at once that there is a maximum angle through

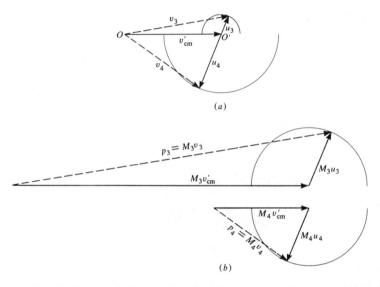

(a)

(b)

Fig. 10-3. Graphical method for transforming from the c.m. frame to the lab frame when the velocities are nonrelativistic. Although point O has been taken outside the figure in this illustration, it may lie anywhere between O and O' depending upon the conditions of the problem. **(a)** In velocity space, each velocity vector in the c.m. frame is added to the same c.m. velocity vector to obtain the corresponding laboratory velocity. **(b)** In momentum space, the momenta in the c.m. frame are equal but the momentum associated with motion of the c.m. depends on the mass of the particle. The figure has been split along the x-axis and the upper and lower halves separated to make it easier to distinguish the vectors $M_3v'_{cm}$ and $M_4v'_{cm}$.

which the impinging particle can be scattered. If it hits M_2 "head on" it loses speed but continues to move forward after the collision. The struck particle can recoil at any angle from 0° up to 90°, but at the latter limit its recoil velocity is zero, indicating a grazing collision by M_1.

The situation like that just discussed, but in which $M_2 > M_1$, is shown in Fig. 10-5. In this case the impinging particle may be scattered through any angle up to 180°. The struck particle, as before, can only recoil at angles from 0° to 90°. In a "head on" collision M_1 has its direction of motion reversed.

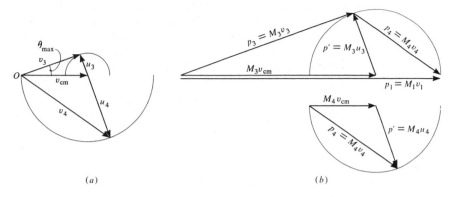

(a) (b)

Fig. 10-4. Graphical representation of nonrelativistic elastic scattering of particle M_1 by an initially stationary particle M_2, where $M_1 > M_2$. (a) Shows the plot in velocity space. (b) Shows the plot in momentum space. It also demonstrates that the lower half of the figure is unnecessary. Since conservation of momentum requires that $\mathbf{p}_3 + \mathbf{p}_4 = \mathbf{p}_1$, $\mathbf{p}_4$ can be obtained by closing the momentum triangle once $\mathbf{p}_3$ is found. Both figures are drawn for the special case where M_1 is scattered through the maximum possible angle.

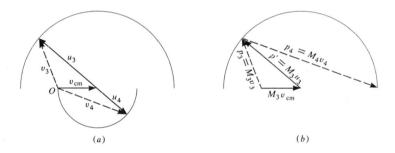

(a) (b)

Fig. 10-5. Graphical representation of nonrelativistic scattering of a particle M_1 by an initially stationary particle M_2 where $M_1 < M_2$. (a) A plot in velocity space. (b) A plot in momentum space.

10-3 Relativistic Collisions

It was seen in the previous section that a change in the total mass of a system, a change which is explained by relativity mechanics, when brought into a nonrelativistic treatment resulted in the center of mass of the system having to change velocity as the result of a collision. It was also found that the energy after the collision was not the same as it was before the collision in case the total mass of the system changed. In relativistic mechanics, one has the invariance of the energy-momentum four-vector rather than the separate laws of conservation of energy and momentum. In keeping with this shift in viewpoint we abandon the center-of-mass frame used in non-relativistic mechanics and adopt a center-of-momentum frame which, in nonrelativistic collisions involving no change in the total mass of the system, was seen (in the last section) to be equivalent to the center-of-mass frame. The center-of-momentum frame for two particles which move along the same straight line is that frame of reference, by definition, in which the momenta of the two particles are equal in magnitude and opposite in direction. The velocity of the c.m. frame (the same abbreviation will be used, since the two frames play the same roles) relative to the lab frame will be denoted by βc, and will be taken to be in the direction of the x-axis.

In the c.m. frame the two particles resulting from the collision will also move away from each other with equal and opposite momenta. The collision remains a relatively simple one in the c.m. frame. The chief problem is to find how this would appear to an observer in the lab frame. To answer this question, one needs the transformation equations which transform the four components of the energy-momentum four-vector from the c.m. to the lab frame. The four components in the c.m. frame are

$$p'_x = \frac{Mu_x}{\sqrt{1 - \beta^2}}, \tag{10-34}$$

$$p'_y = \frac{Mu_y}{\sqrt{1 - \beta^2}}, \tag{10-35}$$

$$p'_z = \frac{Mu_z}{\sqrt{1 - \beta^2}}, \tag{10-36}$$

and

$$p'_{iv} = \frac{iW'}{c}, \tag{10-37}$$

where

$$\beta^2 = \frac{u_x^2 + u_y^2 + u_z^2}{c^2}. \tag{10-38}$$

The invariance of the energy-momentum four-vector is expressed by the relationship

$$(p'_x)^2 + (p'_y)^2 + (p'_z)^2 + (p'_{iv})^2 = M^2 c^2. \tag{10-39}$$

When the substitution (10-37) is made this becomes the familiar relativistic energy expression

$$(W')^2 = (p'_x)^2 c^2 + (p'_y)^2 c^2 + (p'_z)^2 c^2 + M^2 c^4, \tag{10-40}$$

where W' is the *total* energy including mass energy. The transformation equations from the lab frame (p_x, p_y, p_z, p_{iv}) to the c.m. frame (p_x', p_y', p_z', p_{iv}') are

$$p_x' = \frac{1}{\sqrt{1 - \beta^2}}\, p_x + 0 \cdot p_y + 0 \cdot p_z + \frac{i\beta}{\sqrt{1 - \beta^2}}\, p_{iv},$$

$$p_y' = 0 \cdot p_x + p_y + 0 \cdot p_z + 0 \cdot p_{iv},$$

$$p_z' = 0 \cdot p_x + 0 \cdot p_y + p_z + 0 \cdot p_{iv}, \qquad \Biggr\} \quad *(10\text{-}41)$$

$$p_{iv}' = \frac{-i\beta}{\sqrt{1 - \beta^2}}\, p_x + 0 \cdot p_y + 0 \cdot p_z + \frac{1}{\sqrt{1 - \beta^2}}\, p_{iv},$$

or, in more compact form, and substituting for p_{iv}, p_{iv}',

$$p_x' = \frac{p_x}{\sqrt{1 - \beta^2}} - \frac{\beta W}{c\sqrt{1 - \beta^2}},$$

$$p_y' = p_y,$$

$$p_z' = p_z, \qquad \Biggr\} \quad (10\text{-}42)$$

$$W' = -\frac{\beta c p_x}{\sqrt{1 - \beta^2}} + \frac{W}{\sqrt{1 - \beta^2}}.$$

Let

$$b^2 \equiv (p_x')^2 + (p_y')^2 + (p_z')^2 \qquad (10\text{-}43)$$

and substitute from (10-42). This gives

$$b^2 = (1 - \beta^2)\left(p_x - \frac{\beta W'}{c\sqrt{1 - \beta^2}}\right)^2 + p_y^2 + p_z^2. \qquad (10\text{-}44)$$

Now let

$$k^2 \equiv \frac{b^2}{1 - \beta^2}, \qquad (10\text{-}45)$$

and

$$\alpha = \frac{\beta W'}{c\sqrt{1 - \beta^2}}. \qquad (10\text{-}46)$$

Then

$$\frac{(p_x - \alpha)^2}{k^2} + \frac{p_y^2 + p_z^2}{b^2} = 1. \qquad (10\text{-}47)$$

This is just the equation of a prolate ellipsoid of revolution about the x-axis. It is almost obvious that if the x-component of momentum in the c.m. frame (p_x') is zero, then the term ($p_x - \alpha$) is zero, but it can be obtained by returning to (10-42), from which, when $p_x' = 0$,

$$p_{x_0} = \frac{\beta W}{c} = \frac{\beta W'}{c\sqrt{1 - \beta^2}} = \alpha. \qquad (10\text{-}48)$$

* An advantage in writing the transformation equations in this way is that the coordinate transformation has the same form. More explicitly, if p_x' is replaced by x' etc., p_x by x etc., p_{iv}' by $x_{iv}' \equiv ict'$, and p_{iv} by $x_{iv} \equiv ict$, one has the desired transformation equations.

It is seen then that α, which, geometrically, is the displacement along the p_x-axis of the center of the ellipsoid from the origin of the lab momentum coordinates, is just the lab component of momentum in the x-direction associated with motion of the c.m. frame. The graphical method of obtaining the lab momentum $\mathbf{p}_j$ from the c.m. momentum $\mathbf{b}$ is shown in Fig. 10-6(a).

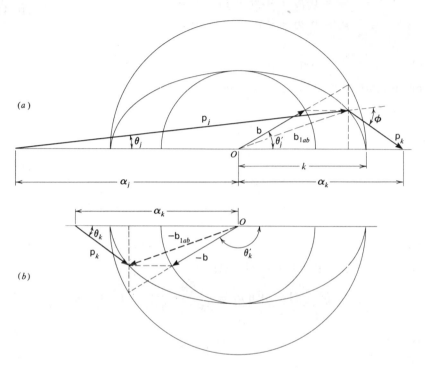

Fig. 10-6. Graphical method for transforming from a momentum $\mathbf{b}$ in the center-of-momentum frame to the corresponding momentum $\mathbf{p}_j$ in the laboratory frame. b, k, and α may be computed from Eqs. (10-30), (10-31), and (10-32) respectively or suitable modifications thereof. The point which is to be the terminus of $\mathbf{p}_j$ can be determined, without actually constructing the ellipse shown, in the following way. If the momentum vector in the c.m. frame makes an angle θ' with the x-axis, one draws $\mathbf{b}$ as shown, and extends the line of $\mathbf{b}$ to its intersection with the circle of radius k. A line perpendicular to the x-axis is dropped from this intersection. A line parallel to the x-axis is then drawn from the terminus of $\mathbf{b}$. The intersection of the latter line with the perpendicular line determines the location of the terminus of $\mathbf{p}_j$. The origin of $\mathbf{p}_j$ is a distance α_j to the left of O. Where two particles result from the collinear collision of two primary particles, the combined momenta of the primary particles is $\alpha_j + \alpha_k$, and $\mathbf{p}_k$ may be obtained as shown in (a) without the second construction (b).

Since the y and z components of $\mathbf{b}$ are unchanged when we transform to the lab frame, it is clear that if one draws a line parallel to the x-axis from the tip of $\mathbf{b}$ to the ellipsoid and then draws a vector from the origin of $\mathbf{b}$ to this point on the ellipsoid, the momentum of the particle relative to the c.m. frame *as seen by an observer in the lab frame* is obtained. The vector sum of the vectors $\mathbf{b}_{lab}$ and $\boldsymbol{\alpha}_j$ gives the lab momentum $\mathbf{p}_j$.

In a collision which results in the emission of two particles, the momentum of the second particle is equal and opposite to the first in the c.m. frame (i.e., is $-\mathbf{b}$). As shown in Fig. 10-6(b), this means that its momentum relative to the c.m. frame as seen by an observer in the lab frame is also equal and opposite to that of the first particle (i.e., is $-\mathbf{b}_{lab}$). The only difference between the two momentum diagrams is brought about by the fact that the momentum associated with the c.m. motion is different for the second particle (α_k) from what it is for the first particle (α_j).

Actually it is unnecessary to draw two figures as was done in Figs. 10-6(a) and (b). A vector from the terminus of $\mathbf{p}_j$ to a point on the axis a distance α_k from the center, O, gives $\mathbf{p}_k$ as shown in Fig. 10-6(a). If Fig. 10-6(b) were rotated $180°$ about an axis perpendicular to the page and passing through O, it would be seen that the geometrical figure formed by α_k, $\mathbf{b}$, and $\mathbf{p}_k$ would be the same as that drawn in Fig. 10-6(a). Conservation of momentum in the lab frame then requires that $\alpha_j + \alpha_k$ be the total momentum of the system before the collision as well as after.

If two particles, M_1 and M_2, before colliding, are moving in the same direction with momenta p_1 and p_2 and energies W_1 and W_2, respectively, then the requirement that their momenta be equal and opposite in the c.m. frame, namely that

$$p_1' = -p_2', \tag{10-49}$$

together with (10-42) gives us the velocity βc of the c.m. The desired result is

$$\beta = \frac{\sqrt{W_1^2 - M_1^2 c^4} + \sqrt{W_2^2 - M_2^2 c^4}}{W_1 + W_2}. \tag{10-50}$$

It is evident, from a comparison of Figs. 10-3 and 10-6, that α_j is the relativistic counterpart of $M_3 v_{cm}$ in the nonrelativistic case.

In most laboratory experiments, the target particle is at rest before the collision. Use of this fact gains a considerable simplification in the analysis, and all discussion from here on will be limited to this special case. The c.m. motion will now be given by

$$\beta = \frac{\sqrt{W_1^2 - M_1^2 c^4}}{W_1 + M_2 c^2} = \frac{\sqrt{W_{K1}(W_{K1} + 2M_1 c^2)}}{W_{K1} + (M_1 + M_2)c^2}, \tag{10-51}$$

where W_{K1} is the kinetic energy of the impinging particle, while the momentum of the impinging particle in the c.m. frame will reduce to

$$b_i = \frac{\beta M_2 c}{\sqrt{1 - \beta^2}}. \tag{10-52}$$

It is interesting to take up several special cases.

Elastic collision with $M_1 > M_2$. In this case, which is illustrated in Fig. 10-7, $M_3 = M_1$ and $M_4 = M_2$. Since the collision is elastic, both initial and both final momenta in the c.m. frame have the magnitude b_i as given by Eq. (10-52). From the constancy of b and the masses, it follows that $W_3 = W_1$

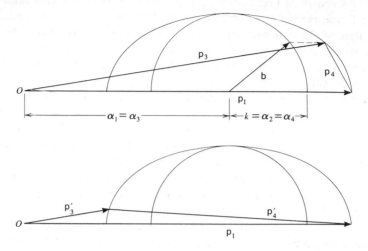

Fig. 10-7. Graphical construction for the elastic collision of a particle M_1 with a particle M_2 which is initially at rest. $M_1 > M_2$. The impinging particle has a momentum $p_1 = \alpha_1 + k$ and the target particle has an initial momentum $p_2 = \alpha_2 - k = 0$. The lower figure demonstrates the fact that when O lies outside the ellipse, there are two sets of momenta compatible with a given direction of motion of one of the particles. In this case $\mathbf{p}_3$ in the upper figure is parallel to $\mathbf{p}_3'$ in the lower.

and $W_4 = W_2$ and hence that $\alpha_3 = \alpha_1$ and $\alpha_2 = \alpha_4$. The graphical construction may be used for both initial and final states of the system in this instance, and it is immediately apparent that the initial momentum, p_1, satisfies the relation

$$p_1 = k + \alpha_1, \tag{10-53}$$

from which

$$\alpha_1 = p_1 - k. \tag{10-54}$$

It is also clear from the figure that

$$\alpha_2 - k = 0, \tag{10-55}$$

or

$$\alpha_2 = k. \tag{10-56}$$

Equation (10-40) states that, for particles of equal momenta, the particle with larger mass will have the greater total energy. Therefore, since $M_1 > M_2$, $\alpha_1 > \alpha_2$. In this case, since $\alpha_4 = k$, p_4 may be obtained simply by drawing a vector from the terminus of $\mathbf{p}_3$ to the point $\alpha_1 + k$ on the x-axis.

Elastic collision with $M_1 < M_2$. This is essentially the same as the case discussed above except for the condition $M_1 < M_2$. Therefore $\alpha_1 < \alpha_2$, as shown in Fig. 10-8.

Elastic collision between equal masses. This is basically not different from the previous two cases except that $M_1 = M_2$. In this case $\mathbf{p}_3$ starts from the point where the left side of the ellipse touches the x-axis. In the low-velocity

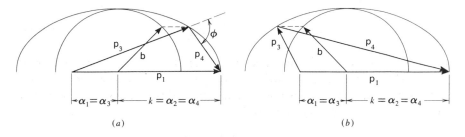

(a)   (b)

Fig. 10-8. Elastic collision of particle M_1 with an initially stationary particle M_2, where $M_1 < M_2$. (a) Shows a case in which M_1 is scattered in the forward direction. (b) Shows a case in which M_1 is scattered in the backward direction. It imparts much more momentum to M_2 in this example than it would in a forward scatter.

case, in which the ellipse degenerates to a circle, a theorem from geometry tells us that the angle between $\mathbf{p}_3$ and $\mathbf{p}_4$ is $90°$. This situation was encountered earlier in the scattering of alpha particles by helium nuclei. In the relativistic case it can be seen that the angle ϕ between $\mathbf{p}_3$ and $\mathbf{p}_4$ is always less than $90°$. Its minimum value occurs when $p_3 = p_4$ and is then given by

$$\cos \phi_{\min} = \frac{W_{K1}}{W_{K1} + 4M_1 c^2}. \tag{10-57}$$

Collisions of massless particles with massive ones. Here we deal with collisions involving photons or neutrinos. This is the case, for example, of a Compton collision between a photon and a massive body which is initially at rest so that $M_1 = 0$. Figure 10-8 is therefore again applicable. Here (10-34) reduces to

$$\bar{\beta} = \frac{p_1}{M_2 c + p_1} = \frac{h\nu_1}{h\nu_1 + M_2 c^2}, \tag{10-58}$$

while

$$\alpha_1 = \alpha_3 = \frac{\bar{\beta} b c}{c \sqrt{1 - \bar{\beta}^2}} = \bar{\beta} k = \bar{\beta} \alpha_2 = \bar{\beta} \alpha_4. \tag{10-59}$$

As $h\nu_1 \longrightarrow \infty, \bar{\beta} \longrightarrow 1$, and $\alpha_1 \longrightarrow \alpha_2$. When $h\nu_1 \longrightarrow 0$, $\bar{\beta} \longrightarrow 0$, and $\alpha_1 \longrightarrow 0$. Therefore the point from which $\mathbf{p}_3$ starts may lie anywhere from the center of the ellipse for zero-energy photons, to the left intersection of the ellipse with the x-axis when the photon energy becomes infinite.

An interesting aspect of photon collision is that the photon is scattered without change in wavelength in the c.m. frame. The difference between the incident and scattered wavelength in the lab frame may then be viewed as differences in the Doppler shift. From the c.m. frame, the source of the impinging photon, which is stationary in the lab frame, appears to be moving away from the c.m. with a velocity of $\bar{\beta}$. The photon, whose frequency is ν_1 in the lab frame, then appears to be a photon of frequency

$$\nu_1' = \nu_1 \sqrt{\frac{1 - \bar{\beta}}{1 + \bar{\beta}}} \tag{10-60}$$

in the c.m. frame. It is reradiated or scattered in the c.m. frame without change in frequency but is emitted at an angle which may be called θ_3 as seen in the lab frame. The Doppler-shift equation for this case in which the motion of the source is not purely radial is

$$\nu_3 = \nu_1' \frac{\sqrt{1 - \bar{\beta}^2}}{1 - \bar{\beta} \cos \theta_3}. \tag{10-61}$$

Combining (10-38) and (10-39),

$$\nu_3 = \frac{\sqrt{\frac{(1 - \bar{\beta})}{(1 + \bar{\beta})}(1 - \bar{\beta}^2)}}{1 - \bar{\beta} \cos \theta_3} \nu_1. \tag{10-62}$$

Substitution for $\bar{\beta}$ from (10-58) then gives

$$\nu_3 = \frac{\nu_1}{1 + (h\nu_1/M_2 c^2)(1 - \cos \theta_3)}, \tag{10-63}$$

which is a useful form of the Compton equation when energies ($h\nu$) rather than wavelengths are being measured.

Nuclear reactions. The equations which apply to nuclear reactions are somewhat less compact. The conditions which must be fulfilled are

$$(1) \quad W_3 + W_4 = W_1 + W_2, \tag{10-64}$$

$$(2) \quad W_3' + W_4' = W_1' + W_2', \tag{10-65}$$

and $$(3) \quad p_3' = -p_4', \tag{10-66}$$

from which it follows that

$$b_f^2 = \frac{[Q(M_1 + M_2 + M_3 + M_4)c^2 + 2W_{K1}M_2 c^2]}{\times [Q(M_1 + M_2 + M_3 + M_4)c^2 + 2W_{K1}M_2 c^2 + 4M_3 M_4 c^4]}{4c^2[2W_{K1}M_2 c^2 + (M_1 + M_2)^2 c^4]} \tag{10-67}$$

where we have introduced the quantity

$$Q \equiv [(M_1 + M_2) - (M_3 + M_4)]c^2, \qquad (10\text{-}29)$$

which is positive in exoergic and negative in endoergic reactions. An exoergic reaction is allowed at any bombardment energy as far as energy considerations alone are concerned. In endoergic reactions, on the other hand, there is a minimum kinetic energy of bombardment, called the threshold energy, below which it is impossible to promote the reaction. In the c.m. frame the threshold energy (which is now the kinetic energy of *both* target and impinging particles) is just $-Q$. The threshold energy in the lab frame can be found from the fact that in the final state of the system

$$b_f = k_f = 0,$$

$$\alpha_{3,4} = \frac{\beta M_{3,4} c}{\sqrt{1 - \beta^2}},$$

and the fact that the incident momentum is

$$\frac{1}{c} \sqrt{W_{K1}(W_{K1} + 2M_1 c^2)} = \alpha_1 + \alpha_2 = \alpha_3 + \alpha_4,$$

where W_{K1} is the threshold kinetic energy for the bombarding particle. This gives

$$\begin{aligned} W_{th} \equiv W_{K1} &= \frac{[(M_3 + M_4)^2 - (M_1 + M_2)^2]c^2}{2M_2} \\ &= -\frac{(M_1 + M_2 + M_3 + M_4)Q}{2M_2}. \qquad (10\text{-}68) \end{aligned}$$

If more than two particles result from the reaction, (10-68) can be modified to accommodate this situation since, at threshold, none of the particles has momentum in the c.m. frame and therefore it doesn't matter how many fragments the final mass is broken up into. The modified equation is

$$W_{th} = W_{K1} = \frac{\left[(\sum_i M_i)^2 - (M_1 + M_2)^2\right]c^2}{2M_2} = \frac{-Q\left[M_1 + M_2 + \sum_i M_i\right]}{2M_2}. \qquad (10\text{-}69)$$

Excitation energy. In compound nucleus formation, it is often necessary to know the amount of excitation of the compound nucleus. As long as the compound nucleus exists as such it is at rest with respect to the c.m. frame. Its excitation then is just the difference between its total energy in the c.m. frame and $M_3 c^2$ of its ground state. The total energy of the compound nucleus in the lab frame is

$$W_3 = W_1 + M_2 c^2 \qquad (10\text{-}70)$$

while its total energy in the c.m. frame is

$$W_3' = W_{ex}' + M_3 c^2 \tag{10-71}$$

where W_{ex}' is the excitation energy of the compound nucleus. These relations, together with (10-42) and (10-52) give

$$W_{ex}' = \sqrt{2W_1 M_2 c^2 + (M_1^2 + M_2^2)c^4} - M_3 c^2, \tag{10-72}$$

or, if expressed in terms of the kinetic energy, W_{K1}, of the bombarding particle,

$$W_{ex}' = \sqrt{2W_{K1} M_2 c^2 + (M_1 + M_2)^2 c^4} - M_3 c^2. \tag{10-73}$$

Decay in flight. In the next chapter we shall be much interested in the decay of a radioactive particle in flight. Where the decay results in just two product particles, the methods of this chapter are applicable. Since there is no target particle in this case,

$$M_2 = 0 \quad \text{and} \quad \bar{\beta} = \frac{\sqrt{W_1^2 - M_1^2 c^4}}{W_1},$$

which is obviously just the velocity (in units of c) of the particle itself in the lab frame. The other conditions are $W_3' + W_4' = M_1 c^2$, and $p_4' = -p_3'$. With some manipulation, these give

$$(p_3')^2 = \frac{[Q^2 - 2(M_1 - M_3)c^2 Q][Q^2 - 2(M_1 - M_3)c^2 Q - 4M_1 M_3 c^4]}{4M_1^2 c^6}, \tag{10-74}$$

or, in terms of masses only,

$$(p_3')^2 = \frac{c^2[M_1^2 - (M_3 + M_4)^2][M_1^2 - (M_3 - M_4)^2]}{4M_1^2}. \tag{10-75}$$

If the primary particle moves without loss of energy, then its velocity is a constant and the proper time of flight (i.e., the time measured in its own rest frame) is

$$t' = \frac{M_1 c^2}{W} t, \tag{10-76}$$

where t is the time of flight measured in the lab frame.

Angular distribution. When one carries out a nuclear bombardment reaction in the laboratory and observes the angular distribution of the product particles, this distribution is markedly affected by the motion of the c.m. In most theoretical analyses of such reactions it is more convenient to examine the distribution of the particles in their rest frame, or c.m. frame as it is called here. The transformation equation for converting differential cross sections per unit solid angle from the lab frame to the c.m. frame for the jth product particle is

$$\sigma_j'(\theta_j') = \sigma_j(\theta_j)\left(\frac{b_j}{p_j}\right)^2 \sqrt{1 - \frac{[(W_j')^2 - b_j^2 c^2]\beta^2}{b_j^2 c^2(1 - \beta^2)} \sin^2 \theta_j}. \quad (10\text{-}77)$$

Three-particle decay at rest. The methods of this chapter can be extended to the case of a particle which is at rest in the lab frame and decays into three particles (beta decay is a good example). Choose a set of coordinates such that particle number one with mass M_1 moves along the negative x-axis while the other two particles, M_3 and M_4, move in the x-y plane. Conservation of momentum requires that the c.m. of the latter two particles move along the positive x-axis. We now examine the motion of the two particles with respect to their c.m. (*not* the c.m. of the whole system of three particles). The situation is exactly like that shown in Fig. 10-6. In this case

$$\alpha_3 + \alpha_4 = -p_1 \quad (10\text{-}78)$$

and the velocity, βc, of the c.m. of the two particles is given by

$$\beta = \frac{-p_1}{W_3 + W_4} = \frac{-p_1}{M_0 c^2 - W_1}, \quad (10\text{-}79)$$

where M_0 is the mass of the parent particle before decay. For any given momentum p_1 which is allowed by energy conservation (for example, the momentum of the recoil ion in beta decay), a construction like Fig. 10-6 then gives all the possible pairs of momenta $\mathbf{p}_3$ and $\mathbf{p}_4$.

10-4 Maximum Momentum Transfer

If often occurs in nuclear and high-energy physics that one needs to know the maximum amount of momentum which can be carried away from some event with a fixed amount of total energy. Sometimes the question arises in the reverse order, namely, given a certain amount of momentum, under what conditions will the energy associated therewith be a minimum? The answer is, "The energy will be a minimum if all the particles move together as though they were a single large mass." We can show this formally in two steps.

In Fig. 10-9 we have chosen a group of momentum vectors whose magnitudes satisfy the total energy specification. It is at once evident that maximum momentum will be achieved when all the $\mathbf{p}_i$ are collinear. The problem then reduces to finding an extremum of

$$p = \sum p_i \quad (10\text{-}80)$$

while satisfying the energy criterion.

The total energy, W, is given by

$$W = \sum W_i = \sum (p_i^2 c^2 + M_i^2 c^4)^{1/2}, \qquad (10\text{-}81)$$

and its variation is

$$\delta W = \sum \frac{1}{2} \frac{2 p_i c^2 \, \delta p_i}{(p_i^2 c^2 + M_i^2 c^4)^{1/2}} = \sum \frac{p_i c^2}{W_i} \, \delta p_i. \qquad (10\text{-}82)$$

Since the total energy is fixed,

$$\delta W = 0, \qquad (10\text{-}83)$$

so that after dividing through by c,

$$\sum \frac{p_i c}{W_i} \, \delta p_i = 0. \qquad (10\text{-}84)$$

To find an extremum for p, we write

$$\delta p = \delta \sum p_i = \sum \delta p_i = 0. \qquad (10\text{-}85)$$

The δp_i are not all independent because of the restriction of constant energy. This suggests the use of Lagrange multipliers. One writes

$$\sum \left(\frac{p_i c}{W_i} - \xi \right) \delta p_i = 0, \qquad (10\text{-}86)$$

where ξ is an undetermined multiplier (i.e., a constant). The usual procedure is now followed. One of the coefficients is made equal to zero by a suitable

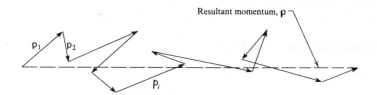

Resultant momentum, ρ

Fig. 10-9. This diagram makes it intuitively evident that when the magnitudes of a group of momentum vectors are given, the vector sum or total momentum is a maximum when the vectors are all collinear and of the same sense.

choice of ξ. The remaining δp_i can then be chosen arbitrarily, which means the remaining coefficients must also be zero. Hence

$$\frac{p_i c}{W_i} - \xi = 0 \qquad (10\text{-}87)$$

or

$$\xi = \frac{p_i c}{W_i}, \qquad (10\text{-}88)$$

which is recognized at once as an expression for β, the velocity of the ith particle (in units of c). Since each of the particles has the same velocity, the proposition is established.

PROBLEMS

10-1 A deuteron of 2-Mev energy strikes a second deuteron at rest. A proton is produced which moves at a 45° angle to the extension of the path of the impinging deuteron. Use nonrelativistic graphical methods to find the angle at which the triton is emitted.   [*Ans.* ∼85°.]

10-2 A nucleus of mass M_2 grams absorbs a photon whose energy is $h\nu_1$ ergs. What is the excitation of the nucleus produced by this event? Show that for very small photon energies, the excitation energy is approximately $h\nu_1$.

$$[Ans. \quad W'_{\mathrm{ex}} = M_2c^2(\sqrt{1 + (2h\nu_1/M_2c^2)} - 1).]$$

10-3 Assuming that the minimum scattering angle, when a particle of mass M_1 and kinetic energy W_{K1} is scattered by a second particle of the same mass which is initially at rest, occurs when $p_3 = p_4$, derive Eq. (10-57).

10-4 Obtain the threshold energy from Eq. (10-73).

10-5 Show that the threshold photon energy for creation of a pair in the vicinity of a free electron is $4mc^2$.

10-6 Show that when a particle of mass M_1 is scattered by a second particle of the same mass which is initially at rest, the minimum scattering angle occurs when $p_3 = p_4$.

10-7 Show, from Eq. (10-77), that in an elastic scattering by a particle of mass M_2 which is initially at rest, the differential cross section per unit solid angle for the ejection of M_2 at an angle θ_4 is

$$\sigma'_4(\theta'_4) = \sigma_4(\theta_4) \frac{(1 - \bar{\beta}^2 \cos^2 \theta_4)^2}{4(1 - \bar{\beta}^2) \cos \theta_4}.$$

HIGH ENERGY PHYSICS

11-1 Introduction

Until fairly recent times, the only source of very high-energy particles available to the physicist was the cosmic radiation. Even today this is the only source of particles whose energies exceed those of the largest man-made particle accelerators. It is natural, then, that this chapter should initially be concerned with cosmic rays. The emphasis, however, will not be on cosmic radiation as such but rather on cosmic radiation as a source of high-energy particles. This means that we shall have to forego a discussion of the correlation between cosmic-ray intensity and solar disturbances, and the fascinating hypotheses on the origin of cosmic radiation.

11-2 Historical Background

Around the turn of the century there was a great deal of activity in the field of ionization and gaseous conductivity. It was found in the course of these researches that no matter what precautions were taken to avoid it, an electroscope always slowly discharged. Wilson (159) and, independently,

Elster and Geitel (55) found that this slow discharge could not be prevented by the most careful insulation and concluded that the discharge was caused by ions being continuously created in the surrounding gas. As it did not seem possible that an appreciable part of the ionization could be due to thermal agitation of the molecules, they concluded that it was produced by some external agent such as x-rays or γ rays. Wilson even suggested at this time the possibility that the responsible radiation might have an extraterrestrial origin, but experiments designed to test this hypothesis were inconclusive and the proposal was generally ignored for many years thereafter.

Rutherford and his coworkers (102, 140) found that when an ionization chamber was surrounded by sufficient lead to absorb substantially all of the radiations from radium, the discharge rate was still about 40 per cent of what it was without the lead absorber. This indicated that if the agent responsible for the ionization of the gas was actually a form of radiation, then it must be a much more penetrating radiation than any then known. In spite of this finding, Wulf (162) and Gockel (72) had come to the conclusion in 1909 that the radiation could all be explained on the basis of γ rays from naturally radioactive substances near the surface of the earth. Wulf himself (163) performed an experiment the following year, however, which upset this conclusion. He measured the rate of ionization at the top of the Eiffel Tower, some 300 meters above the ground, and found that the decrease was much less than anticipated on the basis of absorption of radium γ rays from the earth by this thickness of air. Gockel (73) made a series of balloon flights up to an altitude of 4000 meters, measuring the ionization rate as a function of altitude. He also failed to observe the great decrease in discharge rate with altitude expected on the basis of a source of γ rays on the ground. In fact, he found an initial decrease followed by a slight increase in rate of discharge with increasing altitude, but the interpretation of these results was complicated by the fact that he did not use a pressure-tight vessel, so that the gas density within the ionization chamber varied with altitude. The rate of absorption, in an ionization chamber, of gamma rays, which were the only radiations that could be conceived of at that time possessing such great penetrating power, is proportional to the density of the gas in the chamber. A leaky chamber would accordingly be expected to show a lesser rate of discharge at high altitude than would an identical chamber with gas sealed in at the ambient pressure of some lower elevation.

In 1911, Simpson and Wright (143) found that there was a considerable amount of ionization immediately above the surface of the sea. Since it was known that there is very little radioactive contamination in sea water, it was concluded that the effect was not due to radioactivity. They also made the important incidental observation that the ionization in a *closed vessel* changed with barometric pressure, but could not understand why this should be so. Pacini (121) too observed that the ionization produced in a chamber at the surface of the sea was larger than that anticipated from known radioactive contaminants in sea water, but he made an important further step. He lowered his chamber into the ocean and found that the ionization rate fell from 11.0 ions/cm^3-sec at the surface to 8.9 ions/cm^3-sec at a depth of 3 meters. He repeated this experiment at Lake Bracciano and observed that the rate fell from 12.4 to 10.2. He concluded that these results could not be explained as radiation originating in the earth or the water.

Hess (76), using a pressure-tight ionization chamber so that the gas density within it would be held constant, made a number of balloon flights up to 5000 meters altitude. He found that an initial decrease of discharge rate with increasing altitude was followed by a considerable increase, that the rate was virtually independent of the time of day or night, and was not even influenced by an eclipse of the sun. On the basis of these findings he postulated a source of radiation outside of the solar system. Hess' hypothesis gained very little acceptance at the time it was advanced.

Kolhörster (88) confirmed and extended Hess' work, sending ionization chambers up to as much as 9200 meters elevation. He found that the ionization rate decreased up to 700 meters and then increased. At the highest elevations he found the rate of ionization to be up to ten times that at sea level. From the variation in ionization with altitude he found an absorption coefficient of 10^{-5}/cm of air at NTP. This was a surprising result (though perhaps it should not have been, in the light of Rutherford's earlier work), as the absorption coefficient for the most penetrating γ rays known at that time was eight times as great.

Research languished during the first World War, but a great deal was done in the years immediately thereafter, mostly aimed at determining whether the radiation comes from the earth or is extraterrestrial in origin. In 1925, Millikan and Cameron (108) measured the ionization rate at various depths in snow-fed (and therefore, presumably, relatively free of radioactive substances) Muir Lake, near Mt. Whitney in California. This lake lies at an elevation of 11,800 ft. They found, as had Pacini 13 years earlier, that the intensity decreased with depth, indicating that the rays come from above the water, and found, from the rate of decrease, that they were 18 times more penetrating than the most penetrating γ rays known at that time. Unless the penetrating power decreased at higher altitudes, such rays could easily penetrate the earth's entire atmosphere.

They next took their electroscopes to Lake Arrowhead, also in California, which is situated at an elevation of 5100 ft. They found that the ionization rate measurements here were identical* with those at Muir Lake at depths 6 ft greater than at Lake Arrowhead. Since the layer of air between 5100 and 11,800 ft is just equivalent in absorbing power to 6 ft of water, it was clear

---

* A later extension of these measurements (H. V. Neher and H. G. Stever, *Phys. Rev.*, **58**, 766 (1940)) showed that this result is not quite true. See Sec. 11-5.

that the air is only an absorber, not a source of the penetrating radiation. These results confirmed Hess' hypothesis of the origin of the rays, and Millikan (106, 108) accordingly proposed for the first time the name which is now usually used for these rays, namely *cosmic rays.*

Myssowsky and Tuwim (112) observed in 1926 and Steinke (148) confirmed in the following year that cosmic-ray intensity decreases when the barometric pressure increases. Although this had been observed in 1911, as mentioned earlier, these investigators were the first to realize that the decrease must be attributable to the increased mass of absorbing air. Observations of variation of cosmic-ray intensity as a function of solar and of sidereal time were made in this era, but the effects are so small that the results were not really conclusive.

It was generally believed up until this time that cosmic rays must be very energetic electromagnetic radiation in order to be so extraordinarily penetrating. In 1927, Skobelzyn (145) observed a virtually straight stray track in a cloud chamber which was in a magnetic field. He supposed that the particle was an electron, from the appearance of the track, and concluded that its energy must be at least 20 Mev. He suggested that it was an electron accelerated in the electrostatic field of a thundercloud!

Bothe and Kolhörster (24) used Geiger counters in coincidence to show that there were *charged particles* in the cosmic radiation capable of penetrating 1 cm of lead between the counters. In order to penetrate so much absorber, electrons far more energetic than those emitted by naturally radioactive substances would be required. It was natural for them to suppose, therefore, that the charged particles must be secondaries produced by the interaction of high-energy primary cosmic gamma rays from outer space with the atoms of the earth's atmosphere. They subsequently (25) determined the absorption coefficient of lead for these charged particles by noting the decrease in number of coincidences as the absorber thickness was increased. They found that the absorption coefficient was almost exactly that which had been observed in ionization chamber measurements, and concluded at once that most of the observed cosmic radiation must consist of charged particles. This did not rule out the possibility, of course, that these were secondary particles produced by γ-ray primaries. While the question of primary particles, that is, those coming into the earth's atmosphere from outer space, and secondary particles (those produced by interaction of primary particles with the atoms of the earth's atmosphere) complicates the picture, the motion of any charged particle should be affected by the earth's magnetic field, and it is to this problem that we turn next.

11-3 Deflection of Charged Particles by the Earth's Magnetic Field

It has been known for a very long time that the magnetic field intensities measured at the surface of the earth, aside from local anomalies presumably caused by such things as rock masses or ore bodies, can be approximated fairly well by the field of a magnetic dipole located near the center of the earth. This representation requires a dipole (144) whose magnetic moment is 8.06×10^{25} gauss-cm^3, located 433 km from the center of the earth along a line from the center of the earth to a point on the earth's surface at 15.3° N geographic latitude and 115.1° E geographic longitude. The axis of the dipole intersects the

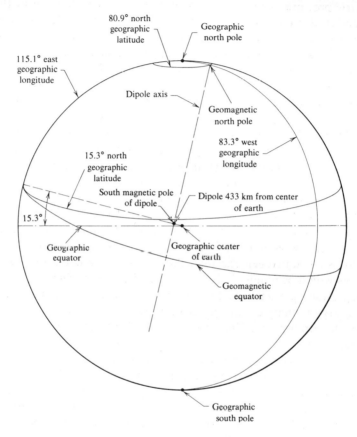

Fig. 11-1. Diagram showing location and orientation of equivalent magnetic dipole whose magnetic field approximates that of the earth at the earth's surface.

earth's surface, in the northern hemisphere, at 80.9° N geographic latitude and 83.3° W geographic longitude. This is to be compared with the "dip pole" (one located by local surface magnetic intensity measurements) which is located at 82.2° N and 142.0° W. The location and orientation are shown pictorially in Fig. 11-1. The adequacy of this model will be touched on later, but it offers such a great mathematical simplification that it seems worthwhile to proceed with its use, since it will yield important qualitative ideas even if they are inexact in detail.

When a moving charged particle is deflected by a static magnetic field its linear momentum undergoes a change in direction but not of magnitude. The constancy of the magnitude of the momentum is required by energy conservation. The angular momentum of the particle about a fixed point is also a constant of the motion. The orbital velocity of the earth is so small in comparison to that of a cosmic-ray particle that the earth may be treated as a fixed object.

It is obvious that a particle* which approaches the earth along the geo-magnetic dipole axis has no component of velocity normal to the magnetic field intensity and therefore will suffer no deflection. This means that there is no lower limit on the energy of particles which may approach the earth from this direction. On the other hand, particles moving in the geomagnetic equatorial plane move at right angles to the magnetic field intensity at all times and therefore suffer maximum deflection. Equation (2-12) shows that the instantaneous radius of curvature in this case is directly proportional to the speed of the particle. Particles of low energy will therefore be deflected away from the earth long before they reach our atmosphere. The actual particle trajectories in the general case, where the particles approach the earth from arbitrary directions, are quite complicated but it is possible, as Störmer (150) showed in 1930, to classify the orbits broadly.

We begin by defining two constants of the motion. Let

$$C = \frac{p_\phi}{pa} \tag{11-1}$$

and

$$a = \sqrt{\frac{\mu q}{pc}} \tag{11-2}$$

where p_ϕ is the orbital angular momentum about the geomagnetic dipole axis of the earth, p is the instantaneous linear momentum of the particle, μ is the magnetic dipole moment of the earth in emu and q/c is the electrical charge in emu borne by the particle. The quantity a, called the Störmer radius, is the radius of the equilibrium circular orbit of a particle having a charge q and momentum p in the geomagnetic equatorial plane. The equations of motion in the earth's magnetic field then yield the expression

$$C = \frac{r}{a} \cos \alpha \cos \theta - \frac{1}{r/a} \cos^2 \theta, \tag{11-3}$$

where θ is the geomagnetic latitude and α the angle between the velocity vector of the particle and the tangent to a latitude circle as shown in Fig. 11-2.

---

* *Particle* will be understood in this section to mean *charged particle*, since these are the only ones which interact significantly with the earth's magnetic field.

Equation (11-3) allows one to divide the C, r/a plane into three regions as shown in Fig. 11-3. In the "forbidden" regions there are no compatible values of C and r/a. Possible values all lie within the area marked "allowed." Since C is a constant for a given particle with given linear and angular momenta, its motion as shown on this plot, no matter how tortuous in three-dimensional space, is confined to motion parallel to the r/a axis. The value

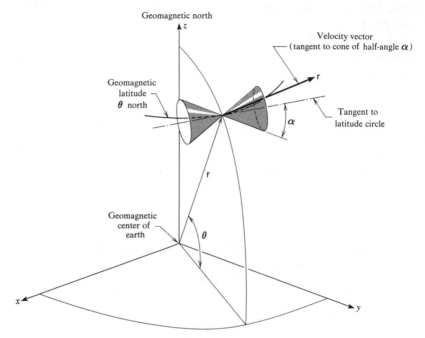

Fig. 11-2. Diagram showing angles α and θ which occur in Eq. (11-3). The radius vector **r** is to some general point in space, *not* to the surface of the earth.

of r/a as a function of *time* may still be complex but that does not detract from the usefulness of the figure. A particle with parameter $C = -2.5$ approaching the earth from some remote point in space can never get closer than about $r/a = 2$ to the center of the earth. Likewise, a particle with $C = -2.5$ initially moving in the close-in part of the allowed region can never leave the vicinity of the earth because it can move, at the most, only to a value of r/a of about 0.46. Such a particle may be said to be "trapped" by the earth's magnetic field, since in the absence of collision with the earth or some other object it is constrained to move forever in the inner allowed region.

According to Störmer's theory, as given above, no particle can reach the earth (if r_{earth}/a is less than one) if C is less than -2. This is certainly correct, but the converse is not true. If a particle has C greater than -2 it is not inconsistent with the conservation conditions for it to reach the earth, but its trajectory may never bring it very close to the earth. More detailed numerical calculations by Lemaitre and Vallarta (97) show that *all* orbits can reach the earth for which $0 > A > -1.57712$. For $-2 < A < -1.57712$ there is a so-called "penumbra" zone in which there are alternate allowed and forbidden regions. In addition some of these "allowed" orbits would require

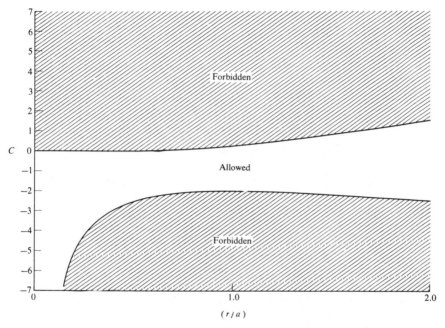

(r/a)

Fig. 11-3. A plot of the quantity C vs. r/a. Since C is a constant which depends only on the initial linear and angular momentum of the particle, orbits are straight horizontal lines on this plot. Not all particles moving in the "Allowed" region will strike the earth, but no particle can reach the earth if it would have to move into the "Forbidden" region to do so. As a is also a constant of the motion, a given value of r/a may represent different distances from the geomagnetic center of the earth for different particles.

the particle to pass through the earth to reach the point of observation. Long numerical calculations are necessary to identify these earth-shadow orbits.

The latitude effect. At low latitudes only those particles which have sufficient energy* can reach the earth, while at higher latitudes the interaction with the geomagnetic field is less and lower-energy particles will strike the

* The term *energy* is used loosely here. The requirements are really on the linear and angular momenta. When the energy is very high, $W = \sqrt{p^2c^2 + M^2c^4} \cong pc$, and in this case it no longer matters whether one speaks of energy or momentum since one is proportional to the other.

earth. This "latitude effect" was first observed by J. Clay (37) in 1927, and was subsequently thoroughly investigated by shipboard measurements made all over the world by Millikan and Neher (107, 109) and by Compton and Turner (40). Figure 11-4 shows results obtained by the latter pair. Since an electron must have an energy greater than 10^3 Bev* and a proton an energy greater than 3 Bev just to penetrate the earth's atmosphere, the lower energy

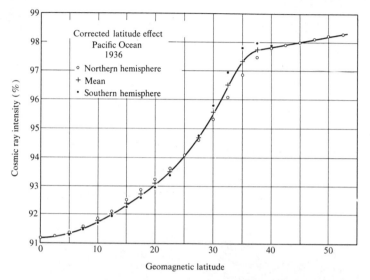

Fig. 11-4. Cosmic-ray intensity, corrected for an apparent atmospheric temperature effect, as a function of geomagnetic latitude. Cosmic-ray intensity was determined by means of a 19.3-liter ionization chamber shielded with lead shot equivalent to 12 cm of solid lead. Within the experimental accuracy of the data, the effect at northern and southern latitudes appears to be the same. [From A. H. Compton and R. N. Turner, *Phys. Rev.*, **52**, 799 (1937).]

particles which are magnetically allowed at higher latitudes have insufficient energy to penetrate the atmosphere. One would expect a greater latitude effect at higher elevations than at sea level, and this has been well demonstrated by a number of investigations such as that of Millikan, Neher, and Pickering (110) the results of which are shown in Fig. 11-5.

The longitude effect. It was discovered by Clay, Van Alphen, and Hooft (39) that the cosmic-ray intensity also varies with longitude at the same value of latitude. Even if one measures intensity as a function of geomagnetic (dipole) longitude at constant geomagnetic latitude one obtains such an effect. The minimum occurs, however, not at the point expected from the

* 1 Bev = 10^9 ev. In foreign literature it is more common to encounter the abbreviation Gev for the same quantity. The G stands for Giga which means 10^9.

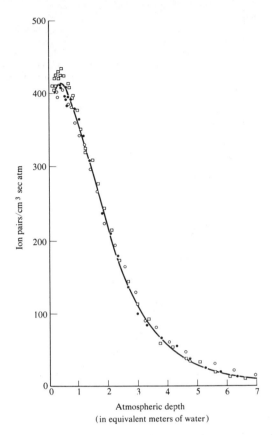

Fig. 11-5. (a) Ionization rate as a function of depth from the top of the earth's atmosphere at 51.3° north geomagnetic latitude (Omaha, Neb.). The three kinds of data points represent three different balloon flights made at different times on the same day. A few points have been omitted from the upper end of the curve, but the spread of data is preserved.

eccentric dipole model, but rather at a point about 65° further west where the local magnetic field is a maximum. In any event it seems certain that it is a magnetically controlled phenomenon. The latitude and longitude effects make it certain that a sizable fraction, at least, of the primary cosmic radiation consists of charged particles. The charged particles which give rise to magnetically linked intensity variations, moreover, must be particles more massive than electrons, since electrons with sufficient energy to penetrate the earth's atmosphere are practically undeviated by the geomagnetic field.

The east-west effect. An inspection of Fig. 11-3 shows that for values of r/a less than 1, particles with C less than -2 will not be able to penetrate the

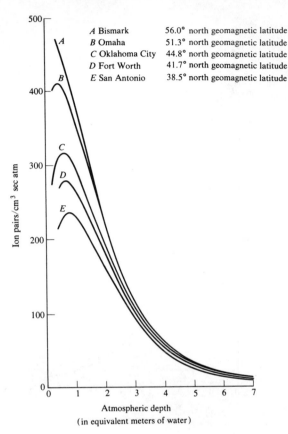

A Bismark	56.0° north geomagnetic latitude
B Omaha	51.3° north geomagnetic latitude
C Oklahoma City	44.8° north geomagnetic latitude
D Fort Worth	41.7° north geomagnetic latitude
E San Antonio	38.5° north geomagnetic latitude

Fig. 11-5. (b) Ionization rate as a function of atmospheric depth at five geomagnetic latitudes. [From Millikan, Neher, and Pickering (110).]

earth's magnetic field. For given values of r, a, and θ one can then use Eq. (11-3) to calculate a "critical angle" α_c defined by

$$-2 = \frac{r_0}{a} \cos \alpha_c \cos \theta_0 - \frac{1}{r_0/a} \cos^2 \theta_0 \qquad (11\text{-}4)$$

or

$$\cos \alpha_c = \frac{\cos \theta_0}{(r_0/a)^2} - \frac{2}{(r_0/a) \cos \theta_0}. \qquad (11\text{-}5)$$

Equation (11-3) can now be rewritten in terms of $\cos \alpha_c$ as

$$C = -2 + \frac{r_0}{a} \cos \theta_0 (\cos \alpha - \cos \alpha_c). \qquad (11\text{-}6)$$

It is seen at once from (11-6) that C will be less than -2 if $\cos \alpha$ is less than cos α_c, from which it follows that particles with the chosen values of a can never reach a point r_0, θ_0 unless α is less than α_c. In other words, those particles (for a given value a) which reach r_0, θ_0 enter through the base of a cone, of half-angle α_c, as shown in Fig. 11-2, which opens to the west for positively charged particles or to the east for negatively charged particles. These cones are called the Störmer cones and open up (α_c increases) as the particle energy increases and as the latitude angle increases.

Experimentally it is found that the intensity of cosmic radiation is a *maximum* in the vertical direction, and decreases roughly as the square of the cosine of the zenith angle. This apparent contradiction with the theory of magnetic deflection is *partially* due to the fact that the earth's atmosphere is effectively thicker for particles entering at large zenith angles, and it is precisely the particles with least energy available for penetration of the earth's atmosphere that must approach the earth with the greatest zenith angle (minimum α).

If what is measured at the earth's surface is *primary* cosmic radiation then, since the effective thickness of absorber is the same for particles entering at a given zenith angle whether they come from the west or the east, a comparison of intensities of cosmic radiation from the two directions and the same zenith angle should show whether the primary particles are principally positively or negatively charged.

Rossi (133) found an indication of an east-west effect in 1931, and this was definitely established soon thereafter by Johnson and Street (86), who give the results shown in Table 11-1, the east-west asymmetry being defined as

$$2\,\frac{\Phi_W - \Phi_E}{\Phi_W + \Phi_E},$$

where Φ_W is the intensity observed at some zenith angle ϕ to the west, and Φ_E is the intensity observed at the same zenith angle to the east. Asymmetries up to 48 per cent have been reported (12, 20, 141) at high altitudes. These results all indicate a preponderance of positively charged primaries. Theory also predicts a small north-south asymmetry from geomagnetic effects. It has been observed (38, 85, 136) in the northern hemisphere that intensity from the south is a little greater than that from the north.

Table 11-1 EAST-WEST ASYMMETRY OF COSMIC-RAY
INTENSITY (86)

Latitude (°N)	Height (m)	Zenith angle (°)	Asymmetry (%)
29	4300	51.5	11
	3300	49	8
	2200	43.6	8
36	1730	35	5.5

In view of the fact that we now know that almost all cosmic-ray particles reaching the earth's surface are secondaries, it is remarkable that an east-west effect is observed. Evidently the secondaries tend to preserve the direction of the primaries. From the discussion in Chap. 10, one would expect this if the incident particles have very great energies.

11-4 Showers

In 1929, Skobelzyn (146) observed a group of stray tracks in a cloud chamber photograph. This was the first observation of a "cosmic-ray shower" as it would now be called, a phenomenon which has since been extensively studied by a number of investigators. An example of such a shower, as observed in a cloud chamber, is shown in Fig. 11-6.

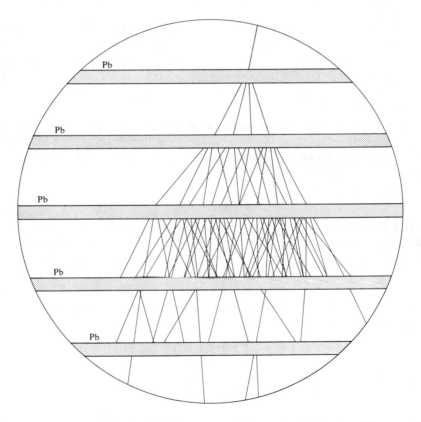

Fig. 11-6. Representation of soft shower produced in a cloud chamber. The cascade process causes a rapid multiplication of particles in the top three lead plates, but then absorption begins to outweigh multiplication and the shower begins to die out after passing through the lower two lead plates.

The first cloud chamber picture showing positron-negatron pairs was obtained by Blackett and Occhialini (22). The discovery of pairs, which of course were predicted by the Dirac theory, led Auger (9) to suggest the following mechanism for the production of showers. A high-energy γ ray produces a pair of fast electrons ($+$ and $-$). As these electrons are decelerated in passing through matter they emit bremsstrahlung or, in other words, create more γ rays. These γ rays obviously must be of much lower energy than the original γ ray, but if sufficiently energetic may each produce a new pair of particles. This chain of events can go on with a continually increasing number of particles until finally the γ rays generated as bremsstrahlung are of insufficient energy to produce a pair (i.e., below about 1 Mev) and the multiplication of particles ceases.

Rossi (134), using an arrangement of counters like that of Fig. 11-7, found that the number of coincidences beneath layers of lead absorber first increased

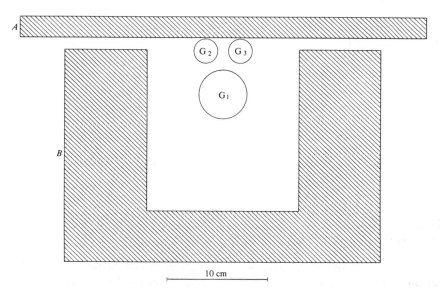

Fig. 11-7. Experimental arrangement employed by Rossi (135) in studying the transition effect. G_1, G_2, and G_3 are GM tubes, B is a lead shield to cut down the background count, and A is one of the lead absorber plates. The simultaneous discharge of the three counters was interpreted as being due to a shower, since a single particle could not pass through all three counters.

and then decreased as the thickness of absorber was increased, as shown in Fig. 11-8. The explanation is that the cascade process causes a multiplication of particles which progresses rapidly at first but levels off as the energy of the bremsstrahlung (γ rays) approaches the threshold for pair-production. As the number of particles in the shower increases, the energies of the particles

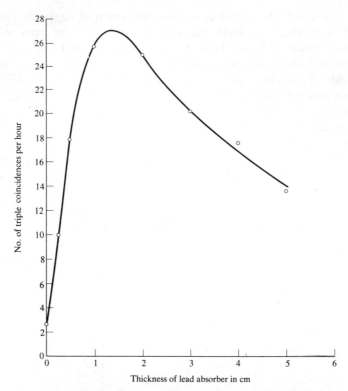

No. of triple coincidences per hour

Thickness of lead absorber in cm

Fig. 11-8. Transition curve obtained by Rossi (135). The number of triple coincidences observed per hour is given as a function of the thickness of the absorber plate *A* (Fig. 11-7).

become correspondingly smaller, so that their range in the absorber becomes less and the number of particles is more rapidly diminished by absorption.

Variation of cosmic-ray intensity with altitude. A comparison of Fig. 11-8 with Fig. 11-5 suggests that the observed variation of total cosmic-ray activity with altitude is to be ascribed to the transition phenomenon discovered by Rossi.

It can now be seen why an electron must have 10^3 Bev of energy to penetrate the earth's atmosphere. What is meant is that a 10^3-Bev electron will produce a shower in the upper atmosphere in which an average of one electron will reach the earth's surface.

11-5 Muons

Rossi (135) found that the cosmic-ray intensity is reduced about 30 per cent by 10 cm of lead, while the remaining radiation is reduced only 50 per cent by a meter of additional lead. This fact has led to the somewhat arbitrary division of cosmic rays into a very penetrating "hard component," which is the radiation remaining after the rays have passed through 10 cm of lead, and a "soft component," which is the easily absorbed part of the radiation removed by 10 cm of lead absorber. The *intensity* of the hard component is

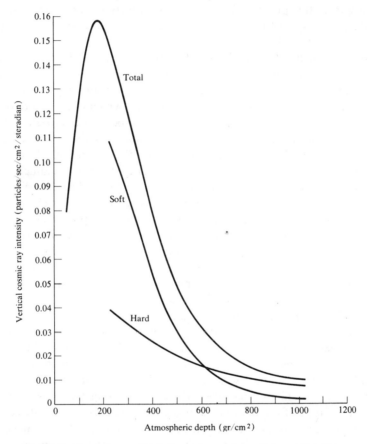

Fig. 11-9. Breakdown of total cosmic-ray intensity near the geomagnetic equator into hard and soft components. [From B. Rossi, *Rev. Mod. Phys.*, **20**, 537 (1948).]

determined by extrapolating the intensity-*vs.*-absorber-thickness curve for absorber thicknesses greater than 10 cm, back to zero absorber thickness. The difference between the measured zero (absorber) thickness intensity and the extrapolated hard-component intensity is taken to be the intensity of the soft component.

When only the hard component of the radiation is measured, the variation with atmospheric depth is quite different from that of the total radiation, as may be seen from Fig. 11-9. The extraordinary penetrating power of some cosmic rays is attested by the fact that they have been observed in mines under rock equivalent in mass to 980 meters of water (15, 161).

According to the Bethe-Heitler (18) theory (see Sec. 3-6), relativistic electrons lose energy primarily by bremsstrahlung. The energy loss per unit path length in this process should increase linearly with the electron energy. This does not appear to be easily reconciled with a hard and soft component of cosmic radiation if both consist of electrons.

To find whether the Bethe-Heitler theory was valid at high energies, Anderson and Neddermeyer undertook an extensive cloud chamber study of the rate of energy loss of cosmic-ray electrons in absorbers. The energies of the electrons were inferred from their momenta, which in turn were obtained from the curvature of the tracks, the curvature being a manifestation of the deflection of the charged particles by a large magnetic field. The momentum is computed from Eq. (1-1) on the assumption that the particle bears a single electronic charge. The energy can be calculated from the momentum provided one assumes a value for the mass of the particle. These studies showed that the Bethe-Heitler theory of electron energy loss was correct up to energies of about 400 Mev, but that particles with an apparent energy greater than this amount showed a smaller rate of energy loss *on the average* than predicted from theory. This conclusion was substantiated by the fact that the number of secondaries observed under lead absorbers struck by high-energy particles was an order of magnitude too small to be in agreement with the rate of energy loss predicted from theory.

In 1933 Kunze (90) had published a cloud chamber photograph of a track, whose momentum and charge could be determined from the magnetically produced track curvature, with the statement "The nature of the particle is unknown; it ionizes too little for a proton and too much for a positron." Apparently little attention was paid to this event, but soon Anderson and others (151) were finding particles whose penetrating power was much too great for electrons if the Bethe-Heitler theory were correct, but whose specific ionizations were too great for electrons. Anderson and Neddermeyer (6) in 1936 found several tracks in which the energy, as deduced from curvature of the track in the upper part of the cloud chamber, was incompatible with the energy of the particle after passing through a lead plate at the center of the chamber unless the particle had a mass intermediate between those of an electron and a proton.

Williams and Pickup (157) obtained a convincing cloud chamber photograph of such an intermediate mass particle in 1938. In the same year, Neddermeyer and Anderson (113) obtained a photograph of a cloud chamber track of a particle which came to rest in the chamber. From the curvature of the track before and after passing through the GM tube at the center of

the cloud chamber and the range of the particle from the p⟨
the GM tube until it came to rest in the gas filling the cloud
possible to make various calculations of its mass, the best ⟨
about 240 electron masses. They also noted three droplets ⟨
intersected the end of the intermediate-mass particle trac⟨
gested might be the track of a positron resulting from the decay ⟨
tively charged heavier particle. Anderson suggested the name *mesotron* for
these particles, while other workers referred to them as mesons, yukons, or
barytrons, but the name now in general use is mu-meson or muon.* It was
also suggested at that time that mesons might be created in pairs by a process
analogous to electron pair production, and that they might exist in several
quantized mass states. A number of early muon mass estimates are given in
Table 11-2. Somewhat more accurate determinations of the muon mass were

Table 11-2 EARLY MUON MASS ESTIMATES

Investigators	Charge of particle	Estimated mass (in electron mass units)	Method*	Reference
Street & Stevenson	−	130	(a)	*Phys. Rev.,* **52,** 1103 (1937)
Nishina, Takeuchi, & Ichimiya	Not reported	184–263	(b)	*Phys. Rev.,* **52,** 1198 (1937)
Ruhlig & Crane	+	120	(c)	*Phys. Rev.,* **53,** 266 (1938)
Corson & Brode	Not reported	Av. 200	(d)	*Phys. Rev.,* **53,** 773 (1938)
Ehrenfest	+	∼ 200	(a)	*Compt. Rend.,* **206,** 428 (1938)
Williams & Pickup	One − Three +	Av. ∼ 200	(a)	*Nature,* **141,** 684 (1938)

  * *Method:*
(a) Droplet count and curvature in magnetic field.
(b) Energy loss in lead plate and curvature in magnetic field.
(c) Rate of change of curvature and curvature in magnetic field.
(d) Droplet count and range.

  * This designation came into use after the discovery of the π-meson (Sec. 11-6) but
is used here to avoid later confusion.

de with nuclear emulsions, but satisfactory accuracy had to await the artificial production of muons (indirectly) by high-energy particle accelerators. Barkas et al. (13) gave a value for the positive muon mass in 1956 of

$$M_{\mu^+} = (206.93 \pm 0.35)m,$$

where m is the mass of an electron.

When negative muons are brought to rest, they are captured by nuclei, initially probably in high quantum number states. As the muon drops to lower quantum number orbits in the region of the atomic electron orbits, the mean electron density is sufficiently high, especially in the heavier elements, that it is likely to give up its transition energy in the ejection of Auger electrons. When it reaches sufficiently low quantum number orbits that it lies wholly within the K-electron orbit,* the mean electron density will be so small that transitions will take place predominantly by photon emission. In heavy elements, the ground-state orbit of the "mesic atom" so formed is so small that the muon moves within the nucleus itself. It is impossible in this case to calculate the ground-state energy level with any degree of exactitude because of ignorance of charge distribution, and hence the coulomb field, within the nucleus. In light elements this is no longer true and one can then apply the simple Bohr formula [Eq. (2-16) with M_{μ^-} replacing m_e in (2-17)] to calculate the transition energies. This approximation becomes even better if the transitions take place between higher quantum number states which still lie inside of the K-electron orbit, since these orbits are larger and the muon spends correspondingly less time within the nucleus. It would appear that one need only measure the energies of x-rays emitted by mesic atoms to determine the muon mass. Actually, a number of small corrections must be made, the largest being the "vacuum polarization" correction. The muon mass, as deduced from mu-mesic x-rays (67) is

$$M_{\mu^-} = (206.76^{+0.03}_{-0.02})m.$$

The experimentally determined masses of the positive and negative muon are so nearly the same that they are commonly assumed to be identical.

Radioactive decay of muons. As mentioned in the discussion of deflection of charged cosmic particles by the earth's magnetic field, the observed intensity is greatest in the vertical direction, whereas one would expect, on the basis of magnetic deflection alone, a minimum intensity in the vertical direction. It was also stated that this was due *in part* to the effectively greater thickness of absorber passed through by particles entering the atmosphere obliquely.

---

* In the Bohr atom model the orbit radius, for circular orbits and for a given total quantum number, is inversely proportional to the reduced mass of the orbiting particle. Muon orbits are therefore on the order of 200 times smaller than the corresponding electron orbits.

Several observers (10, 51, 59) found, however, that when additional absorber is placed above a Geiger counter "telescope" so that the total amount of absorber in the vertical direction is equal to the amount of atmospheric absorber in some direction inclined at an angle ϕ to the vertical, the vertical intensity is still greater than the intensity at the angle ϕ. A possible experimental arrangement is shown schematically in Fig. 11-10.

Kulenkampff (89) showed in 1938 that this absorption anomaly could be understood if one assumes that mesons undergo radioactive decay, for then

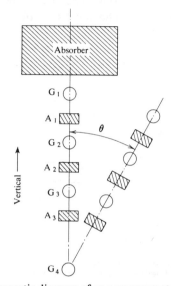

Fig. 11-10. Schematic diagram of an arrangement to demonstrate the absorption anomaly. G_1, G_2, G_3, G_4 are GM tubes. When the block of absorber is equivalent, in mass per unit area, to the additional atmospheric mass per unit area in the direction θ, the number of fourfold coincidences is still greater than when the counter telescope is inclined at the angle θ. A_1, A_2, A_3 are additional absorbers to eliminate as much of the soft component as possible.

the longer inclined path through the atmosphere increases the time during which decay can take place before the mesons reach the earth's surface. Bhabha (19) pointed out that to calculate the effect of spontaneous decay on the apparent absorption of mesons by the atmosphere, account must be taken of the relativistic change in apparent lifetime of the meson, since the meson is moving with a very high speed with respect to the observer. Thus

$$t_{a0} = \sqrt{1 - \beta^2}\, t_a \qquad (11\text{-}7)$$

where t_a is the observed lifetime, t_{a0} is the lifetime when the meson is at rest with respect to the observer, and β is the ratio of the meson velocity to the velocity of light.

In order to avoid the variation in cosmic-ray intensity with zenith angle caused by magnetic deflection of the charged particles, Rossi, Hilberry, and Hoag (137) compared vertical intensities under dense absorbers with *vertical* intensities at various altitudes. Carbon was used as an absorber, as its atomic number is close to that of the nitrogen and oxygen of the air, and therefore there seemed to be less danger in assuming that equal masses of air or carbon absorb the same fraction of mesons. The arrangement of absorber and GM tubes is shown in Fig. 11-11. The results of this experiment are given in

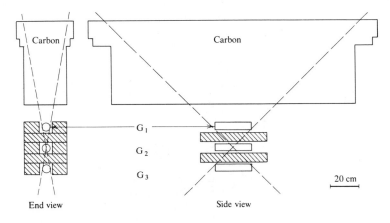

Fig. 11-11. Experimental arrangement used by Rossi, Hilberry, and Hoag (137) to study the absorption anomaly. The coincidence rate with and without the carbon absorber was measured at each altitude.

Fig. 11-12 and show again that the air has an anomalous apparent absorption coefficient. Similar results were obtained by Neher and Stever (114) who measured total ionization rate, with an electrometer, as a function of depth of submergence in Lake Tulainyo (3921 meters above sea level) and in Kerchkoff Reservoir (305 meters above sea level). All of these measurements, after correction for the relativistic time dilation, yield values for the mean life of the meson of 2 to 3 $\times$ 10^{-6} second.

Although Neddermeyer and Anderson had observed a few fog droplets at the end of their stopping muon track and had suggested the possibility that this might be a decay positron, it remained for Williams and Roberts (158) in 1940 to obtain the first definitive cloud chamber photograph of muon decay. Their photograph shows the track of a meson coming to rest in the chamber and the track of a high-speed particle leaving the point where the meson was stopped. By assuming that the decay particle is a positron they estimated its energy to be (70 $\pm$ 35) Mev. Since this is roughly half the mass energy of the muon, they inferred that the muon decayed into a positron and a neutrino. The great kinetic energy of the emitted particle requires the conversion of a large fraction of the mass energy of the muon, which in turn implies that the mass of the emitted particle is small compared to that of the muon. From the fact that there is no visible separation between the end of the

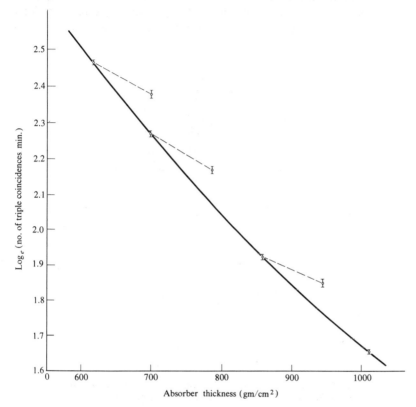

Fig. 11-12. Absorption anomaly data obtained by Rossi, Hilberry, and Hoag (137). The solid line connects points obtained *without* carbon absorber at different altitudes. The dotted lines connect intensities measured under carbon absorber with intensities measured without carbon absorber at the same elevation. One would expect the carbon points to lie on the solid curve rather than lying above it. The discrepancy is explicable on the basis of muon decay-in-flight.

muon track and the beginning of the decay track, they reasoned that the lifetime must have been less than 2×10^{-4} sec if the muon diffused with the mean gas-kinetic velocity, but was likely much shorter since the velocity of the muon at the point where it ceases ionizing is probably much greater than the mean gas-kinetic velocity.

In 1942, Rossi and Nereson (138) determined the mean lifetime of the muon by a more direct method than the atmospheric absorption anomaly. Using an apparatus depicted schematically in Fig. 11-13, they determined when a meson had come to rest or decayed in flight in the brass block by obtaining coincident pulses from G_0, G_1, G_2 without an anticoincident pulse from G_4. They then measured the time which elapsed from the G_0, G_1, G_2 pulse until a pulse (presumably from a decay electron*) came from G_3. Figure 11-14 gives the number of observed decays after any given time lapse. The mean lifetime of the muon can be determined from this curve as though

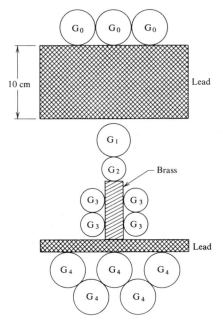

Fig. 11-13. Schematic diagram of apparatus used by Rossi and Nereson (138) to measure the half-life of cosmic-ray muons at rest.

it were an ordinary radioactive decay curve. It is assumed that virtually all decays are from mesons nearly at rest, so that no relativity correction need be applied in this case. The value of the muon mean lifetime which they obtained is $(2.3 \pm 0.2) \times 10^{-6}$ sec, which not only confirms earlier values, but is a striking verification of the relativistic time dilation in a velocity region where the effect is large. A more recent value (128) is (2.211 ± 0.003) μsec.

The assumption that the charged decay product of a muon is an electron is strongly supported by the emulsion event found by Camerini and Fowler (29) in 1949. The decay track emanating from the end of a muon track

---

* The word electron will be used in this chapter for either a positron or a negatron.

suddenly forks into two similar tracks. These tracks are consistent with the interpretation that a decay electron collided with an atomic electron. The calculated masses of the two particles were then found to be $(3 \pm 2)m$ and $(1.5 \pm 1.0)m$.

Although some decays were found which were consistent with a two-body decay scheme, others gave rise to lower-energy electrons. In 1949, Leighton, Anderson, and Seriff (94) made a study of the energy spectrum of μ-decay electrons and obtained the distribution shown in Fig. 11-15. If a single neutrino were emitted, the energy of the decay electron would be unique. The

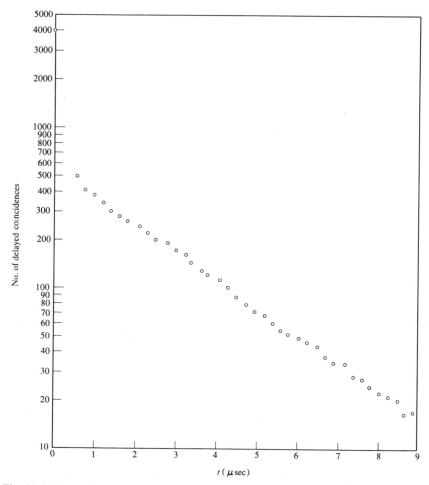

Fig. 11-14. Results obtained by Rossi and Nereson in their study of muon decay. The total number of coincidences in a period of about 538 hours with a delay time equal to or greater than t is plotted against t. This is equivalent to plotting the number of decays per unit time of N muons. Why?

spread in energies, therefore, indicates that at least three bodies participate in the decay. The maximum electron energy gives a value for the muon mass in good agreement with the mass value determined in other ways, but unfortunately the maximum electron energy is independent of the number of neutrinos emitted if the neutrino has zero rest mass.

In 1950 Michel (105) developed a quantum electrodynamical theory of muon decay which introduces a parameter, ρ, now known as the Michel

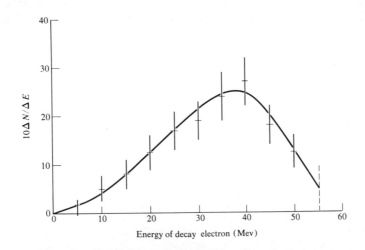

Fig. 11-15. Energy spectrum of muon-decay electrons. The energy of a decay electron is determined from the curvature of its cloud chamber track produced by deflection of the electron in a magnetic field. The number of tracks falling in overlapping 10-Mev intervals is plotted. The upper limit of the spectrum corresponds to a meson mass of $(217 \pm 4)m$. [From R. B. Leighton, C. D. Anderson, and A. J. Seriff, *Phys. Rev.*, **75**, 1432 (1949).]

parameter, which depends on the coupling and which largely determines the shape of the decay spectrum. If the decay is represented by

$$\mu^{\pm} \longrightarrow e^{\pm} + \nu + \bar{\nu}$$

and if the two-component theory of the neutrino is correct, ρ should be equal to 0.75. Early attempts to determine ρ led to quite divergent values, but more recent values (49, 83) lie quite close to 0.75.

Since each of the three decay components in the reaction

$$\mu^{\pm} \longrightarrow e^{\pm} + \nu + \bar{\nu}$$

has a spin of $\frac{1}{2}$, the muon must have a spin of $\frac{1}{2}$ or $\frac{3}{2}$ if this is the actual decay mode. In either case it should be possible for it to decay by the alternate mode

$$\mu^{\pm} = e^{\pm} + \gamma.$$

A number of searches for this mode have been made, but no positive proof of its existence has been found. Lokanathan and Steinberger (100) quote a value for the ratio $(\mu \longrightarrow e + \gamma)/(\mu \longrightarrow e + \nu + \bar{\nu})$ of less than 2×10^{-5}.

If the universal V-A theory of weak interactions is applicable to muons, the muons, aside from their greater mass, should behave as electrons. According to quantum electrodynamics (75), the gyromagnetic ratio* of a Dirac spin $\frac{1}{2}$ particle should be $g = 2 \times 1.00116$. Garwin *et al.* (67) have used a nuclear magnetic resonance technique in which they compare the precession rate of stopped positive muons with that of protons in the same magnetic field. This gives directly the ratio of the magnetic moments,

$$\frac{\mu_\mu^+}{\mu_p} = 3.1865 \pm 0.0022.$$

If $206.76m$ is used as the mass of the muon, this gives

$$g = 2 \times (1.00113^{+0.00016}_{-0.00012}),$$

which is extremely close to the theoretically predicted value. One is almost forced to conclude that, as has long been assumed, the spin of the muon is $\frac{1}{2}$.

As mentioned earlier, the mu-mesic orbits are much smaller than the corresponding electronic orbits, which causes the average density of muons within the nuclear volume to be quite appreciable. One would therefore expect that there might be nuclear interactions, and indeed there are. When muon tracks were found in nuclear emulsions, it was observed that "stars" were produced in many of the cases where a muon came to rest, and it was inferred that these must be caused by nuclear interactions of negatively charged muons. Morinaga and Fry (111) studied the tracks of 24,000 negative muons which stopped in nuclear emulsion. They found that 2.4 per cent produced stars, the great majority of these consisting of a single proton or alpha-particle track whose mean energy was about 15 Mev. Considering that the mass energy of the muon is about 100 Mev, this is a surprisingly small amount of energy to be emitted by the capturing nucleus. Apparently the reaction is primarily

$$p + \mu^- \longrightarrow n + \nu$$

with most of the energy going to the neutrino. This leaves a small amount of energy which may appear as nuclear excitation or as kinetic energy of an emitted neutron. The emission of one or two neutrons per negative muon capture has been confirmed by underground counter experiments.

When the lifetime of negative muons is measured, it is found, as shown in Fig. 11-16, to be smaller than that of positive muons. The reason is that the mean time for nuclear capture is less than the mean life for decay. The number of decays per unit time after any time t is proportional to the number which

---

* The gyromagnetic ratio is defined as the ratio of the magnetic moment to the quantity $eh/2Mc$, where M is the mass of the particle.

remain, but this is determined by the combined rate of loss through decay and capture. The fact that the lifetime is not shortened more than it is gives evidence for the very weak interaction of muons with nucleons. As Wheeler (156) has pointed out, a muon with a 4×10^{-8} sec mean life for nuclear interaction (characteristic of heavy elements) traverses about 5 meters of

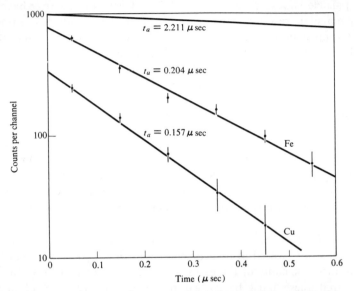

Fig. 11-16. Apparent decay rate of negative cosmic-ray muons in iron and copper. The uppermost curve gives the expected decay rate for positive muons for comparison. [Data from A. M. Hillas, W. B. Gilboy, and R. M. Tennent, *Phil. Mag.*, **3**, 109 (1958).]

nuclear matter before it reacts. Since the density of nuclear matter is about 1.5×10^8 tons/cm³, this involves penetrating about 10^{17} gm/cm² of absorber! Bell and Hincks (16) have found, as seen in Table 11-3, that the shortening

Table 11-3 Z-DEPENDENCE OF μ^- LIFETIMES

Absorber	Mean Lifetime (μsec)*
$_6$C	1.98 ± 0.06
$_4$Be	2.05 ± 0.06
$_3$Li	2.15 ± 0.09

* The μ^+ mean lifetime is (2.211 ± 0.003) μsec.

of the μ^- lifetime through nuclear reaction becomes quite small for elements of low atomic number, tempting one to conclude that the decay lifetimes of positive and negative muons in the free state are probably identical.

The formation of muonium, an atom consisting of a positive muon and a negatron, was not observed for a long time, probably because the positive muons generally decay before they are moving slowly enough to capture negatrons. By contrast, the negative muons can be moving much faster when captured into the relatively high-kinetic-energy orbits around nuclei. Recently, however, muonium has been detected (82) by a magnetic precession experiment like that used to measure the muon magnetic moment. The precession rate in this case depends on the magnetic moment of muonium rather than that of the free muon.

In 1947 Frank (62) discussed the possibility of meson catalyzed fusion. A mesic hydrogen atom, as we have already mentioned is only about $\frac{1}{200}$ as large as an ordinary hydrogen atom, so that it could diffuse through matter almost as easily as a neutron. A meson in a mesic deuterium atom, because of the 5 per cent larger reduced meson mass, would have about 135 ev greater binding energy than it would in a mesic hydrogen atom. In a collision of a mesic hydrogen atom with a deuteron, there is a high probability that the meson will be removed from the proton and become bound to the deuteron. In a hydrogen molecule-ion, the two protons are bound together by one shared electron. The mesic equivalent of interest here is a proton and a deuteron bound together by one shared meson. The internuclear spacing of this mesic molecule-ion will be again roughly $\frac{1}{200}$ of the internuclear spacing of an ordinary H-D molecule-ion. The probability of barrier penetration, allowing the proton and deuteron to combine, is now large enough that the fusion time should be much smaller than the decay lifetime of the muon. The reaction is

$$_1H^1 + {}_1D_\mu^2 \longrightarrow {}_2He_\mu^{3m}$$

where $_2He_\mu^{3m}$ represents a mesic helium atom with an excited nucleus. The excited helium nucleus may then be de-excited by gamma-ray emission or by an internal conversion process that ejects the muon. The excitation energy can be calculated from the masses and is about 5.5 Mev.

Nearly ten years later this process was observed by Alvarez et al. (2) in a ten-inch liquid hydrogen bubble chamber. The discovery was incidental to a study of negative kaons (see Sec. 11-7). In 75,000 photographs, about 2500 negative muons were observed to come to rest. Out of the 2500, there were 15 cases where a particle was emitted from the point where the muon came to rest, traveled 1.7 cm before coming to rest, and then underwent electron decay. The decay energies of the electrons were typical of muon decay. The 1.7-cm range is what one would expect for a muon emitted with nearly 5.5 Mev of kinetic energy. In five of the 15 cases, the beginning of the second muon track was appreciably displaced from the end of the first muon track, indicating that a mesic hydrogen atom had diffused some distance before fusion took place. In the initially observed events the deuterium concentration was only that occurring naturally in hydrogen (0.016 per cent). The results of a subsequent test of the effect of deuterium concentration on reaction rate are given in Table 11-4. One case was observed in which the same muon produced two successive He³ reactions.

Table 11-4 Effect of Deuterium Concentration on
Muon Fusion Catalysis Rate

	Deuterium concentration		
	Natural 0.016%	0.3%	4.3%
Total number of μ^- decays	2541	2959	1269
Number of H + D$_\mu \longrightarrow$ He³ + μ^- events . .	15	57	32
H + D$_\mu \longrightarrow$ He³ + μ^- events/μ^- ending . .	0.6%	2%	2.5%

11-6 Pions

Yukawa (166) developed a theory in 1935 which is an attempt to explain the large binding forces which hold the constituent nucleons of a nucleus together. It is built on an analogy with electromagnetic fields. In this case a new field is envisioned, called the meson field, which governs the motion of mesons in a manner analogous to that in which an electromagnetic field governs the motion of photons. The binding between nucleons is then explained as an "exchange force" due to the exchange of mesons by the nucleons. Exchange forces are explicable only in terms of wave mechanics, but a well-known example is the binding of two hydrogen atoms to form a diatomic molecule, wherein the exchange of an electron between the two atoms gives rise to a binding force. In order to explain the large magnitude of nuclear binding forces it was necessary that the meson have a mass greater than that of an electron, and Yukawa made a rough estimate that its mass should be about 200m.

A very rough estimate of the mass of the particle necessary to explain nuclear forces can be made on the basis of the following argument. Nucleons continually emit and absorb mesons, and it is this process which gives rise to the short-range nuclear forces. When a meson is created and given an average velocity such that $\beta = 0.5$, then an amount of energy $\Delta W = Mc^2/\sqrt{1 - \beta^2}$ must be "borrowed" for its creation. If it is reabsorbed in a very short time this energy change is an unobservable quantity, and thus not in conflict with the law of conservation of energy which applies only to observables. From the uncertainty principle,

$$\Delta W \cdot \Delta t \cong h. \tag{11-8}$$

Therefore
$$\Delta t \cong \frac{h}{W} = \frac{h\sqrt{1 - \beta^2}}{Mc^2}, \tag{11-9}$$

and since the meson has been assumed to travel with a velocity βc, the distance it can travel in time Δt is

$$\Delta R = \beta c\, \Delta t = \frac{\beta \sqrt{1 - \beta^2}\, \hbar}{Mc}. \tag{11-10}$$

The interaction between mesons and nucleons is then limited to a distance of ΔR, which is the range of nuclear forces. Since ΔR is known to be of the order 10^{-13} cm, one obtains for the mass of the meson,

$$M \cong \frac{\beta \sqrt{1 - \beta^2}\, \hbar}{C \Delta R} = \frac{0.5 \sqrt{1 - 0.25} \times 1.055 \times 10^{-27} \times m}{3 \times 10^{10} \times 10^{-13} \times 9.1 \times 10^{-28}} = 163m.$$

By contrast, the photon with zero rest mass gives rise to the long-range coulomb force.

In order to be able to explain β decay also, Yukawa made the further assumption that the new particle would break down spontaneously into an electron and a neutrino, with a half-life of $0.25 + 10^{-6}$ sec. The discovery, shortly after the publication of this theory, of mesons having a mass close to $200m$, together with the absorption anomaly, which could be explained on the basis of radioactive decay of mesons with a half-life of 2 to 3 $\times$ 10^{-6} sec, seemed to be strong evidence that Yukawa's hypothetical particle really existed. The cloud chamber observations of muon beta decay appeared to give additional confirmation.

Theorists, however, were already beginning to find flaws in Yukawa's theory. Nordheim (117) in 1939 pointed out that, if Yukawa had used a coupling constant in better agreement with observed positron decay lifetimes of light elements, the lifetime of the meson would have been 1.6 $\times$ 10^{-9} sec rather than 0.25 $\times$ 10^{-6} sec, so that the apparent muon lifetime of a few microseconds was not a particularly good confirmation of the theory. In the previous year Kemmer (87) had shown that a single type of meson could not include the observed stable triplet state of the deuteron but that a combination, as of a pseudoscalar meson and a vector meson, could. A more basic difficulty lay in the weak interaction of cosmic-ray mesons with nuclei. A meson which is emitted by a proton and absorbed by a neutron as the means of binding these particles together must interact strongly with the nucleons. The copious production of mesons in the upper atmosphere by the incoming cosmic-ray primaries (mostly protons) was in keeping with this idea, but the subsequent ability of the mesons to penetrate the remaining atmosphere with small absorption contradicts such a strong interaction. By taking their detection equipment underground, investigators (160, 161) found that the cosmic-ray mesons could penetrate the equivalent of 980 meters of water in contrast to the mean free path for interaction between nucleons of about one meter of water. At the Shelter Island Conference in New York in June, 1947, Marshak (101) proposed a solution to the copious-production, weak-interaction paradox. He suggested that the primary cosmic rays generated Yukawa-type mesons by their interaction with the nuclei of air atoms, but that these mesons decayed in a time less than the lifetime of the muon, perhaps of the order 10^{-8} sec, into the mesons commonly observed in cosmic rays which interact weakly with matter.

Almost at the same time this proposal was being made, a group led by Powell at the University of Bristol (93), using the newly developed high-density nuclear emulsions exposed to cosmic rays at high altitude, found tracks of mesons which came to rest in the emulsion and then emitted less massive mesons with a consistent range of about 600 microns. The ends of the tracks, where the particles came to rest, were easily identified by the increased

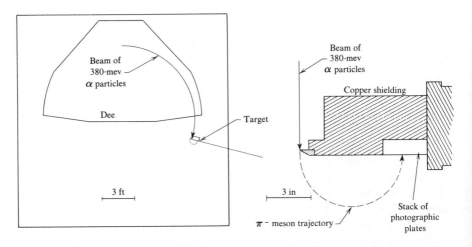

Fig. 11-17. Diagram of apparatus used by Gardner and Lattes (66) to produce and detect negative muons. Since the target is in the magnetic field of the cyclotron, the charged mesons are deflected to the stack of photographic plates as shown.

density of silver grains and often corroborated by increased scattering of the particle as it slowed down. While the absolute masses could still not be determined with high precision, it was possible by the method of grain counting to determine the ratio of the masses of the two mesons, and in this way establish that the primary meson was heavier than the secondary. The name π-meson has been given to the heavier meson and μ-meson to the lighter one. With the development of more sensitive emulsions which could record fast electrons, examples of π-μ-e decay were observed; that is, a pion came to rest and emitted a muon which came to rest and emitted an electron. From the fact that roughly the same number of π-mesons produced nuclear disintegrations (called stars) as underwent spontaneous decay with emission of muons it was inferred (118, 125) that pions of both positive and negative charge were being encountered—the negative ones, because of coulomb attraction, being captured by nuclei and therefore responsible for the nuclear disintegrations.

In 1948, Gardner and Lattes (66) announced the artificial production of π^--mesons by bombardment of Be, Cu, U, and C targets with 380-Mev alpha particles. The targets as well as the nuclear emulsion plates which recorded the tracks of the pions were placed inside an evacuated dee of the 184-inch Berkeley cyclotron, as shown in Fig. 11-17. From the angle at which a pion entered the emulsion and its distance from the target, the value of $B\rho$ could be calculated for the motion of the particle in the magnetic field of the cyclotron. The range of the particle in the emulsion gives information about its energy. The two measurements together permit a calculation of its mass. A 1954 determination (43) of the masses of artificially produced pions gave

$$M_{\pi^+} = M_{\pi^-} = (273.27 \pm 0.11)m,$$

where m is the rest mass of an electron.

Lifetimes of pions. Although cosmic-ray studies (30) had indicated that the lifetime of the pion was in the neighborhood of 10^{-8} sec, the artificial production of pions made much more accurate determinations possible. Richardson (129), for example, allowed π^--mesons produced within one of the dees of the 184-inch Berkeley cyclotron to move around spiral channels within the cyclotron magnetic field, and compared the number which reached a plate π radians from the pion source with the number which reached a plate 3π radians from the source. Then from the calculated time for one complete revolution in the magnetic field, the pion mass, and the fraction decaying in one revolution, he was able to calculate the mean lifetime of the negative pion. One of the channels spiraled upward from the median plane of the dees and the other spiraled downward with the same pitch, so that the channels did not intersect and one would expect as many particles to be deflected into one channel as the other. In order to correct for differences in the numbers of particles reaching the two plates for reasons other than decay in flight, this ratio was measured for α particles emitted by a plutonium source placed in the position normally occupied by the pion source (target). Several recent values of the mean lifetimes, t_a, of positive and negative pions are given in Table 11-5. Just as in the case of negative muons, free decay lifetimes of negative pions at rest cannot be measured because of competition from nuclear capture. Because pions interact so much more strongly than muons with nuclei, they tend to be captured before they can complete radiative transitions to the lower quantum number orbits. The pion rarely reaches the K orbits of nuclei with $Z \geqslant 11$ and is usually captured even before reaching the L orbit with $Z \geqslant 20$. Hydrogen, among all the elements, is exceptional. In this case

Table 11-5 Mean Lifetimes* of Charged Pions

Type of pion	Mean lifetime (sec)	Method†	Reference
π^-	$\left(1.11^{+0.31}_{-0.22}\right) \times 10^{-8}$	(a)	J. R. Richardson, *Phys. Rev.*, **74**, 1720 (1948)
	$(2.92 \pm 0.32) \times 10^{-8}$	(b)	L. M. Lederman, E. T. Booth, H. Byfield, and J. Kessler, *Phys. Rev.*, **83**, 685 (1951)
	$(2.85 \pm 0.25) \times 10^{-8}$	(b)	L. M. Lederman, H. Byfield, and J. Kessler, *Bull. Amer. Phys. Soc.*, **26**, 23 (Oct., 1951)
	$(2.55 \pm 0.19) \times 10^{-8}$	(d)	H. Loar, R. Durbin, and W. W. Havens, Jr., *Bull. Amer. Phys. Soc.*, **27**, 17 (1952)
π^+	$\left(1.97^{+0.14}_{-0.17}\right) \times 10^{-8}$	(a)	E. A. Martinelli and W. K. H. Panofsky, *Phys. Rev.*, **77**, 465 (1950)
	$(1.65 \pm 0.33) \times 10^{-8}$	(c)	W. L. Kraushaar, J. E. Thomas, and V. P. Henri, *Phys. Rev.*, **78**, 486 (1950)
	$(2.65 \pm 0.12) \times 10^{-8}$ $(2.59 \pm 0.12) \times 10^{-8}$	(c)	O. Chamberlain, R. F. Mozley, J. Steinberger, and C. Wiegand, *Phys. Rev.*, **79**, 394 (1950)
	$(2.54 \pm 0.11) \times 10^{-8}$	(c)	M. Jakobson, A. Schultz, and J. Steinberger, *Phys. Rev.*, **81**, 894 (1951)
	$(2.58 \pm 0.14) \times 10^{-8}$	(c)	C. E. Wiegand, *Phys. Rev.*, **83**, 1085 (1951)
	$(2.44 \pm 0.18) \times 10^{-8}$	(d)	H. Loar, R. Durbin, and W. W. Havens, Jr., *Bull. Amer. Phys. Soc.*, **27**, 17 (1952)

* Measured or calculated for particles at rest in the reference frame of the observer.

† *Method:*

(a) From "cyclotron time" (see text).

(b) From mean free path for π-μ decay in cloud chamber.

(c) From time lapse between coincidence caused by passage of meson through two scintillation crystals and pulse caused by decay of π with emission of μ.

(d) From variation of intensity of a 73-Mev pion beam with distance.

the orbital electron becomes detached as soon as the pion is captured into an orbit so that Auger transitions are prohibited, and the pion is forced to lose energy by radiative transitions in moving to the lower quantum number orbits. Experimentally, pi-mesic x-rays from pion capture are observed only in hydrogen. Even in hydrogeneous materials the pi-mesic x-rays are absent, presumably because the pi-mesic hydrogen atom diffuses through the material about like a neutron would, the pion being very quickly captured from the proton by a higher-Z nucleus.

Within experimental uncertainties, the mean lifetimes of positive and negative pions are the same. It is generally assumed that they are identical. If so, a recently determined (8) value for the mean lifetime of the positive pion, $t_a = (2.546 \pm 0.032) \times 10^{-8}$ sec, may be used for either charged pion.

Spins of mesons. When a pion at rest decays to a muon, the decrease in mass is about $67m$ or about 34 Mev. Now the muons coming from π-μ decay have nothing like this amount of energy. The observed mean muon energy is 4.1 Mev (60). Where does the remaining mass energy go? Since the π-meson originally had no momentum, conservation of momentum requires that something carry away an amount of momentum equal and oppositely directed to that given the muon. A particle of very small rest mass could carry away a large energy with a relatively small momentum. This suggests a neutrino or a photon. On the other hand, a new neutral particle might be created in the disintegration. Such a possible particle has sometimes been called a neutretto. In Sec. 11-5 it was shown that the muon has a spin of $\frac{1}{2}$. If the pion breaks down into a muon and a neutrino, each of which has a spin of $\frac{1}{2}$, then it must have a spin of either zero or unity, but if it breaks down into a muon and a gamma ray, it must have half-integral spin.

Panofsky et al. (123, 124) have determined the γ-ray spectrum resulting from bombarding hydrogen with slow π^--mesons. The γ-ray intensity distribution as a function of energy, obtained somewhat later by Crowe and Phillips (44) in a similar experiment of greater precision, is shown in Fig. 11-18. If one interprets the sharp peak centered at about 130 Mev to be due to the reaction

$$\pi^- + p \longrightarrow n + \gamma,$$

then, taking the π^- as being at rest, one can calculate a value for the mass of the π^--meson mass. The result is

$$M_{\pi^-} = (272.7 \pm 0.3)m,$$

which is in good agreement with the value determined in other ways. This close agreement of meson mass values shows that little, if any, energy is carried away by a third particle. It seems plausible, therefore, that the reaction given above is correct, and conservation of angular momentum then requires that the π^--meson have integral spin, since γ emission takes place only when the spin of the system changes by an integral amount. This result rules out the possibility of decay by single-photon emission.

A comparison of the reciprocal reactions

$$p + p \longrightarrow \pi^+ + d$$

and

$$\pi^+ + d \longrightarrow p + p$$

has given strong evidence in favor of a spin value of zero for the π^+-meson (36, 50). Application of the principle of detailed balancing to the reaction allows one to calculate the cross section for the first reaction from the measured

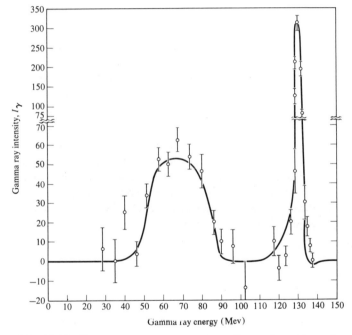

Fig. 11-18. Gamma-ray energy spectrum from absorption of, π^--mesons in H_2 (44). Note scale expansion below $I_y = 75$.

cross section of the second reaction *provided the particles are initially unpolarized.* The calculated value, however, depends upon the spin assumed for the π^+-meson. Figure 11-19 compares the observed cross sections with those calculated from the $\pi^+ + d$ reaction, assuming π^+ spins of either unity or zero. It is seen that the zero-spin curve gives a much better fit, and for this reason the π^+ is believed to be a zero-spin particle.

In these experiments, nothing was known about the states of polarization of the pion beams, but it was assumed that they were unpolarized. More recently, Crewe *et al.* (42) measured scattering and decay asymmetries of the 120-Mev pion beam from the Chicago cyclotron, in an attempt to find whether such a beam is polarized. Their results are given in Tables 11-6 and 11-7.

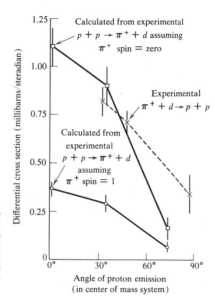

Fig. 11-19. Comparison of measured differential cross section for $\pi^+ + d \rightarrow p + p$ reaction with curves computed from the $p + p \rightarrow \pi^+ + d$ reaction and assuming a π^+ spin of 1 or 0. The much better fit obtained in the latter case indicates that the spin of the π^+ meson is zero. [From Durbin, Loar, and Steinberger (50).]

Table 11-6 SCATTERING ASYMMETRIES OF 120-MEV PION BEAM

Sign of pion charge	Horizontal or vertical scattering	Scattering angle (deg)	Fractional asymmetry (per cent)
−	h	24.9	0.5 ± 5.6
−	h	31.8	2.2 ± 5.0
−	h	36.4	2.6 ± 4.9
−	h	42.6	1.3 ± 4.3
−	h	90	0.2 ± 5.0
−	v	54.2	−1.7 ± 7.1
+	h	42.8	0.6 ± 4.7

Within the accuracy of the measurements, which admittedly is not high, there appears to be no evidence that the tacit assumption of an unpolarized pion beam is incorrect. It is generally conceded now that the positive pion has a spin of zero.

Table 11-7 DECAY ASYMMETRIES OF 120-MEV POSITIVE
PIONS

Azimuthal position of detector	Run 1 (uncorrected for beam spread)	Run 2 (uncorrected for beam spread)	Three-run average (corrected for beam spread)
0° (up)	225 ± 9*	243 ± 11	217 ± 6
45°	237	231	221
90° (right)	245	232	217
135°	234	209	215
180° (down)	222	242	213
225°	220	245	208
270° (left)	231	230	209
315°	224	252	220

* Errors shown are counting statistics only.

Since the electron and muon appear to be so much alike, except for masses, one would expect that pions should undergo beta decay as well as muon decay. In fact beta decay is energetically more favored than muon decay. Ruderman and Finkelstein (139) in 1949 predicted that if the reaction

$$\pi \longrightarrow e + \nu,$$

goes via an axial vector interaction, the rate ratio should be

$$\frac{\pi \longrightarrow e}{\pi \longrightarrow \mu} = 1.3 \times 10^{-4}.$$

The expected recoil energy of the electron is 69.3 Mev, which is enough greater than the maximum energy of muon decay electrons to make possible the certain identification of one in the inevitable presence of the other. Fazzini et al. (57), using a "range telescope," were able to show that the rate ratio was definitely greater than 4×10^{-5}. Impeduglia et al. (83) found six examples of pion beta decay in bubble chamber photographs which showed 65,000 normal muon decays. The statistical accuracy is quite low, but the ratio is in good accord with the predicted value of 1.3×10^{-4}. This gives further evidence in favor of the universal V-A theory of weak interactions.

The idea of a neutral meson or a neutretto cropped up on many occasions in the years following Yukawa's theory, and some experimenters claimed to find evidence for such particles in cosmic-ray data, but it seems probable that these claims are invalid. Oppenheimer (98) suggested that the soft, shower-producing component of cosmic radiation might be caused by neutral mesons generated in impacts of cosmic-ray protons on nucleons in air-atom nuclei. These neutral mesons would be expected to have very short mean lifetimes and to decay into energetic photons. The first direct experimental evidence for neutral pions was obtained in 1950 by Bjorkland, Crandall, Moyer, and York (21). They produced gamma rays by bombarding a carbon target with high-energy protons. The gamma rays both were more abundant than expected from the bremsstrahlung process and showed a spread in energies characteristic of Doppler effect ascribable to motion of a moving source.

If one interprets the somewhat rectangular peak in Fig. 11-18 extending from about 55 to 85 Mev as having its origin in the sequence

$$\pi^- + p \longrightarrow n + \pi^0,$$
$$\pi^0 \longrightarrow \gamma + \gamma,$$

where π^0 represents an uncharged meson, then the maximum energy spread of the two photons will occur when one is emitted in the direction in which the π^0 was traveling and the other is emitted in the opposite direction. Conservation of momentum and energy then leads to a mass of about $265m$ for the neutral pion, a mass which is appreciably less than that of the charged pions. Chinowksy, Sachs, and Steinberger (34) made a study of the angle between coincident pairs of gamma rays from π^0 decay following the $\pi^- + p$ reaction. With the π^0 at rest, the two photons would be emitted at 180° to each other, but if the π^0 is moving, the angle between the two photon emission directions is less than 180°. They utilized this fact to obtain the velocity of the π^0 prior to decay. Their result was

$$\beta = 0.200 \pm 0.009.$$

The corresponding value of

$$M_{\pi^-} - M_{\pi^0} = (8.8 \pm 0.6)m$$

was obtained.

These experiments not only prove the existence of the neutral pion, but also show that it must have spin zero since it is formed in a reaction that allows it to have only a spin of 1 or zero and decays in a manner that is incompatible with conservation of angular momentum if its spin is 1. There is as yet no proof that the spin of the negative pion is zero, but it is hard to believe that the two charged pions could have the same mass and same mean lifetime but different spins. It is assumed therefore that all pions are spin zero particles.

Carlson et al. (31) have shown that the π^0 also decays according to the scheme $\pi^0 \longrightarrow \gamma + e^+ + e^-$. They found electron pairs originating very close to stars in nuclear emulsions. Since, for quantum energies between 10 and 1000 Mev, the mean free path for materialization of a gamma ray in emulsion is about 4.5 cm, the probability that these events represent double gamma decay of a π^0 with subsequent pair production, very close to the point of origin of the π^0, by one of the gamma rays is extremely small. A fairly large number of examples of this decay mode have now been found. The frequency of occurrence ratio is estimated to be

$$\frac{\pi^0 \longrightarrow \gamma + e^+ + e^-}{\pi^0 \longrightarrow \gamma + \gamma} = \frac{1}{80}.$$

Two examples of the decay mode

$$\pi^0 \longrightarrow e^+ + e^- + e^+ + e^-$$

have been found, one in a cloud chamber photograph (78) and the other in emulsion.* This process is estimated, on theoretical grounds, to occur once in about 10^4 normal decays.

The measured energy spread of π^0 mesons is small enough that application of the Heisenberg relation $\Delta W \times \Delta t \geqslant \hbar$ limits the mean lifetime to something greater than 10^{-21} sec. (71). Glasser *et al.** have used the $\pi^0 \longrightarrow \gamma + e^+ + e^-$ mode of decay as a means of studying the lifetime of neutral pions. K^+ mesons (see Sec. 11-7) were allowed to come to rest in nuclear emulsions. In many cases a π^+ and a π^0 were created simultaneously. The π^0 has a unique energy in this event, so its speed can be computed. Its direction of motion must be opposite to that of the π^0 to conserve momentum. In 76 cases the π^0 decayed by electron pair creation. The intersection of either electron track with the extended line of the π^+ track then gives the presumptive point of decay of the π^0. The distance from the end of the K^+ track to the presumed point of decay of the π^0 is a measure of the π^0 lifetime. The mean distance traveled by the π^0 before decay was found to be (0.088 $\pm$ 0.024) microns, from which they deduce a mean lifetime of

$$(1.9 \pm 0.5) \times 10^{-16} \text{ sec.}$$

Since the mean grain size of the silver particles making up the tracks in this experiment was 0.34 micron, our knowledge of the π^0 lifetime is still not precise.

In a two-particle system, the parity is given by the product

$$\text{(parity of particle 1)} \times \text{(parity of particle 2)} \times (-1)^l$$

where l is the orbital angular momentum of the system. In the case of the deuteron, since the parities of the neutron and proton are both taken to be even and since the nucleons have no orbital angular momentum, the parity is even. Chinowsky and Steinberger (35) have shown, by observing the two neutrons in coincidence with each other and with the incoming π^-, that the reaction $\pi^- + d \longrightarrow n + n$ actually occurs. If the spin of the π^- is zero and the reaction takes place from an S state of the $(\pi^- + d)$ system (i.e., one in which the orbital angular momentum is zero), for which there is good experimental evidence, then the total angular momentum of the $(\pi^- + d)$ system

* Glasser, R. G., Seeman, N., and Stiller, B., *Phys. Rev.*, **123**, 1014 (1961).

is 1. After the reaction, the Pauli principle demands that the spins of the two neutrons be antiparallel. This requires them to possess an orbital angular momentum of 1 in order to preserve the angular momentum of the system. The parity of the $(n + n)$ system, then, is

$$(+) \times (+) \times (-1)^1 = (-),$$

or odd. Since the parity of the deuteron is even, the parity of the π^- must be odd. Of the two possible kinds of spinless particles, scalar and pseudoscalar, only the latter has odd parity. It is generally believed, therefore, that pions are pseudoscalar mesons.

In the Yukawa theory one envisions a proton emitting a positively charged meson, thereby becoming a neutron, and a neutron absorbing the positive meson to become a proton. Conversely, a neutron would emit a negatively charged meson, thereby becoming a proton, and a proton would absorb the negative meson and become a neutron. In this way one would hope to account for the attractive forces between neutrons and protons. We have seen, however, that the attractive forces between any pair of nucleons is approximately the same. If protons are to interact with protons and neutrons with neutrons, there must be neutral mesons to be exchanged between like particles. Thus, the known properties of pions are in good qualitative accord with the basic premise of the meson theory of nuclear forces even though there is as yet no satisfactory formulation of this theory.

11-7 Kaons

In 1947 Rochester and Butler (131) reported two very interesting magnet cloud-chamber tracks produced by cosmic rays. In one of these, two straight tracks emanate, in the form of a V, from a common point in the chamber. No third track is visible coming from this point. In the second picture there are likewise two tracks which emanate from a common point in the chamber, but now they form an open V, as though an incoming particle had suffered a large angle deflection in a nuclear encounter. Both examples are accompanied by several hard-shower particles.

In the first picture, the low ion density and the straightness of the tracks in the magnetic field indicate that the decay particles are moving at very high speeds. The plane formed by the two particles passes through the apparent point of origin of the hard-shower particles, so that the two particles could well be due to the disintegration of a neutral particle coming from the event which generated the hard shower. The mass of the supposed neutral particle is estimated to be about $1000m$. This type of particle was originally called a neutral V-particle, or a V^0, but is now designated as $K^0_{\pi 2}$, the symbol K being assigned to any particle of mass approximately $1000m$, the superscript 0 indicating a neutral particle, and the subscript $\pi2$ showing that the particle decays into two pions.

In the second picture, one of the tracks comes from the apparent point of origin of the hard shower and is therefore considered to be the primary particle, while the second particle is believed to be due to the breakup of the primary particle into a charged and a neutral particle. In both events a nuclear scattering is ruled out because the energies are so huge that a recoiling nucleus would almost certainly leave a visible track.

The Caltech group subsequently made a considerable study of V-particles, using the same general technique employed by Rochester and Butler, that is, using coincidence counters to detect a shower, and large blocks of lead above the counters to exclude soft showers. Leighton, Wanlass, and Alford (95) reported two types of V^0 decay, one into particles of equal apparent mass which is interpreted as

$$V_2^0(K_{\pi2}^0) \longrightarrow \pi^+ + \pi^-,$$

and another into particles of unequal mass, one of which is a proton,

$$V_1^0(\Lambda^0) \longrightarrow p^+ + \pi^-.$$

(The latter event will be discussed in Sec. 11-8.) Since the decay particles do not come to rest in the chamber, it is not possible to distinguish a π- from a μ-meson, but some $\pi \longrightarrow \mu$ decays have been observed which could be interpreted as favoring the hypothesis that pions are formed in the breakdown. Assuming that no neutral particles are emitted in the decay, they deduced that the mass of the $K_{\pi2}^0$ must be about 750 to 800m.

When a neutral particle decays in flight into two charged secondary particles, the momentum of the primary is just the vector sum of the momenta of the secondaries. Once the direction of the primary momentum, p_{x1}, is established, the transverse momentum, p_{y1}, of either secondary can be determined. As shown in the last chapter, the transverse momentum is the same in both the laboratory and c.m. frames. If we could transform to the c.m. frame, the secondary particle momentum vectors would all terminate on a circle. In the case of decay in flight, Eq. (10-47),

$$\frac{(p_x - \alpha)^2}{k^2} + \frac{p_y^2 + p_z^2}{b^2} = 1, \tag{10-47}$$

can be put in a somewhat more useful form. The equation may be written for either decay particle, but for definiteness, let us write it for the particle M_3, and let the decay plane be the xy-plane. Then

$$\frac{(p_{x3} - \alpha_3)^2}{k^2} + \frac{p_y^2}{b^2} = 1, \tag{11-11}$$

and since

$$k^2 = \frac{b^2}{1 - \bar{\beta}^2},\qquad\qquad (10\text{-}45)$$

$$p_y^2 + (1 - \bar{\beta}^2)(p_{x3} - \alpha_3)^2 = b^2. \qquad\qquad (11\text{-}12)$$

In a decay in flight, $\bar{\beta}c$ is just the velocity of the primary particle, so that

$$\bar{\beta} = \frac{p_{x1}}{W_1} = \frac{p_{x1}}{\sqrt{p_{x1}^2 c^2 + M_1^2 c^4}},\qquad\qquad (11\text{-}13)$$

where M_1 is the mass of the primary particle. From this it follows at once that

$$1 - \bar{\beta}^2 = \frac{M_1^2 c^4}{p_{x1}^2 c^2 + M_1^2 c^4}.\qquad\qquad (11\text{-}14)$$

Equation (11-12) then becomes

$$p_y^2 + \frac{M_1^2 c^4 (p_{x3} - \alpha_3)^2}{p_{x1}^2 c^2 + M_1^2 c^4} = b^2.\qquad\qquad (11\text{-}15)$$

The quantity $(p_{x3} - \alpha_3)$ is the x-component of what has been called $p_{3\text{ lab}}$ in the previous chapter. Conservation of momentum requires that $\mathbf{p}_{3\text{ lab}}$ and $\mathbf{p}_{4\text{ lab}}$ be equal and oppositely directed vectors. Therefore

$$(p_{x3} - \alpha_3) - (p_{x4} - \alpha_4) = 2(p_{x3} - \alpha_3)\qquad\qquad (11\text{-}16)$$

and $\qquad p_{x3} - \alpha_3 = \frac{1}{2}[(p_{x3} - p_{x1}) - (\alpha_3 - \alpha_4)]$

$$= \frac{1}{2}\left[\left(\frac{p_{x3} - p_{x4}}{p_{x3} + p_{x4}}\right) - \left(\frac{\alpha_3 - \alpha_4}{p_{x3} + p_{x4}}\right)\right](p_{x3} + p_{x4}),$$

$$p_{x3} - \alpha_3 = \frac{p_{x1}}{2}\left[\left(\frac{p_{x3} - p_{x4}}{p_{x3} + p_{x4}}\right) - \left(\frac{\alpha_3 - \alpha_4}{p_{x3} + p_{x4}}\right)\right],\qquad\qquad (11\text{-}17)$$

since conservation of momentum requires that

$$p_{x1} = p_{x3} + p_{x4}.\qquad\qquad (11\text{-}18)$$

Let $\qquad\qquad \gamma \equiv \frac{p_{x3} - p_{x4}}{p_{x3} + p_{x4}}\qquad\qquad (11\text{-}19)$

and $\qquad\qquad \bar{\gamma} \equiv \frac{\alpha_3 - \alpha_4}{p_{x3} + p_{x4}}.\qquad\qquad (11\text{-}20)$

Now $\qquad\qquad \alpha_3 = \frac{\bar{\beta} W_3'}{c\sqrt{1 - \bar{\beta}^2}} = \frac{p_{x1} W_3'}{M_1 c^2}\qquad\qquad (11\text{-}21)$

and $\qquad\qquad \alpha_4 = \frac{p_{x1} W_4'}{M_1 c^2}\qquad\qquad (11\text{-}22)$

so that
$$\bar{\gamma} = \frac{W_3' - W_4'}{M_1 c^2} = \left(\frac{W_3' - W_4'}{M_1 c^2}\right)\left(\frac{W_3' + W_4'}{W_3' + W_4'}\right),$$

and since
$$W_3' + W_4' = M_1 c^2, \tag{11-23}$$

$$\bar{\gamma} = \frac{(W_3')^2 - (W_4')^2}{M_1^2 c^4} = \frac{M_3^2 c^4 + b^2 c^2 - M_4^2 c^4 - b^2 c^2}{M_1^2 c^4},$$

$$\bar{\gamma} = \frac{M_3^2 - M_4^2}{M_1^2}. \tag{11-24}$$

Then Eq. (11-17) becomes

$$p_{x3} - \alpha_3 = \frac{p_{x1}}{2}(\gamma - \bar{\gamma}) \tag{11-25}$$

and (11-15) becomes

$$p_y^2 + \frac{(\gamma - \bar{\gamma})^2}{4(1/M_1^2 c^4 + 1/p_{x1}^2 c^2)} = b^2. \tag{11-26}$$

Equation (11-26) defines a surface for given values of M_1 and $\bar{\gamma}$ upon which the measured quantities p_y and γ should lie. If the primary momentum is very large the term $1/p_{x1}^2 c^2$ may be neglected and the equation reduces to that of an ellipse, which is much more convenient for plotting purposes. It is not really necessary to restrict the analysis to large primary momenta. If a new quantity, γ', defined by

$$\gamma' - \bar{\gamma} = \beta(\gamma - \bar{\gamma}) \tag{11-27}$$

is introduced, (11-15) becomes

$$p_y^2 + \frac{M_1^2 c^4 p_{x1}^2 (\gamma' - \bar{\gamma})^2}{(p_{x1}^2 c^2 + M_1^2 c^4) 4\beta^2} = b^2$$

or
$$p_y^2 + \frac{(\gamma' - \bar{\gamma})^2}{4/M_1^2 c^4} = b^2. \tag{11-28}$$

Thompson, Burwell, and Huggett (154) have used this device to analyze cosmic ray $K_{\pi 2}^0$ decays where only the momenta but not the masses of the decay particles could be determined. They measured the momenta by an analysis of track curvature in a large magnet cloud chamber. Their p_y versus γ' plot is shown in Fig. 11-20. Twenty-four out of 28 points are observed to lie very close to the curve corresponding to $b = 203$ Mev/c and $Q = 214$ Mev. Their quoted values for the mass of the $K_{\pi 2}^0$ and the energy released in its decay are

$$M(K_{\pi 2}^0) = (965 \pm 5)m$$

and
$$Q(K_{\pi 2}^0) = (214 \pm 2.5) \text{ Mev.}$$

Several early rough estimates of the mean $K_{\pi 2}^0$ lifetime indicated that it was around 10^{-10} sec. The Cosmotron, a 3-Bev proton synchrotron at Brookhaven, went into operation in May, 1952, and it was not long before it was demonstrably producing negative kaons. The beam of the Bevatron,

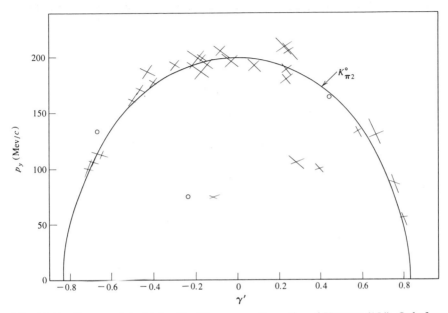

Fig. 11-20. *Q*-curve plot obtained by Thompson, Burwell, and Huggett (154). Only four points lie appreciably removed from the smooth curve expected for a two-body decay-in-flight.

a 6-Bev proton synchrotron at Berkeley, was found in February, 1954, and it, too, soon began producing kaons. Although most kaons were discovered and much information about them obtained from cosmic-ray studies, the small number of events found has often given quantitative results of very low statistical accuracy. The big machines have been invaluable in producing kaons (and other particles) in sufficient numbers to make good statistical studies possible.

Eisler *et al.* (53) observed the decay of neutral kaons in a 12-in liquid propane magnet bubble chamber. The origin of the K^0 could be accurately located by the disappearance of the π^- which produced it by interacting with a proton in the propane. Their results, shown in Fig. 11-21, give

$$t_a(K_{\pi 2}^0) = (0.95 \pm 0.08) \times 10^{-10} \text{ sec.}$$

Evidence for a $K_{\pi 2}^0$ decay has been obtained by Ridgway *et al.* (130) who produced neutral kaons (and other things, of course, which confuse the interpretation somewhat) by bombarding a target with high-energy protons and observing the produced beam of particles with a gamma-ray telescope at right angles to the beam. The telescope was shielded from photons produced before the beam reached a point in front of it. The number of gamma rays reaching the telescope per unit time is proportional to the rate of decay of kaons which have survived from the time they left the target until they

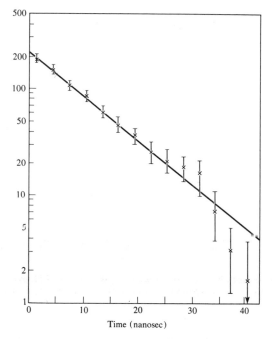

Fig. 11-21. Integral decay curve of neutral kaons which decay via the $K^0 \rightarrow \pi^+ + \pi^-$ mode in a propane bubble chamber (53).

reached the line of sight of the telescope. Since the number of kaons decaying per unit time is proportional to the number present (i.e., to the number which have survived) at this point in the beam, the measured gamma-ray intensity versus distance gives a K^0 decay curve. Their results are shown in Fig. 11-22.

A distinguishing feature of the $K^0_{\pi 2}$ decay, where the line of motion of the kaon can be determined, is that the plane of the decay includes this line of motion. The event is then said to be coplanar. Van Lint *et al.* (155), and later several other investigators, found a few examples which were noncoplanar and which did not satisfy the conservation conditions for a $K^0_{\pi 2}$ decay. The noncoplanarity suggests at least a three-body decay in which one or more neutral particles are emitted. A small number of events gives some evidence for the following neutral kaon decays:

$$K^0_{\beta 3} \longrightarrow \pi^{\pm} + e^{\mp} + \nu,$$
$$K^0_{\mu 3} \longrightarrow \pi^{\pm} + \mu^{\mp} + \nu,$$
$$K^0_{\pi 3} \longrightarrow \pi^+ + \pi^- + \pi^0.$$

There may well be other decays which have been unobserved because of their extreme rarity. Possibilities are

$$K^0_{\pi 2, \gamma} \longrightarrow \pi^+ + \pi^- + \gamma,$$
$$K^0_{\mu \beta 3} \longrightarrow \mu^{\pm} + e^{\mp} + \text{a neutral particle},$$
$$K^0_{\beta \beta 3} \longrightarrow e^{\pm} + e^{\mp} + \text{a neutral particle}.$$

In 1955, Gell-Mann and Pais (69) suggested that there may be two kinds of neutral kaons with differing mean lifetimes. To test this idea, Landé *et al.* (91, 92) placed a cloud chamber at a distance of 6 meters from the target of the Cosmotron. This distance corresponded to a transit time of about 100

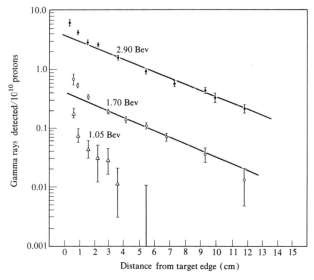

Fig. 11-22. Gamma rays detected as a function of distance between target and detector (130). The distance in which the number of detected gamma rays decreases by a factor e is 4.16 ± 0.1 cm for 2.90-Bev protons and 3.87 ± 0.3 cm for 1.70-Bev protons. To convert these distances into proper mean lifetimes requires a number of assumptions to be made with regard to the velocities and angular distributions of the unstable particles and their decay products. The mean lifetimes based on various assumptions vary from 1.34×10^{-10} to 1.52×10^{-10} sec.

mean lifetimes of the 10^{-10}-sec type of decay so the chance of one of these short-lived kaons reaching the chamber would be negligible. A 400,000-gauss magnet swept charged particles from the beam which was collimated with 4-ft-long lead absorbers. This is necessary to insure that the neutral kaons are not produced in the vicinity of the chamber by charged particles. They

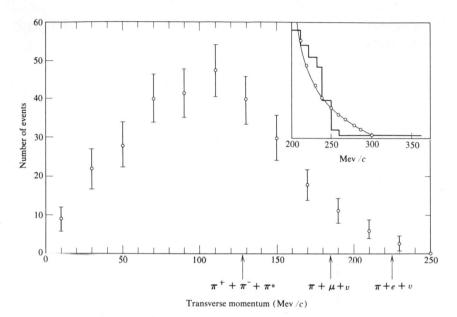

Fig. 11-23. Transverse momentum spectrum of positive, negative, and neutral secondaries from decay of neutral primaries (presumably K° mesons) (91, 92). The momenta of positive and negative particles are measured, those of neutrals deduced from the necessity of transverse momentum balance. The arrows indicate where spectrum should cut off for various possible decay modes. The inset, which is a magnification of the upper end of the curve, compares the measured values with the smooth curve expected for cutoff corrected for resolution of the instrument.

found 100 decay events, measured the transverse momenta of the two charged particles in each case, and calculated the momentum of an assumed single neutral particle necessary to give momentum balance. The resulting transverse momentum spectrum of the 300 decay particles is shown in Fig. 11-23. Since the maximum momentum for a decay particle from

$$K^0 \longrightarrow \pi^+ + \pi^- + \pi^0$$

is about 130 Mev/c and that for

$$K^0 \cdots\rightarrow \pi^{\pm} + \mu^{\mp} + \nu$$

is about 185 Mev/c, while that for

$$K^0 \longrightarrow \pi^{\pm} + e^{\mp} + \nu$$

is about 225 Mev/c, the distribution is good evidence for an appreciable number of the latter type of decay. Among these 100 events they found the following which could be identified with considerable confidence:

Number of events	Charged decay particles
4	$\pi^+ + e^-$
2	$\pi^- + e^+$
1	$\pi^- + \mu^+$
1	$\pi^- + \pi^+$

In an earlier experiment, 25 out of 26 events were noncoplanar. The mean lifetime of these particles appears to be of the order 10^{-6} sec.

Tau-mesons. The Bristol group (27) reported a cosmic-ray event recorded in emulsion in 1949 in which a charged particle, which they called a τ-meson, but which would now be termed a $K_{\pi3}^+$, apparently came to rest and disintegrated into three charged particles, one of which appeared to be a π^-, since it produced a star.

By comparing grain counts on the τ track with those of proton tracks they were able to estimate the mass as $(1080 \pm 160)m$. The three decay tracks were coplanar within experimental error, making it unlikely that any neutral particles were emitted in the event. If the star-producing particle was a π^- then its momentum could be determined. The total momentum of the three decay particles, from a parent particle originally at rest, must be zero. If the other two tracks were made by either electrons or protons, this momentum balance criterion could not be satisfied, but if they were made by either muons or pions, the momentum balanced within experimental error. They favored the view that all three decay products were pions. With this assumption, and present-day values for the charged pion mass, the mass of this kaon would be about 970 m. Since the charge of only one of the decay particles could be determined, the charge of the kaon was unknown. From the observation that decays at rest occur only for positive pions and muons, one might guess that this was also a positive particle. A number of events of this type were subsequently found, but in no case was it possible to deduce the charge of the kaon. Of the first 40 stopping tracks, however, 26 were positive pions, which is consistent with all the particles being K^+. Finally, in 1954, a cosmic-ray event was found (17) in which the kaon was emitted from a multipronged star, came to rest, and emitted three particles. Two of these underwent mu-decay, and one produced a single-prong star. This event was certainly a $K_{\pi3}^+$, and it is likely that the others were also.

In 1951 O'Ceallaigh (119) found two unusual events in emulsions exposed to cosmic rays, in one of which a particle of mass $(1320 \pm 250)m$ came to rest and emitted a high-velocity particle which could not be identified. In the second event a particle of mass $(1125 \pm 200)m$ came to rest and emitted a particle of mass 200 to 300m which underwent beta decay at the end of its range. Since the energies of the decay particles were different in these two cases, he proposed the three-body decay scheme $K_{\mu3}^+ \longrightarrow \mu^+ + \pi^0 + \nu$. Menon and O'Ceallaigh (103) found eight additional events of the same type with decay muon energies from zero to about 200 Mev, which tended to confirm the three-body decay hypothesis. These events give no clue to the identity of the neutral particles, but if the $K_{\mu3}^+$ is the same as the $K_{\pi3}^+$ (which decays into three bosons and is therefore a boson* itself), then one of the neutral particles must be a neutrino to conserve angular momentum. Partial confirmation of the emission of a π^0 came in the discovery of events (77, 164) in which an electron pair and a muon were emitted from the end of the kaon track. These have been interpreted as examples of the rare decay mode,

$$\pi^0 \longrightarrow e^+ + e^- + \gamma,$$

of the neutral pion.

By 1954 there was some evidence for a monoergic kaon decay,

$$K_{\pi2}^+ \longrightarrow \pi^+ + \pi^0,$$

and for an alternative three-pion decay (45),

$$K_{\pi3}'^+ \longrightarrow \pi^+ + \pi^0 + \pi^0.$$

In 1954 a group (74) from l'Ecole Polytechnique in Paris found evidence of a monergic kaon decay in which a muon is emitted. They used two large cloud chambers, one above the other. The uppermost was a magnet cloud chamber, which enabled them to determine the momentum of a charged particle with considerable precision, while the lower was a multiplate cloud chamber. The series of metal plates in the latter makes it possible to determine the energy of a charged particle from its range. No gamma-ray showers were found associated with these events. The decay was therefore interpreted as

$$K_{\mu2}^+ \longrightarrow \mu^+ + \nu.$$

This type of decay is now known to be far more common than the $K_{\mu0}^+$, which was discovered earlier. The reason for the reverse order of discovery probably lies in the great momentum of the muon in $K_{\mu2}^+$ decay. When large stacks of emulsion pellicles began to be used, these events were found in large numbers and thoroughly studied.

In 1954, Friedlander et al. (65) found a cosmic-ray kaon track in which the kaon came to rest and underwent what appeared to be beta decay. The decay track exhibited plateau† grain density (i.e., it was made by a highly

---

* A particle with integral spin (see glossary).

† In emulsion the grain density versus energy curve is very similar to the space-rate-of-energy-loss-$vs.$-energy curve shown in Fig. 4-19 except that, after passing through a minimum, it increases only a small amount and then becomes constant whereas the ionization rate continues to increase.

relativistic particle) until, after traveling 2.3 cm through the emulsion, it suffered a sudden change in direction, following which it could be definitely identified as an electron. If the particle is assumed to have been an electron, then its energy, deduced from grain density, was 90 Mev. An electron of this energy has a mean free path for bremsstrahlung production in emulsion of 2.9 cm, so the identification of the decay particle with an electron seems reasonable. Others (47, 84) have found a few similar events. The energies of the decay electrons in the different events are not the same, leading one to postulate a three-body decay. There is no evidence yet for the nature of the neutral particles, but a reasonable guess would be $K_{\beta3}^{+} \longrightarrow e^{+} + \pi^{0} + \nu$. In addition to the decay mode

$$K_{\beta3}^{+} \longrightarrow e^{+} + 2 \text{ neutral particles,}$$

there is the possibility of the decay

$$K_{\beta2}^{+} \longrightarrow e^{+} + 1 \text{ neutral particle.}$$

Early analyses of charged kaon decay events in cloud chambers and in emulsion indicated a mean lifetime of about 10^{-8} sec. Using cosmic rays, Mezzetti and Keuffel (104), with the apparatus shown schematically in Fig. 11-24, found a mean lifetime of $(0.96 \pm 0.08) \times 10^{-8}$ sec. Their data are shown in Fig. 11-25. With the advent of the big machines it was possible to

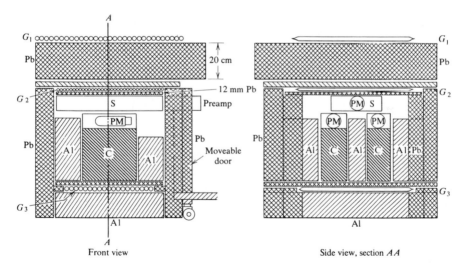

Front view   Side view, section AA

Fig. 11-24. Drawing of apparatus used by Mezzetti and Keuffel (104) to determine the mean lifetime of charged cosmic-ray kaons. Tray G_1 contained 30 1″ × 24″ GM tubes. Tray G_2 contained 48 $\frac{1}{2}$″ × 24″ GM tubes, and tray G_3 20 1″ × 24″ tubes. Scintillations produced in the block labeled S were detected by a photomultiplier (PM) tube. The water-filled tanks labeled C, together with their associated PM tubes, were Čerenkov detectors.

select only positively charged kaons. Fitch and Motley (58) used the apparatus shown in Fig. 11-26 to distinguish between $K_{\mu 2}^{+}$ and $K_{\pi 2}^{+}$ with results shown in Fig. 11-27. The near identity of these lifetimes, taken together with the near identity of masses, is strong presumptive evidence that the observed decays are simply alternate decay modes of a single type of kaon, the K^{+}.

Negative kaons. These particles, like negative pions, interact strongly with nuclei, or perhaps more correctly, with nucleons, thus making it virtually

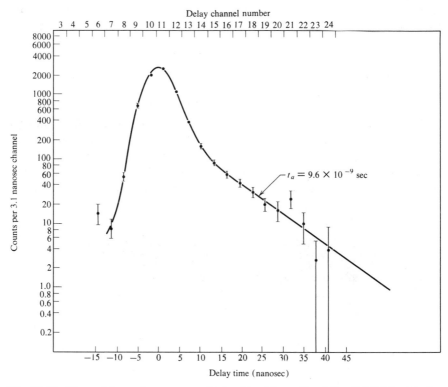

Fig. 11-25. Charged-kaon decay curve obtained by Mezzetti and Keuffel (104) with the apparatus shown in Fig. 11-24. For delay times greater than 15×10^{-9} sec, the points lie reasonably close to a straight line. This straight line portion gives a mean lifetime of 9.6 nanosec.

impossible to observe decays at rest. The following decay processes are each represented by a small number of in-flight decay events (63):

$$K_{\pi 3}^{-} \longrightarrow \pi^{+} + \pi^{-} + \pi^{-},$$

$$K_{\pi 2}^{-} \longrightarrow \pi^{-} + \pi^{0},$$

$$K_{\beta 3}^{-} \longrightarrow e^{-} + 2 \text{ neutral particles.}$$

The best estimate of the K^- mass (14) as of 1957 was

$$M_{K^-} = (965.6 \pm 1.2)m,$$

which is close enough to the mass of the positive kaon to suggest they have identical masses. Barkas *et al.* (14) have determined the lifetime of negative kaons by studying the decay in flight of momentum-separated particles slowing down in emulsion. Their value is

$$t_a(K^-) = (1.32 \pm 0.17) \times 10^{-8} \text{ sec,}$$

again close enough to that of K^+ to lead to the strong suspicion that the two mean lifetimes are the same.

Spin and parity. As we have seen before, the possible spin and parity combinations of the primary particle may be deduced from those of the

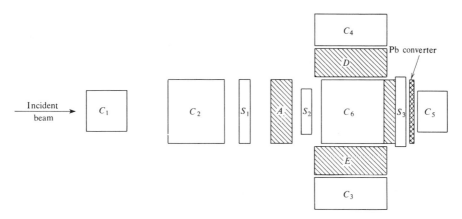

Fig. 11-26. Diagram of apparatus used by Fitch and Motley (58) to determine the mean lifetimes of $K_{\mu 2}^+$ and $K_{\pi 2}^+$. C_1, C_2, C_3, C_4, C_5, and C_6 are Čerenkov detectors, of which C_1 responds only to particles with $0.62 < \beta < 0.78$. The threshold of C_2 lies above the kaon velocity and is used in anticoincidence with C_1 to eliminate pions detected by C_1. A, D, E, and F are absorbers, D and E being of such a thickness that a muon from a $K_{\mu 2}^+$ decay in C_6 can reach C_3 or C_4 but a pion from a $K_{\pi 2}^+$ decay in C_6 cannot. S_1, S_2, and S_3 are scintillation detectors.

secondaries if parity is conserved. Assuming that the 0^- characterization of all pions is correct, one has for the parity of the $K_{\pi 3}^+$,

$$(-)(-)(-)(-1)^l,$$

which leads to the possible spin-parity assignments

$$0^-, 1^+, 2^-, 3^+, \text{ etc.}$$

In the case of the $K_{\pi 2}^+$, one writes

$$(-)(-)(-1)^l$$

and the possible spin-parity assignments are 0^+, 1^-, 2^+, 3^-, etc. If the $K^+_{\pi 3}$ and $K^+_{\pi 2}$ are simply different decay modes of the same particle, as suggested by the near identity of their masses and lifetimes, then a way must be found

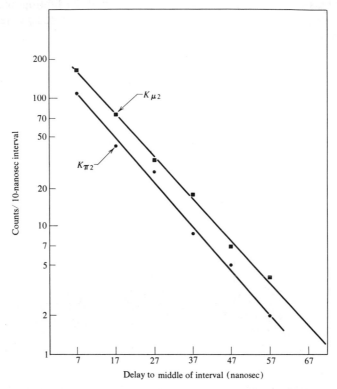

Fig. 11-27. Decay curves of $K^+_{\mu 2}$ and $K^+_{\pi 2}$ obtained by Fitch and Motley (58) with the apparatus shown in Fig. 11-26. The near parallelism of the two straight lines suggests that the muon and pion decays are simply two decay modes of the same particle.

around this apparent nonconservation of parity or it must be that parity is not conserved in these decays. It was this problem which led Lee and Yang to question the general principle of parity conservation in weak interactions.*

---

* Interactions between particles or between particles and fields seem to fall into three distinct classes which have been labeled "strong," "electromagnetic," and "weak." The strong interactions are typified by the production of pions, kaons, and hyperons in nucleon-nucleon encounters. In meson field theory one speaks of a mesonic charge in analogy to the electronic charge in electromagnetic field theory. If one represents the magnitude of the elementary mesonic charge by g, then a dimensionless measure of the strength of strong interactions is the quantity $g^2/4\pi\hbar c \approx 15$.

Electromagnetic interactions are typified by emission of photons by excited atomic

It has not yet been firmly established, but it seems likely that all kaons are spinless.

11-8 Hyperons* and Hypernuclei

A single V-event in emulsion exposed to cosmic rays was found by Hopper and Biswas (81) in 1950. Their analysis indicated that the tracks were produced by a proton and a pion according to the scheme

$$\Lambda^0 \longrightarrow p + \pi^-.$$

From the energies and assumed identities of the decay particles they obtained a mass for the neutral primary of $(2370 \pm 60)m$.

In the following year a number of events of this type were found in the cloud chamber events mentioned at the beginning of the previous section. The mass of the neutral primary was found to average about $2250m$ in these events. As more and more events were found in different laboratories it began to be fairly certain that the decay was monoergic and therefore that no third decay particle was involved. A more recent (70) value for the mass of the Λ^0 is

$$M_{\Lambda^0} = (1115.2 \pm 0.14) \text{ Mev}$$

or $$M_{\Lambda^0} = (2182.5 \pm 0.27)m.$$

Early cloud chamber pictures indicated that the mean lifetime of the Λ^0 was $\sim 10^{-10}$ sec. A statistical analysis of cloud chamber events in 1954 by

---

and nuclear systems, and the decay of the π^0. The strength of electromagnetic interactions is measured by the dimensionless quantity $e^2/4\pi\hbar c \cong 1/137$, which is just the fine structure constant, where e is the charge on an electron.

The weak interactions are typified by beta decay and by the spontaneous decay of muons, charged pions, charged kaons, and hyperons. They are usually measured by the square of the Fermi (i.e., vector) coupling constant of beta decay theory. This coupling constant is

$$C \approx 10^{-49} \text{ erg cm}^3.$$

One can convert C to a dimensionless quantity by dividing by $\hbar c$ and by the square of the Compton wavelength of a pion, namely $(\hbar/m_\pi c)^2$. One can rationalize the use of the Compton wavelength by the argument that it is a measure of the radius of the interaction volume for weak interactions. This procedure gives

$$\frac{(C \text{ erg cm}^3)^2}{(\hbar c \text{ erg cm})^2} \left(\frac{m_\pi c}{\hbar} \text{ cm}^{-1}\right)^4 = \frac{(10^{-49})^2}{(1.1 \times 10^{-27} \times 3 \times 10^{10})^2} \left(\frac{1}{1.4 \times 10^{-13}}\right)^4$$
$$\cong 2 \times 10^{-14}$$

The strengths of these different interactions are then seen to differ from each other by several orders of magnitude.

* The name hyperon is given to any particle whose mass lies between that of the neutron and that of the deuteron.

Page (122) gave $t_a = (3.7 \pm 0.6) \times 10^{-10}$ sec. A more recent value (52) based on the decay of artificially produced Λ^0's in bubble chambers is

$$t_a = (2.42 \pm 0.13) \times 10^{-10} \text{ sec.}$$

This very short length of time actually was puzzlingly long to physicists. Lambdas are produced copiously by $\pi^- + p$ reactions, which indicates a strong interaction with the nucleon-meson field. For example, the reaction might be

$$\pi^- + p \longrightarrow \Lambda^0 + \pi^0 \quad \text{[False]}.$$

One would then expect the Λ^0 to dissociate readily into $\pi^- + p$. Such an argument predicts a lifetime of $\sim 10^{-22}$ sec, so it is seen why 10^{-10} sec is looked upon as a "long" lifetime.

Part of the answer to this paradox was found by Fowler *et al.* (61) in 1953. They allowed 1.5-Bev negative pions produced by the Cosmotron to enter a hydrogen-filled diffusion cloud chamber. They immediately found reactions of the type

$$\pi^- + p \longrightarrow \text{hyperon} + \text{K}$$

and, in one case,

$$\pi^- + p \longrightarrow \Lambda^0 + \text{K}^0.$$

Examples of the latter process were also found by Thompson *et al.* (153) and by Leighton *et al.* (96) in cosmic-ray events in magnet cloud chambers. The production of a pair of new (often called "strange") particles in this way is spoken of as "associated production." The kaons produced in associated production were gradually found to decay by all the known kaon decay modes, thereby giving support to the idea that the various decays are alternate modes for identical particles. In all the early examples of associated production, the kaon was positively charged. When negatively charged kaons were eventually found (64) they were associated, not with hyperons, but with other kaons. The significance of the latter observation will be expanded upon later. Associated production does explain the copious-production, slow-decay paradox. The copious production involves interaction between a hyperon and a kaon. When the hyperon has moved away from the interaction volume, the chance of its meeting another kaon is vanishingly small, so that the decay process, which does not involve a kaon, may be entirely different than the production process. If this is the case, there is no longer a reason to expect the production and decay lifetimes to be similar.

Schwartz *et al.* (142) found events produced by $\pi^- + p$ reactions in a bubble chamber which appeared to be associated production events except that no $\Lambda^0 \longrightarrow p + \pi^-$ decay took place. In some of these the tracks of an electron pair were found. If the electron pair were due to materialization of a gamma ray from the decay $\Lambda^0 \longrightarrow n + \gamma$, the pairs found in the several events would all be expected to have the same energy (about 165 Mev). On the other hand, if the decay mode is

$$\Lambda^0 \longrightarrow n + \pi^0$$

the energy spectrum of the pairs should be flat from about 32 to 134 Mev. The observed energy spectrum is in better agreement with the latter. Eisler *et al.* (52), in a study of a large number of associated production events, find that in almost exactly $\frac{1}{3}$ of all cases, no $\Lambda^0 \longrightarrow p + \pi^-$ decay is found, and from this conclude that $\frac{2}{3}$ of all Λ^0's decay by the familiar

$$\Lambda^0 \longrightarrow p + \pi^-$$

mode, and $\frac{1}{3}$ by the

$$\Lambda^0 \longrightarrow n + \pi^0$$

mode.

From the modes of decay of the Λ^0 it is clear that it has half-integral spin, and it seems likely that its spin is $\frac{1}{2}$. If this is so, then the Λ^0 seems to be very closely akin to a neutron, and in fact it has been speculated that the Λ^0 may be a neutron in an excited state. It is not absolutely clear what one means by an "excited state" in this case, and no particular progress has yet been made along this line in understanding its properties. The idea immediately suggests itself, however, that a Λ^0 might replace a neutron in a nucleus. The resulting structure would have a short lifetime, but long enough to be easily observed.

Danysz and Pniewski (48) observed what they interpreted to be just such an event in 1953. One of the 39 prongs of a cosmic-ray induced star in emulsion started out from the star center as an extremely thick track and gradually narrowed until it apparently came to rest. Such thinning down of a track is characteristic of a stripped multiply charged nucleus and is caused by gradual electron pickup by the nucleus as it slows down. The effective reduction in its net charge by electron pickup causes it to ionize less heavily and the track grows correspondingly thinner. They estimated that $Z \sim 5$. At the end of the thinned track was a four-prong star. Since the particle initiating the four-prong star was either at rest or moving quite slowly, its kinetic energy was far too small to produce a nuclear disintegration. While nuclei can be formed in excited states which disintegrate by particle emission, the time for such a process is only about 10^{-20} sec whereas the travel time of this particle was about 10^{-12} sec. They concluded that the particle was either a nucleus containing a bound Λ^0 (which would explain the long lifetime) or possibly a nucleus with a π^- bound in an orbit which was finally captured by the nucleus, thereby producing a nuclear disintegration.

An event observed by Crussard and Morellet (46) a little later ruled out the bound-pion possibility, for in this case one of the decay particles was a π^- with about 25 Mev of kinetic energy. It is, of course, energetically impossible for a mesic atom to emit a pion. Later events showed that the total energy liberated in the stars was consistent with that expected of a bound Λ^0. These particles, which are now called *hypernuclei* or *hyperfragments*, sometimes emit pions when they decay, but often, especially in the case of hypernuclei of larger Z, undergo nonmesic disintegration. In the former case the total energy liberated is in the neighborhood of 35 Mev, while in the latter it is about 175 Mev, the actual amount being dependent upon the binding energy of the Λ^0 in the hypernucleus. The binding energies of a few hypernuclei are given in Table 11-8. It is seen at once that the binding energies of the Λ^0's

Table 11-8 BINDING ENERGIES* OF Λ^0'S IN HYPERNUCLEI

Hypernucleus†	Binding Energy (Mev) of Λ^0	of neutron‡	Hypernucleus	Binding Energy (Mev) of Λ^0	of neutron
$_\Lambda H^3$	0.12 ± 0.26§	6.26	$_\Lambda Li^8$	6.11 ± 0.35	2.03
$_\Lambda H^4$	2.20 ± 0.14	..	$_\Lambda Li^9$	7.2 ± 0.6	..
$_\Lambda He^4$	2.36 ± 0.12	20.56	$_\Lambda Be^8$	6.6 ± 0.6	18.90
$_\Lambda He^5$	3.08 ± 0.09	-0.96	$_\Lambda Be^9$	6.60 ± 0.31	1.57
$_\Lambda He^7$	3.0 ± 0.7	..	$_\Lambda B^{11}$	9.9 ± 0.6	11.47
$_\Lambda Li^7$	5.71 ± 0.31	7.25	$_\Lambda B^{12}$	9.6 ± 0.6	3.36

* From R. Ammar, R. Levi Setti, W. E. Slater, S. Limentani, P. E. Schlein, and P. H. Steinberg, *Nuovo Cimento*, **15**, 181 (1960).

† The symbol $_\Lambda H^3$ represents a nuclear assemblage consisting of one proton, one neutron, and one Λ^0.

‡ The figure given in the last column is the binding energy of the last added neutron in the corresponding normal nucleus (i.e., 6.26 Mev for $_1H^3$).

§ This is the standard deviation of the average only. It does not include systematic errors estimated to be $\sim \pm 0.2$ Mev.

although of about the same magnitude as neutron binding energies on the average, are quite different from those of the neutrons which they replace in specific nuclides. This is evidence for the operation of the Pauli exclusion principle which now allows Λ^0's in states forbidden to neutrons because of the presence of other neutrons. The lifetimes of hypernuclei are not well known because so few of them decay in flight, but the lifetimes are comparable to that of the free Λ^0.

Σ **hyperons.** In 1953, Bonetti *et al.* (23) observed a cosmic-ray-induced emulsion event in which a protonlike track ended and a lightly ionizing track started from the end of the heavier track. Measurements on the heavier track, which was 15.8 mm long, gave a mass of $(2500 \pm 345)m$. The light track was too short to be analyzed, but they proposed the decay of a hyperon,

$\Sigma \longrightarrow \pi +$ neutral particle. About the same time, two cosmic-ray events were seen in a magnet cloud chamber by York et al. (165) which were interpreted to be of the type

$$\Sigma^+ \longrightarrow p + \pi^0.$$

In these latter events a positively charged particle, which was produced in a lead plate within the chamber, decayed in flight into what appeared to be a proton. Emulsion events were soon found in which decays of the type

$$\Sigma^+ \longrightarrow p + \pi^0$$

were also observed. In these the range of the proton was always about 1680 microns, confirming the idea of a two-body decay. As more and more of these events were found, it became clear that the mass values determined from either the

$$\Sigma^+ \longrightarrow p + \pi^0$$

or

$$\Sigma^+ \longrightarrow n + \pi^+$$

were equal within experimental uncertainties. It seems fairly certain now that there is but one Σ^+ hyperon which undergoes these two modes of decay. In addition, it decays by the mode

$$\Sigma^+ \longrightarrow p + \gamma$$

in an estimated 1 per cent of all decays (127). This mode can be distinguished from the $\Sigma^+ \longrightarrow p + \pi^0$ mode by the fact that its decay proton range in emulsion is about $3000 \, \mu$ (micron) as opposed to $1686.5 \pm 6 \, \mu$ for the π^0 mode.

When hyperons began to be produced by artificially created beams of negative pions, Fowler et al. (61) observed not only the two previously found Σ^+ decay modes but also the process

$$\Sigma^- \longrightarrow \pi^- + n.$$

Large numbers of both positive and negative Σ hyperons have now been studied. Unlike the pions and kaons, the masses of positive and negative Σ hyperons are different. The mass difference can be obtained independently of the absolute masses by a study of the reactions,

$$K^- + p \longrightarrow \Sigma^+ + \pi^-$$

and

$$K^- + p \longrightarrow \Sigma^- + \pi^+.$$

If one writes the mass-energy equations, all quantities understood to be in the same units, he has

$$M_{K^-} + M_p = M_{\Sigma^+} + M_{\pi^-} + Q_1 \tag{11-29}$$

and

$$M_{K^-} + M_p = M_{\Sigma^-} + M_{\pi^+} + Q_2. \tag{11-30}$$

Taking the difference between (11-30) and (11-29), it is seen that

$$M_{\Sigma^-} - M_{\Sigma^+} = Q_1 - Q_2. \tag{11-31}$$

The mass difference (152) determined in this way is

$$M_{\Sigma^-} - M_{\Sigma^+} = (13.5 \pm 2.0)m,$$

which is quite close to the mass difference determined in other ways. The masses of the two particles are

$$M_{\Sigma^-} = (2341.3 \pm 2.0)m,$$

and

$$M_{\Sigma^+} = (2327.9 \pm 0.8)m.$$

The lifetime of Σ^+ hyperons was estimated to be $\sim 10^{-10}$ sec quite early in their study. More recent values (56) are

$$t_a(\Sigma^+) = (0.7^{+0.6}_{-0.4}) \times 10^{-10} \text{ sec}$$

and

$$t_a(\Sigma^+) = (0.83^{+0.06}_{-0.05}) \times 10^{-10} \text{ sec.}$$

Since the Σ^+ can decay by two different pion modes whereas only one mode is available to the Σ^-, one might expect the Σ^- lifetime to be longer than that of Σ^+. Like other negative strange particles and pions, Σ^- hyperons interact strongly with nucleons so that one depends mostly on decays in flight for lifetime information. A recently quoted value of the Σ^- lifetime is (52)

$$t_a(\Sigma^-) = (1.71 \pm 0.16) \times 10^{-10} \text{ sec.}$$

The first indication of a neutral hyperon, Σ^0, occurred in the associated production studies mentioned earlier. In these, the reactions

$$\pi^- + p \longrightarrow \Sigma^- + K^+,$$

and

$$\pi^- + p \longrightarrow \Lambda^0 + K^0$$

were observed. In the latter reaction the Λ^0 and K^0 are ordinarily coplanar, as they must be in such a two-body reaction, with the incoming π^-. Occasionally, however, events were found which were not coplanar that could be explained if a gamma ray of about 70 Mev had also been emitted in the process. Plano et al. (126) confirmed this hypothesis by observing an electron pair created in the chamber by the elusive gamma ray. The total energy released in this event was (73 $\pm$ 3.5) Mev, from which they calculated the mass of the Σ^0 to be (2323 $\pm$ 7)m. Alvarez et al. (3) have caused the Σ^0 to reveal themselves in a slightly different manner. In a study of the interactions of stopped Σ^- hyperons in a hydrogen bubble chamber, they found some monoergic and some polyergic Λ^0's. They were able to explain this on the basis of the two reactions

$$\Sigma^- + p \longrightarrow \Lambda^0 + n$$

and
$$\Sigma^- + p \longrightarrow \Sigma^0 + n$$
$$ \longrightarrow \Lambda^0 + \gamma.$$

In the latter reaction, the Σ^0 would be moving when it decayed, so that the observed laboratory energy of the Λ^0 would depend upon the direction in which the Λ^0 was emitted relative to the direction of motion of the Σ^0. It might be asked at this point, "How could one tell the difference between the simultaneous creation of a K^0, Λ^0, and γ and the creation of a K^0 and Σ^0 with the Σ^0 immediately (in perhaps $\sim 10^{-22}$ sec) breaking down into a Λ^0 and a gamma ray?" In principle it is very easy to distinguish between the two processes, for in the first, which is a three-body decay, the energy of the K^0 in the c.m. frame will vary, whereas in the second, which is a two-body decay, the energy of the K^0 in the c.m. frame will be unique. However, the best proof, thus far, of the reality of the Σ^0 has come about in a somewhat different way.

Stevenson (149) and Eisler *et al.* (54) have both observed events in which an electron pair rather than a gamma ray has been emitted by the decaying Σ^0. The argument here is the same as that advanced in the case of beta decay of the neutral pion, namely that the mean free path for pair production in hydrogen is so long that the probability of a gamma ray, emitted in a three-body breakup, creating a pair within an unresolvable distance from the decay event is extremely small. One is then almost forced to the conclusion that the Σ^0 can undergo a less common decay represented by

$$\Sigma^0 \longrightarrow e^+ + e^- + \Lambda^0.$$

The first of these events gives

$$Q \equiv M_{\Sigma^0} - M_{\Lambda^0} = (76.4 \pm 3.3) \text{ Mev}$$

and
$$M_{\Sigma^0} = (2332.0 \pm 6.5)m.$$

The second gives a Q of (77.4 ± 3.5) Mev. When this is averaged with other quoted values, the authors obtain

$$Q = (75.1^{+1.2}_{-2.0}) \text{ Mev}$$

and
$$M_{\Sigma^0} = (2329.5^{+2.4}_{-3.9})m.$$

From their decay modes we deduce that the Σ hyperons, like the Λ^0 hyperon, are all half-integral spin particles. One would like to think, in keeping with their position as "fundamental particles," that they would have the simplest possible half-integral spin, namely $\frac{1}{2}$. More experimental work will be necessary to decide this point.

The Ξ^- hyperon. In 1952 Armenteros *et al.* (7) observed the track of a cosmic-ray induced negative particle. This track suddenly changed direction and nearby was a V-track. The momentum vector associated with the V-track lay on a line which passed through the deflection point of the "primary" track. They were not able to determine the masses of any of the particles involved, but they surmised that the reaction was

$$\Xi^- \longrightarrow \pi^- + \Lambda^0$$
$$\hphantom{\Xi^- \longrightarrow \pi^-} \longrightarrow p + \pi^-.$$

Assuming this decay scheme they found the Q to be ~ 60 Mev. A number of investigators have now found examples of this decay. The average value (63) of the Q is (65.4 ± 2.2) Mev and $M_{\Xi^-} = (2583 \pm 5.5)m$. Sorrels *et al.* (147) have observed an event in which a Ξ^- is created in conjunction with two neutral kaons. The lifetime of the Ξ^- has not been well established, but is probably $\sim 10^{-10}$ sec. A single event has been reported (4) which is interpreted by its discoverers as evidence for a Ξ^0 hyperon.

11-9   Antiparticles

Dirac's theory of the electron led to the idea of an antiparticle, the positron. The antielectron has two particularly characteristic features. It can be created by a gamma ray but only in conjunction with a normal electron, and when it gets close enough to an electron both particles are annihilated, their entire masses being converted to radiant energy. Physicists speculated for a number of years on the possibility of other antiparticles, especially antiparticles of other spin-$\frac{1}{2}$ particles such as the proton. Evidence for their existence was actively sought in cloud-chamber and nuclear-emulsion events but without great success. Bridge *et al.* (26) found a single cosmic-ray event in a cloud chamber in which a slowly moving heavy particle was brought to rest in a brass plate. Three electron showers were observed which indicated the emission of three gamma rays from the region of the plate in which the heavy particle was presumably arrested. The estimated combined energy of these three gamma rays was more than 1 Bev, and since there was no other apparent source of this energy it was proposed that the heavy track was that of an antiproton which annihilated a proton at the end of its range in the brass plate. Others found connected stars in nuclear emulsions which might have been caused by antiprotons, but the evidence was usually not conclusive.

The completion of the Bevatron at last provided enough energy to produce antiprotons, and the Berkeley physicists (33) were not long in proving that they were indeed being produced by impacts of high-energy protons. This was such an impressive experiment that it seems worthwhile to describe it in some detail. The physical arrangement of equipment is shown in Fig. 11-28. The high-energy protons from the Bevatron struck the target at T. Negative particles produced in the resulting interaction were deflected outward by the

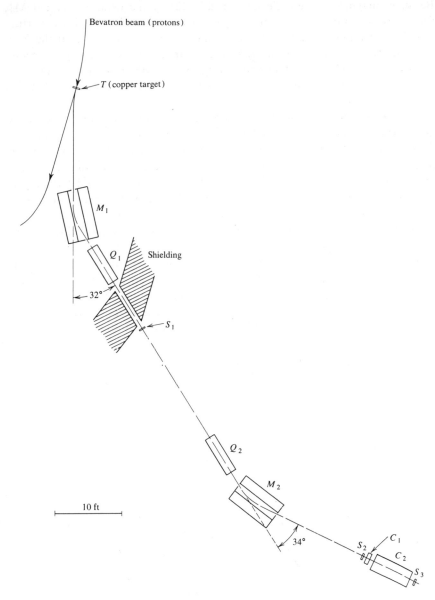

Fig. 11-28. Arrangement of equipment used by Chamberlain *et al.* (33) to detect anti-protons. Singly charged negative particles with a momentum of 1.19 Bev/c created at the target were deflected through an angle of 21° in the opposite sense from that of the beam protons by the Bevatron magnet. Q_1 is a set of three consecutive quadrupole focusing magnets which bring the particles to a focus at S_1. Q_2 brings the particles to a focus again at S_2. S_1, S_2, and S_3 are scintillation detectors. C_1 and C_2 are Čerenkov detectors.

Bevatron magnets, were deflected through 32° by the bending magnet M1, focused by a quadrupole focusing magnet Q1, and passed through an aperture in heavy shielding to the first scintillation detector S1, which was at the focal point of Q1. After passing through S1, the particles passed through a second quadrupole lens Q2, were deflected through 34° by M2 and again brought to a focus at the second scintillator, S2. Particles which reached S2 all had a momentum of 1.19 Bev/c ± 2 per cent.

One of the chief difficulties in this experiment was the detection of a few antiprotons in the presence of large numbers of pions (about 1 proton to 50,000 pions). One of the means for discriminating against pions was the use of the two Čerenkov counters C1 and C2. At the momentum used here, pions would have a $\beta(v/c)$ of 0.99 while the antiprotons would have a β of 0.78 as they entered S2. By selection of material of the proper dielectric constant for C1 it was possible to make it count all particles with $\beta > 0.79$. A count in C1 then showed that the particle was a pion and it was disregarded. C2 was a special type of Čerenkov counter which responded only to particles with $0.75 < \beta < 0.78$. Therefore a count in C2 was very likely to represent an antiproton. This was not enough by itself, however, for there are always random particles passing through the counters which might give a count. It was required that counts be produced in S1, S2, C2, and S3. Moreover, the flight time over the 40-foot path from S1 to S2 was 51 millimicroseconds for

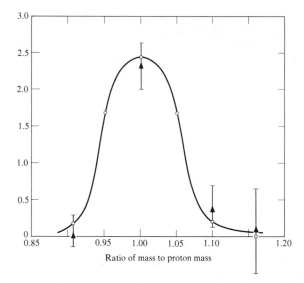

Fig. 11-29. Mass resolution of equipment depicted in Fig. 11-28. The solid curve and round dots give the measured intensity (to an arbitrary scale) when the equipment was adjusted to accept positive protons. The points (⊤) are for antiprotons, the scale at the left giving the number of antiprotons per 10^5 negative pions.

an antiproton, but only 40 mμ sec for a pion. The system was tested by moving the target in the Bevatron and reversing the magnetic field so that protons would be accepted.

The mass sensitivity of the system was tested by measuring the number of detected protons as a function of the magnet currents when the equipment was arranged to accept positive particles. The resulting curve is shown in Fig. 11-29. The number of antiproton counts as a function of magnet setting is also shown on the same figure. It seems clear that the instrument was measuring mass correctly and further that the antiproton mass differs by no more than 5 per cent from the proton mass.

If it is necessary to produce a proton-antiproton pair, for example by the reaction

$$p + p \longrightarrow p + p + \bar{p} + p$$

or

$$p + n \longrightarrow p + n + \bar{p} + p,$$

where $\bar{p}$ represents an antiproton, then the impinging proton must have a kinetic energy of 5.6 Bev if it strikes a proton at rest. If it strikes a nucleus, then the nucleons which are moving within the nucleus will sometimes be moving toward the impinging proton. This increases the excitation energy in the c.m. frame and lowers the required proton energy to about 4.3 Mev. If the proton strikes a nucleon which is moving toward it and produces a pion which strikes another nucleon producing an antiproton, the threshold energy may be lowered to 3.08 Mev. It was not possible to make an absolute excitation function determination in this first experiment, but the relative number of antiprotons per pion was measured as a function of beam energy. The data are shown in Fig. 11-30. One might imagine a process in which a neutron is struck with sufficient energy to cause it to emit a positive pion and be transformed into a negatively charged particle of roughly protonic mass. If such a process were possible it would have a very much lower threshold than that for $\bar{p}$-p pair production. The observed drop in the relative number of antiprotons to zero at about 4 Bev is a good indication that the particles observed were produced in pairs.

The reality of antiprotons was subsequently confirmed by measuring the Čerenkov radiation produced by charged particles resulting from their annihilation, and by observing their annihilation in bubble chambers and in nuclear emulsion. An extensive study with emulsions (32) has shown that, unlike positron annihilation, no measurable direct gamma radiation is produced in antiproton annihilation. Instead, each annihilation emits an *average* of 5.36 $\pm$ 0.3 pions (charged and neutral combined) with an average energy of 380 $\pm$ 18 Mev/pion, and 4.1 $\pm$ 0.3 protons with a total energy release in protons and neutrons of 490 $\pm$ 40 Mev. In addition a K-$\overline{\text{K}}$ pair, (where $\overline{\text{K}}$ is a presumed antikaon) is emitted in (3.5 $\pm$ 1.5) per cent of the annihilations. One $\Sigma^{\pm}$ (charge not determinable) and one Σ^{+} as well as one Dalitz pair

$(e^+ + e^-)$ have been observed in annihilation stars. Among those pions which stop in the emulsion stack—that is, those of lower energy—the ratio of π^+/π^- is 0.45 ± 0.12. Conservation of charge would require equal numbers of π^+ and π^- to be emitted in a $\bar{p}$-p interaction, whereas one more π^- than π^+ would be required in a $\bar{p}$-n interaction. This may possibly explain the observed ratio, but the interpretation is made uncertain by the fact that not all pions escape from the nucleus within which the annihilation takes place.

In 1956 Cork *et al.* (41) succeeded in producing antineutrons by passing antiprotons through a liquid scintillator in which some of them underwent charge exchange. The antineutrons had to pass through a lead plate thick

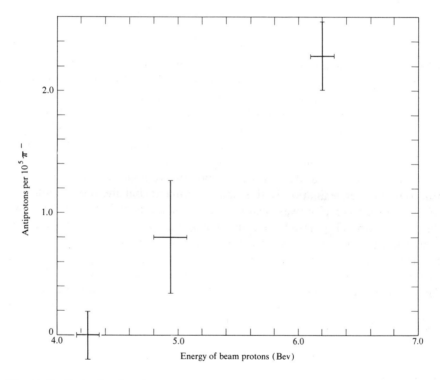

Fig. 11-30. Excitation function for production of antiprotons as a function of the energy of the bombarding protons. The large threshold energy is evidence that antiprotons and protons must be produced in pairs.

enough to stop most of the gamma rays generated in the charge exchange tank, and then through a scintillator without producing a count (thus showing they were uncharged), and were finally captured in a lead glass Čerenkov detector which counted large pulses brought about by annihilation of the antineutrons. Later, a bubble chamber picture was obtained (1) showing the disappearance of an antiproton, presumably by charge exchange, and somewhat farther along in the chamber, an antineutron annihilation star.

The discovery of these two new antiparticles has increased speculation upon the possibility of antihyperons. Baldo-Ceolin and Prowse (11) have described a nuclear emulsion event in which there was a V-track which appeared very much like the usual $\Lambda^0 \longrightarrow p + \pi^-$. When the apparent π^- track was followed, however, it came to rest and underwent μ-decay which is characteristic of π^+ rather than π^-. The apparent proton track, moreover, suffered an interaction in flight, the star so produced containing two tracks with nearly minimum ionization. This type of star is rather characteristic of annihilation stars, so they were led to postulate that they had observed the decay of an antilambda according to the reaction $\bar{\Lambda}^0 \longrightarrow \bar{p} + \pi^+$.

Amaldi et al. (5) have described another emulsion event in which an antiproton produces a two-pronged star, one branch of which appears to be due to a proton and the other, they believe, to an antisigma.* The latter undergoes a sharp change in direction which they interpret as a decay in flight according to the scheme

$$\bar{\Sigma}^- \longrightarrow \bar{p} + \pi^0.$$

The supposed $\bar{p}$ then produces a star in which at least 1.6 Bev of energy is released, whereas the kinetic energy of the incoming particle, if of protonic mass, is only 400 Mev. For this reason they believe it to be an annihilation star.

Button et al. (28) have reported a bubble chamber event in which two V-tracks are associated with a stopping $\bar{p}$. One V appears to be a Λ^0 while the other appears to be a $\bar{\Lambda}^0$. They believe the reaction is either

$$\bar{p} + p \longrightarrow \bar{\Sigma}^0 + \Lambda^0, \qquad \bar{\Sigma}^0 \longrightarrow \bar{\Lambda}^0 + \gamma$$

or

$$\bar{p} + p \longrightarrow \Sigma^0 + \bar{\Lambda}^0, \qquad \Sigma^0 \longrightarrow \Lambda^0 + \gamma,$$

and favor the first interpretation.

Two different groups of investigators have each found a single event which they interpret as the production of a Ξ^-, $\bar{\Xi}^+$ pair (i.e., a Ξ^- and its antiparticle.) In one case† a $\bar{p}$ from a separated beam of 3.3 Bev/c momentum,

---

* The antiparticle of the Σ^+ would be a negatively charged particle, so the symbol $\bar{\Sigma}^-$ is used here, but oftentimes the confusing symbol $\overline{\Sigma^+}$ is used instead.

† Brown, H. N., Culwick, B. B., Fowler, W. B., Gailloud, M., Kalogeropoulos, T. E., Kopp, J. K., Lea, R. M., Louttit, R. I., Morris, T. W., Shutt, R. P., Thorndike, A. M., Webster, M. S., Baltay, C., Fowler, E. C., Sandweiss, J., Sanford, J. R., and Taft, H. D., *Phys. Rev. Lett.*, **8**, 255 (1962).

struck a proton in a 20-inch liquid hydrogen bubble chamber producing a V-shaped track which is interpreted as a Ξ^-, $\bar{\Xi}^+$ pair. The reactions are

$$\bar{p} + p \longrightarrow \Xi^- + \bar{\Xi}^+$$
$$\Xi^- \longrightarrow \pi^- + \Lambda^0$$
$$\bar{\Xi}^+ \longrightarrow \pi^+ + \bar{\Lambda}^0$$
$$\bar{\Lambda}^0 \longrightarrow \bar{p} + \pi^+.$$

The Λ^0 and $\bar{\Lambda}^0$, being uncharged, do not produce tracks, of course, so their presence has to be inferred. The charge signs of the charged particles involved can be determined from the magnetically produced curvatures of the tracks. From the assumed reactions, they calculate the following masses:

$$M_{\bar{\Xi}^+} = (2587.2 \pm 2.5)m$$
$$M_{\bar{\Lambda}^0} = (2193.1 \pm 4.9)m.$$

The second group* found a very similar hydrogen bubble chamber event produced by a $\bar{p}$ of momentum 3 Bev/c. Assuming the same reactions, they obtain the following calculated masses:

$$M_{\bar{\Xi}^+} = (2585.6 \pm 4.7)m$$
$$M_{\bar{\Lambda}^0} = (2179.0 \pm 4.9)m.$$

One cannot be sure, from such a few isolated events, that these anti-hyperons actually exist, but it seems quite probable that more exciting dis-coveries will soon be made. The decay modes of the hyperons show that they all have half-integral spins, but do they each have spin of $\frac{1}{2}$ as is commonly supposed? And what are the magnetic moments and parities? It is *assumed* that the antiproton and antineutron are stable particles, but as mentioned in the discussion of positrons, this is next to impossible to prove because of annihilation reactions. In the antiproton experiments the total flight time was about 10^{-7} sec. The lifetime cannot be much shorter than this or no appreciable number of antiprotons would have survived. A lower limit of even 10^{-7} sec is a rather unsatisfactory figure for a lifetime (against decay) which is presumed to be infinite.

11-10 Strangeness

The enormous success of quantum ideas in physics made it inevitable, upon the discovery of the muon, that speculations concerning a spectrum of quantized masses should arise. The discoveries since that time make such an idea even more attractive, but the fact is that no theory that predicts the

---

* CERN and Centre d'Etudes Nucléaires, *Phys. Rev. Lett.*, **8**, 257 (1962).

observed masses has yet been put forward. Two quantum concepts that bring some order out of the chaos of observations have been put forward. These are "isotopic spin" and "strangeness."

If one examines all the fundamental particles, he notices that, in addition to mass, spin, parity, and electric charge which help characterize any given particle, there are "family" characteristics. The neutron and proton appear to belong together, with one positively charged and one neutral member of the family. The antiproton is negatively charged to be sure, but the antiproton and antineutron are a sort of mirror image (called charge conjugates) of the proton-neutron group. The electron exists only in the negatively charged state (again ignoring its charge conjugate, the anti-electron or positron) but not in a neutral or positively charged form. The neutrino exists only in the neutral state. Other particles exhibit all charges, but the question arises whether some members of the group are antiparticles.

The experiments which led to the downfall of the parity conservation hypothesis also showed that invariance under charge conjugation was invalid in weak interactions. The *CPT* theorem requires invariance under the combined operations of charge conjugation (C), space inversion (P), and time reversal (T). That is, if one has a real physical situation, the combined operations of C, P, and T must lead to another realizable physical situation. One of the consequences of this theorem is that there must be certain relations between the physical parameters of particles and their antiparticles. These are shown in Table 11-9.

Table **11-9** RELATIONSHIP BETWEEN PARTICLE AND ANTI-
PARTICLE PROPERTIES

Physical property	Antiparticle value relative to that of particle
Mass	Same
Spin	Same
Lifetime	Same
Charge	Opposite
Magnetic moment	Opposite

In Sec. 9-7 we defined a quantity called the isobaric spin. The idea embodied in that quantum number has been taken over, with modifications, into fundamental particle theory. In an attempt to avoid confusion, the term "isotopic spin" will be used for this new quantity whose projection on some ζ-axis in isotopic spin space is given by

$$T_\zeta = \frac{q}{e} - \frac{1}{2} Y, \qquad (11\text{-}32)$$

where q is the charge of the particle concerned and Y is the sum of the charges of the isotopic spin multiplet, of which the particle is a member, divided by e. For example, the charge of a proton is e, and $Y = (e + 0)/e = 1$, so that

$$T_\zeta = 1 - \frac{1}{2} = \frac{1}{2}.$$

For a neutron*

$$T_\zeta = \frac{0}{e} - \frac{1}{2}\left(\frac{e + 0}{e}\right) = -\frac{1}{2}.$$

For an antiproton,

$$T_\zeta = \frac{-e}{e} - \frac{1}{2}\left(\frac{-e + 0}{e}\right) = -\frac{1}{2},$$

and for an antineutron,

$$T_\zeta = \frac{0}{e} - \frac{1}{2}\left(\frac{-e + 0}{e}\right) = \frac{1}{2}.$$

The neutron and proton are then members of an isotopic spin doublet with $T = \frac{1}{2}$, and the antineutron and antiproton are also members of an isotopic spin doublet with $T = \frac{1}{2}$. The pions are members of an isotopic spin triplet with $T = 1$, etc.

A "baryon" is defined as any particle whose mass is equal to or greater than that of a proton. Essentially it means nucleons and hyperons. Antibaryons are the corresponding antiparticles. One may now define a baryon number, N, which is the number of baryons minus the number of antibaryons. As applied to particles, $N = +1$ for baryons and $N = -1$ for antibaryons.

Gell-Mann (68) and Nishijima (115, 116) in 1953 proposed the introduction of a new quantum number, the strangeness, S. It is defined by

$$S = Y - N. \qquad (11\text{-}33)$$

Since it is determined by other quantum numbers, it can tell us nothing that the others do not, but it is a much more convenient quantity. Like the isotopic spin it really characterizes a multiplet rather than an individual particle. The neutron-proton, antineutron-antiproton, and pion groups all have $Y = N$ and hence have a strangeness of zero.

The Λ^0 seems to be a hyperon apart, in that no other particle has a mass very close to the Λ^0 mass. One assumes, therefore, that the Λ^0 is an isotopic

---

* The signs of the isotopic spins of neutron and proton are just opposite to those obtained from the definition of isobaric spin in Sec. 9-7. There is no particular significance to this, as the sign is arbitrary, but it is a bit confusing to have the two different sign conventions in the two contexts. We have preferred to follow convention here rather than be consistent and at odds with common usage.

singlet, which means that it must have $T = 0$. This is obviously consistent with its lack of charge which requires that $T_\zeta = 0$. It is also seen that $Y = 0$ and hence $S = 0 - 1 = -1$. Therefore the Λ "family" is an isotopic singlet with a strangeness of -1.

If it now is assumed that strangeness is conserved in "strong interactions" but not conserved in weak interactions, we can deduce possible strangeness of other particles. In the reaction

$$\pi^- + p \longrightarrow K^0 + \Lambda^0$$

strangeness conservation requires that

$$0 + 0 = S_{K^0} + (-1),$$

from which $$S_{K^0} = 1$$

and $$T_\zeta(K^0) = \frac{q}{e} - \frac{1}{2} \, Y = \frac{q}{e} - \frac{1}{2}(S + N)$$

$$= 0 - \tfrac{1}{2}(1 + 0) = -\tfrac{1}{2}.$$

The K^0 may then be a member of an isotopic spin doublet with $T = \frac{1}{2}$ or an isotopic spin quadruplet with $T = \frac{3}{2}$ or some higher half-integral isotopic spin multiplet. If $T = \frac{3}{2}$ and $Y = 1$, then the possible values of $T_\zeta(\frac{3}{2}, \frac{1}{2}, -\frac{1}{2}, -\frac{3}{2})$ correspond to values of q/e of 2, 1, 0, -1, which gives $Y = 2$, a value inconsistent with the assumed value $Y = 1$. There is a feeling, moreover, that fundamental particles should not be multiply charged, and this is borne out, thus far, by failure to find doubly charged strange particles. If multiple charges are ruled out, then we are left with a doublet, K^0, K^+.

The reaction which competes with the one above, namely,

$$\pi^- + p \longrightarrow \Sigma^- + K^+,$$

gives the strangeness relation

$$0 + 0 = S_{\Sigma^-} + 1,$$

from which it follows that the strangeness of the Σ hyperons is -1. This gives, for the Σ^-, if it is a particle rather than an antiparticle,

$$T_\zeta = -1 - \tfrac{1}{2}(-1 + 1) = -1.$$

Again, if one rules out multiple charges it must be a member of an isotopic spin triplet, Σ^+, Σ^0, Σ^-. In this way the Σ^0 was predicted before it was observed experimentally.

In the case of Ξ^- there is less information and consequently more choice. One can eliminate $S = 0$ if he excludes multiple charges. $S = -1$ leads to an isotopic triplet, which raises the question why neither of the other charge states has been observed. $S = -2$ gives a doublet (Ξ^-, Ξ^0) in which one member has not been observed, while $S = -3$ gives a singlet. The choice between these two can be made if one invokes a selection rule on slow-decay into strongly interacting particles of

$$\Delta S = \pm 1$$

(which is equivalent to $\Delta T_\zeta = \pm \frac{1}{2}$). In Λ^0 decay, $\Lambda^0 \longrightarrow p + \pi^-, \Delta S = +1$. The observed Ξ^- decay, $\Xi^- \longrightarrow \Lambda^0 + \pi^-$ would give $\Delta S = +1$ if $S = -2$ and $\Delta S = +2$ if $S = -3$. The selection rule is also supported by the failure to observe

$$\Xi^- \longrightarrow n + \pi^-,$$

which would involve a change in strangeness of $+2$ or $+3$ depending on whether S is -2 or -3. The assignment $S = -2$ would likewise be in keeping with the simultaneous production of a Ξ^- and two kaons mentioned in Sec. 11-8, if the event was produced by "ordinary" particles—for example,

$$n + \pi^- \longrightarrow \Xi^- + K^0 + K^0,$$

which gives the conservation-of-strangeness equation

$$0 + 0 = -2 + 1 + 1.$$

The accuracy of the assignment depends on observing a Ξ^0 or on a study of Ξ^- production reactions.

The strangeness assignments of the antiparticles follow directly from those of the particles. If each particle has an antiparticle, then the antiparticles form isotopic spin multiplets of the same multiplicity as their corresponding particles. More simply stated, the total isotopic spin is the same for a particle or antiparticle multiplet. The fact that charge and baryon number of an antiparticle are opposite in sign to the corresponding particle requires that the strangeness of an antiparticle multiplet be the negative of the strangeness of the corresponding particle multiplet. The strangeness assignments are shown in Fig. 11-31.

The requirement of conservation of strangeness in strong interactions leads directly to the observed necessity for associated production. This can be accomplished by creation of a particle-antiparticle pair or by creation of two different strange particles of opposite strangeness. It is consistent with the observed reactions

$$\pi^- + p \longrightarrow K^0 + \Lambda^0$$

and
$$\pi^- + p \longrightarrow K^+ + K^-,$$

which conserve strangeness, and with the failure to observe the reaction

$$\pi^- + p \longrightarrow K^0 + \pi^0,$$

which is forbidden because it involves a change in strangeness.

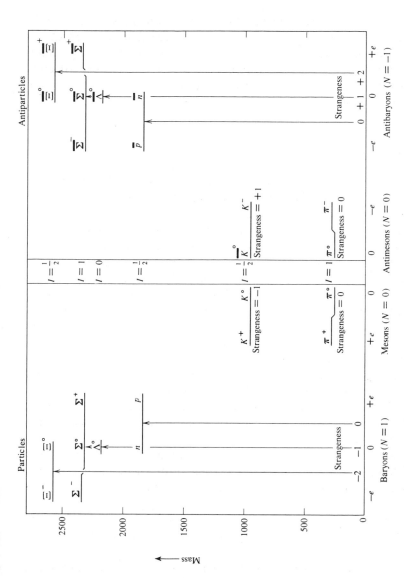

Fig. 11-31. This chart, adapted from a somewhat similar chart used by Gell-Mann and Rosenfeld (70), shows the strangeness assignments of the various particles and antiparticles. The masses (in electron mass units) are given at the left. Isotopic spins are given in the central column. Baryon numbers and charges are given at the bottom of the figure.

That most of the strange particles have long lifetimes is consistent with this theory, since decay can only take place with a change in strangeness and is therefore a forbidden process as far as the fast, strong interactions are concerned.

All experimental observations thus far are in agreement with the strangeness scheme. It is not a theory in the sense that it is derivable from well-known laws of interaction between the particles, for such laws are still lacking, but it provides rules which bring a great amount of order into the experimental observations and should be invaluable for testing out laws of interaction when such are proposed.

11-11 Structure of Nucleons

Physicists have speculated for many years on the possibility that the fundamental particles, and in particular nucleons, have some sort of structure or internal architecture. An allied speculation is that hyperons might be nucleons in excited states, an idea which carries with it the implication that the nucleon has a structure. In the case of the proton, a knowledge of its charge distribution might make it possible to compute a magnetic moment in agreement with the experimentally determined value. A neutron would then have to consist of equal amounts of positive and negative charge distributed in such a way that the angular momentum would be $\hbar/2$ and the magnetic moment in agreement with experiment. Since no charge smaller than that of the electron has ever been observed, it seems strange to speak of a distribution of charge, for how can something be distributed if it is indivisible? The meson theory of nuclear forces requires that nucleons constantly emit and reabsorb virtual pions, so the nucleon may be looked upon as surrounded by a pion cloud. The existence of such a pion cloud would not change the total nucleon charge but would give rise to a charge-density distribution about the nucleon.

The differential cross section for elastic scattering of electrons by a point proton without spin (and, by implication, with no magnetic moment), often referred to as the Mott scattering cross section, is given by

$$\left(\frac{d\sigma}{d\Omega}\right)_M = \left(\frac{e^2}{2W_K}\right)^2 \frac{\cos^2 \theta/2}{\sin^4 (\theta/2)[1 + (2W_K/M_p c^2) \sin^2 (\theta/2)]}, \quad (11\text{-}34)$$

where θ is the laboratory angle through which the electron is scattered, W_K is the laboratory kinetic energy of the impinging electron, $d\Omega$ is the solid angle between θ and $\theta + d\theta$ into which the electron is scattered, and M_p is the proton mass. Rosenbluth (132) has shown that the differential cross section for elastic scattering of electrons by a point proton with a magnetic moment,

μ_p ($= 1 + \kappa_p$), can be written in terms of the Mott scattering differential cross section.

$$\left(\frac{d\sigma}{d\Omega}\right)_R = \left(\frac{d\sigma}{d\Omega}\right)_M \left\{1 + \frac{\hbar^2 G^2}{4M_p^2 c^2}\left[2(1 + \kappa_p)^2(\tan^2 \theta/2) + \kappa_p^2\right]\right\} \quad (11\text{-}35)$$

where*
$$G = \frac{2W_K}{\hbar c} \frac{\sin \theta/2}{[1 + (2W_K/M_p c^2)\sin^2 \theta/2]^{1/2}}. \quad (11\text{-}36)$$

The quantity G is called the electron (four-vector) energy-momentum transfer and is defined by the expression

$$(\hbar c G)^2 = (p_p c)^2 - W_{Kp}^2, \quad (11\text{-}37)$$

where p_p and W_{Kp} are the momentum and kinetic energy respectively given

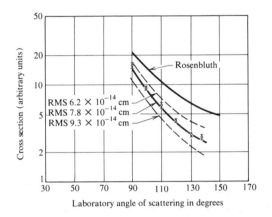

Fig. 11-32. Differential cross sections for scattering of 236-Mev (lab) electrons by protons (hydrogen). The data points with indicated margin of error are shown as ⌽ . The point-charge, point-anomalous magnetic moment model theoretical curve is labeled Rosenbluth. The theoretical curves for model protons of various RMS radii as shown were calculated on the assumption that $F_{1p} = F_{2p} \simeq 1 - G^2\bar{r}^2/6$, where $(\bar{r^2})^{1/2}$ is the RMS radius. [From R. Hofstadter, F. Bumiller, and M. R. Yearian, *Rev. Mod. Phys.*, **30**, 482 (1958).]

to the scattering proton. G thus has the dimensions of a reciprocal length and is often given in (fermi)$^{-1}$.

Hofstadter and McAllister's (80) high-energy electron scattering experiments showed that the angular dependence of the differential cross section did not agree with the Rosenbluth formula, the deviation becoming greater as the scattering angle was increased, as seen in Fig. 11-32. Olson, Schopper, and

* In the literature, the symbol q is usually used for this quantity.

Wilson (120) have found departures from the Rosenbluth equation which increase with incident electron energy, becoming quite large at 1.2 Bev as shown in Fig. 11-33.

A possible interpretation of these results is that the laws of electro-dynamics break down at very small distances. A more interesting hypothesis is that the proton is not a point particle but a structure of finite size. When

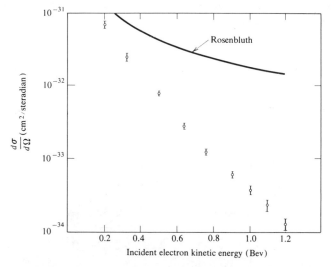

Fig. 11-33. Differential cross section for scattering of electrons by protons at 112° (lab). [From D. N. Olson, H. F. Schopper, and R. R. Wilson, *Phys. Rev. Lett.*, **6**, 286 (1961).]

x-rays are scattered by the electrons of an atom, the finite size of the atom results in interference between waves which are scattered by electrons in different parts of the atom. For those rays which are scattered at a small angle to the transmitted rays, the path differences are very small for waves scattered from different parts of the atom so that the finite size of the atom has little effect on the intensity of the scattered radiation. On the other hand, for rays which are scattered through larger angles, the path-length differences for waves scattered from different parts of the atom become greater as the scattering angle is increased and reach a maximum at a scattering angle of 180°. If the wavelength of the radiation is long compared to the dimensions of the atom, the path differences produce only small phase differences between waves scattered from different parts of the atom so that the intensity of the scattered radiation is only slightly less than that expected from a point atom. At higher photon energies the wavelength becomes shorter and the phase difference begins to be significant. When the wavelength is comparable to or less than an atomic diameter, the effect of finite atom size becomes quite large. It is seen then that the departures of electron scattering from the point proton model are just like the departures from a point atom model observed in the scattering of x-rays, the departures increasing with increasing scattering angle and with increasing energy of the incident particle.

In x-ray scattering, the finite size of the atom is taken into account by introduction of a "form factor" into the scattering formulas. Rosenbluth has shown that one may similarly introduce form factors into the electron scattering equations to take account of a proton of finite size. The modification of Eq. (11-35) is

$$\left(\frac{d\sigma}{d\Omega}\right)_p = \left(\frac{d\sigma}{d\Omega}\right)_M \left\{F_{1p}^2 + \frac{\hbar^2 G^2}{4M_p^2 c^2}\left[2(F_{1p} + F_{2p})^2\left(\tan^2\frac{\theta}{2}\right) + F_{2p}^2\right]\right\}. \quad (11\text{-}38)$$

F_1 is called the "charge form factor," and F_2 is called the "anomalous magnetic moment form factor." F_1 and F_2 are functions of G. Equation (11-38) fits the experimental scattering data quite well as can be seen from Fig. 11-32, but does so for a variety of charge and magnetic moment distributions. Since the rms (root mean square) radius depends on the precise form of distribution which is assumed, there is still considerable uncertainty in what radius one should assign to the proton.

Presumably, with suitable neutron form factors, Eq. (11-38) could also be applied to electron scattering by neutrons. Thus

$$\left(\frac{d\sigma}{d\Omega}\right)_n = \left(\frac{d\sigma}{d\Omega}\right)_M \left\{F_{1n}^2 + \frac{\hbar^2 G^2}{4M_n^2 c^2}\left[2(F_{1n} + F_{2n})^2\left(\tan^2\frac{\theta}{2}\right) + F_{2n}^2\right]\right\}. \quad (11\text{-}39)$$

Unfortunately the elastic scattering of electrons by neutrons is not as readily studied as that of electrons by protons for the reason that there are no sources of free neutrons with a sufficient concentration of neutrons per unit volume. The next best thing is the deuteron, but now the scattering is a combination of proton scattering and neutron scattering, which depends somewhat on relative motions of the two nucleons in the deuteron nucleus. A point neutron should scatter 500-Mev electrons at 135° some three times as strongly as the apparently more diffuse proton. The deuteron elastic scattering experiments indicated that neutron scattering was much less than this, implying that the neutron, too, is a structure of finite size. It has been found more satisfactory to use inelastic scattering or electrodisintegration of deuterons by electrons rather than elastic scattering.

Arguments can be advanced (79) to justify the approximate validity of the equation

$$\left(\frac{d\sigma}{d\Omega}\right)_D = \left(\frac{d\sigma}{d\Omega}\right)_p + \left(\frac{d\sigma}{d\Omega}\right)_n, \quad (11\text{-}40)$$

where $(d\sigma/d\Omega)_D$ is the differential cross section for inelastic scattering of electrons by deuterons, while $(d\sigma/d\Omega)_p$ and $(d\sigma/d\Omega)_n$ are the differential cross sections for elastic scattering of electrons by protons and neutrons respectively. Approximate values of $(d\sigma/d\Omega)_n$ are then obtained by subtracting measured values of $(d\sigma/d\Omega)_p$ from measured values of $(d\sigma/d\Omega)_D$.

If neutron and proton are assumed to be two different states of a fundamental nucleon, then the neutron should be the image in isotopic spin space of the proton. In order for the neutron to be neutral while the proton is positively charged, the charge form factor at $G = 0$, namely $F_1(0)$, must contain a scalar part which does not change sign in a reflection in isospace and a vector part which does change sign. Thus

$$F_{1p} = F_{1s} + F_{1v} \tag{11-41}$$

and
$$F_{1n} = F_{1s} - F_{1v}. \tag{11-42}$$

By analogy, we assume for the anomalous magnetic moment form factors

$$F_{2p} = F_{2s} + F_{2v} \tag{11-43}$$

and
$$F_{2n} = F_{2s} - F_{2v}. \tag{11-44}$$

At low electron energy (and therefore necessarily small G) the nucleons will act as point scatterers so that Eq. (11-38) should reduce to (11-35). From this and the fact that the uncharged neutron does not scatter low-energy electrons it follows at once that

$$F_{1p}(0) = F_{1s}(0) + F_{1v}(0) = 1,$$

$$F_{1n}(0) = F_{1s}(0) - F_{1v}(0) = 0,$$

$$F_{2p}(0) = F_{2s}(0) + F_{2v}(0) = \mu_p - 1,$$

$$F_{2n}(0) = F_{2s}(0) - F_{2v}(0) = \mu_n - 1.$$

From the first two relationships,

$$F_{1s}(0) - F_{1v}(0) = \tfrac{1}{2},$$

while from the second two,

$$F_{2s}(0) = \frac{\mu_p + \mu_n}{2} - 1$$

and
$$F_{2v}(0) = \frac{\mu_p - \mu_n}{2}.$$

Littauer, Schopper, and Wilson (99) go further and break up the isoscalar form factors into two parts, a core of small radius and a more extensive isoscalar meson cloud. They tentatively identify the isoscalar meson cloud with a $T = 1$, $J = 1$ (where J is the angular momentum quantum number) two-pion resonant state with a resonance energy of four times the mass energy of a pion, and the isovector cloud with a three-pion resonant state, probably a $T = 0, J = 1$ state, with a resonance energy of 2.9 times the mass energy of a pion. The charge and anomalous magnetic moment distributions which they find best fit their data are given in Fig. 11-34. According to their picture, the neutron consists of a core of positive charge surrounded by negative

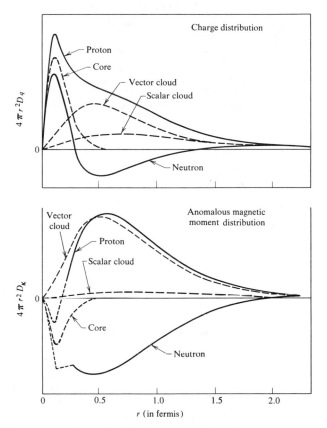

Fig. 11-34. Charge distribution (upper figure) and anomalous magnetic moment distribution (lower figure) of proton and neutron as deduced from electron scattering. D_q is the charge density (charge/unit volume) and D_κ is the anomalous magnetic moment density. [From R. M. Littauer, H. F. Schopper, and R. R. Wilson, *Phys. Rev. Lett.*, 7, 144 (1961).]

charge and this in turn surrounded by a small amount of positive charge at a considerable distance from the center of the neutron. As in the scattering of x-rays, the charge form factor can be calculated from a Fourier integral if the charge density as a function of position is known. Conversely, by application of the Fourier integral theorem, if the charge form factor is known for all values of G, the charge distribution can be calculated. Thus, increased precision of the experiments, coupled with scattering of electrons of greater energy, should make it possible in time to describe the nucleon charge distribution with considerable exactness.

Table 11-10 SUMMARY OF ELEMENTARY PARTICLE PROPERTIES*

	Particle	Spin ($\hbar$)	Mass (Mev/c^2)	Mean lifetime (sec)	Decay modes
Photon	γ	1	0	stable	
Leptons	ν	$\frac{1}{2}$	0	stable	
	$e^{\mp}$	$\frac{1}{2}$	0.510976 ± 0.000007	stable	
	$\mu^{\mp}$	$\frac{1}{2}$	105.655 ± 0.010	$(2.212 \pm 0.001) \times 10^{-6}$	$\mu^{\mp} \longrightarrow e^{\mp} + \nu + \bar{\nu}$
Mesons	$\pi^{\pm}$	0	139.59 ± 0.05	$(2.55 \pm 0.03) \times 10^{-8}$	$\pi^+ \longrightarrow \mu^+ + \nu$
					$\pi^+ \longrightarrow e^+ + \nu$
					$\pi^- \longrightarrow \mu^- + \bar{\nu}$
					$\pi^- \longrightarrow e^- + \bar{\nu}$
	π^0	0	135.00 ± 0.05	$(2.2 \pm 0.8) \times 10^{-16}$	$\pi^0 \longrightarrow \gamma + \gamma$
					$\pi^0 \longrightarrow e^+ + e^- + \gamma$
					$\pi^0 \longrightarrow e^+ + e^- + e^+ + e^-$
	$K^{\pm}$	0	493.9 ± 0.2	$(1.224 \pm 0.013) \times 10^{-8}$	$K_{\mu 2}^+ \longrightarrow \mu^+ + \nu$
					$K_{\mu 3}^+ \longrightarrow \mu^+ + \nu + \pi^0$
					$K_{\pi 2}^+ \longrightarrow \pi^+ + \pi^0$
					$K_{\pi 3}^+ \longrightarrow \pi^+ + \pi^+ + \pi^-$
					$K_{\pi 3}'^+ \longrightarrow \pi^+ + \pi^0 + \pi^0$
					$K_{\beta 3}^+ \longrightarrow e^+ + (\nu) + (\pi^0)$
					$K_{\mu 2}^- \longrightarrow (\mu^- + \bar{\nu})$
					$K_{\pi 2}^- \longrightarrow \pi^- + \pi^0$
					$K_{\pi 3}^- \longrightarrow \pi^- + \pi^+ + \pi^-$
					$K_{\beta 3}^- \longrightarrow e^- + (\bar{\nu}) + (\pi^0)$
	K^0 K^1 K^2	0	497.8 ± 0.6	50% K$_1$, 50% K$_2$ K$_1$: $(1.00 \pm 0.038) \times 10^{-10}$ K$_2$: $(6.1^{+1.6}_{-1.1}) \times 10^{-8}$	$K_{\mu 3}^0 \longrightarrow \mu^+ + \pi^- + \nu$
					$K_{\mu 3}^0 \longrightarrow \mu^- + \pi^+ + \bar{\nu}$
					$K_{\pi 2}^0 \longrightarrow \pi^+ + \pi^-$
					$K_{\pi 0}^0 \longrightarrow \pi^0 + \pi^0$
					$K_{\pi 3}^0 \longrightarrow \pi^+ + \pi^- + \pi^0$
					$K_{\beta 3}^0 \longrightarrow e^+ + \pi^- + \nu$
					$K_{\beta 3}^0 \longrightarrow e^- + \pi^+ + \bar{\nu}$
Baryons	p	$\frac{1}{2}$	938.213 ± 0.01	stable	
	n	$\frac{1}{2}$	939.507 ± 0.01	$(1.013 \pm 0.029) \times 10^3$	$n \longrightarrow e^- + \bar{\nu}$
	Λ	$\frac{1}{2}$	1115.36 ± 0.14	$(2.69^{+0.20}_{-0.15}) \times 10^{-10}$	$\Lambda \longrightarrow p + \pi^-$
					$\Lambda \longrightarrow n + \pi^0$
	Σ^+	$\frac{1}{2}$	1189.40 ± 0.20	$(0.81^{+0.06}_{-0.05}) \times 10^{-10}$	$\Sigma^+ \longrightarrow p + \pi^0$
					$\Sigma^+ \longrightarrow p + \gamma$
	Σ^-	$\frac{1}{2}$	1195.96 ± 0.30	$(1.61^{+0.1}_{-0.09}) \times 10^{-10}$	$\Sigma^+ \longrightarrow n + \pi^+$
					$\Sigma^- \longrightarrow n + \pi^-$
	Σ^0	$\frac{1}{2}$	1191.5 ± 0.5	$< 10^{-11}$	$\Sigma^0 \longrightarrow \Lambda + \gamma$
					$\Sigma^0 \longrightarrow \Lambda + e^+ + e^-$
	Ξ^-	?	1318.4 ± 1.2	$(1.28^{+0.38}_{-0.30}) \times 10^{-10}$	$\Xi^- \longrightarrow \Lambda + \pi^-$
	Ξ^0	?	1311 ± 8	1.5×10^{-10} (1 event)	$\Xi^0 \longrightarrow \Lambda + \pi^0$

* The spins, masses, and mean lifetimes in this table are taken from the data cards prepared by W. H. Barkas and A. H. Rosenfeld (UCRL-8030) which appeared in *Physics Today*, **14**, 70 (1961). The table is based on the assumption that particles and antiparticles have identical masses and mean lifetimes. Most of the values given are slightly different from those given in the text.

PROBLEMS

11-1 The concentration of C^{14} in our atmosphere is believed to be due to the reaction

$$N^{14} + n \rightarrow C^{14} + p,$$

brought about by cosmic-ray neutrons. Living organisms contain the same ratio of C^{14} to C^{12} as that of atmospheric carbon, but when they die the C^{14} which is bound up in stable chemical compounds begins to decay. C^{14} has a half-life of 5600 years. A piece of cypress wood from the tomb of Zoser was found to give 7.62 counts per minute per gram of carbon, while a piece of new wood gave 12.5 counts per minute per gram of carbon. How old was the piece of cypress wood? [See W. F. Libby, E. C. Anderson, and J. R. Arnold, *Science*, **109**, 227 (1949).]   [*Ans.* 4000 yr.]

11-2 To find the trajectory of a particle between two points in a nonuniform magnetic field (the fringing field of a proton synchrotron, for example) a wire is stretched between the two points and a current passed through it. If the gravitational force acting on the wire can be neglected, the wire should assume the shape of the trajectory. Show that $T/I = p/e$, where I is the current in the wire in amperes, e is the charge borne by the particle in coulombs, T is the tension in the wire in newtons, and p is the particle momentum in kg-meters/sec.

11-3 Find an approximate mass absorption coefficient for cosmic rays near sea level from the ionization-*vs.*-altitude curve of Fig. 11-4.

[*Ans.* $\sim 6 \times 10^{-3}$ cm^2/gm.]

11-4 If the maximum momentum given to an electron in the decay of a muon is 52.9 Mev/c and if the neutrino and antineutrino have zero rest-mass, what is the mass of the muon?   [*Ans.* 207.05*m*.]

11-5 (a) What would be the radius of the ground-state orbit of the mu-mesic lead atom if the nucleus could be treated as a point charge?
(b) What is the smallest quantum number which corresponds to an orbit outside the nucleus?
(c) What is the largest atomic number for which the mu-mesic K orbit lies outside the nucleus?
[*Ans.* (a) 3.13×10^{-13} cm; (b) 2; (c) 38 if $r_0 = 1.5 \times 10^{-13}$ cm.]

11-6 Certain mu-mesic x-rays emitted by phosphorus are found [S. Koslov, V. Fitch, and J. Rainwater, *Phys. Rev.*, **95**, 291 (1954)] to have an energy very close to the K-absorption edge energy of lead which lies at 88,014 ev and has a width of about 100 ev. Calculate the mass of the muon from this information on the basis of the simple Bohr formula, and identify the values of n_1 and n_2 involved in the transition.   [*Ans.* 207*m*; $n_1 = 2$, $n_2 = 3$.]

11-7 The muon emitted in pion decay has a kinetic energy of 4.1 Mev. Using $M_\pi = 273.27m$, $M_\mu = 206.93m$, calculate the apparent rest mass of the neutral particle emitted in the decay.   [*Ans.* 2.6*m*.]

11-8 From the pion mass and the decay muon kinetic energy given in Prob. 11-7, calculate the mass of the positive muon. Assume the neutrino rest mass to be zero.   [*Ans.* 207.05*m*.]

11-9 What is the average distance traveled by 1-Bev pions (in the absence of any energy loss in transit) before they decay?   [*Ans.* 62.2 meters.]

11-10 Panofsky *et al.* found the gamma ray produced in the reaction

$$\pi^- + p \rightarrow n + \gamma$$

to have an energy of 130 Mev. What does this give for the mass of a negative pion?   [*Ans.* 275.2*m*.]

11-11 In the competing reaction

$$\pi^- + p \rightarrow \pi^0 + n,$$
$$\pi^0 \rightarrow \gamma + \gamma,$$

Panofsky *et al.* found γ rays with energies from (53.6 ± 2.8) Mev to (85 ± 2.8) Mev. Calculate the mass of the neutral pion from the most probable values of the γ-ray energy limits.   [*Ans.* 264.6*m*.]

11-12 Show that when a proton collides with a proton which is at rest, it must have a minimum kinetic energy of $6M_p c^2$ in order to create a proton-antiproton pair. Assume that the mass of proton and antiproton are each equal to M_p.

11-13 Show that the strangeness of an antiparticle isotopic spin multiplet is the negative of the corresponding particle multiplet.

11-14 Explain the relatively great stability of hypernuclei against mesonic decay on the basis of strangeness.

REFERENCES

1. Agnew, L. E., Elioff, T., Fowler, W. B., Gilly, L., Lander, R., Oswald, L., Powell, W., Segrè, E., Steiner, H., White, H., Wiegand, C., and Ypsilantis, T., *Phys. Rev.*, **110**, 994 (1958); *Phys. Rev. Lett.*, **1**, 27 (1958).

2. Alvarez, L. W., Bradner, H., Crawford, F. S., Jr., Crawford, J. A., Falk-Vairant, P., Good, M. L., Gow, J. D., Rosenfeld, A. M., Solmitz, F., Stevenson, M. L., Ticho, H. K., and Tripp, R. D., *Phys. Rev.*, **105**, 1127 (1957).

3. Alvarez, L. W., Bradner, H., Falk-Vairant, P., Gow, J. D., Rosenfeld, A. H., Solmitz, F., and Tripp, R. D., *Nuovo Cimento*, **5**, 1026 (1957).

4. Alvarez, L. W., Eberhard, P., Good, M. L., Graziano, W., Ticho, H. K., and Wojcicki, S. G., *Phys. Rev. Lett.*, **2**, 215 (1959).

5. Amaldi, E., Barbaro-Galtieri, A., Baroni, G., Castagnoli, C., Ferro-Luzzi, M., Manfredini, A., Muchnik, M., Rossi, V., and Severi, M., *Nuovo Cimento*, **16**, 392 (1960).

6. Anderson, C. D., and Neddermeyer, S. H., *Phys. Rev.*, **50**, 263 (1936).

7. Armenteros, R., Barker, K. H., Butler, C. C., Cachon, A., and York, C. M., *Phil. Mag.*, **43**, 597 (1952).

8. Ashkin, J., Fazzini, T., Fidecaro, G., Goldschmidt-Clermont, Y., Lipman, N. H., Merrison, A. W., and Paul, H., *Nuovo Cimento*, **16**, 490 (1960).

9. Auger, P., *Nature*, **135**, 820 (1935).

10. Auger, P., Ehrenfest, P., Freon, A., and Fournier, A., *Compt. Rend.*, **204**, 257 (1937).

11. Baldo-Ceolin, M., and Prowse, D. J., *Nuovo Cimento*, **10**, 635 (1958). See also Prowse, D. J., and Baldo-Ceolin, M., *Phys. Rev. Lett.*, **1**, 179 (1958).

12. Barber, W. C., *Phys. Rev.*, **75**, 590 (1949).

13. Barkas, W. H., Birnbaum, W., and Smith, F. M., *Phys. Rev.*, **101**, 778 (1956).

14. Barkas, W. H., Dudziak, W. F., Giles, P. C., Heckman, H. H., Inman, F. W., Mason, C. J., Nichols, N. A., and Smith, F. M., *Phys. Rev.*, **105**, 1417 (1957).

15. Barnóthy, J., and Forró, M., *Phys. Rev.*, **55**, 870 (1939).

16. Bell, W. E., and Hincks, E. P., *Phys. Rev.*, **88**, 1424 (1952).

17. Belliboni, G., Sechi, B., and Vitale, B., *Suppl. Nuovo Cimento*, **12**, 195 (1954).

18. Bethe, H., and Heitler, W., *Proc. Roy. Soc.*, **A146**, 83 (1934).

19. Bhabha, H. J., *Nature*, **141**, 117 (1938).

20. Biehl, A. T., Neher, H. V., and Roesch, W. C., *Phys. Rev.*, **75**, 688 (1949).

21. Bjorkland, R., Crandall, W. E., Moyer, B. J., and York, H. F., *Phys. Rev.*, **77**, 213 (1950).

22. Blackett, P. M. S., and Occhialini, G. P. S., *Proc. Roy. Soc.*, **A139**, 699 (1933).

23. Bonetti, A., Levi Setti, R., Panetti, M., and Tomasini, G., *Nuovo Cimento*, **10**, 345 (1953).

24. Bothe, W., and Kolhörster, W., *Naturwiss.*, **16**, 1045 (1928).

25. Bothe, W., and Kolhörster, W., *Z. Physik*, **56**, 751 (1929).

26. Bridge, H. S., Courant, H., De Staebler, H., Jr., and Rossi, B., *Phys. Rev.*, **95**, 1101 (1954).

27. Brown, R., Camerini, U., Fowler, P. H., Muirhead, H., Powell, C. F., and Ritson, D. M., *Nature*, **163**, 82 (1949).

28. Button, J., Eberhard, P., Kalbfleisch, G. R., Lannutti, J. E., Lynch, G. R., Maglić, B. C., and Stevenson, M. L., *Phys. Rev. Lett.*, **4**, 530 (1960).

29. Camerini, U., and Fowler, P. H., *Reports on Progress in Physics* (London: The Physical Society, 1950), and p. 215 of Powell, C. F., Fowler, P. H., and Perkins, D. H., *The Study of Elementary Particles by the Photographic Method* (New York: Pergamon Press, 1959).

30. Camerini, U., Muirhead, H., Powell, C. F., and Ritson, D. M., *Nature*, **162**, 433 (1948).

31. Carlson, A. G., Hooper, J. E., and King, D. T., *Phil. Mag.*, **41**, 701 (1950).

32. Chamberlain, O., Goldhaber, G., Jaunneau, L., Kalogeropoulos, T., Segrè, E., and Silberberg, R., *Phys. Rev.*, **113**, 1615 (1959).

33. Chamberlain, O., Segrè, E., Wiegand, C., and Ypsilantis, T., *Phys. Rev.*, **100**, 947 (1955); *Nature*, **177**, 11 (1956).

34. Chinowsky, W., Sachs, A., and Steinberger, J., *Phys. Rev.*, **93**, 917 (1954).

35. Chinowsky, W., and Steinberger, J., *Phys. Rev.*, **95**, 1561 (1954).

36. Clark, D. L., Roberts, A., and Wilson, R., *Phys. Rev.*, **83**, 649 (1951).

37. Clay, J., *Proc. Acad. Amst.*, **30**, 1115 (1927); **31**, 1091 (1928); **33**, 711 (1930).

38. Clay, J., *Physica*, **2**, 861, 867 (1935).

39. Clay, J., Van Alphen, P. M., and 'T Hooft, C. G., *Physica*, **1**, 829 (1934).

40. Compton, A. H., and Turner, R. N., *Phys. Rev.*, **52**, 799 (1937).

41. Cork, B., Lambertson, G. R., Piccioni, O., and Wenzel, W. A., *Phys. Rev.*, **104**, 1193 (1956).

42. Crewe, A. V., Kruse, U. E., Miller, R. H., and Pondrom, L. G., *Phys. Rev.*, **108**, 1531 (1957).

43. Crowe, K. M., *Nuovo Cimento*, **5**, 541 (1957).

44. Crowe, K. M., and Phillips, R. H., *Phys. Rev.*, **96**, 470 (1954).

45. Crussard, J., Kaplon, M. F., Klarman, J., and Noon, J. H., *Phys. Rev.*, **93**, 253 (1954).

46. Crussard, J., and Morellet, D., *Compt. Rend.*, **236**, 64 (1953).

47. Dahanayake, C., Francois, P. E., Fujimoto, Y., Iredale, P., Waddington, C. J., and Yasin, M., *Phil. Mag.*, **45**, 1219 (1954).

48. Danysz, M., and Pniewsky, J., *Phil. Mag.*, **44**, 348 (1953).

49. Dudziak, W. F., Sagane, R., and Vedder, J., *U.C.R.L.*-8202 (1958).

50. Durbin, R., Loar, H., and Steinberger, J., *Phys. Rev.*, **83**, 646 (1951).

51. Ehmert, A., *Z. Physik*, **106**, 751 (1937).

52. Eisler, F., Plano, R., Prodell, A., Samios, N., Schwartz, M., Steinberger, J., Conversi, M., Franzini, P., Manelli, I., Santangelo, R., and Silvestrini, V., *Phys. Rev.*, **112**, 979 (1958).

53. Eisler, F., Plano, R., Samios, N., Schwartz, M., and Steinberger, J., *Nuovo Cimento*, **5**, 1700 (1957).

54. Eisler, F., Plano, R., Samios, N., Steinberger, J., and Schwartz, M., *Phys. Rev.*, **110**, 226 (1958).

55. Elster, J., and Geitel, H., *Physik. Z.*, **2**, 560 (1900–1).

56. Erwin, E. R., Jr., Kopp, J. K., and Shapiro, A. M., *Phys. Rev.*, **115**, 669 (1959).

57. Fazzini, T., Fidecaro, G., Merrison, A. W., Paul, H., and Tollestrup, A. V., *Phys. Rev. Lett.*, **1**, 247 (1958).

58. Fitch, V., and Motley, R., *Phys. Rev.*, **101**, 496 (1956).

59. Follet, D. H., and Crawshaw, J. D., *Proc. Roy. Soc.*, **A155**, 546 (1936).

60. Fowler, P. H., *Phil. Mag.*, **41**, 169 (1950). See also, General Reference 1.

61. Fowler, W. B., Shutt, R. P., Thorndike, A. M., and Whittemore, W. L., *Phys. Rev.*, **91**, 1287 (1953); **93**, 861 (1954).

62. Frank, F. C., *Nature*, **160**, 525 (1947).

63. Franzinetti, C., and Morpurgo, G., *Suppl. Nuovo Cimento*, **6**, 469 (1957).

64. Friedlander, M. W., Keefe, D., and Menon, M. G. K., *Nuovo Cimento*, **1**, 694 (1955); **2**, 666 (1955); **3**, 663 (1955).

65. Friedlander, M. W., Keefe, D., Menon, M. G. K., and Van Rossum, L., *Phil. Mag.*, **45**, 1043 (1954).

66. Gardner, E., and Lattes, C. M. G., *Science*, **107**, 270 (1948).

67. Garwin, R. L., Hutchinson, D. P., Penman, S., and Shapiro, G., *Phys. Rev.*, **118**, 271 (1960).

68. Gell-Mann, M., *Phys. Rev.*, **92**, 833 (1953); *Suppl. Nuovo Cimento*, **4**, 848 (1956).

69. Gell-Mann, M., and Pais, A., *Phys. Rev.*, **97**, 1387 (1955).

70. Gell-Mann, M., and Rosenfeld, A. H., *Annual Review of Nuclear Science* (Stanford: Annual Reviews, Inc., 1957).

71. Gettner, M., Holloway, L., Kraus, D., Lande, K., Leboy, E., Selove, W., and Siegel, R., *Phys. Rev. Lett.*, **2**, 471 (1959).

72. Gockel, A., *Physik. Z.*, **10**, 845 (1909).

73. Gockel, A., *Physik. Z.*, **11**, 280 (1911); **12**, 595 (1911).

74. Gregory, B., Lagarrigue, A., Leprince-Ringuet, L., Muller, F., and Peyrou, Ch., *Nuovo Cimento*, **11**, 292 (1954).

75. Heitler, W., *The Quantum Theory of Radiation* (3rd ed.; New York: Oxford University Press, 1954).

76. Hess, V. F., *Physik. Z.*, **12**, 998 (1911); **13**, 1084 (1912); **14**, 610 (1913); *Wien. Ber.*, **II A 121**, 2001 (1912).

77. Hoang, T. F., Kaplon, M. F., and Yekutielli, G., *Phys. Rev.*, **101**, 1834 (1956).

78. Hodson, A. L., Ballam, J., Arnold, W. H., Harris, D. R., Rau, R. R., Reynolds, G. T., and Treiman, S. B., *Phys. Rev.*, **96**, 1089 (1954).

79. Hofstadter, R., *Ann. Rev. of Nuc. Sci.*, **7**, 231 (1957). See p. 266 *et seq.*

80. Hofstadter, R., and McAllister, R. W., *Phys. Rev.*, **98**, 217 (1955).

81. Hopper, V. D., and Biswas, S., *Phys. Rev.*, **80**, 1099 (1950).

82. Hughes, V. W., McColm, D. W., Ziock, K., and Prepost, R., *Phys. Rev. Lett.*, **5**, 63 (1960).

83. Impeduglia, G., Plano, R., Prodell, A., Samios, N., Schwartz, M., and Steinberger, J., *Phys. Rev. Lett.*, **1**, 249 (1958).

84. Johnson, R. W. H., and O'Ceallaigh, C., *Phil. Mag.*, **46**, 393 (1955).

85. Johnson, T. H., *Phys. Rev.*, **47**, 91 (1935).

86. Johnson, T. H., and Street, J. C., *Phys. Rev.*, **43**, 381 (1933).

87. Kemmer, N., *Proc. Camb. Phil. Soc.*, **34**, 354 (1938).

88. Kolhörster, W., *Physik. Z.*, **14**, 1066 (1913); *Ber. deut. physik. Ges.*, **16**, 719 (1914–19).

89. Kulenkampff, H., *Verhandl. deut. Ges.* (1938).

90. Kunze, P., *Z. Physik*, **83**, 1 (1933). See his Fig. 5 on p. 10 of the article.

91. Landé, K., Booth, E. T., Impeduglia, J., Lederman, L. M., and Chinowsky, W., *Phys. Rev.*, **103**, 1901 (1956).

92. Landé, K., Lederman, L. M., and Chinowsky, W., *Phys. Rev.*, **105**, 1925 (1957).

93. Lattes, C. M. G., Muirhead, H., Occhialini, G. P. S., and Powell, C. F., *Nature*, **159**, 694 (1947).

94. Leighton, R. B., Anderson, C. D., and Seriff, A. J., *Phys. Rev.*, **75**, 1432 (1949).

95. Leighton, R. B., Wanlass, S. D., and Alford, W., *Phys. Rev.*, **83**, 843 (1951). See also Armenteros, R., Barker, K. H., Butler, C. C., Cachon, A., and Chapman, A. H., *Nature*, **167**, 501 (1951).

96. Leighton, R. B., Wanlass, S. D., and Anderson, C. D., *Phys. Rev.*, **89**, 148 (1953).

97. Lemaitre, G., and Vallarta, M. S., *Univ. of Toronto Studies*, Appl. Math. Ser., No. 3 (1938). These calculations are also given by Johnson, T. H., *Rev. Mod. Phys.*, **10**, 219 (1938).

98. Lewis, H. W., Oppenheimer, J. R., and Wouthuysen, S. A., *Phys. Rev.*, **73**, 127 (1948). See also Oppenheimer, J. R., *Phys. Rev.*, **71**, 462 (1947), and Kemmer, N., *Proc. Camb. Phil. Soc.*, **34**, 354 (1938).

99. Littauer, R. M., Schopper, H. F., and Wilson, R. R., *Phys. Rev. Lett.*, **7**, 141 (1961).

100. Lokanathan, S., and Steinberger, J., *Phys. Rev.*, **98**, 240 (1955).

101. Marshak, R. E., and Bethe, H., *Phys. Rev.*, **72**, 506 (1947).

102. McLennan, J. C., and Burton, E. F., *Phys. Rev.*, **16**, 184 (1903).

103. Menon, M. G. K., and O'Ceallaigh, C., *Proc. Roy. Soc.*, **A221**, 294 (1954).

104. Mezzetti, L., and Keuffel, W., *Nuovo Cimento*, **4**, 1096 (1956).

105. Michel, L., *Proc. Phys. Soc.*, **A63**, 514 (1950). See also Bouchiat, C., and Michel, L., *Phys. Rev.*, **106**, 170 (1957); Kinoshita, T., and Sirlin, A., *Phys. Rev.*, **106**, 1110 (1957); **107**, 593 (1957).

106. Millikan, R. A., *Proc. Nat. Acad. Sci.*, **12**, 48 (1926).

107 Millikan, R. A., *Phys. Rev.*, **43**, 661 (1933).

108. Millikan, R. A., and Cameron, C. H., *Phys. Rev.*, **28**, 851 (1926).

109. Millikan, R. A., and Neher, H. V., *Phys. Rev.*, **47**, 205 (1935); **50**, 15 (1936).

110. Millikan, R. A., Neher, H. V., and Pickering, W. H., *Phys. Rev.*, **66**, 295 (1944).

111. Morinaga, H., and Fry, W. F., *Nuovo Cimento*, **10**, 308 (1953).

112. Myssowsky, L., and Tuwim, L., *Z. Physik*, **36**, 615 (1926).

113. Neddermeyer, S. H., and Anderson, C. D., *Phys. Rev.*, **54**, 88 (1938).

114. Neher, H. V., and Stever, H. G., *Phys. Rev.*, **58**, 766 (1940).

115. Nishijima, K., *Prog. Theor. Phys. (Japan)*, **12**, 107 (1954); **13**, 285 (1954).

116. Nishijima, K., and Nakano, T., *Prog. Theor. Phys. (Japan)*, **10**, 581 (1953).

117. Nordheim, L., *Phys. Rev.*, **55**, 506 (1939).

118. Occhialini, G. P. S., and Powell, C. F., *Nature*, **159**, 186 (1947).

119. O'Ceallaigh, C., *Phil. Mag.*, **42**, 1032 (1951).

120. Olson, D. N., Schopper, H. F., and Wilson, R. R., *Phys. Rev. Lett.*, **6**, 286 (1961).

121. Pacini, D., *Nuovo Cimento*, **3**, 93 (1912).

122. Page, D. L., *Phil. Mag.*, **45**, 863 (1954).

123. Panofsky, W. K. H., Aamodt, L., Hadley, J., and Phillips, R., *Phys. Rev.*, **80**, 94 (1950).

124. Panofsky, W. K. H., Aamodt, L., and York, H. F., *Phys. Rev.*, **78**, 825 (1950).

125. Perkins, D. H., *Nature*, **159**, 126 (1947).

126. Plano, R., Samios, N., Schwartz, M., and Steinberger, J., *Nuovo Cimento*, **5**, 216 (1957).

127. Quareni, G., and Vignudelli, A. G., *Nuovo Cimento*, **14**, 1179 (1959).

128. Reiter, R. A., Romanowski, T. A., Sutton, R. B., and Chidley, B. G., *Phys. Rev. Lett.*, **5**, 22 (1960).

129. Richardson, J. R., *Phys. Rev.*, **74**, 1720 (1948).

130. Ridgway, S. L., Berley, D., and Collins, G. B., *Phys. Rev.*, **104**, 513 (1956).

131. Rochester, G. D., and Butler, C. C., *Nature*, **160**, 855 (1947).

132. Rosenbluth, M. N., *Phys. Rev.*, **79**, 615 (1950).

133. Rossi, B., *Z. Physik*, **68**, 64 (1931).

134. Rossi, B., *Physik. Z.*, **33**, 304 (1932).

135. Rossi, B., *Z. Physik*, **82**, 151 (1933).

136. Rossi, B., *Ricerca Sci.*, **5**, 569 (1934).

137. Rossi, B., Hilberry, N., and Hoag, J. B., *Phys. Rev.*, **57**, 461 (1940).

138. Rossi, B., and Nereson, N., *Phys. Rev.*, **62**, 417 (1942). See also Rasetti, F., *Phys. Rev.*, **60**, 198 (1941).

139. Ruderman, M. A., and Finkelstein, R. J., *Phys. Rev.*, **76**, 1458 (1949).

140. Rutherford, E., and Cooke, H. L., *Phys. Rev.*, **16**, 183 (1903).

141. Schein, M., Yngwe, V. H., and Kraybill, H. L., *Phys. Rev.*, **73**, 928 (1948).

142. Schwartz, M., Steinberger, J., Plano, R., and Samios, N., *Nuovo Cimento*, **5**, 216 (1957).

143. Simpson, G. C., and Wright, C. S., *Proc. Roy. Soc.*, **A85**, 175 (1911).

144. Singer, S. F., in *Elementary Particle and Cosmic Ray Physics*, Vol. 4 (New York: Interscience Publishers, Inc., 1958).

145. Skobelzyn, D., *Z. Physik*, **43**, 354 (1927).

146. Skobelzyn, D., *Z. Physik*, **54**, 686 (1929).

147. Sorrels, J. D., Leighton, R. B., and Anderson, C. D., *Phys. Rev.*, **100**, 1457 (1955).

148. Steinke, E., *Z. Physik*, **42**, 570 (1927).

149. Stevenson, M. L., *Phys. Rev.*, **111**, 1707 (1958).

150. Störmer, C., *Z. Astr. Phys.*, **1**, 237 (1930); *Terr. Mag. and Elec.*, **37**, 375 (1932); *Astrophys. Norv.*, **1**, 1 (1934).

151. Street, J. C., Woodward, R. H., and Stevenson, E. C., *Phys. Rev.*, **47**, 891 (1935).

152. Swami, M. S., *Phys. Rev.*, **114**, 333 (1959).

153. Thompson, R. W., Burwell, J. R., Cohn, H. O., Huggett, R. W., and Karzmark, C. J., *Phys. Rev.*, **95**, 661 (1954).

154. Thompson, R. W., Burwell, J. R., and Huggett, R. W., *Suppl. Nuovo Cimento*, **4**, 286 (1956).

155. Van Lint, V. A. J., Anderson, C. D., Cowan, E. W., Leighton, R. B., and York, C. M., Jr., *Phys. Rev.*, **94**, 1732 (1954).

156. Wheeler, J. A., *Phys. Rev.*, **92**, 812 (1953).

157. Williams, E. J., and Pickup, E., *Nature*, **141**, 684 (1938).

158. Williams, E. J., and Roberts, G. E., *Nature*, **145**, 102 (1940).

159. Wilson, C. T. R., *Proc. Camb. Phil. Soc.*, **11**, 32 (1901).

160. Wilson, V. C., *Phys. Rev.*, **55**, 6 (1939).

161. Wilson, V. C., and Hughes, D. J., *Phys. Rev.*, **63**, 161 (1943).

162. Wulf, T., *Physik. Z.*, **10**, 152 (1909).

163. Wulf, T., *Physik. Z.*, **11**, 811 (1910).

164. Yekutielli, G., Kaplon, M. F., and Hoang, T. F., *Phys. Rev.*, **101**, 506 (1956).

165. York, C. M., Leighton, R. B., and Bjornerud, E. K., *Phys. Rev.*, **90**, 167 (1953).

166. Yukawa, H., *Proc. Phys. Math. Soc. Japan* (3), **17**, 48 (1935).

GENERAL REFERENCES

The following books are filled with excellent and fascinating pictures which help tremendously in gaining a feeling of the reality of elementary particles. These books are expensive, but they belong in every physics library.

1. Gentner, W., Maier-Leibnitz, H., and Bothe, W., *An Atlas of Typical Expansion Chamber Photographs* (London: Pergamon Press, 1954).

2. Powell, C. F., Fowler, P. H., and Perkins, D. H., *The Study of Elementary Particles by the Photographic Method* (New York: Pergamon Press, 1959).

3. Rochester, G. D., and Wilson, J. G., *Cloud Chamber Photographs of the Cosmic Radiation* (New York: Academic Press, 1952).

APPENDIXES

CHARGED-PARTICLE ACCELERATORS

A-1 Introduction

A large part of our knowledge in nuclear physics has been obtained through nuclear reactions made possible by charged-particle accelerators. The development of accelerators did not come about through discovery of new principles of physics, but rather by solution of engineering problems of great complexity. The basic ideas behind many accelerators were recognized several years before the first successful embodiments of these ideas were realized. For that reason we shall not follow the historical order of development of accelerators, but instead discuss them in terms of the features which characterize each type.

A-2 Potential Difference Accelerators

Although one does not usually think of it in these terms, an ordinary x-ray machine is a particle accelerator belonging to this class. In these devices, ions are given a single acceleration by falling through a relatively large potential difference between the source of the ions and the target upon which they impinge. The potential difference either is constant or varies slowly enough that the change is small during the time it takes an ion to go from source to target. The maximum potential difference in such accelerators is severely limited by insulation and air-breakdown problems. Highly ionized atoms such as C^{++++++} will be given more energy by the same potential difference, since the kinetic energy given to the ion is

$$W_{KE} = ZeV$$

where Z is the net number of electronic charges borne by the ion. On the other hand the coulomb barrier of the target nucleus is raised by the same factor, so the only gain in going to heavier highly ionized atoms has to do with a reduction in the center of mass motion.

Cockcroft-Walton accelerator. Cockcroft and Walton (1, 2) were the first to succeed in producing nuclear reactions with accelerator particles. The potential difference in their device was produced in a voltage multiplier circuit devised by Greinacher (3). A schematic circuit diagram is shown in Fig. A-1.

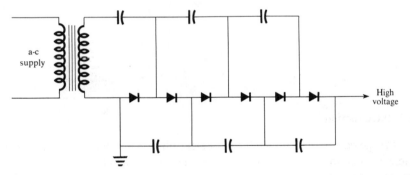

Fig. A-1. Cockcroft-Walton generator. A transformer steps up the alternating potential difference from that of the supply mains to as high a value as can be safely handled by the capacitors and rectifiers.

The charge transferred per cycle decreases as one proceeds up the ladder of rectifiers and capacitors. This must evidently be so, since the high potential difference power output cannot be greater than the lower potential difference power input and hence the steady output current must be much smaller than the rms input current. Since the condensers are charged by a rectified alternating current there is a "ripple" or fluctuation in the output potential difference. Many modern Cockcroft-Walton generators reduce this ripple by employing a relatively high-frequency (30 to 50 kilocycles per sec) input instead of the conventional 60 cycles per second furnished by the power mains. These accelerators are most commonly used at potential differences less than 10^6 volts. They are widely used as neutron sources as mentioned in

Chap. 6. They sometimes serve to pre-accelerate particles which are fed into higher-energy accelerators.

Cascade transformer. This method of obtaining potential differences up to 10^6 volts has been used by Lauritsen (5, 6, 7) at Caltech. A schematic circuit diagram is shown in Fig. A-2. Unlike the Cockcroft-Walton generator, this device furnishes an alternating potential difference. When used as an electron accelerator to produce x-rays, the variation in electron energy is not a

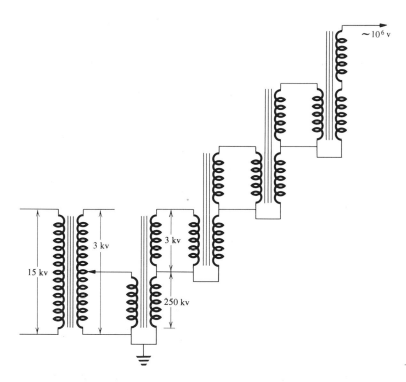

Fig. A-2. Circuit diagram of cascaded transformers used by Lauritsen *et al.* (5, 6, 7).

serious drawback since the x-rays are polyergic even when produced by monoergic electrons. The energy variation is quite objectionable when nuclei are being accelerated, as the energy dependence of the resulting nuclear reactions cannot be studied in detail. The energy spread of the particles can be reduced by placing a biasing grid near the source so that the net electric field near the source repels ions back toward the source until the potential difference has reached a large fraction of its maximum value. In principle, one could make the energy spread very small in this way if he desired, but the time during which ions would pass through the grid and be accelerated would be so short that the average beam current would become too small to be useful.

Electrostatic generators. While other types of electrostatic generators have been used, the only one of importance today is the charged-belt type known as the Van de Graaff generator. In this device, a schematic diagram of which

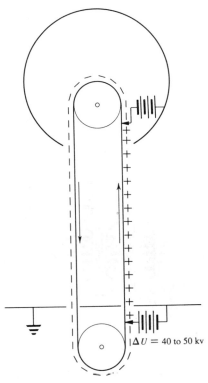

Fig. A-3. Schematic cross section of a Van de Graaff type electrostatic generator. Negative charges are removed and a positive charge excess created on the belt at the lower charging points. At the upper charging points, electrons are sprayed onto the belt, thereby in effect transferring positive charge to the upper sphere and leaving an excess of negative charge on the belt.

is shown in Fig. A-3, charge is sprayed from pointed electrodes onto a belt (usually made of fabric) at the grounded end of the generator. The charge is then carried to the high-potential storage element where it is removed. The electrical energy is supplied by mechanical work done on the charges transported by the belt against the attractive forces of the charges of opposite sign left behind and against the repulsive forces of charges of the same sign on the storage element. Oftentimes, the belt carries charge in both directions as shown in Fig. A-3. One does not usually think of the work required to operate an electrostatic generator as being significant, but if the charge transported amounts to a current of 1 ma and the potential difference maintained is 1.5 Mv, then, even a 100 per cent efficient system would require nearly 2 horse-power to drive the belt. While steady currents as high as 1 or 2 ma and pulses whose instantaneous currents were several ma have been generated with machines of this type, the useful average proton beam current is usually only about 20 to 50 μa. The potential differences used are commonly in the 1 to 4 Mv range, with a maximum useful potential difference of 8 Mv having been attained. Compact high-potential difference machines are pressurized to prevent discharges through the gas. The pressurizing gas is usually dry air or dry nitrogen containing 3 to 10 per cent of Freon or sulfur hexafluoride.

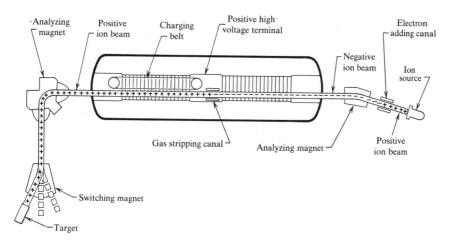

Fig. A-4. Schematic diagram of a tandem Van de Graaff accelerator. [Courtesy of High Voltage Engineering Corporation.]

The great asset of Van de Graaff accelerators is the small energy spread of the particles which reach the target. This can be kept as small as 1 part in 10^4 by various control devices, one of which is an automatically controlled variable electron beam which acts as a variable shunt from the high-potential electrode to ground. A disadvantage of this method of control is that x-rays are generated by the electrons when they strike the anode.

In the "tandem Van de Graaff accelerator," shown in Figs. A-4 and A-5, negative ions are accelerated by the full potential difference of the generator, suffer charge exchange at the high-potential anode, and are accelerated again (as positive ions) by the potential difference between anode and ground. In this way the ion acquires twice the usual amount of energy. In addition, both source and target can be at ground potential, which is a great convenience in operation.

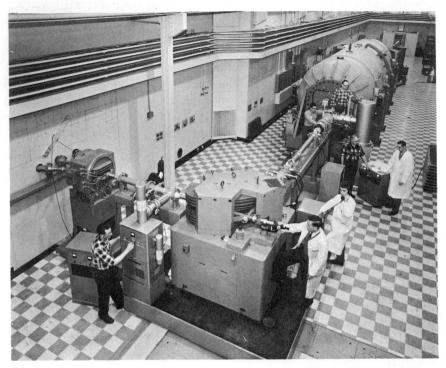

Fig. A-5. Photo of a 12-Mev tandem Van de Graaff installation. [Photo courtesy of High Voltage Engineering Corporation.]

A-3 Linear Accelerators

In these devices, the charged particle is accelerated repeatedly in approximately a straight path from source to target. An electron reaches a velocity of 98 per cent of that of light at 2 Mev, so that it moves at nearly constant speed through the greater part of its path in a high-energy linear electron accelerator. On the other hand, a proton must have an energy of nearly 4 Bev before its velocity is 98 per cent of that of light. The designs of linear proton and electron accelerators tend, therefore, to be rather different.

Proton accelerators. Various types of heavy-ion accelerators have been built. A schematic diagram of an early device built by Sloan and Lawrence (12) to accelerate mercury and other heavy ions is shown in Fig. A-6. Ions which arrive at the gap between cylindrical electrodes 1 and 2 at the proper time are given an acceleration. They then drift through the "drift tube" at essentially constant velocity until they reach the gap between electrodes 2 and 3. In order to be accelerated again at this second gap, the length b_2 must be so chosen that

$$b_2 = \frac{\bar{v}_2 \tau}{2} = \frac{\bar{v}_2}{2f} = \frac{\bar{\beta}_2 c}{2f} = \frac{\bar{\beta}_2 \lambda}{2},$$

(A-1)

where $\tau, f,$ and λ are the period, frequency, and free-space wavelength respectively of the radio-frequency potential difference, and $\bar{v}_2$ is the average speed of the ion along the path b_2. It is clear that the drift tubes must grow longer as the particle gains energy and moves at higher speeds. If the energy becomes large enough that $\bar{\beta} \cong 1$, then the succeeding drift tubes have a constant length of $\lambda/2$. Since the upper limit on the frequency obtainable for an r-f oscillator to power the accelerator was not very high at the time this device was built, it could be used to accelerate protons either at the expense of very long drift tubes or the acceptance of relatively small ion energy (about 1 Mev).

The modern proton accelerator, known as a "linac," makes use of subsequently developed oscillators which operate at very high frequencies (a typical value is 200 megacycles/sec). The drift tubes are surrounded by a large coaxial chamber with conductive walls, the whole assemblage acting as a

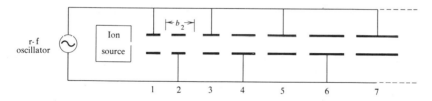

Fig. A-6. Schematic diagram of early proton linear accelerator built by Sloan and Lawrence (12).

large resonant cavity in which electromagnetic standing waves are established. When a coaxial cylindrical cavity of this type is excited in the TM_{010} mode, the electric field lines are parallel to the axis of the cylinder as shown in Fig. A-7(a). Since this field changes rapidly with time it is not possible simply to allow the ion to be accelerated continuously from one end of the cavity to the other. Instead, the ion must be accelerated for a short time and then pass into the relatively field-free region of a drift tube until the field is again in the correct direction to accelerate it. This suggests a structure with accelerating fields being developed in the gaps between drift tubes. These gaps perturb the field structure in such a way that it is necessary to vary the external diameters of the drift tubes. The TM_{010} mode may be looked upon as one in which cylindrical waves move out radially, are reflected at the outer conductor, move inward and are reflected by the inner conductor, etc. The gaps in the central conductor then introduce a phase shift at reflection from the inner conductor, the phase shift being greater where the gap length per unit length of central conductor is greater (i.e., at the low-energy end of the accelerator). This phase shift can be compensated by shortening the distance between inner and outer conductors, as shown in Fig. A-7(b). Unlike the earlier generator

Fig. A-7. (a) Conjectural sketch of the electric field intensity (dashed) lines in a cylindrical cavity with a concentric cylindrical center conductor resonating in the TM_{010} mode.

shown in Fig. A-4, the distance between gaps n and $n+1$ in the linac must be

$$b_n = \beta_n \lambda. \tag{A-2}$$

Ions will be given maximum energy if they are accelerated at each gap at the peak of the r-f potential difference. Suppose, however, that an ion reaches the first gap a little after the peak (A in Fig. A-8). Then it will receive a smaller acceleration than will an ion which reaches the gap at the peak. If the radio frequency has been chosen such that an ion which receives maximum acceleration will reach the next gap at the next peak in the r-f potential difference,

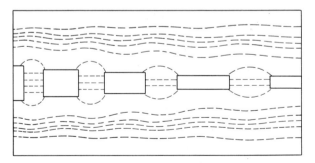

Fig. A-7. (b) Conjectural sketch of the electric field intensity (dashed) lines in a cylindrical cavity similar to that used in a linac. The field structure between the drift tubes would have the shape shown only if the ends of the drift tubes were covered with conducting grids or foils.

then the ion accelerated at time A will take a time greater than the r-f period τ to reach the next gap. As a result it will reach the next gap at some time B and will receive a still smaller acceleration, with the result that it will reach the third gap at time C. If time A is only slightly greater than $\tau/4$, then the

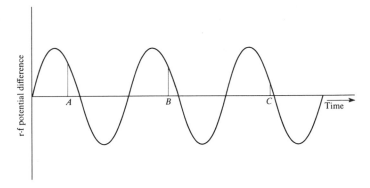

Fig. A-8. If the gaps between drift tubes are so spaced that a particle which is accelerated by the maximum r-f potential difference at the first gap will reach the next gap when the potential difference is again a maximum, then a particle which reaches the first gap at time A will receive a less-than-normal acceleration and hence will reach the next gap at an even later phase of the cycle, such as time B. The ion will reach the third gap at a time C when the potential difference is yet smaller and may eventually reach a gap in which the potential difference will actually decelerate the particle.

ion will reach the target but with less energy than the maximum possible. If A exceeds $\tau/4$ as much as shown in Fig. A-8 the ion will arrive at later gaps when the r-f potential difference is negative, in which case the particle will be decelerated and may even fail to reach the target.

It might appear than an ion which arrives early at the first gap would fare better, since, although it would receive a smaller than normal acceleration, it would thereby take a longer than normal time to reach the next gap so that it would arrive at a time closer to the peak. It can never regain the velocity which it failed to acquire in the first few gaps, however, so, even though it reaches some gap at the peak, it will reach the next gap late and thereafter its fate will be the same as that of a particle which reached the first gap late.

The preceding analysis suggests that it might be better to choose the radio frequency to stay in phase with particles which receive less than the maximum acceleration as shown in Fig. A-9. Now, if an ion reaches the first gap late, as at time A, it will receive more than the normal amount of acceleration and will arrive at the next gap in a time less than τ. It will then receive an acceleration at the second gap which is smaller than that received at the first gap but larger than the normal amount. When it finally reaches a gap at the proper phase of the r-f potential difference it will be moving at a velocity greater than normal. It will thus arrive early at the next gap and receive a less than normal acceleration. It is easy to see, then, that as long as the ions arrive at the first gap while the r-f potential difference is increasing, they will oscillate in phase about the phase at which particles move in perfect synchronism with the r-f. This situation is known as "phase stability."

The increase of r-f potential difference with time which leads to phase stability also may lead to defocusing of the ion beam. A positive ion which enters a gap between drift tubes will be subjected to the action of an electrostatic field somewhat like that sketched in Fig. A-10. If the potential difference between the tubes is constant, then the ion will experience a radial

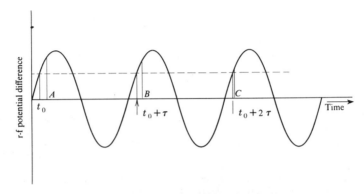

Fig. A-9. Demonstration of possibility of phase stability in a linac. The spacing between accelerating gaps is now chosen so that a particle which reaches the first gap at t_0 with the correct velocity will arrive at succeeding gaps at the same phase of the r-f cycle.

inward acceleration in the left half of the gap and a radial outward acceleration in the right half of the gap. As a result it will receive no net inward velocity, to a first approximation, in crossing the gap but will be displaced toward the axis. On the other hand, if the potential difference between the tubes is increasing with time, then by the time the ion reaches the right half

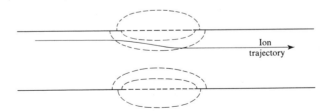

Fig. A-10. Conceptual drawing of electrostatic field between drift tubes. The trajectory of an ion in such a static field is also shown. If the field increases as the ion crosses the gap, the particle acquires a net outward component of velocity in crossing the gap, thus causing the beam to diverge as it moves down the drift tube.

of the gap, the electric intensity and hence the outward acceleration will be greater than the corresponding quantities encountered in the left half of the gap. The ion will then acquire a net outward velocity which will cause the beam to grow in cross section as it proceeds down the accelerator, possibly even striking the walls of a drift tube before it reaches the target.

If the mouth of the right-hand drift tube is covered with a conducting foil or grid, the electric field will be somewhat like that shown in Fig. A-11. In

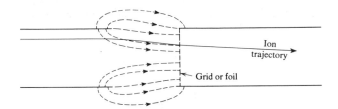

Fig. A-11. Conceptual drawing of electrostatic field between drift tubes when the face of the right-hand tube is covered by a conducting grid or foil. The trajectory of an ion is also shown. The ion acquires a net inward velocity in passing across the gap in this case, thus producing a convergence or "focusing" of the beam.

this case a positive ion experiences only inward accelerations, which results in a contraction or focusing of the beam. Such foils and grids have not been very satisfactory, but are often used on the first few gaps where defocusing action is most serious.

Electron accelerators. Traveling-wave accelerators have found favor over standing-wave accelerators for electrons. Electromagnetic waves travel down straight-sided hollow waveguides with a phase velocity greater than c. If conducting diaphragms, with holes in their centers to transmit the beam, are placed in the waveguide, the phase velocity can be lowered to c or even less if desired. When the electron moves at the same speed as the wave which is accelerating it, the defocusing effect, which is troublesome in proton accelerators, vanishes. By injecting electrons into the linear accelerator with an initial energy of, say, 2 Mev, defocusing by the accelerator tubes can be made negligible.

If neither focusing nor defocusing forces were active, then the momentum of the particle transverse to the beam would remain constant and equal to its initial transverse momentum, p_t. It might appear that this would be very serious in a long accelerator, but fortunately relativistic dynamics shows that this is not the case. The relativistic expression for the transverse momentum of the particle is

$$p_t = \frac{mv_t}{\sqrt{1 - \beta^2}}, \tag{A-3}$$

where m is the rest mass of the particle, v_t is its transverse velocity, and βc is its *total* velocity. Solving for v_t, one obtains

$$v_t = \frac{p_t}{m} \sqrt{1 - \beta^2},\qquad\text{(A-4)}$$

from which it is seen that as β approaches unity v_t approaches zero. Thus the sideward motion of the electron is very small when the particle reaches a velocity close to that of light. We can obtain a somewhat more quantitative estimate of the spreading of the beam by considering the energy, W, of the particle.

$$W = \frac{mc^2}{\sqrt{1 - \beta^2}}.\qquad\text{(A-5)}$$

From this

$$\sqrt{1 - \beta^2} = \frac{mc^2}{W},\qquad\text{(A-6)}$$

which allows (A-4) to be written

$$v_t = \frac{p_t c^2}{W}.\qquad\text{(A-7)}$$

Assuming that the particle moves at the same speed as the wave, to a good approximation the energy of the particle is proportional to the distance traveled. (If the particle is injected with some initial energy, we can add a fictitious length to the beginning of the accelerator tube, so that the energy of the particle is proportional to this increased "effective distance" traveled by the particle.) Then

$$W \propto x$$

and (A-7) may be written

$$v_t = \frac{k}{x},\qquad\text{(A-8)}$$

where k is a constant for an electron with a particular initial transverse momentum, and x is the effective distance which the particle has traveled down the accelerator tube. The radial displacement, r, of the particle is then

$$\int_{r_1}^{r_2} dr = \int_{t_1}^{t_2} v_t \, dt = \int_{x_1}^{x_2} \frac{k \, dx}{x \, \beta c}.\qquad\text{(A-9)}$$

If we take β to be approximately unity, then

$$r_2 = r_1 + \frac{k}{c} \ln \frac{x_2}{x_1}.\qquad\text{(A-10)}$$

As an example, suppose the particle moves $\frac{1}{16}$ inch radially between $x = 2$ ft and $x = 10$ ft. Then

$$\frac{k}{c} = \frac{r_2 - r_1}{\ln (x_2/x_1)} = \frac{\frac{1}{16} - 0}{\ln 5}.$$

At the end of 250 ft it will have moved a radial distance

$$r = \frac{1}{16} + \frac{1}{16 \ln 5} \ln \frac{240 + 10}{10} \cong \frac{3}{16} \text{ inch,}$$

and after another mile will have reached a radial distance

$$r = \frac{3}{16} + \frac{1}{16 \ln 5} \ln \frac{5280 + 250}{250} \cong \frac{5}{16} \text{ inch.}$$

One may look at the situation in an interesting alternative way. To an observer traveling along the beam axis with the same speed as that of the electron, the radial speed of the electron will appear to be constant, but the tube will appear, because of its high relative speed, to be of length

$$b' = b\sqrt{1 - \beta^2} = \frac{bmc^2}{W} \tag{A-11}$$

where b is the length of the tube as measured in laboratory coordinates. For example, to an electron moving at a constant energy of 1 Bev along a mile-long tube, the tube length would appear to be

$$b' = 5280 \times \frac{0.51}{10^3} = 2.7 \text{ ft.}$$

Thus, even though the transverse speed of the electron remains constant in the moving frame of the observer traveling along the beam, the electron will not move far radially while the 2.7-ft tube is passing by.

A-4 Induction Accelerators

In devices of this type, usually known as "betatrons" since they are used only as electron accelerators, the path of the particle is bent into a circle by a transverse magnetic field called the "guide field" and the particle is accelerated by the electric field associated with a time rate of change of a magnetic field. If we use the relativistically valid equation

$$\mathbf{f} = \frac{d\mathbf{p}}{dt} \tag{A-12}$$

where $\mathbf{f}$ is the force acting on the particle, then for a particle which moves in a perfectly circular orbit,

$$\frac{B_z ev}{c} = p\omega = \frac{pv}{r}, \tag{A-13}$$

where B_z is the magnetic flux density perpendicular to the plane of the orbit, e is the electronic charge, p is the momentum of the particle, r is the radius of the orbit, and ω is the angular orbit frequency. From this, we find that

$$r = \frac{pc}{B_z e}, \tag{A-14}$$

and, since
$$\beta\left(=\frac{v}{c}\right) = \frac{pc}{W}, \tag{A-15}$$

$$\omega = \frac{B_z ev}{pc} = \frac{B_z ec}{W}, \tag{A-16}$$

where
$$W = (p^2c^2 + m^2c^4)^{1/2}. \tag{A-17}$$

If r is to remain constant (which greatly simplifies the design of the machine), then B_z must increase as the momentum of the electron increases. The increase in energy of the particle is easily obtained from a consideration of the electromotive force around the orbit produced by a changing flux, Φ, through the orbit.

$$dW/\text{revolution} = \frac{e}{c}\frac{d\Phi}{dt}, \tag{A-18}$$

$$\frac{dW}{dt} = \frac{v}{2\pi r}\frac{e}{c}\frac{d\Phi}{dt} \tag{A-19}$$

or
$$dW = \frac{ve}{2\pi rc}\,d\Phi. \tag{A-20}$$

From (A-17)
$$pc^2\,dp = W\,dW. \tag{A-21}$$

Equation (A-21) together with (A-15) gives

$$dW = v\,dp. \tag{A-22}$$

Hence, (A-20) becomes

$$v\,dp = \frac{ve}{2\pi rc}\,d\Phi$$

or
$$dp = \frac{e}{2\pi rc}\,d\Phi. \tag{A-23}$$

From (A-13)
$$p = \frac{B_z er}{c} \tag{A-24}$$

and
$$dp = \frac{er}{c}\,dB_z. \tag{A-25}$$

Equating dp from (A-23) and (A-25), one obtains

$$d\Phi = 2\pi r^2\,dB_z, \tag{A-26}$$

which is known as the "flux condition" in betatron design. A change in the flux density in a uniform magnetic field would result in a change in flux of only πr^2 times the change in flux density. It is clear then that a betatron cannot be built with a uniform magnetic field. Because of the "2-for-1 rule," as the flux condition is sometimes called, many betatrons have a separate magnetic circuit called the "induction field" which contributes the greater part of the total flux through the orbit.

To the extent that the permeability of the magnetic material is a constant, Φ and B will be proportional to the currents in the coils which provide the induction and guide fields respectively. In this case, the flux condition can be satisfied by a suitable proportionality between the induction field current, i_i, and the guide field current i_g. If we neglect the effect of the resistance of a coil, the rate of current increase will be related to the potential difference U applied to its terminals by

$$U = L\frac{di}{dt}. \tag{A-27}$$

Thus

$$\frac{di_i}{di_g} = \frac{L_g}{L_i}, \tag{A-28}$$

so that a proper choice of turns ratio of the two sets of coils will allow the flux condition to be satisfied while powering the coils from a common source. If one places a turn of wire (called the "orbit coil") near the electron orbit but sufficiently far above or below the median plane of the orbit that it does not interfere with the circulating electrons, it will have an emf induced in it proportional to and approximately equal to the quantity $d\Phi/dt$ which we have been discussing. A small coil (called the "field coil"), placed near the electron orbit with the guide field magnetic flux lines perpendicular to the plane of the coil, will have an emf induced in it proportional to dB_z/dt. By connecting these two coils to a suitable resistance network, one can obtain an output potential difference

$$U = U_0\left(\frac{d\Phi}{dt} - 2\pi r^2 \frac{dB_z}{dt}\right). \tag{A-29}$$

When U is zero,

$$\frac{d\Phi}{dt} = 2\pi r^2 \frac{dB_z}{dt}, \tag{A-30}$$

which means that the flux condition (A-26) is being satisfied. If U is displayed on an oscilloscope, the operator can adjust the machine so that the flux condition is very nearly satisfied throughout each cycle of operation.

If the guide field is uniform, a radial displacement of the electron will simply shift the center of its orbit. If it has a small transverse velocity (i.e., in the direction of the magnetic field lines) it will not move in a circle but along a helix. Its transverse motion will then eventually cause it to strike the walls of the evacuated chamber within which it moves. The latter situation can be avoided if there is a radially inward component of the field above the nominal orbit plane and a radially outward component below it. If the magnetic field lines are convex outward, as shown in Fig. A-12, then, since the principal component of the electron's velocity is normal to the page, the acceleration will be inward along a line perpendicular to the field lines at the point where the electron finds itself. We may consider the nominal orbit plane to be the median plane of the vacuum chamber, *E*. If the electron drifts above this plane it will experience a transverse force driving it back toward the nominal orbit plane. The velocity which it acquires in the transverse direction will carry it across the nominal orbit plane, where it will now experience an upward force. It will thus oscillate back and forth about the nominal orbit plane, which we may call the equilibrium plane, since a particle moving in this plane will not execute transverse oscillations. It is instructive

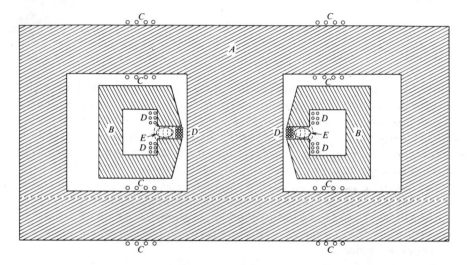

Fig. A-12. Schematic cross-sectional drawing of a betatron. *A* is the induction field magnet with energizing coils *C*. *B* is a ring magnet of C-shaped cross section which furnishes the guide field. *B* is energized by coils *D*. *E* is the evacuated hollow torus in which the beam circulates. The dotted lines indicate the guide field structure.

to examine this motion in greater detail since the same phenomena are encountered in other types of accelerators where the particle path is bent into a "closed" orbit by a magnetic field.

If we ignore the small current constituting the beam itself, then the current density in the region where the electrons are moving is zero and hence

$$\text{curl } \mathbf{B} = 0 \tag{A-31}$$

and, in particular, the component of the curl along the beam direction is

$$\frac{\partial B_r}{\partial z} - \frac{\partial B_z}{\partial r} = 0,$$

or

$$\frac{\partial B_z}{\partial r} = \frac{\partial B_r}{\partial z}, \tag{A-32}$$

where z is the distance perpendicular to the equilibrium plane. Thus a variation of B with z requires a corresponding variation of B_z with r. The variation of B_z with r over a small range in r may be expressed as

$$\frac{B_z}{B_{z0}} = \left(\frac{r_0}{r}\right)^n, \tag{A-33}$$

where B_{z0} is the flux density at r_0, B_z is the flux density at r, and n is a suitably chosen exponent.*

For small values of z one may approximate the r-component of the magnetic flux density by

$$B_r = \left(\frac{\partial B_r}{\partial z}\right)_{z=0} \times z = \left(\frac{\partial B_z}{\partial r}\right)_{z=0} \times z, \tag{A-34}$$

which, with the use of (A-33) may be written

$$B_r = -B_{z0}\,n\,\frac{r_0^n}{r^{n+1}}\,z \cong -\frac{nB_{z0}}{r_0}\,z. \tag{A-35}$$

The force acting in the z-direction, f_z, is then

$$f_z = \frac{e}{c}\,B_r v = \frac{ev}{c}\left(\frac{-nB_{z0}}{r_0}\right)z \tag{A-36}$$

or

$$\frac{dp_z}{dt}\,(=f_z) = -\frac{nevB_{z0}}{cr_0}\,z = -\frac{ne\beta B_{z0}}{r_0}\,z \tag{A-37}$$

$$\frac{d}{dt}\left(\frac{mv_z}{\sqrt{1-\beta^2}}\right) = -\frac{ne\beta B_{z0}}{r_0}\,z. \tag{A-38}$$

If we assume that β changes very slowly with time, then (A-38) becomes

$$m\,\frac{dv_z}{dt} = -\frac{n\beta\sqrt{1-\beta^2}\,eB_{z0}}{r_0}\,z \tag{A-39}$$

or

$$\frac{d^2z}{dt^2} = -\frac{n\beta\sqrt{1-\beta^2}\,eB_{z0}}{mr_0}\,z. \tag{A-40}$$

The equilibrium orbit rotation angular frequency, ω_0, is given by (A-16) as

$$\omega_0 = \frac{B_{z0}ec}{W} = \frac{B_{z0}e\sqrt{1-\beta^2}}{mc}. \tag{A-41}$$

With this substitution, (A-40) becomes

$$\frac{d^2z}{dt^2} = -\frac{n\beta c}{r_0}\,\omega_0 z = -n\omega_0^2 z. \tag{A-42}$$

* n is regretfully used here because it is a time-honored symbol. It is usually *not* an integer.

It follows at once from (A-42) that the particle will move continuously in the z-direction if n is negative, but will execute simple harmonic vibrations in this direction with an angular frequency

$$\omega_z = \sqrt{n}\, \omega_0 \qquad \text{(A-43)}$$

if n is positive (i.e., field lines convex outward as shown in Fig. A-12). The energy associated with this oscillation is

$$W_z = \frac{1}{2} \omega_z^2 z_{\max}^2 = \frac{n}{2} \omega_0^2 z_{\max}^2. \qquad \text{(A-44)}$$

If the oscillation exists because of the initial conditions of direction under which the particle was injected into its orbit, then W_z will remain constant, and as the energy of the particle increases, ω_z will increase, which requires that the amplitude of oscillation $z_{\max}$ decrease as the energy increases. This is obviously a desirable situation, as it means that the beam contracts in the z-direction before striking the target.

For small excursions in the radial coordinate, r, the equation of motion is

$$\frac{dp_r}{dt} - p\omega = -\frac{e}{c} v B_z \qquad \text{(A-45)}$$

or

$$\frac{d}{dt}\left(\frac{mv_r}{\sqrt{1-\beta^2}}\right) = -e\beta B_z + \frac{m\beta c}{\sqrt{1-\beta^2}} \omega_0 \frac{r_0}{r}. \qquad \text{(A-46)}$$

Again assuming that β varies very slowly with time, (A-46) may be written

$$\frac{d^2 r}{dt^2} = -\beta c \frac{e\sqrt{1-\beta^2}\, B_{z0}}{mc} \frac{B_z}{B_{z0}} + \beta c \omega_0 \frac{r_0}{r} \qquad \text{(A-47)}$$

$$= -\beta c \omega_0 \left(\frac{B_z}{B_{z0}} - \frac{r_0}{r}\right)$$

$$= -r_0 \omega_0^2 \left(\frac{r_0^n}{r^n} - \frac{r_0}{r}\right)$$

$$= -r_0 \omega_0^2 \frac{r_0}{r}\left[\left(\frac{r_0}{r}\right)^{n-1} - 1\right]. \qquad \text{(A-48)}$$

Let

$$\rho = \frac{r - r_0}{r_0}. \qquad \text{(A-49)}$$

Then (A-48) becomes

$$r_0 \frac{d^2 \rho}{dt^2} = -r_0 \omega_0^2 \frac{1}{1+\rho}\left[\frac{1}{(1+\rho)^{n-1}} - 1\right],$$

or

$$\frac{d^2 \rho}{dt^2} = -\frac{\omega_0^2}{1+\rho}[1 - (n-1)\rho + \cdots - 1],$$

or

$$\frac{d^2 \rho}{dt^2} \simeq -(1-n)\omega_0^2 \rho. \qquad \text{(A-50)}$$

If $n > 1$, ρ will increase indefinitely, but if $n < 1$, ρ will oscillate at an angular frequency

$$\omega_r = \sqrt{1 - n}\ \omega_0. \tag{A-51}$$

We see then that for stable motion in both the radial and transverse directions, n must lie between zero and one. The energy associated with the radial oscillations is

$$W_r = \frac{1}{2}\,\omega_r^2\rho_{\max}^2 = \frac{1 - n}{2}\,\omega_0^2\rho_{\max}^2, \tag{A-52}$$

so, as the energy of the electron increases, ω_0 increases and $\rho_{\max}$ decreases. Thus the beam contracts both transversely and radially before it strikes the target.

The radial and transverse oscillations have been treated here as though they were independent. Actually there is some coupling with a resulting flow of energy from one mode of oscillation to the other at certain frequencies. For example, when $n = 0.5$, the two oscillations take place at the same frequency and energy flows back and forth between the two modes quite readily. Other values of n which one tries to avoid are 0.2, 0.25, 0.75, and 0.8.

It was assumed, in deriving the flux condition, (A-26), that the energy obtained from the changing magnetic field all went into increasing the energy of the electron. This is not exactly true. The circular motion of the electron involves a steady inward radial acceleration. When a charged particle is accelerated, according to classical theory, it radiates electromagnetic energy. The amount of energy radiated per circuit of the orbit, according to classical theory, is

$$\Delta W_{\mathrm{rad}} = \frac{4\pi}{3}\frac{e^2}{r}\left(\frac{W}{mc^2}\right)^4, \tag{A-53}$$

an equation which is satisfactory except when the beam current becomes large (11), under which conditions coherent radiation becomes appreciable. The loss of energy by radiation is usually great enough above 100 Mev that it must be compensated for. The part of the emitted radiation which lies in the visible portion of the spectrum is easily seen in betatrons with transparent vacuum chambers or specially provided viewing ports.

Betatrons are usually used to produce x-rays by allowing the electrons to strike a target within the vacuum chamber. Since the target must not be in the way of the beam while the electrons are being accelerated, when the desired particle energy has been reached, the orbit is expanded by decreasing (or contracted by increasing) the guide field strength. When the particles have been shifted far enough from their normal orbit, they strike the internal target. It is also possible to expand the orbit into a magnetic channel where a weaker field allows the particles to pass out of the machine to an external target.

A-5 Magnetic Resonance Accelerators

In this class of device, the particle trajectories are bent by a magnetic field into "closed" orbits, while the particle is accelerated one or more times per circuit of the orbit by, or primarily by, an oscillating electric field. We shall discuss, first, machines in which both the magnetic field and the frequency of the accelerating potential difference are held constant (cyclotron and electron cyclotron), next, a type of machine in which the magnetic field is held constant but the radio frequency is varied (synchrocyclotron), then a type in which the radio frequency is held constant but the magnetic field is varied (synchrotron), and finally a type of machine in which both the magnetic field and radio frequency are varied (proton synchrotron).

Cyclotron. The cyclotron utilizes an approximately homogeneous magnetic field formed between large plane pole faces as shown in cross section in

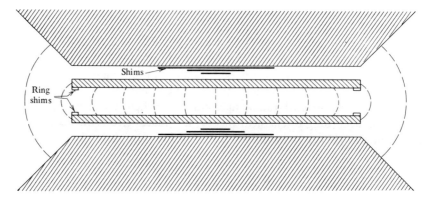

Fig. A-13. The pole faces of a cyclotron magnet are shown above and below. The central shims in the space between the pole face and a second plate of iron (in order to make the shims easily visible, the space is not drawn to scale) are for the purpose of producing some convexity to the magnetic field near the center. The ring shims are to prevent the convexity of the field from becoming too large near the edge of the magnet. The magnetic field lines are shown dotted.

Fig. A-13. An ion emitted from an ion source near the center of the field is accelerated by the potential difference applied between the two D-shaped hollow conducting boxes called dees, then moves in a circular arc within one of the dees and arrives back at the gap between the dees one half cycle (of the alternating potential difference applied between the dees) after the first acceleration. The electric field between dees is now in the correct direction to accelerate the ion a second time. The ion spirals outward as shown in Fig. A-14, the radii of the orbital segments increasing as the square root of the number of times the ion has crossed the gap between the dees. The dees must be within an evacuated chamber in order that an excessive number of ions not collide with gas molecules.

Equation (A-16) shows that, at nonrelativistic speeds in a steady homogeneous magnetic field, the angular frequency of rotation of the ion is a constant. This means that the dees may be energized by a constant-frequency generator.

If a steady, homogeneous magnetic field is used and the constant-frequency electric field passes through the same odd number of half-cycles between each transit across the gap between dees, then the maximum attainable particle energy in a cyclotron is limited by the necessity that the particle velocity be small compared to c. For protons, this sets the upper limit at something on the order of 20 Mev. It might appear that higher speeds could be accommodated by shaping the magnetic field such that the flux density increases with r, but we have seen, in the analysis of betatron oscillations, that this requires

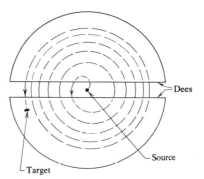

Fig. A-14. Approximate shape of particle trajectory in a cyclotron.

the field lines to be concave rather than convex outward, a condition which leads to unstable orbits. Thomas (13) and Schiff (10) showed, however, in 1938 that azimuthal magnetic field variations may be used to produce stable orbits even when the average flux density increases with r. These ideas have been incorporated in a model (4) which has successfully accelerated electrons to a velocity of $\frac{1}{2}c$, and a spiral ridge cyclotron capable of producing 50-Mev protons is in operation at the University of California at Los Angeles.

The analysis of the beam oscillations is more involved in a cyclotron than in a betatron because the nominal orbit radius changes rather rapidly, but we may use the results of the betatron oscillation analysis to make qualitative predictions for the cyclotron. The orbit frequency ω_0 which occurs in Eqs. (A-44) and (A-52) is now a constant, so that only changes in the field index, n, can change the amplitude of the oscillations. Since n increases with the radial distance r in a cyclotron, the transverse oscillations must decrease in amplitude as the particle energy increases. On the other hand, the radial oscillations increase in amplitude as the particle energy increases.

The cyclotron has one characteristic which makes it different from the higher-energy machines to be discussed later, namely, that it produces a pulse of particles with each cycle of the radio frequency, thus making it possible to obtain rather large average beam currents.

Electron cyclotron. In this device, which is also called a microtron, the transit time between accelerations increases by an integral number times the period of oscillation of the accelerating electric field after each acceleration. From Eq. (A-16) we see that the period of rotation is

$$\tau = \frac{2\pi}{\omega} = 2\pi \frac{W}{B_z ec}. \tag{A-54}$$

If the accelerating field imparts an energy of mc^2 at each transit, then after N transits the energy will be

$$W = mc^2 + Nmc^2 = (1 + N)mc^2 \tag{A-55}$$

and the period of revolution will become

$$\tau = (1 + N)\left(\frac{2\pi mc}{B_z e}\right). \tag{A-56}$$

If B_z is now chosen so that the period of the electric field oscillation, τ_{osc}, is given by

$$\tau_{osc} = \frac{2\pi mc}{B_z e}. \tag{A-57}$$

then

$$\tau = (1 + N)\tau_{osc}. \tag{A-58}$$

A sketch of the orbits corresponding to this type of operation is given in Fig. A-15.

Synchrocylotron. In this type of machine, as in the cyclotron, the magnetic field is constant in time but decreases slightly with increasing radial distance from the center to give orbital stability to the circulating ions. In order to be able to go to higher energies, the frequency is decreased at such a rate that it remains in synchronism with a group of particles which started at approximately the same time. The result, of course, is that the output is no longer continuous but comes in spurts, resulting in a lower average beam current.

In a cyclotron, a particle which does not arrive at the gap between dees at the time of maximum potential difference receives a smaller amount of energy than one which does arrive at the time of maximum potential difference. Its period of revolution remains equal to the radio frequency, nevertheless, so that it simply makes a larger number of revolutions before it reaches full energy. All particles, moreover (having the same value of q/M, of course), reach a given radius with the same energy. In a synchrocyclotron, on the other hand, the orbital period of particles which have reached relativistic speeds increases as their energy increases. If the rate of change of the radio frequency is chosen to maintain synchronism with particles accelerated each time by the maximum potential difference between the dees, then, as in the linear accelerator, particles which arrive either before or after the peak in the r-f potential difference will drop out of synchronism and be lost from the beam. On the other hand, if the rate of change of frequency is chosen to

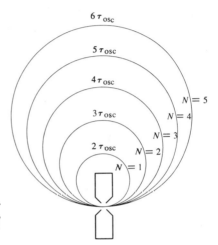

Fig. A-15. Electron trajectory in a microtron. [After C. Henderson, F. F. Heymann, and R. E. Jennings, *Proc. Phys. Soc.*, **66B**, 41 (1953).]

maintain synchronism with particles which arrive at the dees when some fraction of the maximum r-f potential difference is reached, such as point *A* in Fig. A-16, then a particle which arrives late (*B* in the figure) will receive a smaller acceleration than normal. Its period of revolution will then be smaller than normal, causing it to arrive at the next dee gap more nearly in synchronism. If one pursues this line of argument, then he finds, just as in the linear accelerator, that it is possible to have phase stability with the particles oscillating back and forth in phase about the normal or synchronous phase. For convenience of illustration, accelerations only at every other gap crossing (i.e., when the potential difference is positive) are considered in Fig. A-16. The principle of phase stability was discovered independently by McMillan (8) and by Veksler (14) and was first successfully tested in a cyclotron which simulated the operation of a synchrocyclotron (9).

The 184-in. synchrocyclotron at Berkeley can produce 740-Mev protons at an average current of about 0.8 μa, of which about 5 per cent can be extracted as an external proton beam of approximately 25 cm² cross section. Each pulse of the internal beam lasts about 500 μsec.

Synchrotron. In the electron synchrotron, as in the betatron, the electrons are held in a constant-radius orbit by a magnetic field which increases as the particle energy increases. Unlike the betatron, however, the greater part of the acceleration comes from an r-f potential difference across a single gap in the orbit rather than from the changing magnetic field. Since the applied radio frequency is constant and equal to the circumference of the orbit divided by c, it is necessary to bring the particles up to a speed close to c before the synchrotron acceleration can be started. This is usually done by a "betatron start." Small flux bars through the inside of the orbit are used to provide the initial induction acceleration. Then the radio frequency is turned on and true synchrotron acceleration takes place. The synchrotron, too, may be made to operate in a phase-stable manner. If a particle arrives late at the

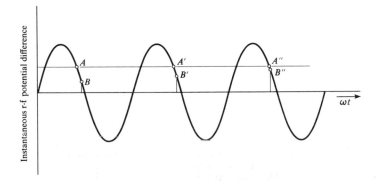

Fig. A-16. In a synchrocyclotron, a particle that arrives at the dee gap at the proper phase, as at A, will reach the gap in subsequent crossings at the same phase (A', A''). A particle that arrives late in phase, as at B, will arrive less late, as at B', on the next crossing, and still less late, as at B'' on the following crossing. At some subsequent crossing it will arrive early at the gap and, because of its energy deficit, will arrive even earlier on the next crossing. It is now receiving extra acceleration at each crossing, however, so that as its velocity increases its period increases and it begins to arrive less and less early at subsequent crossings. Thus it oscillates in phase about the equilibrium phase.

accelerating gap, it will receive less than a normal energy increment. Since the magnetic flux density is changing at such a rate that a particle which receives the normal energy increment will move in an orbit of constant radius, a particle of smaller momentum, as shown by Eq. (A-14), will move in an orbit of smaller radius. Since it is moving essentially with the velocity c, it will complete a full turn about the orbit in less than the normal time, thus arriving at the gap less late than on the previous passage. It is clear that the argument is analogous to that invoked to explain phase stability of the synchrocyclotron. A 1.5-Bev synchrotron, shown diagrammatically in Fig. A-17, is in operation at Caltech. The Cambridge accelerator at Harvard

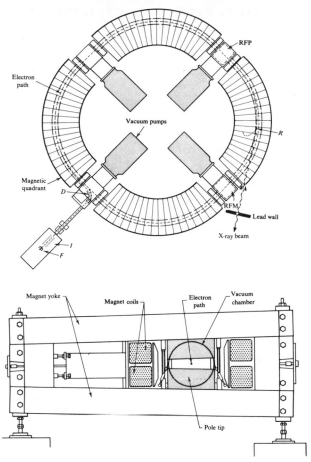

Fig. A-17. (a) Schematic diagram of 1.5 Bev synchrotron. A short pulse of electrons emitted from a hot filament (F) is accelerated to 1 Mev in the injector (I). After passing through a vacuum pipe surrounded by focusing coils the electrons enter the main vacuum and are deflected through 90° by an electrostatic deflector (D). The electrons then enter the first magnetic quadrant and are constrained to move in a circular path by the magnetic field. The electrons make approximately twenty turns around the more or less circular path shown, spiraling in to smaller radii as the magnetic field increases. The radio-frequency modulated cavity (RFM) is then turned on to accelerate the electrons from 1 Mev to about 10 Mev. This acceleration increases the electron velocity from 94% to nearly 100% of the velocity of light. The radio frequency power (RFP) cavity then takes over from the (RFM) to accelerate the electrons to as much as 1.5 Bev. At this point the accelerating voltage is turned off and the electrons spiral inward, striking a thin wire target or radiator (R). The electrons' energy is converted into x-rays in the radiator and the beam of x-rays emerges from the machine in a straight line. The magnetic field increases from a small value, at the time the 1 Mev electrons are injected, to a peak value of 15,000 gauss. The RF potential difference must increase even more rapidly to compensate for light radiated by the high-energy electrons. The acceleration cycle takes about 1/5 second, and each electron travels 2×10^6 revolutions or 37,000 miles. After reaching peak field, the magnet energy is restored in the flywheel of a large motor-generator set. **(b)** Cross sectional diagram showing details of one of the eighteen 5° sections (such as the one marked *A*) making up a quadrant.

457

University is an alternating-gradient synchrotron designed to produce 7-Bev electrons. A design advantage which synchrotrons possess vis-à-vis betatrons is that no correction needs to be applied for radiation loss by the electron. Such loss simply causes the center of the phase oscillations to shift to a phase where the potential difference is enough higher to offset the radiation loss. In the Cambridge accelerator the higher radiation loss associated with greater electron momentum will be partially offset by using an orbit of larger radius but will still be about 10 Mev per turn near the end of each acceleration cycle.

Proton synchrotron. The magnetic flux density, as in the electron synchrotron, must increase as the proton gains energy in order to hold it in an orbit of constant radius. It is not feasible, however, to inject protons with a velocity comparable to c. As a consequence, the radio frequency must be increased as the proton gains energy. The orbital frequency of revolution of the proton is

$$\omega = \frac{B_z ec}{W}. \tag{A-16}$$

From Eq. (A-14)

$$B_z e = \frac{pc}{r}. \tag{A-59}$$

When this is substituted into (A-16), the expression for ω becomes

$$\omega = \frac{pc}{r}\frac{c}{W} = \frac{c}{r}\sqrt{1 - \frac{M_p^2 c^4}{W^2}}. \tag{A-60}$$

If r is constant, then ω must increase as W increases. ω will be zero when the proton has no kinetic energy (i.e., $W = M_p c^2$) and will approach the constant frequency c/r as W becomes large compared to $M_p c^2$.

The 3-Bev accelerator at Brookhaven (Cosmotron) and the 6.2-Bev accelerator at Berkeley (Bevatron) are proton synchrotrons of the type we have been considering. The proton synchrotrons at CERN (Geneva, Switzerland) and at Brookhaven, which are designed for 25 Bev and 30 Bev respectively, employ a newer principle known as "alternating-gradient focusing." We have seen earlier that in a uniform-gradient magnetic field, n must lie between zero and one. In a typical magnet in an AG machine, the value of n is much greater than 1. One aspect of the alternating-gradient principle can be easily illustrated, as in Fig. A-18(a), (b), by a slight oversimplification involving the use of d'Alembert's principle. When the particle is moving in an equilibrium orbit in the median plane of radius r_0, the magnetic force $(e/c)B_{z0}v$ and the apparent force in the rotating coordinate system of the particle, Mv^2/r_0, are equal. If the particle were displaced outward along r

and imagined to move in a new orbit of radius r, the increase in the apparent outward force would be

$$df_{d'Al} = d\left(\frac{Mv^2}{r}\right) = -\frac{f_{d'Al}}{r}\, dr,$$ (A-61)

and the increase in magnetic force,

$$df_{mag} = \frac{ev}{c}\, dB = -\frac{nf_{mag}}{r}\, dr.$$ (A-62)

Since $f_{d'Al} = f_{mag}$ when the particle is moving along the equilibrium orbit of radius r_0, it is clear that when $|n| > 1$, the magnetic force will be dominant in determining the nature of the particle's motion. Figure A-18(a) represents

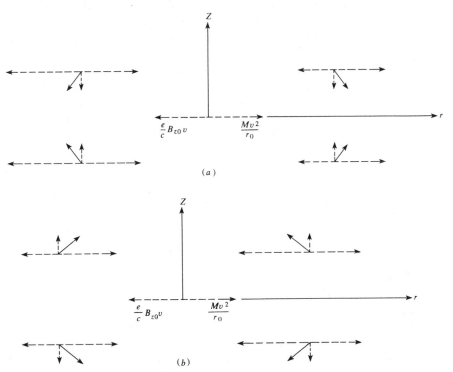

(a)

(b)

Fig. A-18. (a) At the center of the figure, the particle is in dynamic equilibrium in the median plane in an orbit of radius r_0. Since n has been taken to be positive in this figure, any displacement from the median plane results in a restoring force toward the median plane. With the same velocity, a path of radius r greater than r_0 (to the right in the figure) would require a larger centripetal force than that provided by the particles' motion through the magnetic field. Hence, if the particle is displaced outward from its equilibrium orbit it will spiral outward. Conversely, a displacement to the left ($r < r_0$) will cause it to spiral inward.

(b) When n is negative, a displacement in either direction along r will cause the particle to move back toward the equilibrium radius, r_0. Now, however, displacements in the z-direction produce defocusing.

the situation when n is positive. It appears from the figure that there is effectively a net outward force when the particle is displaced outward from its equilibrium orbit where n is positive. Actually, of course, the radius of curvature of the path will be such that the mass times the centripetal acceleration of the particle is equal to the magnetic force. This means that the particle will move in a path whose radius of curvature is greater than r, causing the particle to spiral outward. On the other hand, a displacement inward from the equilibrium orbit will cause the particle to spiral inward. One says that the magnet "defocuses" the beam radially. As we have seen before, a positive value of n gives rise to restoring forces along the z-direction when the particle is displaced from the median plane. We may say, then, that a magnet with large positive n will produce focusing in the z-direction and defocusing in the r direction. Conversely, as shown in Fig. A-18(b), a magnet with large negative n will defocus the beam in the z-direction but will focus it in the r-direction.

One might suppose, at first sight, that such alternating focusing and defocusing would accomplish no useful purpose, but in fact the net effect is to focus the beam. This is most easily seen by resorting to a simple optical analogue. If two thin lenses of focal lengths F and $-F$ are separated from each other by a distance b, the focal length of the pair of lenses is

$$F' = \frac{F^2}{b},$$ (A-63)

where F' is the focal length of a simple lens which would give the same magnification of distant objects as the pair of lenses gives. It is seen at once that if a finite distance separates the lenses, then they act together as a convergent lens. In the same way, the AG magnets focus the beam in both the z- and r-directions. This squeezing of the orbits into a beam of small cross section is known as "momentum compaction." It allows a smaller beam tube to be used and this in turn permits the use of smaller magnets with a consequent reduction in cost.

A situation similar to that of alternating gradients is encountered in magnetic quadrupole lenses. In a quadrupole lens, as shown schematically in cross section in Fig. A-19, charged particles moving parallel to the axis of the lens (i.e., normal to the page) are focused for displacements along one axis (the y-axis in the case of positively charged particles), and defocused for displacements along the other axis. If one such lens is followed by a second which is rotated 90° about the axis of the lens system, focusing in both the x- and y-directions will take place. Quadrupole lenses are often used within the drift tubes of linacs to compensate for the defocusing action of the electric field in the gap between drift tubes when foils or grids are not used at the entrances of the drift tubes. Quadrupole lenses have also been of great importance in preventing the external beams of particles generated in the targets of the high-energy accelerators from spreading out to such an extent that very few particles would finally strike the detecting devices.

FFAG accelerators. The momentum compaction which takes place in an alternating-gradient accelerator has suggested the possibility of a fixed-field alternating gradient (FFAG) accelerator. This device is essentially a synchro-cyclotron with alternating-gradient focusing. If the particles are injected into

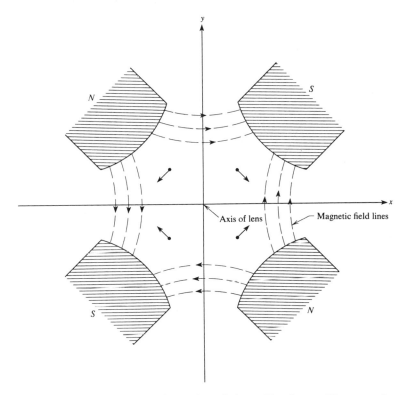

Fig. A-19. Cross section of magnetic quadrupole lens. The short solid arrows show the directions of the magnetic forces exerted on positively charged particles moving normally into the page at the points shown as dots at the origins of the arrows. The lens axis would be the z-axis in this figure. It is seen that the lens causes particles to converge toward the x,z-plane and to diverge from the y,z-plane.

the machine with several Mev of energy, the total change in orbit radius during acceleration is relatively small. Thus a ring magnet like that of a synchrotron rather than the solid pole-face magnet of the conventional cyclotron may be used. The MURA (Midwest Universities Research Association) group has made extensive studies of FFAG designs including theoretical analyses, numerical computations, and model studies. As yet, no full-scale FFAG accelerator has been built.

A-6 Accelerators of the Future

In addition to the two-mile long linear accelerator to produce 15- to 45-Bev electrons which is to be constructed at Stanford University, a number of other concepts including plasma accelerators have been or are now being studied. One of the most interesting groups of ideas concerns "colliding-beam" or "intersecting-beam" machines. The reason for this interest lies in the fact that at relativistic speeds a larger and larger part of the total kinetic

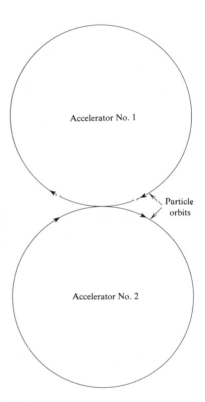

Fig. A-20. Where the beams of these two accelerators overlap at the point of tangency, particles may occasionally collide head-on.

energy of the impinging particle goes into the center-of-momentum motion of the system if the target particle is initially at rest. This "waste" of energy can be avoided, in principle, by allowing two particles with equal and opposite momenta to collide head-on, in which case no energy whatever goes into c.m. motion. For example, two 15-Bev protons, striking head-on, have the same energy, in the c.m. frame, as that of a 540-Bev proton striking a proton at rest. Two 1-Bev electrons colliding head-on have the same energy, in the c.m. frame, as a 1000-Bev electron striking an electron at rest.

The obvious advantages of colliding beams tend to be offset by the small probability of collision between the constituent beam particles, but a number of ideas for circumventing the latter problem have been put forward. In one suggestion, two tangent accelerators would be arranged so that the beam from each passed through a common section in opposite directions as in Fig. A-20. This common section could be a straight section so that the region in which the beams can interact would be increased. The perturbations of the orbits by the guiding magnetic fields near the point of tangency give rise to rather great technical problems in designing this type of machine. To avoid this difficulty, it has been suggested that the particles be removed from the two accelerators and guided into a separate magnetic "storage ring" where the two beams would circulate in opposite directions. Here the difficulty would be that of extracting a large enough fraction of the beam from an accelerator and bringing it into the storage ring. One ingenious idea for avoiding these

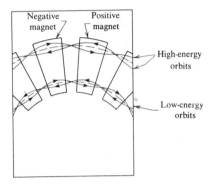

Fig. A-21. Schematic diagram of orbits in a proposed colliding-beam accelerator of the FFAG type in which particles of the same mass and charge circulate simultaneously about the ring magnet in opposite directions. This seemingly paradoxical behavior is traceable to the increase of magnetic field, in each sector magnet, with increasing radial distance. In the stable orbits shown, those particles which are moving along the inward-curved arcs are in stronger magnetic fields than those which are moving along outward-curved arcs. The inward-curved arcs are, therefore, more strongly curved (i.e., have smaller radii of curvature) than the outward-curved arcs with the result that the particles moving in either direction suffer a net inward curvature. The "positive" segment magnetic fields are perpendicular to and into the page if the particles are positively charged. The "negative" segment magnetic fields are perpendicular to and out of the page for positively charged particles.

problems involves accelerating the particles in opposite directions around the same ring structure, as shown in Fig. A-21. The particles now have the chance to collide between each pair of magnet segments, but where the beam current is small, the number of such collisions will be negligible since this number is proportional to the beam current (in either direction) squared. To build up the high-energy beam current to a magnitude which would give a reasonable number of collisions per unit time, it is contemplated that "beam stacking" would be used. Successive groups (sometimes referred to as "buckets") of particles would be brought up to maximum energy and allowed to circulate in storage. Particles would be lost from storage both by the desired collisions and also by unwanted collisions with residual air molecules. In order to obtain a reasonable lifetime against scattering by residual air molecules for the stored particles, it will be necessary to reduce the pressure from the usual 10^{-5} to 10^{-6} mm of Hg, to as little as 10^{-9} mm of Hg. Both beams can be accelerated by a common r-f cavity. Stable phase (relative to the r-f accelerating potential difference) for particles moving in one direction will, of course, differ from stable phase for countercirculating particles by 180°.

REFERENCES

1. Cockcroft, J. D., and Walton, E. T. S., *Proc. Roy. Soc.*, **A136**, 619 (1932).

2. Cockcroft, J. D., and Walton, E. T. S., *Proc. Roy. Soc.*, **A137**, 229 (1932).

3. Greinacher, H., *Z. Physik*, **4**, 195 (1921).

4. Kelly, E. L., Pyle, R. V., Thornton, R. L., Richardson, J. R., and Wright, B. T., *Rev. Sci. Instr.*, **27**, 493 (1956).

5. Lauritsen, C. C., and Bennett, R. D., *Phys. Rev.*, **32**, 850 (1928).

6. Lauritsen, C. C., and Cassen, B., *Phys. Rev.*, **36**, 988 (1930).

7. Lauritsen, C. C., and Crane, R., *Rev. Sci. Instr.*, **4**, 497 (1933).

8. McMillan, E. M., *Phys. Rev.*, **68**, 143 (1945).

9. Richardson, J. R., MacKenzie, K. R., Lofgren, E. J., and Wright, B. T., *Phys. Rev.*, **69**, 669 (1946).

10. Schiff, L. I., *Phys. Rev.*, **54**, 1114 (1938).

11. Schiff, L. I., *Rev. Sci. Instr.*, **17**, 6 (1946).

12. Sloan, D. H., and Lawrence, E. O., *Phys. Rev.*, **38**, 2021 (1931).

13. Thomas, L. H., *Phys. Rev.*, **54**, 580 (1938).

14. Veksler, V., *J. Phys. U.S.S.R.*, **9**, 153 (1945).

GENERAL REFERENCES

1. Flügge, S., ed., *Handbuch der Physik*, Vol. 44 (Berlin: Springer-Verlag, 1959). This is a very thorough account. All of the articles but one are in English.

2. Judd, D. L., "Conceptual Advances in Accelerators," in *Annual Review of Nuclear Science*, Vol. 8 (Palo Alto, Calif.: Annual Reviews, Inc., 1958), p. 181.

3. Livingston, M. S., *High Energy Accelerators* (New York: Interscience Publishers, Inc., 1954). This short and highly readable book by one of the pioneers in accelerator development is not as out-of-date as the publication date might indicate.

4. McMillan, E. M., "Particle Accelerators," in *Experimental Nuclear Physics*, Vol. 3 (New York: John Wiley & Sons, Inc., 1959), p. 639. The first part of this article gives an interesting historical account of accelerator development. The latter part goes into somewhat more detail than does the Livingston book.

NUCLEAR REACTORS

B-1 Flux

Virtually all of the nuclear physical phenomena involved in nuclear reactors have been discussed at various points in the text, but certain modifications of previously used ideas may be employed to advantage in reactor analysis. One of these is the concept of a "neutron flux," Φ, which is defined to be the product of neutron density, N, and average neutron speed, $\bar{v}$. Thus*

$$\Phi = N\bar{v}.$$

This differs from the usual concept of flux as the number of particles crossing a given unit area of a surface per unit time. The dimensions, nevertheless, are the same and it will be seen that the quantity is appropriate to the purpose for which it is used.

B-2 Macroscopic Cross Section

If a neutron of velocity v moves through a material in which the cross section for some type of interaction (scattering, absorption, fission, etc.) is

* In this appendix, in order to employ notation commonly used in nuclear reactor analysis, many of the symbols are given meanings differing from those in the text proper.

σ_i, then the probability of interaction per unit thickness of material (i.e., unit path length of the neutrons) is given by

$$P_x = N_1\sigma_i, \tag{B-1}$$

where N_1 is the number of nuclei, per unit volume of the material, with which neutrons may interact in the specified process. Since the time required for the neutron to travel unit distance is $1/v$, the probability of interaction per unit time is

$$P_t = vP_x = vN_1\sigma_i. \tag{B-2}$$

If the material through which the neutron moves is isotropic, the probability of a reaction is independent of the direction in which the neutron is moving. The rate at which N neutrons per unit volume, each moving with speed $\bar{v}$ but in random directions, will react is then

$$R_i = N\bar{v}N_1\sigma_i \tag{B-3}$$

reactions per unit volume per unit time. Because the product $N_1\sigma_i$ always occurs in the reaction rate equation, it is convenient to define a "macroscopic cross section," Σ_i.

$$\Sigma_i \equiv N_1\sigma_i. \tag{B-4}$$

It should be noted that the "macroscopic cross section" actually has the dimensions of a reciprocal length rather than those of a true "cross section." One can show, in the manner of Sec. 4-3, where the collision mean free path of a particle was calculated, that Σ_i is the reciprocal of the mean distance traveled by neutrons of a given velocity before they undergo a reaction of the specified type. If σ_i is not a function of neutron speed, the reaction rate for polyergic neutrons will be

$$R_i = N\bar{v}\,\Sigma_i = \Phi\Sigma_i. \tag{B-5}$$

Usually σ_i *is* a function of neutron speed. If the spectrum of neutron energies is known, then we may say that there are $N(v)\,dv$ neutrons with speeds between v and $v + dv$, and

$$R_i = \int N(v)\,vN_1\sigma_i(v)\,dv, \tag{B-6}$$

where the integral is over the range of speeds comprising the neutron velocity spectrum, which, in the case of thermal neutrons, is usually taken as zero to infinity. We may then define an "average macroscopic cross section" by

$$\bar{\Sigma}_i = \frac{\int N(v)\,vN_1\sigma_i(v)\,dv}{\Phi} \tag{B-7}$$

so that the reaction rate expression can be put in the same form as (B-5), namely

$$R_i = \Phi\bar{\Sigma}_i. \tag{B-8}$$

In many cases, the cross section is very nearly inversely proportional to the neutron speed. In this case

$$\bar{\Sigma}_i = \frac{\int N(v)\, v\, \Sigma_i(v)\, dv}{\Phi} \tag{B-9}$$

$$= \frac{\int N(v)\, v\, \dfrac{\Sigma_i(v_0)\, v_0}{v}\, dv}{N\bar{v}}$$

$$= \frac{\Sigma_i(v_0)\, v_0 \int N(v)\, dv}{N\bar{v}} = \frac{v_0\, \Sigma_i(v_0)\, N}{N\bar{v}}$$

$$= \frac{v_0}{\bar{v}}\, \Sigma_i(v_0). \tag{B-10}$$

Tables (1) usually give Σ_i for the most probable neutron thermal velocity at room temperature (i.e., 2200 m/sec). Since the ratio of most probable to average thermal velocity, in a Maxwellian velocity distribution, is

$$\frac{v_p}{\bar{v}} = \frac{\sqrt{\pi}}{2}, \tag{B-11}$$

it follows, in the case of $1/v$ cross sections, that

$$\bar{\Sigma}_i = \frac{\sqrt{\pi}}{2}\, \Sigma_i(v_p). \tag{B-12}$$

The tables also give a correction factor (which is exact only when the velocity spectrum is that of a Maxwellian distribution at room temperature) which, when multiplied into $(\sqrt{\pi}/2)\Sigma_i(v_p)$, gives the correct value of $\bar{\Sigma}_i$ taking account of departures of cross sections from $1/v$ dependence. These correction factors are usually less than 3 per cent. To a good approximation, therefore, the ratio of two average cross sections is the same as the ratio of the cross sections measured at v_p.

B-3 Neutron Multiplication

The following discussion sidesteps a host of complicating phenomena which occur in an actual nuclear reactor but serves, nevertheless, to convey some of the most basic principles of reactor kinetics.

We imagine that N_0 neutrons are liberated at time $t = 0$, move about within the reactor for a time l, known as the "generation time," and then are absorbed or otherwise disappear from the reactor. Let us suppose that those which are absorbed liberate a new "generation" of kN_0 neutrons which then likewise last for a time l, etc. At the end of a time t, which is an integral multiple of l, the number of neutrons, N, is

$$N = N_0 k^{t/l}. \tag{B-13}$$

The increase in number of neutrons in one generation is

$$\Delta N = kN - N = (k - 1)N \tag{B-14}$$

and the average rate of change is

$$\frac{\Delta N}{\Delta t} = \frac{(k - 1)N}{l}. \tag{B-15}$$

If k differs only slightly from unity, the stepwise growth may be approximated by a continuous one. Then

$$\frac{dN}{dt} = \frac{(k - 1)N}{l} \tag{B-16}$$

and

$$N = N_0 e^{[(k - 1)/l]t}. \tag{B-17}$$

When $k = 1$, the number of neutrons stays constant. As shown in Fig. B-1, the number of neutrons decreases exponentially with time when k is less than one and increases exponentially with time when k is greater than one. When $k = 1$, the reactor is said to be "critical." When k is less than one, it is said to be subcritical and when k is greater than one, to be supercritical.

Most nuclear reactors contain a neutron source, such as a radium-beryllium source, which produces neutrons at a steady rate whether or not the reactor is in operation. If the source produces neutrons at the rate of N_s neutrons per unit time, then Eq. (B-16) must be modified to

$$\frac{dN}{dt} = N_s + \left(\frac{k - 1}{l}\right)N, \tag{B-18}$$

whose easily verified solution is

$$N = \frac{N_s l}{k - 1} (e^{[(k - 1)/l]t} - 1). \tag{B-19}$$

When k is less than one, the number of neutrons builds up to a maximum value of $N_s l/(1 - k)$ as shown in Fig. B-2. When k is equal to or greater than one, the number of neutrons increases without limit. It is thus possible to operate a reactor which contains a neutron source at a constant, stable level subcritically. Because of the inherent safety of subcritical reactors, they are widely used as training devices.

Since the reaction rate in the case of monoergic neutrons is proportional to the neutron density, the rate of energy evolution (power) is proportional to N. Thus the neutron build-up curves of Figs. B-1 and B-2 may be looked upon as power build-up curves. The time required for the power level to increase by a factor e is called the "reactor period."

In thermal fission of U^{235}, 0.76 per cent of all the neutrons liberated come from delayed-neutron emitting fission fragments. If k were suddenly increased from 1 to 1.0076, therefore, there would be no increase in power until new generations of delayed neutrons began to be produced. Since the delayed-neutron precursors have mean lives up to 80 sec, the effective value of l is very large for values of k between 1 and 1.0076. This extra sluggishness in reactor

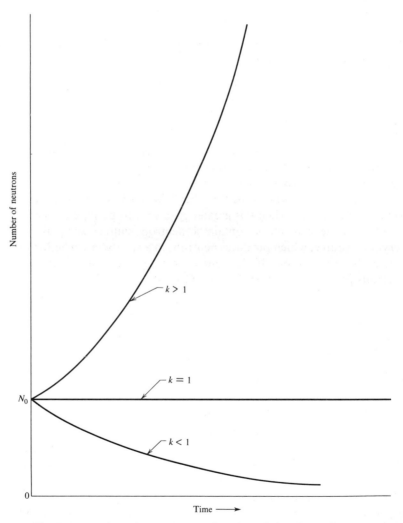

Fig. B-1. Number of neutrons as a function of time for various values of k.

response makes the reactor easier to control because the control devices do not need to be able to respond with great speed. When k is greater than 1.0076, power build-up can proceed without the extra contribution of the delayed neutrons so it can increase at a much greater rate. The reactor is

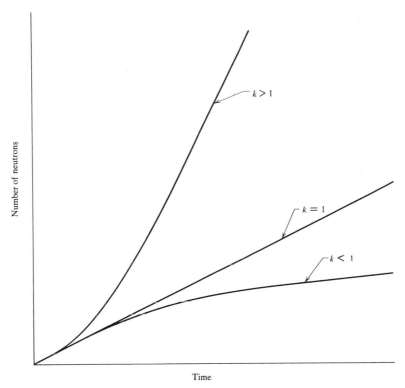

Fig. B-2. Number of neutrons as a function of time when a time-independent neutron source is present.

then said to be "prompt critical" since it is critical even with only the prompt neutrons being taken into consideration.

B-4 Neutron Economy

This section might aptly be called "neutron bookkeeping," for it is concerned with keeping track of where the neutrons come from and what happens to them. Aside from source neutrons, which may be neglected except during reactor start-up, the neutrons come from fissions. The energy spectrum of fission neutrons extends to several Mev, as seen in Fig. B-3. Some of these fast neutrons produce new fissions, and some escape ("leak") from the reactor before being slowed down greatly. Others are slowed down by collisions but are captured in (n, γ) processes before reaching thermal velocities. In the case of natural uranium reactors the (n, γ) capture by U^{238} is particularly

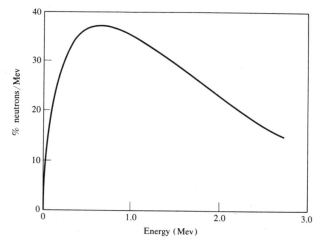

Fig. B-3. Energy spectrum of neutrons from thermal fission of U^{235}. The curve shown is an empirical fit to the data given by $N_n(W) = 2b^{3/2} \sqrt{w/\pi} e^{-bw}$ where $b = 0.775$ and W is the kinetic energy of the neutrons in Mev.

troublesome because of the large capture resonances, evident in Fig. B-4, in the energy region from about 6 to 200 ev.

Of those neutrons which are finally slowed down to thermal velocities within the reactor, some leak away without reacting, an almost negligible fraction undergo spontaneous decay, and some are absorbed by nonfuel nuclei (i.e., nuclei which cannot undergo thermal fission). The remaining neutrons are captured by fuel nuclei. A small fraction of such captures lead to (n, γ) reactions, but the majority produce new fissions.

In a natural uranium reactor, the neutrons captured by U^{238} in (n, γ) processes produce U^{239}.

$$U^{239} \xrightarrow{\beta^-} Np^{239} \xrightarrow{\beta^-} Pu^{239}.$$

The end result is that for each such neutron captured, one atom of Pu^{239} is created. Since Pu^{239} is fissionable by thermal neutrons, it is essentially as useful as U^{235}. The U^{238}, in this case, is called the "fertile material." The process is known as conversion, and one defines the "conversion ratio," K_c, as

$$K_c = \frac{\text{number of new thermally fissionable nuclei created}}{\text{number of nuclei destroyed through thermal fission}}.$$

In the Hanford reactors, which are operated exclusively as converters so that the Pu^{239} can be separated from the U^{238} by chemical rather than the physical methods necessary to separate U^{235} from U^{238}, the conversion ratio is less than one. In other words, more than one U^{235} atom is used up for each Pu^{239} atom created. In a reactor containing Pu^{239}, as the fuel, and U^{238}, as the fertile material, or U^{233}, as the fuel, and Th^{232}, as the fertile material, this process leads to a continuous (at least partial) replenishment of the fuel. In this case one speaks of "breeding" and defines the breeding ratio, K_b, in the same way as K_c was defined.

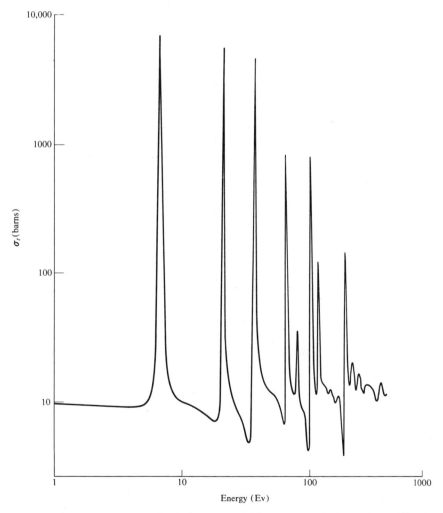

Fig. B-4. Total cross section for interaction of low-energy neutrons with U^{238}. The peaks are ascribable to (n, γ) capture events.

B-5 Evaluation of Multiplication Factor

It is convenient to break the fission chain up into a number of separate steps and examine these one by one. We define the multiplication factor, k, as the ratio of the number of thermal neutrons absorbed by fissionable nuclei in one generation to the number absorbed in the previous generation. Consider, first, an infinite reactor. In this case there can be no leakage of neutrons from the system. Diagram B-1 represents the chain of events described in Sec. B-4.

Diagram B–1.

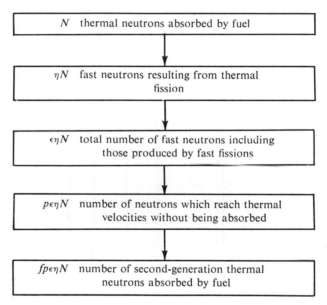

It is evident from this diagram that the symbols used have the following definitions:

$$\eta = \frac{\text{number of fast thermal-fission neutrons produced}}{\text{number of thermal neutrons absorbed by fuel}},$$

$$\epsilon = \frac{\text{total number of fast neutrons produced}}{\text{number of fast thermal-fission neutrons produced}},$$

$$p = \frac{\text{number of neutrons which reach thermal velocities}}{\text{total number of fast neutrons produced}},$$

$$f = \frac{\text{number of thermal neutrons absorbed by fuel}}{\text{number of neutrons which reach thermal velocities}}.$$

ϵ is called the "fast fission factor," p the "resonance escape probability" (i.e., the probability of escaping resonance capture), and f the "thermal utilization factor." In the case of an infinite reactor, then, we may write

$$k_{\infty} = \frac{fp\epsilon\eta N}{N} = fp\epsilon\eta. \tag{B-20}$$

In a reactor of finite size, some of the neutrons are lost by leakage from the reactor. The probability that a neutron will not be lost by leakage is called the nonleakage probability P. Then

$$k = Pfp\epsilon\eta. \tag{B-21}$$

The quantities f, p, ϵ, and η depend on the spatial and velocity distributions of the neutrons. Since these distributions are not the same in finite and in infinite reactors, the quantities f, p, ϵ, η also differ somewhat in the two cases. Nevertheless, as a first approximation, one assumes that f, p, ϵ, η are constants and writes

$$k = Pk_{\infty}. \tag{B-22}$$

This approximation enables us to treat those aspects of the reactor which depend on its actual size and shape, namely, the nonleakage probability, separately from other details involving types of fuel, moderator, etc.

It would appear logical to refer only to fissionable nuclei when speaking of fuel. It is customary, however, in the case of natural uranium reactors, to refer to all of the uranium as fuel. In this case

$$\eta = \frac{\nu}{1 + \alpha}, \tag{B-23}$$

where ν is the average number of thermal-fission neutrons released per thermal fission, and

$$\alpha = \frac{\text{number of thermal neutrons lost through radiative capture by fuel}}{\text{number of neutrons producing thermal fissions}}.$$

If suitably averaged values of the macroscopic fission and capture cross sections are used,

$$\alpha = \frac{\bar{\Sigma}_c}{\bar{\Sigma}_f}. \tag{B-24}$$

In a natural uranium reactor (fractional abundance, C, of U^{235} is 0.0072),

$$\alpha = \frac{\bar{\Sigma}_c}{\bar{\Sigma}_f} = \frac{C\,\bar{\sigma}_c^{235} + (1 - C)\bar{\sigma}_a^{238}}{C\,\bar{\sigma}_f^{235}} \tag{B-25}$$

$$= \frac{0.0072 \times (602 - 502) + 0.9928 \times 2.43}{0.0072 \times 502}$$

$$= \frac{0.72 + 2.41}{3.61} = 0.867,$$

where $$\sigma_a = \sigma_c + \sigma_f, \tag{B-26}$$

σ_c is the radiative capture cross section, σ_f is the fission cross section, and where all cross sections have been given in barns. Then

$$\eta = \frac{\nu}{1 + \alpha} = \frac{2.47}{1.867} = 1.32.$$

Since U^{238} is so much more abundant than U^{235}, the fast effect in a natural uranium reactor is almost entirely due to fast fission of U^{238}. In the elastic collision of a neutron with such a massive nucleus as that of U^{238}, the maximum fractional energy loss, from Eq. (B-32), is only

$$(1 - a) = \frac{4A}{(A + 1)^2} = \frac{4 \times 238}{(239)^2} = 0.0167.$$

If all scattering collisions were elastic, the neutron would be very likely to be absorbed before its energy was brought below the U^{238} fission threshold (about 0.9 Mev).

Table B-1 U^{238} CROSS SECTIONS USED IN FAST-EFFECT COMPUTATIONS

Type of interaction	Cross section (barns)
Inelastic scattering	$\sigma_i = 2.47$
Elastic scattering	$\sigma_e = 1.5$
Fission	$\sigma_f = 0.29$
(n, γ)	$\sigma_\gamma = 0.04$
Total	$\sigma_t = 4.3$

Because, as shown in Table B-1, the inelastic scattering cross section is greater than the elastic, the average neutron will lose enough energy in the first one or two collisions to be below the U^{238} fission threshold. The fraction of neutrons absorbed in two collisions is only about

$$2 \frac{(\sigma_f + \sigma_\gamma)}{\sigma_t} = \frac{2 \times 0.33}{4.3} = 0.15,$$

so the majority of the neutrons cannot produce fissions with the result that, in an infinitely large piece of natural uranium, ϵ, instead of being some very large number, would be only about 1.2. Since a reactor using pure U^{238} as a fuel would depend entirely on fast fissions, the arguments just advanced show that such a reactor would be incapable of supporting a self-sustaining reaction.

Use of a natural mixture of U^{238} and U^{235} opens up the possibility that those neutrons which are slowed below the U^{238} fission threshold will be captured eventually by the U^{235} nuclei. A large solid piece of natural uranium, in addition to being unable to have any useful amount of power generated within it without melting, cannot become critical because of the large (n, γ) cross section of U^{238} in the 6 to 200 ev region. It is necessary, therefore, to make the fuel element small enough that very few neutrons will be slowed down within it to the resonance absorption region, and then to surround it with a "moderator," a material of low mass number and small absorption cross section which will slow most of the neutrons to a speed below the resonance region before they reach another fuel element. Reducing the size of the fuel elements and surrounding them with moderator (in which a single collision usually drops the neutron energy below the U^{238} fission threshold) greatly reduces the probability that a neutron will produce a fast fission before it has lost too much energy. As a result, ϵ, in most natural uranium reactors, has a value in the vicinity of 1.03.

In a breeder reactor it is desirable, and in fact almost a necessity, to make each factor in the multiplication factor formula as large as possible without simultaneously reducing other factors. The fast-fission factor, ϵ, is one of the more promising of these. It is fairly obvious from the previous discussion that natural uranium offers little hope for increasing ϵ appreciably. If a substance such as U^{233}, U^{235}, or Pu^{239}, which has no fission threshold, is used as a fuel, the restrictions which limited ϵ are no longer operative. These three nuclides not only offer greater possibilities of obtaining breeding ratios greater than one; they also are the only materials which can be used as fuel in a "fast reactor," that is, one in which the greater part of the fissions are produced by neutrons with an energy exceeding 10^5 ev.

The resonance escape probability, p, like ϵ, depends very much on the actual arrangement of fuel and moderator. A homogeneous mixture consisting of 1 atom of natural uranium to 400 atoms of graphite has a resonance escape probability of about 0.68. Increasing the fractional concentration of graphite increases the resonance escape probability somewhat, but it simultaneously decreases the thermal utilization factor. The result is that the product pf has a maximum value of about 0.55 for such a homogeneous mixture. This is too small a value to give $k = 1$, and one therefore concludes that it is impossible to build a homogeneous reactor using natural uranium. By segregating the fuel into discrete lumps or rods with moderator filling the remaining space (a "heterogeneous" reactor) it is possible to increase p to values on the order of 0.9.

If one takes $f = 0.9$ to be a reasonable value in a natural uranium heterogeneous reactor, then

$$k = P \times 0.9 \times 0.9 \times 1.03 \times 1.30 = 1.085P.$$

In order for such a reactor to be critical, k must be 1, from which we conclude that the nonleakage probability must be at least

$$P = \frac{1}{1.085} = 0.92.$$

A considerable part of reactor design is concerned, therefore, with calculations of P.

B-6 Slowing Down of Neutrons

Fission neutrons are released with rather large energies. When they collide with nuclei and are scattered, their energies are reduced by the amounts of energy given to the recoiling nuclei. In addition to the random path lengths between scattering events, the amount of energy lost depends on

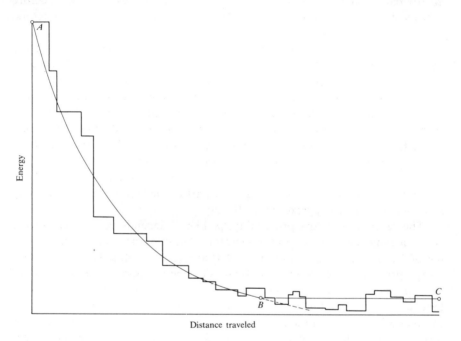

Fig. B-5. Schematic representation of energy *vs.* distance-traveled history of a neutron. The actual histories of neutrons may be approximated by that of a hypothetical average neutron which loses energy in a continuous manner from birth (A) to thermalization (B) and then moves with constant energy (B to C) until captured or lost from the reactor.

the angle through which the neutron is scattered. The energy loss is accordingly a ragged function of distance traveled as shown in Fig. B-5. At the higher energies the thermal velocities of the scattering nuclei are ordinarily so small compared with the neutron energies that they may be neglected. As a consequence, one may say that the neutron loses energy in each collision in this energy range. As the neutron velocity approaches thermal velocities, however, the neutron may either gain or lose energy in any given collision, although it is more likely to lose than to gain energy. Ultimately the neutron comes into thermal equilibrium with the medium and energy losses or gains become equally probable.

It is clear that the thermal and epithermal (above-thermal) regions need to be treated differently, but what is to be done with the transition region? One approximate method which is widely used is to treat the slowing-down region (*A-B* in Fig. B-4) as though the scattering nuclei were at rest and then, when the energy reaches the energy of a neutron with the average speed of a thermal neutron, to treat the problem as one of diffusion of monoergic neutrons.

It has been shown in Chap. 10 that when a neutron ($M_n \cong 1$ amu) of velocity v_1 strikes a nucleus ($M_s \cong A$ amu) at rest, the c.m. velocity is

$$v_{\text{cm}} = \frac{v_1}{1 + A}, \tag{B-27}$$

while the velocity of the neutron in the c.m. frame (both before and after collision) is

$$v' = \left(\frac{A}{A + 1}\right) v_1. \tag{B-28}$$

If the neutron is scattered through an angle θ in the c.m. frame, its velocity, after scatter, in the laboratory frame is

$$v_2^2 = v_{\text{cm}}^2 + (v')^2 + 2v'v_{\text{cm}} \cos \theta \tag{B-29}$$

$$= \frac{(A^2 + 2A \cos \theta + 1)}{(A + 1)^2} v_1^2. \tag{B-30}$$

Let

$$a \equiv \left(\frac{A - 1}{A + 1}\right)^2. \tag{B-31}$$

Then

$$1 - a = \frac{4A}{(A + 1)^2}, \tag{B-32}$$

and

$$1 + a = \frac{2(A^2 + 1)}{(A + 1)^2}. \tag{B-33}$$

With these substitutions, Eq. (B-30) becomes

$$v_2^2 = [(1 + a) + (1 - a) \cos \theta] \frac{v_1^2}{2}. \tag{B-34}$$

In terms of kinetic energies of the neutron,

$$W_2 = \frac{[(1 + a) + (1 - a) \cos \theta]}{2} W_1. \tag{B-35}$$

In a grazing collision, $\theta = 0$ and $W_2 = W_1$. In a head-on collision, $\theta = 180°$ and $W_2 = aW_1$. The energy loss in a collision can vary, therefore, from zero to a maximum of $(1 - a)W_1$.

At thermal energies, when a neutron and a nucleus are close enough together to interact appreciably, they will not usually have enough angular momentum, as a system, to be in a quantized angular momentum state other than a state of zero angular momentum (i.e., an s state). According to quantum mechanics, the scattering must be isotropic in the c.m. frame in this case. At the higher energies in which we are interested here, one cannot rule out anisotropic scattering. As a simplifying approximation we shall, nonetheless, assume isotropic scattering in the c.m. frame. The probability of a scatter through an angle between θ and $\theta + d\theta$ is then just proportional to the solid angle into which such particles would be scattered. Thus

$$P(\theta)\,d\theta = \frac{d\Omega}{4\pi} = \frac{2\pi \sin\theta\,d\theta}{4\pi} = \frac{\sin\theta}{2}\,d\theta. \tag{B-36}$$

From Eq. (B-35)

$$dW_2 = -\frac{W_1}{2}(1 - a)\sin\theta\,d\theta. \tag{B-37}$$

The occurrence of the minus sign in (B-37) simply means that W_2 decreases as θ increases. Since we are interested only in the relative magnitudes of the intervals dW_2 and $d\theta$, we may disregard this negative sign. Then

$$P(W_2)\,dW_2 = \frac{\sin\theta}{2}\frac{2dW_2}{(1 - a)W_1 \sin\theta},$$

$$P(W_2)\,dW_2 = \frac{dW_2}{(1 - a)W_1}. \tag{B-38}$$

It is convenient to introduce a quantity called the "lethargy" which is defined by

$$u \equiv \ln\frac{W_0}{W} \tag{B-39}$$

where W_0 is some reference energy, usually taken large enough that the lethargies of essentially all fission neutrons are positive. Then

$$du = -\frac{dW}{W} \tag{B-40}$$

and

$$u_2 - u_1 = \ln\frac{W_1}{W_2}. \tag{B-41}$$

Ignoring the minus sign in (B-40) for the same reason that the minus sign was ignored in (B-37), we may transform (B-38) to a lethargy distribution,

$$P(u_2)\,du_2 = \frac{W_2\,du_2}{(1 - a)W_1} = \frac{e^{-(u_2 - u_1)}\,du_2}{1 - a}. \tag{B-42}$$

The natural logarithm of the ratio of initial to final energy, averaged over all possible values of the ratio from 1 to $1/a$, is called the "average logarithmic energy decrement." Then

$$\xi = \overline{\ln \frac{W_1}{W_2}} = \overline{u_2 - u_1} = \int_{u_1}^{u_1 - \ln a} \frac{(u_2 - u_1)e^{-(u_2 - u_1)}}{(1 - a)} \, du_2. \qquad \text{(B-43)}$$

If this expression is integrated by parts it yields

$$\xi = \frac{1}{1 - a} \left[-(u_2 - u_1)e^{-(u_2 - u_1)} \Big|_{u_1}^{u_1 - \ln a} + \int_{u_1}^{u_1 - \ln a} e^{-(u_2 - u_1)} \, du_2 \right]$$

$$= \frac{1}{1 - a} \left[a \ln a + 0 - e^{-(u_2 - u_1)} \Big|_{u_1}^{u_1 - \ln a} \right]$$

$$\xi = \frac{1}{1 - a} [a \ln a - a + 1] = 1 + \frac{a}{1 - a} \ln a. \qquad \text{(B-44)}$$

The interesting aspect of Eq. (B-44) is that, on the average, when a neutron is scattered, its lethargy increases by a constant amount irrespective of its energy (or lethargy) before scattering. In particular, for hydrogen ($a = 0$, $\xi = 1$), the lethargy increases by one, on the average, at each collision, or in other words, the energy is reduced by a factor e, on the average, at each collision.

Suppose that we have an infinite, homogeneous, isotropic medium made of a single kind of nuclide, and that fission neutrons are being generated within this material at the rate of S_f neutrons per unit volume per unit time. Let us idealize the fission process by requiring that all fission neutrons be given the same initial energy. For convenience, then, we may take all fission neutrons to have an initial lethargy of zero.

The number of neutrons crossing from some lethargy less than a given value, u, to some value greater than u per unit volume per unit time, is called the "slowing-down density," $q(u)$. In the absence of absorption, in the steady state,

$$q(u) = S_f. \qquad \text{(B-45)}$$

In the lethargy interval from 0 to $-\ln a$, the fraction of neutrons with initial energy u_1 scattered into the lethargy interval u_2 to $u_2 + du_2$ will be,

$$P(u_2) \, du_2 = \frac{e^{-(u_2 - u_1)} \, du_2}{(1 - a)}. \qquad \text{(B-46)}$$

The number singly scattered into du_2 from an initial lethargy of zero is just

$$S_f P(u_2) \, du_2 = \frac{S_f e^{-u_2} \, du_2}{1 - a}. \qquad \text{(B-47)}$$

In addition, there will be multiply scattered neutrons which are scattered from the lethargy interval du_1 to du_2. The total number of neutrons scattered in du_1 will be

$$\Phi(u_1)\, \Sigma_s(u_1)\, du_1 \;=\; F(u_1)\, du_1, \tag{B-48}$$

where, by definition,

$$F(u_1) \;\equiv\; \Phi(u_1)\, \Sigma_s(u_1). \tag{B-49}$$

Adding these two contributions, then, and integrating over all possible values of u_1, while holding u_2 constant, one obtains

$$F(u_2)\, du_2 \;=\; \frac{S_f e^{-u_2}}{1-a}\, du_2 \;+\; \frac{du_2}{1-a} \int_0^{u_2} e^{-(u_2-u_1)}\, F(u_1)\, du_1 \tag{B-50}$$

or

$$F(u_2) \;=\; \frac{S_f e^{-u_2}}{1-a} \;+\; \frac{e^{-u_2}}{1-a} \int_0^{u_2} F(u_1)\, e^{u_1}\, du_1, \tag{B-51}$$

where the number of neutrons scattered *into* du_2 per unit time has been set equal to the number scattered *out* of du_2 per unit time, $F(u_2)\, du_2$, a condition which holds, of course, only in the steady state. If one takes the derivative of each side of Eq. (B-51) with respect to u_2 and then drops the subscript, he obtains

$$dF \;=\; -\frac{S_f e^{-u}\, du}{1-a} \;-\; \frac{e^{-u}\, du}{1-a} \int_0^{u} F(u_1)\, e^{u_1}\, du_1 \;+\; \frac{e^{-u}}{1-a}\, F(u)e^{u}\, du$$

$$dF \;=\; \left(-F + \frac{F}{1-a} \right) du \;=\; \frac{a}{1-a}\, F\, du, \tag{B-52}$$

which can then be integrated to

$$\ln F \;=\; \frac{a}{1-a}\, u \;+\; \text{const.} \tag{B-53}$$

At $u = 0$, from Eq. (B-51), it is seen that

$$F(0) \;=\; \frac{S_f}{1-a}. \tag{B-54}$$

Hence

$$\ln F(0) \;=\; \ln \left(\frac{S_f}{1-a} \right) \;=\; \text{const}$$

and

$$F(u) \;=\; \frac{S_f}{1-a}\, e^{[a/(1-a)]u}. \tag{B-55}$$

In the special case of hydrogen ($a = 0$),

$$F_{\mathrm{H}}(u) \;=\; S_f. \tag{B-56}$$

Scatterers heavier than hydrogen give a collision density, F, which rises with u from $u = 0$ to $u = \ln(1/a)$ at which there is a discontinuous drop in F, as shown in Fig. B-6, because single scattering can no longer contribute to the total for lethargies greater than $\ln(1/a)$.

In a medium which does not absorb neutrons, the number of neutrons passing per unit time from a higher to a lower value of the lethargy than some chosen value, u, must, in the steady state, be equal to the production rate, S_f. This number of neutrons (per unit volume) which pass any point u on the

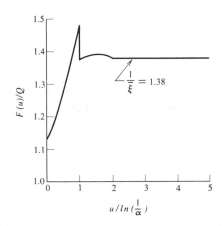

Fig. B-6. In contrast to hydrogen, for which $F(u) = Q$ at all lethargies, the collision density for heavier scatterers has a discontinuity at $\ln(1/a)$ where single collisions cease to play a role. The plot here is for deuterium ($A = 2$, $a = \frac{1}{9}$). The discontinuity in F at $\ln(1/a)$ is reflected in a discontinuity in slope at $2\ln(1/a)$. The function quickly approaches its asymptotic value of 1.38.

lethargy axis per unit time is called the "slowing-down density." Since the number of neutrons scattered per unit time from du_1 into du_2 is

$$F_1(u_1)\, du_1 \frac{e^{u_1 - u_2}}{1 - a}\, du_2,$$

we may, by integrating over all allowable values of u_1 and u_2 as illustrated in Fig. B-7, find the total rate at which neutrons with lethargies less than u are scattered to lethargies greater than u. Thus

$$S_f = \int_u^{u - \ln a} \frac{e^{-u_2}\, du_2}{1 - a} \int_{u_2 + \ln a}^{u_2} F_1(u_1)\, e^{u_1}\, du_1. \tag{B-57}$$

Now if $F(u)$ approaches a constant value for large u (as it appears to do in

Fig. B-6), Eq. (B-57) may be integrated to find what this asymptotic value, F_{as}, is. Then

$$S_f = \frac{F_{as}}{1-a} \int_u^{u-\ln a} e^{-u_2} \, du_2 \int_{u_2+\ln a}^u e^{u_1} \, du_1, \qquad \text{(B-58)}$$

$$S_f = \frac{F_{as}}{1-a} \int_u^{u-\ln a} (e^u - e^{u_2+\ln a}) e^{-u_2} \, du_2$$

$$= \frac{F_{as}}{1-a} \left[-e^u e^{-u_2} - au_2 \right]_u^{u-\ln a},$$

$$S_f = F_{as}\left(1 + \frac{a \ln a}{1-a}\right) = \xi F_{as} \qquad \text{(B-59)}$$

or
$$F_{as} = \frac{S_f}{\xi}. \qquad \text{(B-60)}$$

In the case of a mixture of nuclides a similar equation results,

$$F_{as} = \frac{S_f}{\xi_m}, \qquad \text{(B-61)}$$

where ξ_m is defined by

$$\xi_m \Sigma_s = \sum_j \xi_j \Sigma_{sj}, \qquad \text{(B-62)}$$

ξ_j being the average logarithmic energy decrement for the jth nuclear species and Σ_{sj} being the macroscopic scattering cross section for the jth nuclear species.

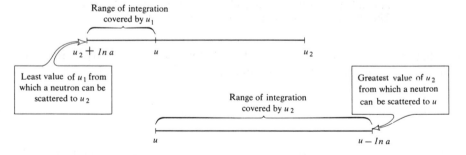

Fig. B-7. Schematic representation of the ranges of integration appropriate to the integral of Eq. (B-57).

Now suppose there is a single sharp absorption resonance at u_i. We shall idealize this resonance as one in which the macroscopic absorption cross section is Σ_{ai} between u_i and $u_i + \Delta u_i$ and zero elsewhere. Those neutrons scattered from lethargies less than u_i to lethargies greater than $u_i + \Delta u_i$ will be unaffected by the resonance. Only those which are scattered into Δu_i can possibly be absorbed. The number of neutrons scattered into Δu_i is equal, in the asymptotic region of F, to

$$F_{as}\,\Delta u_i = \frac{S_f}{\xi_{mi}}\,\Delta u_i. \tag{B-63}$$

The number scattered *out of Δu_i or absorbed* is

$$\Sigma(u_i)\,\Phi(u_i)\,\Delta u_i,$$

where $\Sigma = \Sigma_s + \Sigma_a$, and this number must be equal to the number of neutrons scattered *into Δu_i*. Therefore,

$$\Sigma(u_i)\,\Phi(u_i)\,\Delta u_i = \frac{S_f}{\xi_{mi}}\,\Delta u_i,$$

$$\Phi(u_i) = \frac{S_f}{\xi_{mi}\Sigma(u_i)}. \tag{B-64}$$

The number absorbed in Δu_i will be

$$\Sigma_a(u_i)\,\Phi(u_i)\,\Delta u_i = \frac{\Sigma_a(u_i)S_f}{\Sigma(u_i)\xi_{mi}}\,\Delta u_i. \tag{B-65}$$

The resonance escape probability, p (the fraction of neutrons *not* absorbed), will then be

$$p = \frac{S_f - \dfrac{\Sigma_a(u_i)S_f\,\Delta u_i}{\Sigma(u_i)\xi_{mi}}}{S_f} = 1 - \frac{\Sigma_a(u_i)\,\Delta u_i}{\Sigma(u_i)\xi_{mi}}. \tag{B-66}$$

Now

$$e^{-\left(\frac{\Sigma_a(u_i)\,\Delta u_i}{\Sigma(u_i)\xi_{mi}}\right)} = 1 - \frac{\Sigma_a(u_i)\,\Delta u_i}{\Sigma(u_i)\xi_{mi}} + \cdots, \tag{B-67}$$

so that if $\dfrac{\Sigma_a(u_i)\,\Delta u_i}{\Sigma(u_i)\xi_{mi}} \ll 1$, we may write, approximately,

$$p = e^{-\left(\frac{\Sigma_a(u_i)\,\Delta u_i}{\Sigma(u_i)\xi_{mi}}\right)}. \tag{B-68}$$

If there are a number of such narrow resonances, which are widely enough spaced that they do not interfere (i.e., more than $3 \ln (1/a)$ apart), the total resonance escape probability will be the product of the resonance escape probabilities associated with the several absorption peaks. Then

$$p = \exp\left[-\sum_i \frac{\Sigma_a(u_i)\,\Delta u_i}{\Sigma(u_i)\xi_{mi}}\right]. \tag{B-69}$$

It will be noted that a few absorption peaks, even if infinitely high, will, if sufficiently narrow, not reduce the resonance escape probability appreciably.

The reason for this is simple. Even though neutrons scattered into Δu_i are certain to be absorbed, very few neutrons are scattered into Δu_i, most being scattered *across* Δu_i and therefore escaping absorption. On the other hand, an infinitely high absorption peak as wide as $\ln (1/a)$ would catch and absorb *all* neutrons as none could be scattered across Δu_i in this case.

B-7 Slowing Down with Diffusion—Fermi-Age Treatment

At the beginning of this section a model of the slowing-down process was discussed in which all neutrons start with the same initial energy and subsequently lose energy continuously at the same rate until they become thermalized. Such a model is the basis for Fermi-age theory. According to this model, the energy of a neutron is a unique function of its elderliness, E, that is, the time which has elapsed since its birth. The neutron population of a region can then be characterized by a density function

$$N(\mathbf{r}, E),$$

where $\mathbf{r}$ is the position vector locating the differential volume element being considered.

In Sec. B-8 it will be shown that thermal neutrons obey a diffusion equation. We shall assume that neutrons which are being slowed down also obey a diffusion equation. The neutron current density will then be given* by

$$\mathbf{J}(\mathbf{r}, E) = -D_s \operatorname{grad} N(\mathbf{r}, E) = -D_s \nabla N(\mathbf{r}, E), \tag{B-70}$$

where $\mathbf{J}(\mathbf{r}, E)$ is the neutron current density of neutrons of elderliness E at $\mathbf{r}$, that is, the *net* number of such neutrons passing through unit area of a surface, perpendicular to $\mathbf{J}$, per unit time, and D_s is a slowing-down diffusion coefficient.

The number of neutrons per unit volume, at $\mathbf{r}$, which reach an elderliness E must, in the assumed absence of absorption, either become, in time dt, neutrons of elderliness $E + dt$ or leak out of the volume being considered. The number of neutrons of elderliness E which leak out of the volume in time dt is

$$\nabla \cdot \mathbf{J}(\mathbf{r}, E).$$

---

* In Sec. B-8, the diffusion equation is given as

$$\mathbf{J} = -D \operatorname{grad} \Phi.$$

Since all neutrons with the same value of E move with the same speed, irrespective of their positions ($\mathbf{r}$),

$$\Phi(\mathbf{r}, E) = N(\mathbf{r}, E)v(E).$$

Since v is not a function of $\mathbf{r}$, one could write

$$\mathbf{J}(\mathbf{r}, E) = -Dv(E) \operatorname{grad} N(\mathbf{r}, E).$$

Therefore $N(\mathbf{r}, E) = N(\mathbf{r}, E + dt) + \nabla \cdot \mathbf{J}(\mathbf{r}, E) \, dt$, or

$$\nabla \cdot \mathbf{J}(\mathbf{r}, E) \, dt = -[N(\mathbf{r}, E + dt) - N(\mathbf{r}, E)]$$

$$= -\frac{\partial N(\mathbf{r}, E)}{\partial E} \, dt,$$

from which
$$\nabla \cdot \mathbf{J}(\mathbf{r}, E) = -\frac{\partial N(\mathbf{r}, E)}{\partial E}. \tag{B-71}$$

This equation looks like, and in fact is very closely related to, the ordinary continuity equation, but it is to be noted that the partial derivative is taken with respect to E rather than t.

When (B-71) is substituted in (B-70), the result is

$$D_s \nabla^2 N(\mathbf{r}, E) = \frac{\partial N(\mathbf{r}, E)}{\partial E}. \tag{B-72}$$

The distribution function, $N(\mathbf{r}, E)$, could alternatively be expressed as a function of $\mathbf{r}$ and the lethargy, u, of neutrons which have been diffusing and slowing down for a length of time equal to the neutron elderliness, E. Thus

$$N(\mathbf{r}, E) \, dE = N(\mathbf{r}, u) \, du \tag{B-73}$$

or
$$N(\mathbf{r}, E) = N(\mathbf{r}, u) \frac{du}{dE}. \tag{B-74}$$

Since the average logarithmic energy decrement, ξ, is the average increase in lethargy per collision, the increase in lethargy, du, in a time dE must be

$$du = \xi \frac{\Sigma_s(u) \Phi(\mathbf{r}, u)}{N(\mathbf{r}, u)} \, dE$$

$$= \frac{\xi \Sigma_s(u) N(\mathbf{r}, u) v}{N(\mathbf{r}, u)} \, dE,$$

whence
$$\frac{du}{dE} = \xi \Sigma_s(u) v. \tag{B-75}$$

Equations (B-75) and (B-74) now give

$$N(\mathbf{r}, E) = N(\mathbf{r}, u) \xi \Sigma_s(u) v = \xi \Sigma_s(u) \Phi(\mathbf{r}, u). \tag{B-76}$$

When this expression is substituted in Eq. (B-72), the latter becomes

$$D_s \nabla^2 [\xi \Sigma_s(u) \Phi(\mathbf{r}, u)] = \xi \Sigma_s(u) v \frac{\partial}{\partial u} [\xi \Sigma_s(u) \Phi(\mathbf{r}, u)], \tag{B-77}$$

where use has been made of the fact that

$$\frac{\partial N}{\partial u} \frac{du}{dE} = \frac{\partial N}{\partial E}.$$

From Eqs. (B-45) and (B-60) it is seen that the quantity in brackets in Eq. (B-77) is just the slowing-down density. We therefore make the substitution

$$q(\mathbf{r}, u) = \xi F_{as}(\mathbf{r}, u) = \xi \Sigma_s(u)\Phi(\mathbf{r}, u), \tag{B-78}$$

and (B-77) becomes

$$\nabla^2 q(\mathbf{r}, u) = \frac{\xi \Sigma_s(u)v}{D_s} \frac{\partial q(\mathbf{r}, u)}{\partial u}. \tag{B-79}$$

Now let

$$\tau = \int_0^u \frac{D_s}{\xi \Sigma_s(u)v} \, du, \tag{B-80}$$

from which it follows that

$$d\tau = \frac{D_s}{\xi \Sigma_s(u)v} \, du. \tag{B-81}$$

Then

$$\nabla^2 q(\mathbf{r}, u) = \frac{\partial q(\mathbf{r}, u)}{\partial \tau}, \tag{B-82}$$

or, since u is uniquely related to τ,

$$\nabla^2 q(\mathbf{r}, \tau) = \frac{\partial q(\mathbf{r}, \tau)}{\partial \tau}. \tag{B-83}$$

This differential equation is known as the Fermi-age equation.

If the reader has an uneasy feeling, at this point, that the development of the Fermi-age equation is based on assumptions that have not been well justified, he is absolutely right. It is characteristic of reactor analysis that in order to obtain mathematically tractable equations it is necessary to make approximations which are known to be not wholly satisfactory. The alternative is to go to digital computers and make detailed numerical integrations. The latter alternative is being used more and more in reactor analysis, but the approximate methods are still necessary as a guide and as a means for gaining a semiquantitative appreciation of the factors influencing reactor design. The great virtue of the Fermi-age equation is that it is mathematically identical to the heat-flow equation, many solutions to which, for various boundary conditions, are well known (2). The word "age" is used because τ plays the same role here as time plays in the heat-flow equation. It should be noted that τ does *not* have the dimensions of time, but rather of area. The solution to the problem of a point source, located in an infinite medium, which emits s_p neutrons per unit time, is

$$q(r, \tau) = \frac{s_p}{(4\pi\tau)^{3/2}} e^{-r^2/4\tau}. \tag{B-84}$$

An infinite plane source which emits s_a neutrons per unit area per unit time and which is adjacent to semiinfinite media on each side of its plane gives a slowing-down density

$$q(x, \tau) = \frac{S_a}{\sqrt{4\pi\tau}} e^{-x^2/4\tau}.$$ (B-85)

where x is the distance normal to the source plane.

It is of interest to determine the mean square displacement which will have been attained by neutrons of age τ. It is convenient to consider the neutrons coming from a point source, in which case Eq. (B-84) will be applicable. Then

$$\overline{[r(\tau)]^2} = \frac{\int_0^\infty r^2(4\pi r^2 q)\, dr}{\int_0^\infty 4\pi r^2 q\, dr}$$ (B-86)

$$= \frac{\int_0^\infty \dfrac{r^4 s e^{-r^2/4\tau}}{(4\pi\tau)^{3/2}}\, dr}{\int_0^\infty \dfrac{r^2 s e^{-r^2/4\tau}}{(4\pi\tau)^{3/2}}\, dr},$$

$$\overline{[r(\tau)]^2} = \frac{\int_0^\infty r^4 e^{-r^2/4\tau}\, dr}{\int_0^\infty r^2 e^{-r^2/4\tau}\, dr} = 6\tau.$$ (B-87)

The "slowing-down length" is defined as the square root of the age at which neutrons reach thermal velocities.

$$\sqrt{\tau_{th}} = \sqrt{\overline{r_{th}^2}/6}.$$ (B-88)

Equation (B-83) was derived on the assumption that a steady state existed. In such a case q is not a function of time. If a quasi-steady state exists in which the rate of change of q is very small in the time required for a neutron to be moderated to thermal energies, we may write

$$\nabla^2 q(\mathbf{r}, \tau, t) = \frac{\partial q(\mathbf{r}, \tau, t)}{\partial \tau}.$$ (B-89)

As is usual in partial differential equations, one attempts to separate variables by writing q as the product of functions of the single variables. Thus

$$q(\mathbf{r}, \tau, t) = \mathscr{R}(\mathbf{r})\, \theta(\tau)\, T(t).$$ (B-90)

When this is substituted into (B-89), the latter becomes

$$\frac{\nabla^2 \mathscr{R}}{\mathscr{R}} = \frac{1}{\theta} \frac{d\theta}{d\tau}.$$ (B-91)

This equation can only be satisfied if both sides are equal to the same constant, say $-B^2$. This gives

$$\theta = \theta_0 e^{-B^2\tau}$$ (B-92)

and
$$\nabla^2 \mathscr{R} + B^2 \mathscr{R} = 0, \tag{B-93}$$

where B^2 is limited to positive values since the slowing-down density cannot increase with age. Since B is any eigenvalue of Eq. (B-93), there are many possible solutions corresponding to the different eigenvalues, but the only solution of importance when $k \cong 1$ is the smallest eigenvalue. This value of B is called the "buckling."

The number of neutrons entering the system at $\tau = 0$ per unit time per unit volume is
$$q(\mathbf{r}, 0, t) = \theta_0 \mathscr{R} T. \tag{B-94}$$

The slowing-down density at τ_{th} will be this quantity multiplied by the resonance escape probability, p, and the slowing-down nonleakage probability, P_{sl}. The slowing-down density at τ_{th}, multiplied by the thermal nonleakage probability, P_{th}, must be just k times the number of neutrons absorbed per unit time and unit volume in the previous generation, namely $\Sigma_a \Phi(\tau_{th})$. Thus

$$P_{th} P_{sl} p q(\mathbf{r}, 0, t) = k \Sigma_a \Phi(\tau_{th}), \tag{B-95}$$

so that
$$q(\mathbf{r}, 0, t) = \frac{k \Sigma_a \Phi(\tau_{th})}{p P_{sl} P_{th}} = \theta_0 \mathscr{R} T.$$

Hence
$$\mathscr{R} T = \frac{k \Sigma_a \Phi(\tau_{th})}{P_{sl} P_{th} p \theta_0},$$

and
$$q(\mathbf{r}, \tau, t) = \frac{k \Sigma_a \Phi(\tau_{th})}{P_{sl} P_{th} p} e^{-B^2 \tau}. \tag{B-96}$$

Since the slowing-down density used here is the slowing-down density which would exist in the absence of absorption, the actual slowing-down density at τ_{th} will be (to a good approximation)

$$p q(\mathbf{r}, \tau_{th}, t) = \frac{k \Sigma_a \Phi(\tau_{th})}{P_{th}} = \frac{k \Sigma_a \Phi(\tau_{th}) e^{-B^2 \tau_{th}}}{P_{th} P_{sl}} \tag{B-97}$$

from which we conclude that the slowing-down nonleakage probability is

$$P_{sl} = e^{-B^2 \tau_{th}}. \tag{B-98}$$

B-8 Diffusion of Neutrons

In a reactor, the concentration of neutrons is so small compared to the concentration of scattering nuclei that collisions of neutrons with each other are very rare compared to collisions with nuclei. It is justifiable, therefore, in treating neutron diffusion, to ignore neutron-neutron collisions. The number of scattering collisions of neutrons with nuclei per unit time per unit volume is $\bar{\Sigma}_s\Phi$. The number, then, which will undergo scattering within some volume element dV, as shown in Fig. B-8, per unit time is

$$\bar{\Sigma}_s\Phi\ dV.$$

The fraction of these which will be scattered toward the element of area, dS, will be proportional to the solid angle subtended by dS at dV. The number of neutrons scattered in dV toward dS per unit time, then, is

$$\frac{dS\cos\theta}{4\pi r^2}\bar{\Sigma}_s\Phi\ dV.$$

The fraction of these which reach dS without being scattered or absorbed is

$$e^{-\bar{\Sigma}r}$$

where $$\bar{\Sigma} = \overline{(\Sigma_a + \Sigma_s)}.$$ (B-99)

Now if Φ is changing slowly enough with time that it is not altered appreciably

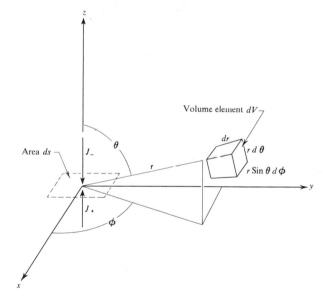

Fig. B-8. Diagram illustrating the quantities involved in the computation of a neutron current, **J**.

during the time required for a neutron to go from dV to dS we may set the number of neutrons, originating in dV, which pass through dS in some small interval of time equal to the number arriving at dS which originated at dV in the same time interval. If we then define a neutron current density, J_z , as being the number of neutrons passing through unit area of the x,y-plane in the downward direction per unit time, we may write

$$J_{z^-} \, dS = \int e^{-\bar{\Sigma}r} \frac{dS \cos \theta}{4\pi r^2} \Sigma_s \Phi \, dV$$

or

$$J_{z^-} = \frac{1}{4\pi} \int_{r=0}^{\infty} \int_{\theta=0}^{\pi/2} \int_{\phi=0}^{2\pi} \Phi \Sigma_s e^{-\bar{\Sigma}r} \sin \theta \cos \theta \, dr \, d\theta \, d\phi. \qquad \text{(B-100)}$$

In order to carry out the required integration, we need to know Φ as a function of position. Because of the term $e^{-\bar{\Sigma}r}$, the major contribution to the integral will come in the first few mean free paths of neutron motion. It is therefore reasonable to expand Φ about the origin in a Taylor's series and use only the leading terms in the expansion, since the region in which Φ will then not be given accurately contributes almost nothing to the integral anyway.

$$\Phi(x, y, z) = \Phi_0 + x \left(\frac{\partial \Phi}{\partial x}\right)_0 + y \left(\frac{\partial \Phi}{\partial y}\right)_0 + z \left(\frac{\partial \Phi}{\partial z}\right)_0 \qquad \text{(B-101)}$$

$$+ x^2 \left(\frac{\partial^2 \Phi}{\partial x^2}\right)_0 + y^2 \left(\frac{\partial^2 \Phi}{\partial y^2}\right)_0 + z^2 \left(\frac{\partial^2 \Phi}{\partial z^2}\right)_0$$

$$+ 2xy \left(\frac{\partial^2 \Phi}{\partial x \, \partial y}\right)_0 + 2xz \left(\frac{\partial^2 \Phi}{\partial x \, \partial z}\right)_0 + 2yz \left(\frac{\partial^2 \Phi}{\partial y \, \partial z}\right)_0 + \cdots.$$

If one now makes the substitutions

$$x = r \sin \theta \cos \phi, \qquad \text{(B-102)}$$

$$y = r \sin \theta \sin \phi, \qquad \text{(B-103)}$$

$$z = r \cos \theta, \qquad \text{(B-104)}$$

and integrates, he discovers that the x, y, xy, xz, and yz terms all drop out, leaving

$$J_{z^-} = \frac{\Sigma_s}{\bar{\Sigma}} \frac{\Phi_0}{4} + \frac{\Sigma_s}{6\bar{\Sigma}^2} \left(\frac{\partial \Phi}{\partial z}\right)_0 + \frac{\Sigma_s}{8\bar{\Sigma}^3} \left(\frac{\partial^2 \Phi}{\partial x^2}\right)_0$$

$$+ \frac{\Sigma_s}{8\bar{\Sigma}^3} \left(\frac{\partial^2 \Phi}{\partial y^2}\right)_0 + \frac{\Sigma_s}{4\bar{\Sigma}^3} \left(\frac{\partial^2 \Phi}{\partial z^2}\right)_0 + \cdots. \qquad \text{(B-105)}$$

Next, we consider the upward current density, J_{z^+}, through dS. From (B-105) we see that a reversal of the z-axis will change, of those terms we have considered, only the second. Thus

$$J_{z^+} = \frac{\Sigma_s}{\bar{\Sigma}} \frac{\Phi_0}{4} - \frac{\Sigma_s}{6\bar{\Sigma}^2} \left(\frac{\partial \Phi}{\partial z}\right)_0 + \frac{\Sigma_s}{8\bar{\Sigma}^3} \left(\frac{\partial^2 \Phi}{\partial x^2}\right)_0$$

$$+ \frac{\Sigma_s}{8\bar{\Sigma}^3} \left(\frac{\partial^2 \Phi}{\partial y^2}\right)_0 + \frac{\Sigma_s}{4\bar{\Sigma}^3} \left(\frac{\partial^2 \Phi}{\partial z^2}\right)_0 + \cdots. \qquad \text{(B-106)}$$

The net current density in the z-direction, J_z, is then seen to be

$$J_z = J_{z^+} - J_{z^-} = -\frac{\bar{\Sigma}_s}{3\bar{\Sigma}^2}\left(\frac{\partial \Phi}{\partial z}\right)_0,$$ (B-107)

if we neglect higher-order terms such as $\left(\dfrac{\partial^3 \Phi}{\partial z^3}\right)_0$. Similarly,

$$J_z = -\frac{\bar{\Sigma}_s}{3\bar{\Sigma}^2}\left(\frac{\partial \Phi}{\partial x}\right)_0$$ (B-108)

and

$$J_y = -\frac{\bar{\Sigma}_s}{3\bar{\Sigma}^2}\left(\frac{\partial \Phi}{\partial y}\right)_0.$$ (B-109)

The total current density, $\mathbf{J}$, is

$$\mathbf{J} = -\frac{\bar{\Sigma}_s}{3\bar{\Sigma}^2}\left(\mathbf{i}\frac{\partial \Phi}{\partial x} + \mathbf{j}\frac{\partial \Phi}{\partial y} + \mathbf{k}\frac{\partial \Phi}{\partial z}\right),$$

or

$$\mathbf{J} = -\frac{\bar{\Sigma}_s}{3\bar{\Sigma}^2}\,\text{grad }\Phi.$$ (B-110)

If we define a thermal diffusion coefficient

$$D = \frac{\bar{\Sigma}_s}{3\bar{\Sigma}^2}$$ (B-111)

then the diffusion equation becomes

$$\mathbf{J} = -D\,\text{grad }\Phi.$$ (B-112)

If

$$\Sigma_a \ll \Sigma_s, \qquad D \cong \frac{1}{3\bar{\Sigma}_s}.$$ (B-113)

It will be noted that (B-112) has the same form as Ohm's law for electrical current flow in a continuous medium if we let $\mathbf{J}$ represent the electrical current density, Φ the electrical potential, and D the specific conductivity of the medium (i.e., the reciprocal of the resistivity).

If we have a region in which S_{th} thermal neutrons are being created per unit volume per unit time, conservation of neutrons leads to the expression

$$S_{th} - \text{div }\mathbf{J} - \bar{\Sigma}_a\Phi = \frac{\partial N}{\partial t},$$ (B-114)

where N is the number of neutrons per unit volume. This may also be written

$$D\,\nabla^2\Phi - \bar{\Sigma}_a\Phi + S_{th} = \frac{\partial N}{\partial t}.$$ (B-115)

In reactor analysis this is usually referred to as "the diffusion equation." In the *steady state*, $\partial N/\partial t = 0$ and (B-115) becomes

$$D\,\nabla^2\Phi - \bar{\Sigma}_a\Phi + S_{th} = 0.$$ (B-116)

If we are interested in steady-state diffusion of neutrons in a region free of sources,

$$\nabla^2 \Phi - \frac{\overline{\Sigma}_a \Phi}{D} = 0 \qquad \text{(B-117)}$$

or
$$\nabla^2 \Phi - \kappa^2 \Phi = 0, \qquad \text{(B-118)}$$

where, by definition,
$$\kappa^2 = \frac{\overline{\Sigma}_a}{D}. \qquad \text{(B-119)}$$

One can now solve (B-118) for certain cases if proper boundary conditions can be specified. Two conditions which must always be satisfied are

1. The neutron flux must be everywhere finite and positive or zero (i.e., negative values are excluded).
2. The normal component of the neutron current must be continuous at any boundary.

It is customary, in addition, to use two boundary conditions which are only approximately true.

3. The flux must be continuous at any boundary.
4. The quantity $D(\partial \Phi / \partial \zeta)$, where ζ is a coordinate normal to the boundary, must be continuous at any boundary.

The last condition follows from condition (2) if the media on the two sides of the boundary are identical, but where they differ the diffusion equation is not strictly valid. It will be remembered, in fact, that it was necessary to assume that the media on both sides of the boundary were identical in order to derive the diffusion equation.

Let us examine the case of a point source, in an infinite medium, which emits s_p neutrons per unit time. At all points for which $r > 0$, the equation

$$\nabla^2 \Phi - \kappa^2 \Phi = 0$$

will hold. From the spherical symmetry of the problem,

$$\frac{\partial \Phi}{\partial \theta} = \frac{\partial \Phi}{\partial \phi} = 0.$$

In spherical coordinates, then,

$$\frac{1}{r} \frac{\partial^2 (r\Phi)}{\partial r^2} - \kappa^2 \Phi = 0, \qquad \text{(B-120)}$$

$$\frac{\partial^2 (r\Phi)}{\partial r^2} - \kappa^2 (r\Phi) = 0. \qquad \text{(B-121)}$$

The solution to this equation is

$$r\Phi = b_1 e^{\kappa r} + b_2 e^{-\kappa r}, \qquad \text{(B-122)}$$

but this makes Φ become infinite at large r unless $b_1 = 0$. Therefore,

$$\Phi = b_2 \frac{e^{-\kappa r}}{r}. \tag{B-123}$$

The net outward current of particles across a spherical surface of radius r is

$$J_r \cdot 4\pi r^2 = 4\pi r^2 \left(-D \frac{\partial \Phi}{\partial r} \right) \tag{B-124}$$

$$= \frac{-\overline{\Sigma}_a}{\kappa^2} 4\pi r^2 b_2 \left[\frac{-\kappa e^{-\kappa r}}{r} - \frac{e^{-\kappa r}}{r^2} \right]. \tag{B-125}$$

If there were no absorption of neutrons this would be a constant and equal to the source strength, s_p. The number of neutrons which have been removed by absorption becomes smaller and smaller as r becomes smaller. Hence, in the limit of vanishing r,

$$s_p = \lim_{r \to 0} \left\{ \frac{\overline{\Sigma}_a}{\kappa^2} \cdot 4\pi b_2 \left[\kappa r e^{-\kappa r} + e^{-\kappa r} \right] \right\} \tag{B-126}$$

$$= \frac{4\pi b_2 \overline{\Sigma}_a}{\kappa^2}, \tag{B-127}$$

or $$b_2 = \frac{\kappa^2 s_p}{4\pi \overline{\Sigma}_a}. \tag{B-128}$$

Thus $$\Phi = \frac{s_p \kappa^2}{4\pi \overline{\Sigma}_a} \frac{e^{-\kappa r}}{r}. \tag{B-129}$$

Consider next an infinite sheet source in the y,z-plane which emits s_a neutrons per unit area per unit time, and which has semiinfinite media on each side of the sheet source. Let the source plane be located at $x = 0$. From symmetry,

$$\frac{\partial \Phi}{\partial y} = \frac{\partial \Phi}{\partial z} = 0,$$

so the diffusion equation becomes

$$\frac{d^2 \Phi}{dx^2} - \kappa^2 \Phi = 0, \tag{B-130}$$

the solution to which is the same as that of (B-121) except that Φ occurs here where $r\Phi$ occurred in (B-121), namely

$$\Phi = b_3 e^{\kappa x} + b_4 e^{-\kappa x}, \tag{B-131}$$

and, as before, if Φ is to remain finite at large x, b_3 must be zero, and

$$\Phi = b_4 e^{-\kappa x}. \tag{B-132}$$

As x approaches zero, the current density in the x-direction must approach $s_a/2$ since half of the neutrons will flow toward positive x and half toward negative x. Thus

$$\frac{s_a}{2} = \lim_{x\to 0}\left\{-\frac{\overline{\Sigma}_a}{\kappa^2}\frac{d\Phi}{dx}\right\} = \lim_{x\to 0}\left\{\frac{\overline{\Sigma}_a}{\kappa^2}b_4\kappa e^{-\kappa x}\right\} \tag{B-133}$$

$$= \frac{\overline{\Sigma}_a}{\kappa}b_4 \tag{B-134}$$

or

$$b_4 = \frac{\kappa s_a}{2\overline{\Sigma}_a}, \tag{B-135}$$

and

$$\Phi = \frac{s_a\kappa}{2\overline{\Sigma}_a}e^{-\kappa x}. \tag{B-136}$$

Let us now ask, "What will be the mean square displacement of a neutron from its source when it is captured?" We may use the result which we have already obtained for the flux caused by a point source of strength s_p in an infinite medium and take the average value of r^2 in the usual way. The number of neutrons absorbed in a spherical shell between r and $r + dr$ will be $4\pi r^2\overline{\Sigma}_a\Phi(r)\,dr$, so

$$\overline{r^2} = \frac{\int_0^r r^2 4\pi r^2 \overline{\Sigma}_a\Phi(r)\,dr}{s_p} \tag{B-137}$$

$$= \frac{4\pi\overline{\Sigma}_a}{s_p}\int_0^r r^4\frac{s_p\kappa^2}{4\pi\overline{\Sigma}_a}\frac{e^{-\kappa r}}{r}\,dr$$

$$= \kappa^2\int_0^r r^3 e^{-\kappa r}\,dr.$$

When integrated by parts, this yields

$$\overline{r^2} = \frac{6}{\kappa^2}. \tag{B-138}$$

If one defines a "diffusion length," L, by

$$L = \frac{1}{\kappa}, \tag{B-139}$$

then

$$L = \left(\frac{\overline{r^2}}{6}\right)^{1/2}. \tag{B-140}$$

Suppose a neutron suffers a displacement $\mathbf{r}_1$ during slowing-down and another displacement $\mathbf{r}_2$ during diffusion (until captured). Then the total displacement, $\mathbf{r}$, will be

$$\mathbf{r} = \mathbf{r}_1 + \mathbf{r}_2 \tag{B-141}$$

and

$$r^2 = r_1^2 + r_2^2 + 2r_1r_2\cos\theta, \tag{B-142}$$

where θ is the angle between the vectors $\mathbf{r}_1$ and $\mathbf{r}_2$. The mean value of $r^2/6$ will then be defined as the "migration area," $\mathcal{M}^2$, and will be

$$\mathcal{M}^2 = \frac{\overline{r^2}}{6} = \frac{\overline{r_1^2}}{6} + \frac{\overline{r_2^2}}{6} + \frac{\overline{2r_1r_2\cos\theta}}{6},$$

$$\mathcal{M}^2 = \tau_{th} + L^2 + \tfrac{1}{3}\overline{r_1r_2\cos\theta}. \tag{B-143}$$

Since r_1, r_2, and θ are independent (or at least assumed to be)

$$\overline{r_1r_2\cos\theta} = \overline{r_1}\,\overline{r_2}\,\overline{\cos\theta} = \overline{r_1}\,\overline{r_2}\int\cos\theta\,\frac{d\Omega}{4\pi}$$

where $d\Omega$ is the solid angle containing all values of θ between θ and $\theta + d\theta$.

$$\overline{r_1r_2\cos\theta} = \overline{r_1}\,\overline{r_2}\int_0^\pi \cos\theta\,\frac{2\pi\sin\theta\,d\theta}{4\pi} = 0. \tag{B-144}$$

Therefore

$$\mathcal{M}^2 = \tau_{th} + L^2, \tag{B-145}$$

and $\mathcal{M}$, which is called the "migration length," is

$$\mathcal{M} = \sqrt{\tau_{th} + L^2}. \tag{B-146}$$

It is common practice to surround the reactor core (the part where fissions take place) by a nonreacting medium whose purpose is to scatter as many neutrons back toward the core as possible. This outer medium is called a "reflector." A "reflection coefficient" or "albedo," β, may be defined for the reflector by

$$\beta = \frac{J_{\text{back}}}{J_{\text{in}}}, \tag{B-147}$$

where J_{back} is the neutron current density flowing back across the boundary from the reflector toward the source medium and J_{in} is the neutron current density flowing from the source medium into the reflector. *Approximate* values for the current densities may be obtained by using the expressions for current densities in a *continuous* medium. Thus

$$\beta = \frac{J-}{J+} = \frac{\dfrac{\Phi}{4} + \dfrac{D}{2}\dfrac{\partial\Phi}{\partial\zeta}}{\dfrac{\Phi}{4} - \dfrac{D}{2}\dfrac{\partial\Phi}{\partial\zeta}}. \tag{B-148}$$

Let the boundary between source medium and reflector be a plane perpendicular to ζ at $\zeta = 0$, and let the source medium and reflector be semiinfinite. Then the expression for the flux within the reflector will be of the form

$$\Phi_r = \Phi_0 e^{-\kappa\zeta} \tag{B-149}$$

and

$$\beta = \frac{\dfrac{\Phi_0}{4} - \dfrac{D\kappa}{2}\,\Phi_0}{\dfrac{\Phi_0}{4} + \dfrac{D\kappa}{2}\,\Phi_0} = \frac{1 - 2\,D\kappa}{1 + 2\,D\kappa},$$ (B-150)

and if $D\kappa \ll 1$,

$$\beta \cong 1 - 4\,D\kappa.$$ (B-151)

If $\bar{\Sigma}_a \ll \bar{\Sigma}_s$ in the reflector,

$$D\kappa = (D\bar{\Sigma}_a)^{1/2} = \left(\frac{\bar{\Sigma}_a}{3\bar{\Sigma}_s}\right)^{1/2}.$$ (B-152)

A good reflector should have a reflection coefficient as near as possible to unity, which means that $D\kappa$ should be as small as possible, and (B-152) shows

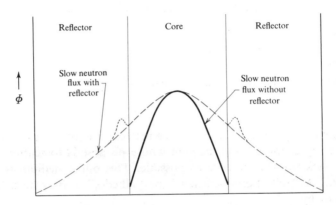

Fig. B-9. A sketch to show how the slow neutron flux in a bare infinite slab reactor would differ from that in an infinite slab reactor with infinite slab reflectors on both faces. The small dotted humps shown in the reflector regions occur in an actual reactor because fast neutrons which pass into the reflector and are moderated there are much less strongly absorbed than are moderated neutrons in the core.

that this demands as small a ratio as possible of absorption to scattering cross section. As shown in Fig. B-9, the reflector not only saves neutrons but flattens the flux distribution, thus spreading heat generation more uniformly in the core.

B-9 Diffusion with Distributed Source—Fermi-Age Treatment

In the preceding section, an expression for the diffusion of thermal neutrons where a source is present was written down. This expression is

$$D\,\nabla^2\Phi - \bar{\Sigma}_a\Phi + S_{th} = \frac{\partial N}{\partial t}.$$ (B-115)

To be a reasonably tractable equation, it would be necessary that the source neutrons have the same energy distribution as the diffusion neutrons. As an approximation, we shall assume that the slowing-down density at τ_{th} provides such a source even though the Fermi-age model would give a monoergic source. Then

$$D \nabla^2 \Phi - \overline{\Sigma}_a \Phi + pq(\mathbf{r}, \tau_{th}, t) = \frac{\partial N}{\partial t}, \tag{B-153}$$

or

$$D \nabla^2 \Phi - \overline{\Sigma}_a \Phi + \frac{k\overline{\Sigma}_a \Phi}{P_{th}} = \frac{\partial N}{\partial t}, \tag{B-154}$$

and, in the steady state where $\partial N/\partial t = 0$,

$$\nabla^2 \Phi + \left(\frac{k}{P_{th}} - 1\right) \frac{\overline{\Sigma}_a}{D} \Phi = 0 \tag{B-155}$$

or, since $\overline{\Sigma}_a/D = \kappa^2 = 1/L^2$,

$$\nabla^2 \Phi + \left(\frac{k}{P_{th}} - 1\right) \frac{1}{L^2} \Phi = 0. \tag{B-156}$$

In the section on slowing-down of neutrons, an equation for the slowing-down density was obtained. This expression is

$$\nabla^2 q(\mathbf{r}, \tau, t) = \frac{\partial q(\mathbf{r}, \tau, t)}{\partial \tau}. \tag{B-157}$$

Substituting for q from Eq. (B-96), this gives

$$\nabla^2 \left(\frac{k\overline{\Sigma}_a \Phi(\mathbf{r}, \tau_{th}, t)e^{-B^2\tau}}{P_{sl}P_{th}p}\right) = \frac{\partial}{\partial \tau}\left(\frac{k\overline{\Sigma}_a \Phi(\mathbf{r}, \tau_{th}, t)e^{-B^2\tau}}{P_{sl}P_{th}p}\right).$$

Since $\Phi(\mathbf{r}, \tau_{th}, t)$ is not a function of τ, this becomes simply

$$\nabla^2 \Phi + B^2 \Phi = 0. \tag{B-158}$$

A comparison of (B-158) with (B-156) shows that

$$B^2 = \left(\frac{k}{P_{th}} - 1\right) \frac{1}{L^2}, \tag{B-159}$$

from which

$$P_{th} = \frac{k}{1 + B^2L^2}.$$

Since we specified a steady state when we set $\partial N/\partial t = 0$, we have implied that $k = 1$. We conclude that

$$P_{th} = \frac{1}{1 + B^2L^2}. \tag{B-160}$$

This result can also be obtained more directly by letting

$$P_{th} = \frac{\overline{\Sigma}_a \Phi}{\overline{\Sigma}_a \Phi + \text{leakage}} = \frac{\overline{\Sigma}_a \Phi}{\overline{\Sigma}_a \Phi + \nabla \cdot \mathbf{J}} \tag{B-161}$$

or
$$P_{th} = \frac{\bar{\Sigma}_a \Phi}{\bar{\Sigma}_a \Phi - D\,\nabla^2 \Phi}. \tag{B-162}$$

Substitution of $\nabla^2\Phi$ from Eq. (B-158) gives

$$P_{th} = \frac{\bar{\Sigma}_a \Phi}{\bar{\Sigma}_a \Phi + DB^2\Phi} = \frac{1}{1 + DB^2/\bar{\Sigma}_a},$$

$$P_{th} = \frac{1}{1 + B^2L^2}. \tag{B-163}$$

Since
$$k = k_\infty P = k_\infty P_{sl} P_{th}, \tag{B-22}$$

$$k = \frac{k_\infty e^{-B^2\tau_{th}}}{1 + B^2L^2}. \tag{B-164}$$

If $B^2\tau_{th}$ is small (usually true in large reactors),

$$k = \frac{k_\infty}{(1 + B^2L^2)e^{B^2\tau_{th}}} = \frac{k_\infty}{(1 + B^2L^2)(1 + B^2\tau_{th} + \cdots)},$$

$$k = \frac{k_\infty}{1 + B^2(L^2 + \tau_{th}) + \cdots} \cong \frac{k_\infty}{1 + B^2 \mathscr{M}^2}. \tag{B-165}$$

B-10 Reactor Kinetics

We are now in a position to re-examine the subject of power build-up and power decay in a reactor, a subject which was discussed in a greatly over-simplified way in Sec. B-3. Equation (B-154) can be rewritten as

$$D\,\nabla^2\Phi + \left(\frac{k}{P_{th}} - 1\right)\Sigma_a\Phi = \frac{\partial N}{\partial t}. \tag{B-166}$$

If we now make the approximation that all neutrons move with the same speed, this becomes

$$L^2\,\nabla^2\Phi + \left(\frac{k}{P_{th}} - 1\right)\Phi = \frac{1}{v\Sigma_a}\frac{\partial(Nv)}{\partial t} = \frac{1}{v\Sigma_a}\frac{\partial\Phi}{\partial t}. \tag{B-167}$$

A neutron, in an infinite medium, will move, on the average, a distance $1/\Sigma_a$ before being captured. It will, therefore, move for a time, l_0, called the "generation time," before capture, where

$$l_0 = \frac{1}{v\Sigma_a}. \tag{B-168}$$

Then (B-167) becomes

$$L^2\,\nabla^2\Phi + \left(\frac{k}{P_{th}} - 1\right)\Phi = l_0\frac{\partial\Phi}{\partial t}. \tag{B-169}$$

If k is exactly one,

$$\nabla^2 \Phi = -B^2 \Phi. \tag{B-158}$$

Let us assume that this relationship will hold for k near unity. Then

$$[-B^2 L^2 - 1 + k(1 + B^2 L^2)]\Phi = l_0 \frac{\partial \Phi}{\partial t}$$

or

$$(k - 1)(1 + B^2 L^2)\Phi = l_0 \frac{\partial \Phi}{\partial t}. \tag{B-170}$$

Let

$$\Phi = R(\mathbf{r})T(t). \tag{B-171}$$

Then

$$\frac{(k - 1)(1 + B^2 L^2)}{l_0} = \frac{1}{T}\frac{dT}{dt} \tag{B-172}$$

or

$$T = T_0 e^{\frac{(k-1)(1+B^2L^2)}{l_0} t}, \tag{B-173}$$

where T_0 is the value of T at $t = 0$.

Thus it is seen that the flux builds up in just the way it did in our over-simplified model. The development has thus far tacitly assumed that there were no delayed neutrons. We may take account of the delayed neutrons by substituting a new generation time in place of l_0. If a fraction β_i of all neutrons are delayed neutrons which come from precursors with a mean lifetime t_{ai}, then the mean generation time will be

$$l_0 = (1 - \beta)l_0 + \sum_i \beta_i(t_{ai} + l_0),$$

$$\bar{l}_0 = l_0 + \sum_i \beta_i t_{ai} = l_0 + \bar{t}_a, \tag{B-174}$$

where

$$\bar{t}_a = \sum_i \beta_i t_{ai} \tag{B-175}$$

and

$$\beta = \sum_i \beta_i. \tag{B-176}$$

Typically, in a thermal reactor,

$$l_0 \sim 10^{-3} \text{ sec} \quad \text{and} \quad \bar{t}_a \sim 10^{-1} \text{ sec}$$

so that

$$\bar{l}_0 \cong \bar{t}_a \tag{B-177}$$

and

$$T = T_0 e^{\frac{(k-1)(1+B^2L^2)}{\bar{t}_a} t} \tag{B-178}$$

from which it is clear that the power build-up, for a given value of k, depends primarily on the delayed neutrons as long as k is below the prompt-critical value. When the reactor is shut down (k reduced appreciably below one) the power decreases more slowly than it would if delayed neutrons were not present.

Poison build-up. Fission products which have extraordinarily large thermal neutron capture cross sections are known as poisons. The chief of these are Xe^{135}, which has an (n, γ) cross section of 2.6 megabarns, and Sm^{149} with a cross section of 5.3×10^4 barns. Only about 0.003 atoms of Xe^{135} are produced directly per U^{235} fission, but another 0.056 atoms of Te^{135} are produced directly per fission. The decay chain of Te^{135} is

$$Te^{135} \xrightarrow[\text{2 min}]{\beta^-} I^{135} \xrightarrow[\text{6.7 hr}]{\beta^-} Xe^{135} \xrightarrow[\text{9.2 hr}]{\beta^-} Cs^{135} \xrightarrow[\text{2} \times 10^6 \text{ yr}]{\beta^-} Ba^{135}.$$

Since the lifetime of I^{135} is so long compared to that of Te^{135}, we may consider I^{135} to be a direct product of fission with 0.056 atoms of I^{135} produced per fission. The equation for build-up of the number, N_I, of I^{135} atoms is

$$\frac{dN_I}{dt} = \gamma_1 \bar{\Sigma}_f \Phi - \lambda_1 N_I - \bar{\sigma}_1 N_I \Phi, \tag{B-179}$$

where γ_1 is the number of I^{135} atoms formed per fission (0.056), $\bar{\Sigma}_f$ is the average macroscopic cross section for fission, λ_1 is the decay constant of I^{135}, and $\bar{\sigma}_1$ is the average (n, γ) thermal neutron capture cross section of I^{135}. Since $\bar{\sigma}_1$ is only about 7 barns, $\bar{\sigma}_1 \Phi$ will be only 7×10^{-9} even when Φ has the very large value of 10^{15} neutrons/cm²/sec. By contrast, $\lambda_1 = 2.9 \times 10^{-5}$ sec^{-1}, so that the term $\bar{\sigma}_1 \Phi N_I$ may be neglected by comparison. Then (B-179) reduces to

$$\frac{dN_I}{dt} = \gamma_1 \bar{\Sigma}_f \Phi - \lambda_1 N_I. \tag{B-180}$$

When a steady state has been reached, dN_I/dt will be zero and the I^{135} concentration given by

$$N_{I_{st}} = \frac{\gamma_1 \bar{\Sigma}_f \Phi}{\lambda_1}. \tag{B-181}$$

When Φ and N_I are changing, the solution to (B-180) is

$$N_I = e^{-\lambda_1 t} \left[N_{I_0} + \gamma_1 \bar{\Sigma}_f \int_0^t e^{\lambda_1 t} \Phi \, dt \right]. \tag{B-182}$$

The build-up of the number, N_{Xe}, of Xe^{135} atoms is given by

$$\frac{dN_{Xe}}{dt} = \gamma_2 \bar{\Sigma}_f \Phi + \lambda_1 N_I - \lambda_2 N_{Xe} - \bar{\sigma}_2 N_{Xe} \Phi, \tag{B-183}$$

where γ_2 is the number (0.003) of Xe^{135} atoms formed directly per fission, λ_2 is the decay constant of Xe^{135}, and $\bar{\sigma}_2$ is the average (n, γ) cross section of

Xe^{135}. When a steady state has been reached dN_{Xe}/dt will be zero and the Xe^{135} concentration given by

$$N_{Xe_{st}} = \frac{\gamma_2 \bar{\Sigma}_f \Phi + \lambda_1 N_{I_{st}}}{\lambda_2 + \bar{\sigma}_2 \Phi},$$

$$N_{Xe_{st}} = \frac{(\gamma_1 + \gamma_2)\bar{\Sigma}_f \Phi}{\lambda_2 + \bar{\sigma}_2 \Phi}. \tag{B-184}$$

The time-varying solution to (B-183) is

$$N_{Xe} = e^{-\int_0^t (\lambda_2 + \bar{\sigma}_2 \Phi)dt'} \left[\int_0^t (\lambda_1 N_I + \gamma_2 \bar{\Sigma}_f \Phi) e^{\int_0^t (\lambda_2 + \bar{\sigma}_2 \Phi)dt'} dt + N_{Xe_0} \right], \tag{B-185}$$

where N_{Xe_0} is the concentration of Xe^{135} atoms at $t = 0$.

It is seen from Eq. (B-184) that the large capture cross section of Xe^{135} prevents the Xe^{135} concentration from building up to large values in the steady state, but that the concentration of I^{135} may become quite large. If a reactor which has been operating steadily at a high power level is suddenly shut down, the accumulated I^{135} continues to decay to Xe^{135} and, since there are no thermal neutrons to be captured, the concentration of Xe^{135} begins to increase. The xenon concentration will reach its maximum value in about 12 hours. If the reactor is not restarted quickly, the Xe^{135} concentration may become so large that it will be impossible to restart the reactor for a few days. In a liquid homogeneous reactor it is possible to remove the xenon gas continuously and thus greatly reduce the poison problem.

Temperature effects. The temperature of a reactor affects its operation in a number of ways. An increase in temperature shifts the energy spectrum of thermal neutrons to higher energy values with a corresponding increase in mean velocity. Since

$$\Phi = N\bar{v}$$

this means an increase in neutron flux if the neutron concentration is kept constant. This, in itself, would tend to increase the thermal neutron reaction rate, $\bar{\Sigma}\Phi$, but $\bar{\Sigma}$ depends on both $\bar{v}$ and the number of nuclei per unit volume. Usually the cross section, σ, decreases with increasing velocity. A rise in temperature ordinarily results in an expansion of the reactor material, which in turn decreases the density of nuclei. On both counts, then, $\bar{\Sigma}$ tends to decrease with increasing temperature.

In our earlier discussion of slowing-down, we ignored the thermal motions of the scattering nuclei. This thermal motion changes the relative velocity of neutron and nucleus. The energy at which a resonance absorption can occur is therefore changed because of the different amount of energy associated with center-of-mass motion. It is customary to speak of this phenomenon as Doppler broadening of the resonance peaks. The effective broadening of the resonance peaks decreases the resonance escape probability and hence decreases k.

It may seem surprising that neutron leakage increases with increasing temperature. The path length of the neutron through the reactor increases as the linear dimensions of the reactor increase with expansion, but the density of nuclei varies inversely as the *cube* of the linear dimensions. Thus the non-leakage probabilities and consequently k tend to decrease with temperature because of this effect.

It can be seen that it is not easy to predict whether k in a given reactor will

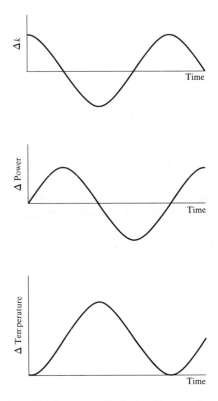

Fig. B-10. A sudden increase, Δk, in k will cause the power level and temperature of the reactor to oscillate if the temperature coefficient of reactivity is negative. The effect of delayed neutrons, which has been neglected in this figure, is to introduce damping of these oscillations so that Δk oscillates about zero with decreasing amplitude as time goes on. The temperature oscillation will also gradually die out, leaving the reactor at a new, stable, higher temperature. The flux will increase more on the larger upswings of Δk than it will decrease on the following, smaller, downswings. Consequently, the final stable flux, and therefore also power, will be greater than the initial flux and power.

increase or decrease with temperature. It is very desirable, however, that k decrease with temperature. Then if k is made slightly greater than one, the power level in the reactor will begin to increase and this will result in an increase of temperature which will, in turn, cause a decrease in k. Thus the reactor will be self-limiting in the power level it will reach. For this reason nearly all reactors have negative temperature coefficients of reactivity, $-\Delta k/k$ per degree temperature rise, falling roughly in the range 10^{-2} to 10^{-5} per °C. A sudden small change in k will not merely cause the power level to shift to a new stable value, however, but will result in oscillations about such a new stable value. This is perhaps best seen by referring to Fig. B-10. The increase in k causes the power to begin rising, but since the power has not yet changed appreciably, the rise in temperature is very small and consequently the reduction in k is small. The power will continue to increase as long as Δk is positive. The temperature will increase more and more rapidly as the power level rises. The power will reach its maximum value when Δk is zero and the rate of change of temperature will be a maximum at this time. As k becomes negative, the power level begins to drop, but since it is still above its mean value, the temperature will continue to rise. Since the mean temperature is higher than it was before the increase in k, it is clear that the mean power level must be correspondingly higher than its former value. The power plot in Fig. B-10 is therefore the variation in power about the new mean power level. A minor disadvantage of a negative temperature coefficient is the fact that the maximum reactivity of the reactor with the control and safety rods (both thermal neutron absorbers) removed is greater than normal if the reactor is allowed to become very cold, thus increasing the possibility of a reactor "accident."

REFERENCES

1. Hughes, D. J., and Harvey, J. A., *Neutron Cross Sections*, Brookhaven National Laboratory Report No. BNL 325 (1955).

2. Carslaw, H. S., and Jaeger, J. C., *Conduction of Heat in Solids* (Oxford: Clarendon Press, 1947).

GENERAL REFERENCES

1. Glasstone, S., and Edlund, M. C., *The Elements of Nuclear Reactor Theory* (Princeton, N.J.: D. Van Nostrand Company, 1952).

2. Meghreblian, R. V., and Holmes, D. K., *Reactor Analysis* (New York: McGraw-Hill Book Company, 1960).

3. Weinberg, A. M., and Wigner, E. P., *The Physical Theory of Neutron Chain Reactors* (Chicago: University of Chicago Press, 1958).

THE WAVE-MECHANICAL
TREATMENT OF THE
PENETRATION OF POTENTIAL
BARRIERS BY CHARGED
PARTICLES

C-1 The Schrödinger Equation

It is convenient, in such a brief presentation as this, to simply accept the Schrödinger equation as a basic law of wave mechanics, just as one accepts the law

$$f = M \frac{dv}{dt}$$

in classical mechanics. The Schrödinger equation may be written

$$-\frac{\hbar^2}{2M} \nabla^2 \Psi + U\Psi = i\hbar \frac{\partial \Psi}{\partial t}, \qquad \text{(C-1)}$$

where U is the potential energy of the system, Ψ is a function of the spatial coordinates (x, y, z) and the time (t) and is a complex quantity (one having both real and imaginary parts). The quantity Ψ, which is referred to as the "wave function," has no physical interpretation, but the square of the magnitude of Ψ is interpreted as a probability density; for example, the probability of finding a particle in one cubic centimeter of volume at x, y, z, at the time t.

Since Ψ is a complex quantity, it may be written as

$$\Psi = u + iw \tag{C-2}$$

where u and w are real quantities (both functions of x, y, z, and t), and $i = \sqrt{-1}$. The complex conjugate of the wave function, namely Ψ^*, is defined by

$$\Psi^* = u - iw. \tag{C-3}$$

If one replaces each of the quantities in (C-1) by its complex conjugate, he obtains an equation in Ψ^* which must be satisfied.

$$-\frac{\hbar^2}{2M} \nabla^2 \Psi^* + U\Psi^* = -i\hbar \frac{\partial \Psi^*}{\partial t}. \tag{C-4}$$

Equation (C-4) may also be obtained in the following way. Substitute (C-2) into (C-1). This gives

$$-\frac{\hbar^2}{2M} (\nabla^2 u + i \nabla^2 w) + U(u + iw) = i\hbar \left(\frac{\partial u}{\partial t} + i \frac{\partial w}{\partial t} \right). \tag{C-5}$$

Since both the real and imaginary parts of (C-5) must be satisfied independently, (C-5) may be broken up into a pair of coupled equations:

$$-\frac{\hbar^2}{2M} \nabla^2 u + Uu = -\hbar \frac{\partial w}{\partial t} \tag{C-6}$$

and

$$-\frac{\hbar^2}{2M} \nabla^2 w + Uw = \hbar \frac{\partial u}{\partial t}. \tag{C-7}$$

If (C-7) is now multiplied through by $-i$ and added to (C-6), the result is

$$-\frac{\hbar^2}{2M} (\nabla^2 u - i \nabla^2 w) + U(u - iw) = -i\hbar \left(\frac{\partial u}{\partial t} - i \frac{\partial w}{\partial t} \right),$$

$$-\frac{\hbar^2}{2M} \nabla^2 (u - iw) + U(u - iw) = -i\hbar \frac{\partial}{\partial t} (u - iw),$$

or

$$-\frac{\hbar^2}{2M} \nabla^2 \Psi^* + U\Psi^* = -i\hbar \frac{\partial \Psi^*}{\partial t}. \tag{C-4}$$

The probability density, D, is then given by

$$D = |\Psi|^2 = \Psi\Psi^* = (u + iw)(u - iw) = u^2 + w^2. \tag{C-8}$$

Where U is not a function of the time, it is possible to effect a separation of variables by letting

$$\Psi(x, y, z, t) = \psi(x, y, z)\phi(t) \tag{C-9}$$

and substituting (C-9) in (C-1). After dividing through by $\psi \phi$, the result is

$$\frac{1}{\psi}\left(-\frac{\hbar^2}{2M} \nabla^2\psi + U\psi\right) = i\hbar \frac{1}{\phi} \frac{d\phi}{dt}. \tag{C-10}$$

The only way a function of x, y, z alone can be equal to a function of t alone is for each to be a constant, say W. Then

$$\frac{d\phi}{dt} = \frac{W}{i\hbar} \phi \tag{C-11}$$

and

$$\nabla^2\psi + \frac{2M}{\hbar^2} (W - U)\psi = 0. \tag{C-12}$$

From (C-12) it is evident that W must have the same dimensions as U (i.e., energy). The solution to (C-11) is

$$\phi = \phi_0 e^{-(iW/\hbar)t}, \tag{C-13}$$

where ϕ_0 is a constant determined by the initial condition of the system. The solution to (C-12) becomes particularly simple if U is not a function of x, y, z. To simplify the discussion, only the one-dimensional case will be considered from this point on. In this case, (C-12) becomes

$$\frac{d^2\psi}{dx^2} + \frac{2M}{\hbar^2} (W - U)\psi = 0. \tag{C-14}$$

It is instructive to consider the solutions which result according as W is greater or less than U.

CASE I. $W > U$. If one lets

$$K = \frac{\sqrt{2M(W - U)}}{\hbar} \tag{C-15}$$

then

$$\frac{d^2\psi}{dx^2} + K^2\psi = 0, \tag{C-16}$$

where K is a positive constant. This is just the familiar simple-harmonic-motion equation, to which the solution is

$$\psi = A_0 \sin (Kx + \alpha), \tag{C-17}$$

where A_0 is a *complex* constant and α is a constant phase-angle. It is more convenient to write the solution in the alternative form

$$\psi = A_1 e^{iKx} + B_1 e^{-iKx}. \tag{C-18}$$

From this, it follows that

$$\Psi(x, t) = \psi(x)\phi(t) = \phi_0 A_1 e^{-i[(W/\hbar)t - Kx]} + \phi_0 B_1 e^{-i[(W/\hbar)t + Kx]}. \quad \text{(C-19)}$$

The first term, that involving $[(W/\hbar)t - Kx]$ in the exponent, represents a wave traveling in the positive x-direction, while the second term represents a wave traveling in the negative x-direction. It is now apparent why Ψ is called a wave function.

CASE II. $W < U$. Let

$$L = \frac{\sqrt{2M(U - W)}}{\hbar}, \quad \text{(C-20)}$$

then

$$\frac{d^2\psi}{dx^2} - L^2\psi = 0, \quad \text{(C-21)}$$

where L is a positive constant. The solution to (C-21) is similar to that of (C-19) except that the exponents are real.

$$\psi = A_2 e^{Lx} + B_2 e^{-Lx}. \quad \text{(C-22)}$$

C-2 Probability Density Current

The flow of probability density past a point per unit time is called the *probability density current*. For example, suppose a beam of particles, whose average density is one particle per thousand centimeters, is moving in the positive x-direction with a velocity of 10^8 cm/sec. Then the probability density, that is, the probability of finding a particle in one centimeter, is $D = 10^{-3}$. The probability density current is the probability density times its (group) velocity of flow or $10^8 \times 10^{-3} = 10^5$. In other words, the number of particles passing any point, on the average, is 10^5 per second.

Let the probability density, D, within an element of length δx, be changing at a rate $\partial\rho/\partial t$. Let the probability density current flowing into δx from the left be J, and that flowing out of δx toward the right be $J + \delta J$, which may also be expressed as

$$J + \frac{\partial J}{\partial x}\delta x.$$

The conservation of probability, which becomes the conservation of matter when summed over all space, demands that the gain in probability density in δx must equal the excess of the flow of probability density into δx over the flow out of δx. That is

$$\left(\frac{\partial D}{\partial t}\delta t\right)\delta x = -\left(\frac{\partial J}{\partial x}\delta x\right)\delta t \quad \text{(C-23)}$$

or
$$\frac{\partial D}{\partial t} = -\frac{\partial J}{\partial x}.$$
(C-24)

But
$$\frac{\partial D}{\partial t} = \frac{\partial}{\partial t}(\Psi\Psi^*) = \Psi\frac{\partial \Psi^*}{\partial t} + \Psi^*\frac{\partial \Psi}{\partial t}.$$
(C-25)

Substituting for $\partial\Psi/\partial t$ and $\partial\Psi^*/\partial t$ from Eqs. (C-1) and (C-4), we have

$$\frac{\partial D}{\partial t} = \Psi\left(\frac{-1}{i\hbar}\right)\left(-\frac{\hbar^2}{2M}\frac{\partial^2\Psi^*}{\partial x^2} + U\Psi^*\right) + \Psi^*\left(\frac{1}{i\hbar}\right)\left(-\frac{\hbar^2}{2M}\frac{\partial^2\Psi}{\partial x^2} + U\Psi\right)$$

$$= \frac{-i\hbar}{2M}\left(\Psi\frac{\partial^2\Psi^*}{\partial x^2} - \Psi^*\frac{\partial^2\Psi}{\partial x^2}\right) = -\frac{\partial}{\partial x}\left[\frac{i\hbar}{2M}\left(\Psi\frac{\partial\Psi^*}{\partial x} - \Psi^*\frac{\partial\Psi}{\partial x}\right)\right].$$

Comparison with (C-24) shows that

$$J = \frac{i\hbar}{2M}\left(\Psi\frac{\partial\Psi^*}{\partial x} - \Psi^*\frac{\partial\Psi}{\partial x}\right) + F(t),$$
(C-26)

where F is an arbitrary function of the time. In the particular case where Ψ is continuously zero in some region, $F(t)$ must be zero. It will be assumed that $F(t)$ is zero in all cases of practical interest, in which case

$$J = \frac{i\hbar}{2M}\left(\Psi\frac{\partial\Psi^*}{\partial x} - \Psi^*\frac{\partial\Psi}{\partial x}\right).$$
(C-27)

C-3 De Broglie Wavelength of a Particle

Let a particle of mass M, moving in the positive x-direction, be represented by a plane wave moving in the same direction. Then

$$\Psi = Ge^{-i[(W/\hbar)t - Kx]},$$
(C-28)

and
$$\Psi^* = G^*e^{i[(W/\hbar)t - Kx]}.$$
(C-29)

The current will be

$$J = \frac{i\hbar}{2M}[-Ge^{-i[(W/\hbar)t - Kx]}ikG^*e^{i[(W/\hbar)t - Kx]} - G^*e^{i[(W/\hbar)t - Kx]}ikGe^{-i[(W/\hbar)t - Kx]},$$

$$J = \frac{\hbar K}{M}GG^* = \frac{\hbar K}{M}\Psi\Psi^* = \frac{\hbar KD}{M}.$$
(C-30)

From (C-28) it is seen that Ψ returns to the same value each time Kx increases by 2π. The wavelength, then, is

$$\lambda = \frac{2\pi}{K}$$
(C-31)

and the frequency is

$$\frac{W}{2\pi\hbar},$$

so that

$$J = \frac{D\hbar}{M}\frac{2\pi}{\lambda}. \tag{C-32}$$

But J is also equal to the linear particle density, D, multiplied by the particle velocity, or

$$J = Dv_g. \tag{C-33}$$

From (C-32) and (C-33) it follows that

$$\lambda = \frac{2\pi\hbar}{Mv_g} = \frac{h}{Mv_g}, \tag{C-34}$$

which is the well-known de Broglie wavelength for a particle of mass M moving with a velocity v_g. Moreover, from Eqs. (C-15), (C-30), and (C-33), we obtain

$$\frac{D\sqrt{2M(W - U)}}{M} = Dv_g, \tag{C-35}$$

which yields

$$(W - U) = \tfrac{1}{2}mv_g^2 \tag{C-36}$$

or

$$W = U + \tfrac{1}{2}mv_g^2, \tag{C-37}$$

so that W is seen to be the total energy, kinetic plus potential, of a moving particle. Equations (C-34) and (C-37) justify the representation of a freely moving particle by a plane wave as was done in (C-28). It should be noted that the group velocity, according to (C-35), is

$$v_g = \frac{\sqrt{2M(W - U)}}{M}, \tag{C-38}$$

whereas the wave (or phase) velocity is

$$v_w = \lambda \times (\text{frequency}) = \frac{2\pi}{K} \times \frac{W}{2\pi\hbar},$$

$$v_w = \frac{W\hbar}{\hbar\sqrt{2M(W - U)}} = \frac{W}{\sqrt{2M(W - U)}} \tag{C-39}$$

so that

$$\frac{v_g}{v_w} = \frac{2(W - U)}{W}. \tag{C-40}$$

Where $U = 0$, the group velocity is twice the wave velocity

C-4 Boundary Conditions

If there is a sudden change in the potential U at a point $x = a$, then the solution for Ψ will be different for $x < a$ than it is for $x > a$ (see Fig. C-1).

A sufficient condition that the probability density be single-valued at the boundary is that

$$\Psi_1\big|_a = \Psi_2\big|_a. \tag{C-41}$$

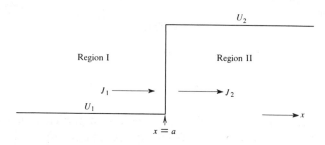

Fig. C-1. A one-dimensional potential step is encountered at $x = a$. The current, J, must be continuous at the boundary between region I and region II.

If the probability density is not to accumulate or be generated at the boundary,

$$J_1\big|_a = J_2\big|_a$$

and
$$\left[\Psi_1 \frac{\partial \Psi_1^*}{\partial x} - \Psi_1^* \frac{\partial \Psi_1}{\partial x}\right]_a = \left[\Psi_2 \frac{\partial \Psi_2^*}{\partial x} - \Psi_1^* \frac{\partial \Psi_2}{\partial x}\right]_a. \tag{C-42}$$

From (C-41) it follows that

$$\Psi_1^*\big|_a = \Psi_2^*\big|_a \tag{C-43}$$

so that (C-42) becomes

$$\Psi_1\big|_a \left(\frac{\partial \Psi_1^*}{\partial x}\bigg|_a - \frac{\partial \Psi_2^*}{\partial x}\bigg|_a\right) = \Psi_1^*\big|_a \left(\frac{\partial \Psi_1}{\partial x}\bigg|_a - \frac{\partial \Psi_2}{\partial x}\bigg|_a\right). \tag{C-44}$$

A sufficient condition that (C-44) be true is that

$$\frac{\partial \Psi_1}{\partial x}\bigg|_a = \frac{\partial \Psi_2}{\partial x}\bigg|_a. \tag{C-45}$$

We have not shown that it is a necessary condition, but shall assume that the slope of the wave function must be continuous at boundaries. As a matter of fact, (C-45) is often taken as one of the postulates of wave mechanics.

C-5 Reflection by a Small Potential Step

A particle whose total energy is W is moving in a region in which its potential energy, which is less than W, is U_1. What is the probability that the particle will be reflected if it comes to a region in which its potential energy would be U_2, where U_2 is also less than W? (See Fig. C-2.)

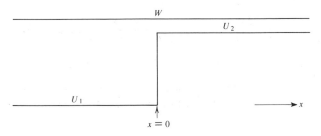

Fig. C-2. A particle of total energy W approaches from the left. It encounters a potential step such that $U_2 < W$ at $x = 0$.

A particle incident from the left may be represented by

$$\Psi_1 = A_1 e^{-i(\omega t - K_1 x)}, \tag{C-46}$$

where ω has been written for $W/\hbar$.

At the boundary ($x = 0$) it may be either reflected or transmitted. The probability of reflection is related to

$$\Psi_1' = B_1 e^{-i(\omega t + K_1 x)}, \tag{C-47}$$

since this represents a particle moving away from the boundary in the negative x-direction, while the probability of transmission is related to

$$\Psi_2 = A_2 e^{-i(\omega t - K_2 x)}. \tag{C-48}$$

The probability of finding the particle to the left of the boundary is enhanced by the fact that it may be found there as either an incident or a reflected particle. Application of the first boundary condition (C-41), then gives

$$[\Psi_1 + \Psi_1']_{x=0} = [\Psi_2]_{x=0} \tag{C-49}$$

or

$$A_1 e^{-i\omega t} + B_1 e^{-i\omega t} = A_2 e^{-i\omega t},$$

which gives

$$A_1 + B_1 = A_2. \tag{C-50}$$

The second boundary condition, (C-45), may be written

$$\left[\frac{\partial}{\partial x}(\Psi_1 + \Psi_1')\right]_{x=0} = \left[\frac{\partial}{\partial x}\Psi_2\right]_{x=0} \tag{C-51}$$

or
$$A_1 i K_1 e^{-i\omega t} - B_1 i K_1 e^{-i\omega t} = A_2 i K_2 e^{-i\omega t},$$

which becomes
$$K_1(A_1 - B_1) = K_2 A_2. \tag{C-52}$$

From (C-50) and (C-52) it is found that

$$B_1 = \left(\frac{K_1 - K_2}{K_1 + K_2}\right) A_1 = \left(\frac{\sqrt{W - U_1} - \sqrt{W - U_2}}{\sqrt{W - U_1} + \sqrt{W - U_2}}\right) A_1 \tag{C-53}$$

and

$$A_2 = \left(\frac{2K_1}{K_1 + K_2}\right) A_1 = \left(\frac{2\sqrt{W - U_1}}{\sqrt{W - U_1} + \sqrt{W - U_2}}\right) A_1. \tag{C-54}$$

Now the reflection probability, or reflection coefficient, may be defined by

$$P_r = \frac{\text{probability current density flowing away from discontinuity toward left}}{\text{probability current density flowing toward discontinuity from left}}.$$

$$P_r = \frac{J_1'}{J_1}. \tag{C-55}$$

It has already been shown (C-30), that

$$J_1 = \frac{\sqrt{2M(W - U_1)}}{M} D_1 = \frac{\sqrt{2M(W - U_1)}}{M} A_1 A_1^* \tag{C-56}$$

and
$$J_1' = \frac{\sqrt{2M(W - U_1)}}{M} B_1 B_1^*, \tag{C-57}$$

so that

$$P_r = \frac{J_1'}{J_1} = \frac{B_1 B_1^*}{A_1 A_1^*} = \left(\frac{\sqrt{W - U_1} - \sqrt{W - U_2}}{\sqrt{W - U_1} + \sqrt{W - U_2}}\right)^2. \tag{C-58}$$

Similarly, a transmission coefficient, T, may be defined by

$$P_{tr} = \frac{J_2}{J_1} = \frac{\frac{1}{M}\sqrt{2M(W - U_2)}\, A_2 A_2^*}{\frac{1}{M}\sqrt{2M(W - U_1)}\, A_1 A_1^*} = \frac{4\sqrt{W - U_1}\,\sqrt{W - U_2}}{(\sqrt{W - U_1} + \sqrt{W - U_2})^2}, \tag{C-59}$$

and it is evident that
$$P_r + P_{tr} = 1, \tag{C-60}$$

as must be the case from conservation of probability.

NUMERICAL EXAMPLE I. Let $W = 9$ Mev, $U_1 = 0$, $U_2 = 5$ Mev. Then

$$P_r = \left(\frac{\sqrt{9 - 0} - \sqrt{9 - 5}}{\sqrt{9 - 0} + \sqrt{9 - 5}}\right)^2 = \left(\frac{3 - 2}{3 + 2}\right)^2 = \frac{1}{25} \text{ or } 4\%,$$

while
$$P_{tr} = \frac{4\sqrt{9 - 0}\,\sqrt{9 - 5}}{(\sqrt{9 - 0} + \sqrt{9 - 5})^2} = \frac{24}{25} \text{ or } 96\%.$$

NUMERICAL EXAMPLE II. Let $W = 9$ Mev, $U_1 = 0$, $U_2 = 9$ Mev. Then

$$P_r = \left(\frac{\sqrt{9-0} - \sqrt{9-9}}{\sqrt{9-0} + \sqrt{9-9}}\right)^2 = \frac{9}{9} = 100\%,$$

while

$$P_{tr} = \frac{4\sqrt{9-0}\quad \sqrt{9-9}}{(\sqrt{9-0} + \sqrt{9-9})^2} = 0.$$

NUMERICAL EXAMPLE III. Let $W = 9$ Mev, $U_1 = 5$ Mev, $U_2 = 0$, Then

$$P_r = \left(\frac{\sqrt{9-5} - \sqrt{9-0}}{\sqrt{9-5} + \sqrt{9-0}}\right)^2 = \left(\frac{-1}{5}\right)^2 = \frac{1}{25} = 4\%,$$

while

$$P_{tr} = \frac{4\sqrt{9-5}\quad \sqrt{9-0}}{(\sqrt{9-5} + \sqrt{9-0})^2} = \frac{24}{25} = 96\%.$$

It will be noted that the particle fares no better in getting into a region of lower potential than into one of higher potential, whereas the reflection coefficient would be zero for either case for a particle obeying the laws of classical mechanics.

C-6 Reflection by a Large Potential Step

A particle of total energy W is incident from the left, which is a region where its potential energy U_1 is less than W. At $x = 0$ a region is encountered where its potential energy U_2 would be greater than W, as shown in Fig. C-3.

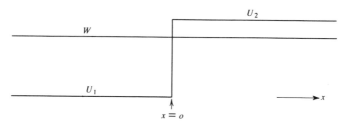

Fig. C-3. A particle of total energy W approaches from the left. It encounters a potential step such that $U_2 > W$ at $x = 0$.

As in Sec. C-5, the incident particle may be represented by

$$\Psi_1 = A_1 e^{-i(\omega t - Kx)} \tag{C-61}$$

and the reflected particle by

$$\Psi_1' = B_1 e^{-i(\omega t + Kx)}, \tag{C-62}$$

but, since $U_2 > W$, the transmitted particle must be represented by

$$\Psi_2 = A_2 e^{-i(\omega t - iLx)}. \tag{C-63}$$

(The second solution to Ψ_2, involving $+iLx$, is ruled out by the fact that this would introduce a factor

$$e^{+Lx}$$

which would make the probability infinite for infinite x.) At $x = 0$,

$$[\Psi_1 + \Psi_1']_{x=0} = [\Psi_2]_{x=0},$$

which yields

$$A_1 + B_1 = A_2, \tag{C-64}$$

while

$$\left[\frac{\partial}{\partial x}(\Psi_1 + \Psi_1')\right]_{x=0} = \left[\frac{\partial}{\partial x}\Psi_2\right]_{x=0}$$

leads to

$$iKA_1 e^{-i\omega t} - iKB_1 e^{-i\omega t} = -LA_2 e^{-i\omega t}$$

or

$$K(A_1 - B_1) = iLA_2. \tag{C-65}$$

From (C-64) and (C-65) it follows that

$$B_1 = \left(\frac{K - iL}{K + iL}\right)A_1 = \left(\frac{\sqrt{W - U_1} - i\sqrt{U_2 - W}}{\sqrt{W - U_1} + i\sqrt{U_2 - W}}\right)A_1 \tag{C-66}$$

and

$$A_2 = \left(\frac{2K}{K + iL}\right)A_1 = \left(\frac{2\sqrt{W - U_1}}{\sqrt{W - U_1} + i\sqrt{U_2 - W}}\right)A_1. \tag{C-67}$$

The reflection coefficient is

$$P_r = \frac{\dfrac{1}{M}\sqrt{2M(W - U_1)}\,B_1 B_1^*}{\dfrac{1}{M}\sqrt{2M(W - U_1)}\,A_1 A_1^*} = \frac{(\sqrt{W - U_1})^2 + (\sqrt{U_2 - W})^2}{(\sqrt{W - U_1})^2 + (\sqrt{U_2 - W})^2} = 100\%. \tag{C-68}$$

The transmission coefficient must be computed using (C-27), so

$$P_{tr} = \frac{\dfrac{i\hbar}{2M}\left(\Psi_2 \dfrac{\partial \Psi_2^*}{\partial x} - \Psi_2^* \dfrac{\partial \Psi_2}{\partial x}\right)}{\dfrac{1}{M}\sqrt{2M(W - U_1)}\,A_1 A_1^*}. \tag{C-69}$$

But

$$\Psi_2 \frac{\partial \Psi_2^*}{\partial x} - \Psi_2^* \frac{\partial \Psi_2}{\partial x}$$

$$= A_2 e^{-i\omega t} e^{-Lx}(-L)A_2^* e^{i\omega t} e^{-Lx} - A_2^* e^{i\omega t} e^{-Lx}(-L)A_2 e^{-i\omega t} e^{-Lx} = 0, \tag{C-70}$$

so that $P_{tr} = 0$, as of course it must to be consistent with (C-68).

C-7 Barrier Penetration

A particle of total energy W moving in a region of potential energy U_1, where U_1 is less than W, encounters a limited region in which the potential energy U_2 is greater than W, as shown in Fig. C-4. It is desired to find the probability of transmission through this region.

In region I the incident particle may be represented by

$$\Psi_1 = A_1 e^{-i(\omega t - Kx)} \qquad\qquad (\text{C-71})$$

and the reflected particle by

$$\Psi_1' = B_1 e^{-i(\omega t + Kx)}. \qquad\qquad (\text{C-72})$$

In region II, in contrast to the situation in Sec. C-6, both solutions to the

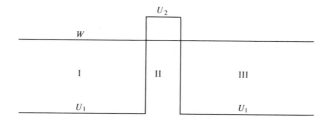

Fig. C-4. A particle of total energy W, approaching from the left, encounters a potential barrier ($U_2 > W$) in region II.

Schrödinger equation are allowable, as x remains finite within the region. Thus

$$\Psi_2 = A_2 e^{-i(\omega t - iLx)} + B_2 e^{-i(\omega t + iLx)}. \qquad\qquad (\text{C-73})$$

In region III, the transmitted particle may be represented by

$$\Psi_3 = A_3 e^{-i(\omega t - Kx)}. \qquad\qquad (\text{C-74})$$

At the first boundary, $x = 0$,

$$[\Psi_1 + \Psi_1']_{x=0} = [\Psi_2]_{x=0}, \qquad\qquad (\text{C-75})$$

$$A_1 e^{-i\omega t} + B_1 e^{-i\omega t} = A_2 e^{-i\omega t} + B_2 e^{-i\omega t},$$

or $\qquad\qquad A_1 + B_1 = A_2 + B_2 \qquad\qquad (\text{C-76})$

and $\qquad\qquad \left[\dfrac{\partial}{\partial x}(\Psi_1 + \Psi_1')\right]_{x=0} = \left[\dfrac{\partial}{\partial x}\Psi_2\right]_{x=0}, \qquad\qquad (\text{C-77})$

$$iKA_1 e^{-i\omega t} - iKB_1 e^{-i\omega t} = -LA_2 e^{-i\omega t} + LB_2 e^{-i\omega t},$$

or $\qquad\qquad K(A_1 - B_1) = iL(A_2 - B_2). \qquad\qquad (\text{C-78})$

At the second boundary, $x = a$,

$$[\Psi_2]_a = [\Psi_3]_a, \tag{C-79}$$

$$A_2 e^{-i\omega t} e^{-La} + B_2 e^{-i\omega t} e^{La} = A_3 e^{-i\omega t} e^{iKa},$$

or
$$\frac{A_2}{b} + B_2 T = A_3 e^{iKa}, \tag{C-80}$$

where
$$T \equiv e^{La} \tag{C-81}$$

$$\left[\frac{\partial \Psi_2}{\partial x}\right]_a = \left[\frac{\partial \Psi_3}{\partial x}\right]_a, \tag{C-82}$$

$$-LA_2 e^{-i\omega t} e^{-La} + LB_2 e^{-i\omega t} e^{La} = iKA_3 e^{-i\omega t} e^{iKa},$$

$$L\left(\frac{A_2}{T} - B_2 T\right) = -iKA_3 e^{iKa}. \tag{C-83}$$

From (C-76), (C-78), (C-80), and (C-83) one obtains

$$A_3 = \frac{4KLTe^{-iKa}}{2KL(1 + T^2) + i(K^2 - L^2)(1 - T^2)} A_1. \tag{C-84}$$

The transmission coefficient P_{tr} is then

$$P_{tr} = \frac{\dfrac{1}{M}\sqrt{2M(W - U_1)}\, A_3 A_3^*}{\dfrac{1}{M}\sqrt{2M(W - U_1)}\, A_1 A_1^*} = \frac{A_3 A_3^*}{A_1 A_1^*}$$

$$= \frac{16(W - U_1)(U_2 - W)T^2}{4(W - U_1)(U_2 - W)(1 + T^2)^2 + (2W - U_1 - U_2)^2(1 - T^2)^2}. \tag{C-85}$$

SCATTERING OF ALPHA PARTICLES BY THE COULOMB FIELD OF A NUCLEUS

In textbooks and treatises on mechanics it is shown that a particle moving about in an inverse square repulsive field always follows a hyperbolic orbit. From Fig. D-1, the following useful relations can be deduced:

$$\frac{a}{\epsilon a} = \frac{1}{\epsilon} = \cos \theta, \tag{D-1}$$

or
$$\epsilon = \sec \theta. \tag{D-2}$$

$$F'A = F'O + OA = F'O \left(1 + \frac{OA}{F'O}\right) = F'O \left(1 + \frac{1}{\epsilon}\right)$$

$$= F'O(1 + \cos \theta) = \frac{R}{\sin \theta}(1 + \cos \theta),$$

$$F'A = R \cot \left(\frac{\theta}{2}\right). \tag{D-3}$$

The nucleus of the scattering atom, which is located at F', will be assumed, in the following development, to be so massive that its motion may be neglected. For a head-on or central collision, conservation of energy gives

$$\frac{1}{2} M v_0^2 = \frac{q_1 \cdot q_2}{C},\tag{D-4}$$

where M is the mass of the α particle, v_0 is the initial velocity of the α particle, q_1 is the nuclear charge, q_2 is the α-particle charge, and C is the distance of closest approach. Since the coulomb force is a central or radial force, it

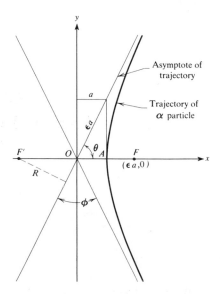

Fig. D-1. Hyperbolic trajectory of an alpha particle in the repulsive coulomb field of a heavy nucleus located at F'.

produces no torque about F', so that the angular momentum of the α particle about F' must be constant. Hence

$$M v_0 R = M v \overline{F'A}$$

or
$$v_0 R = v \overline{F'A},\tag{D-5}$$

where v is the velocity of the α particle at A. From conservation of energy, and using (D-4),

$$\frac{1}{2} M v_0^2 = \frac{1}{2} M v^2 + \frac{q_1 q_2}{\overline{F'A}} = \frac{1}{2} M v^2 + \frac{1}{2} M v_0^2 \frac{C}{\overline{F'A}},\tag{D-6}$$

which reduces to

$$v^2 = v_0^2 \left(1 - \frac{C}{\overline{F'A}} \right).\tag{D-7}$$

Substituting from (D-5), one obtains

$$v_0^2 \frac{R^2}{F'A^2} = v_0^2 \left(1 - \frac{C}{F'A}\right),$$

from which, utilizing (D-3),

$$R^2 = F'A(F'A - C) = \left(R \cot \frac{\theta}{2}\right)\left(R \cot \frac{\theta}{2} - C\right),$$

or

$$R = \cot \frac{\theta}{2}\left(R \cot \frac{\theta}{2} - C\right). \tag{D-8}$$

If we solve (D-8) for C, we obtain

$$C = R \frac{\cot^2 \frac{\theta}{2} - 1}{\cot \frac{\theta}{2}} = 2R \cot \theta, \tag{D-9}$$

or, since $\phi = \pi - 2\theta$,

$$R = \frac{C}{2 \cot \left(\frac{\pi}{2} - \frac{\phi}{2}\right)} = \frac{C}{2} \cot \frac{\phi}{2}. \tag{D-10}$$

The following table gives the relation between the ratio of the scattering parameter, R, to the distance of closest possible approach, C, and the scattering angle, ϕ.

R/C	10	5	2	1	0.5	0.25	0.125
ϕ	5.7°	11.4°	28°	53°	90°	127°	152°

The probability that an α particle be deflected through an angle ϕ *or greater* is evidently the same as the probability that the projection of its initial path will come within a distance R *or less* of the nucleus. If one treats the α particle as a point charge, then the probability that it will be deflected through an angle ϕ or greater is

$$P = \pi R^2 N_a b, \tag{D-11}$$

where N_a is the number of scattering nuclei per unit volume, and b is the thickness of the scattering foil.

The probability that the α particle will be deflected through some angle between ϕ and $\phi + d\phi$ is then

$$-dP = 2\pi R N_a b \frac{dR}{d\phi} d\phi,$$

$$dP = \frac{\pi N_a b C^2}{4} \cot \frac{\phi}{2} \csc^2 \frac{\phi}{2} d\phi. \tag{D-12}$$

If the fluorescent screen is a distance r from the point where the α-ray beam strikes the foil, and if it moves about this point as a center, then the probability per unit area of screen that an α particle will be deflected through an angle of approximately ϕ and strike an area, dS, of the screen is given by

$$\frac{dP}{dS} = \frac{\frac{\pi}{4} N_a b C^2 \cot \frac{\phi}{2} \csc^2 \frac{\phi}{2} \, d\phi}{2\pi r \sin \phi \, r \, d\phi},$$

$$\frac{dP}{dS} = \frac{N_a b C^2}{16 r^2 \sin^4 \frac{\phi}{2}}, \tag{D-13}$$

$$\frac{dP}{dS} = \frac{N_a b q_1^2 q_2^2}{4 M^2 v_0^4 r^2 \sin^4 \frac{\phi}{2}}. \tag{D-14}$$

TABLE OF NUCLIDIC DATA

TABLE OF NUCLIDIC DATA[a]

Z	Element Symbol[b]	A	Mass (amu)	Mass (Mev/c²)	Binding energy (Mev)	B.E. per nucleon (Mev)	Nuclear[c] magnetic moment (n. m.)	Nuclear[d] spin	Decay[e] Mode	Half-life	Abundance (%)
0	n	1	1.008983	939.5054	—	—	-1.913141	$\frac{1}{2}$	β^-	13. m	
1	H	1	1.008144	938.7242	—	—	2.792743	$\frac{1}{2}$			99.985
1	H	2	2.014740	1876.007	2.223	1.111	0.857407	1			0.015
1	H	3	3.017005	2809.257	8.478	2.826	2.97884	$\frac{1}{2}$	β^-	12.26 y	
2	He	3	3.016986	2809.239	7.715	2.572	-2.127544	$\frac{1}{2}$			$\sim 1.3 \times 10^{-4}$
2	He	4	4.003874	3728.171	28.288	7.0720		0			~ 100
2	He	5	5.01389	4668.64	27.33	5.465			α		
2	He	6	6.02083	5506.24	29.23	4.871			β^-	0.82 s	
3	Li	5	5.01395	4568.69	26.49	5.298			α		
3	Li	6	6.017034	5502.707	31.982	5.3303	0.82200	1			7.5
3	Li	7	7.018232	6534.964	39.231	5.6044	3.25631	$\frac{3}{2}$			92.5
3	Li	8	8.025033	7472.437	41.263	5.1578			β^-	0.86 s	
4	Be	6	6.0216	5607.0	26.9	4.49				$\geq 4 \times 10^{-21}$ s	
4	Be	7	7.019159	6535.827	37.586	5.3695			ϵ	53.6 d	
4	Be	8	8.007849	7456.436	56.482	7.0603			α	$< 5 \times 10^{-14}$ s	
4	Be	9	9.015060	8394.292	58.132	6.4591	-1.1771	$\frac{3}{2}$			100
4	Be	10	10.016716	9326.9750	64.9545	6.49545			β^-	2.5×10^6 y	
4	Be	11	11.02514	10265.96	65.48	5.952		$(\frac{1}{2})$	β^-	13.7 s	
5	B	8	8.0268	7474.1	38.1	4.76			β^+	0.6 s	
5	B	9	9.016195	8395.349	56.294	6.2549			α	instant.	
5	B	10	10.016119	9326.4191	64.7292	6.47292	1.8008	3			18.7
5	B	11	11.012795	10254.465	76.189	6.9263	2.68852	$\frac{3}{2}$			81.3
5	B	12	12.018168	11190.609	79.550	6.6292			β^-	0.022 s	
6	C	10	10.02024	9330.256	60.111	6.0111			β^+	19.1 s	

Z	El	A	Mass (MeV)	B (MeV)	B/A (MeV)	μ	I	decay	$T_{1/2}$	abundance
6	C	11	11.014922	10256.445	73.427	6.6752			β^+	20.40 m	
6	C	12	12.003816	11177.245	92.133	7.6777		0			98.89
6	C	13	13.007478	12111.796	97.087	7.4683	0.702381	$\tfrac{1}{2}$			1.11
6	C	14	14.007687	13043.132	105.257	7.51836		0	β^-	5.6×10^3 y	
6	C	15	15.01416	13980.30	107.59	7.1730		$(\tfrac{1}{2})$	β^-	2.3 s	
7	N	12	12.02278	11194.90	73.69	6.141			β^+	0.0125 s	
7	N	13	13.009877	12114.030	94.072	7.2363		1	β^+	9.98 m	
7	N	14	14.007520	13042.976	104.631	7.47367	0.40371	$\tfrac{1}{2}$			99.635
7	N	15	15.004862	13971.642	115.471	7.69805	−0.28313				0.365
7	N	16	16.011171	14908.658	117.961	7.37254			β^-	7.36 s	
7	N	17	17.0140	15842.4	123.7	7.276			β^-	4.14 s	
8	O	14	14.013069	13048.143	98.683	7.0488		0	β^+	74. s	
8	O	15	15.007767	13974.347	111.985	7.46564		$\tfrac{5}{2}$	β^+	2.05 m	
8	O	16	16.000000	14898.256	127.581	7.97383		0			99.759
8	O	17	17.004537	15833.622	131.721	7.74830	−1.8930				0.037
8	O	18	18.004855	16765.059	139.789	7.76608					0.204
8	O	19	19.00959	17700.61	143.74	7.5655		(2)	β^-	29.4 s	
8	O	20	20.01038	18632.48	151.37	7.5687			β^-	13.6 s	
9	F	17	17.007506	15836.386	128.175	7.53972		(1)	β^+	66. s	
9	F	18	18.006646	16766.726	137.341	7.63003	(0.8)	$\tfrac{1}{2}$	β^+	1.87 h	
9	F	19	19.004448	17695.821	147.752	7.77640	−2.62850	(1)			100
9	F	20	20.006350	18628.733	154.345	7.71725			β^-	11.2 s	
9	F	21	21.0066	19560.1	162.5	7.737			β^-	5. s	
10	Ne	18	18.01144	16771.19	132.10	7.3386		0	β^+	1.4 s	
10	Ne	19	19.007945	17699.077	143.714	7.56390		$(\tfrac{3}{2})$	β^+	19. s	
10	Ne	20	19.998798	18621.701	160.596	8.02979	$<2 \times 10^{-4}$	(0)			90.92
10	Ne	21	21.000499	19554.426	167.376	7.97030	(−0.5)	$(\tfrac{5}{2})$			0.257
10	Ne	22	21.998354	20483.569	177.738	8.07900					8.82
10	Ne	23	23.001795	21417.914	182.898	7.95211			β^-	37.6 s	
10	Ne	24	24.00120	22348.50	191.82	7.9924			β^-	3.38 m	
11	Na	20	20.0152	18637.0	144.5	7.227			β^+	0.3 s	
11	Na	21	21.00428	19557.95	163.07	7.7654			β^+	23. s	

Z	Element Symbol[b]	A	Mass (amu)	Mass (Mev/c²)	Binding energy (Mev)	B. E. per nucleon (Mev)	Nuclear magnetic moment (n. m.)[c]	Nuclear spin[d]	Decay[e] mode	Half-life	Abundance (%)
11	Na	22	22.001404	20486.409	174.117	7.91440	1.747	3	β^+, ϵ	2.60 y	
11	Na	23	22.997091	21413.534	186.497	8.10858	2.2166	$\frac{3}{2}$			100
11	Na	24	23.998565	22346.048	193.489	8.06205	1.688	4	β^-	15.0 h	
11	Na	25	24.99778	23276.46	202.58	8.1034			β^-	60. s	
12	Mg	23	23.00145	21417.59	181.66	7.8981		$(\frac{3}{2})$	β^+	11.6 s	
12	Mg	24	23.99266	22340.55	198.21	8.2586		(0)			78.70
12	Mg	25	24.993752	23272.707	205.554	8.22216	-0.85532	$\frac{5}{2}$			10.11
12	Mg	26	25.990854	24201.150	216.617	8.33142	$-0-$	(0)			11.29
12	Mg	27	26.99287	25134.17	223.10	8.2631			β^-	9.45 m	
12	Mg	28	27.99271	26065.16	231.62	8.2721			β^-	21.4 h	
13	Al	24	24.0077	22354.6	183.4	7.643			β^+	2.10 s	
13	Al	25	24.99831	23276.95	200.53	8.0211			β^+	7.6 s	
13	Al	26	25.995171	24205.170	211.816	8.14677		5	β^+, ϵ	7.4×10^5 y	
13	Al^m	26	25.995416	24205.398	211.588	8.13799		(0)	β^+	6.6 s	
13	Al	27	26.990081	25131.571	224.920	8.33037	3.64142	$\frac{5}{2}$			100
13	Al	28	27.990771	26063.354	232.642	8.30864			β^-	2.30 m	
13	Al	29	28.98992	26993.70	241.80	8.3379			β^-	6.56 m	
14	Si	26	26.0002	24209.9	206.4	7.937		(0)	β^+	2.1 s	
14	Si	27	26.995265	25136.398	219.312	8.12265			β^+	4.9 s	
14	Si	28	27.985775	26058.703	236.513	8.44688	$-0-$	(0)			92.18
14	Si	29	28.98566	26989.74	244.98	8.4477	-0.55525	$\frac{1}{2}$			4.71
14	Si	30	29.983252	27918.635	255.591	8.51969	$-0-$	(0)			3.12
14	Si	31	30.98515	28851.54	262.19	8.4577			β^-	2.65 h	
14	Si	32	31.984134	29781.739	271.498	8.48432			β^-	$\sim 7 \times 10^2$ y	
15	P	28	28.0006	26072.5	221.9	7.926			β^+	0.28 s	
15	P	29	28.99099	26994.70	239.24	8.2496			β^+	4.45 s	
15	P	30	29.98788	27922.94	250.50	8.3500			β^+	2.55 m	

Z	El	A	Mass				μ	I	Decay	Half-life	%
15	P	31	30.98356	28850.06	262.89	8.4802	1.13162	$\frac{1}{2}$			100
15	P	32	31.98403	29781.64	270.81	8.4629			β^-	14.30 d	
15	P	33	32.98216	30711.04	280.92	8.5127			β^-	24.4 d	
15	P	34	33.9841	31644.0	287.5	8.455			β^+	12.4 s	
16	S	31	30.98940	28855.50	256.67	8.2796			β^+	2.6 s	
16	S	32	31.982240	29779.975	271.699	8.49061	–0–	0			95.018
16	S	33	32.98189	30710.79	280.39	8.4967	0.64342	$\frac{3}{2}$			0.750
16	S	34	33.97864	31638.90	291.78	8.5818		(0)			4.215
16	S	35	34.97844	32569.86	300.33	8.5809	1.00	$\frac{3}{2}$	β^-	87.1 d	
16	S	36	35.97844	33501.00	308.70	8.5749		(0)			0.017
16	S	37	36.9826	34436.0	313.2	8.464			β^-	5.04 m	
16	S	38	37.98318	35367.70	321.01	8.4477			β^-	2.87 h	
17	Cl	32	31.9962	29793.0	257.9	8.060			β^+	0.31 s	
17	Cl	33	32.98774	30716.24	274.16	8.3079			β^+	2.4 s	
17	Cl	34	33.98457	31644.43	285.48	8.3964		(0)	β^+	1.5 s	
17	Cl^m	34	33.98473	31644.58	285.33	8.3920	(1.4)	(3)	β^+	32.4 m	
17	Cl	35	34.97990	32571.22	298.19	8.5197	0.82181	$\frac{3}{2}$			75.53
17	Cl	36	35.97969	33502.16	306.75	8.5208	1.28538	2	β^-, ϵ	3.2×10^5 y	
17	Cl	37	36.97754	34431.30	317.12	8.5707	0.68409	$\frac{3}{2}$			24.47
17	Cl	38	37.98001	35364.74	323.18	8.5048		2	β^-	37.5 m	
17	Cl	39	38.97982	36295.71	331.72	8.5057			β^-	55.5 m	
18	A	35	34.9862	32577.1	291.5	8.330			β^+	1.83 s	
18	A	36	35.97892	33501.45	306.69	8.5191		(0)			0.34
18	A	37	36.97842	34432.12	315.52	8.5275			ϵ	34.1 d	
18	A	38	37.97479	35359.88	327.26	8.6121		(0)			0.06
18	A	39	38.97664	36292.75	333.90	8.5616			β^-	$\sim 2.6 \times 10^2$ y	
18	A	40	39.97505	37222.41	343.75	8.5937		(0)			99.60
18	A	41	40.97753	38155.86	349.80	8.5318			β^-	1.83 h	
19	K	38	37.98110	35365.76	320.60	8.4369	(1.4)	(3)	β^+	7.75 m	
19	K	39	38.97604	36292.19	333.68	8.5559	0.3915	$\frac{3}{2}$			93.08
19	K	40	39.976709	37223.953	341.421	8.53554	–1.2964	4	β^-, ϵ	1.27×10^9 y	0.0118
19	K	41	40.97476	38153.28	351.60	8.5756	0.21517	$\frac{3}{2}$			6.91

Z	Element Symbol [b]	A	Mass (amu)	Mass (Mev/c²)	Binding energy (Mev)	B. E. per nucleon (Mev)	Nuclear [c] magnetic moment (n. m.)	Nuclear [d] spin	Decay [e] mode	Half-life	Abundance (%)
19	K	42	41.97583	39085.42	358.97	8.5469	−1.137	2	β^-	12.47 h	
19	K	43	42.97433	40015.16	368.73	8.5751			β^-	22.4 h	
19	K	44	43.9759	40947.8	375.6	8.537			β^-	22.0 m	
20	Ca	38	37.9869	35371.2	314.4	8.274			β^+	0.66 s	
20	Ca	39	38.98308	36298.74	326.34	8.3678			β^+	0.90 s	
20	Ca	40	39.97523	37222.58	342.02	8.5504	−0−	(0)			96.96
20	Ca	42	41.97189	39081.75	361.86	8.6156		2			0.64
20	Ca	43	42.97235	40013.32	369.79	8.5998	−1.31720	$\frac{7}{2}$			0.145
20	Ca	44	43.96934	40941.66	380.96	8.6582		(0)			2.07
20	Ca	45	44.97035	41873.74	388.38	8.6307			β^-	164. d	
20	Ca	47	46.96946	43735.19	405.94	8.6370			β^-	4.9 d	
20	Ca	48	47.9677	44664.7	415.9	8.666		(0)		$> 2 \times 10^{16}$ y	0.185
20	Ca	49	48.9712	45599.1	421.0	8.593			β^-	8.8 m	
21	Sc	40	39.9902	37236.5	327.3	8.182			β^+	0.22 s	
21	Sc	41	40.98163	38159.68	343.64	8.3815			β^+	0.87 s	
21	Sc	43	42.97473	40015.53	366.80	8.5301			β^+, ϵ	3.92 h	
21	Sc	44	43.97326	40945.30	376.53	8.5575			β^+, ϵ	3.96 h	
21	Sc^m	44	43.97355	40945.58	376.26	8.5513				2.44 d	
21	Sc	45	44.97007	41873.48	387.86	8.6192	4.7563	$\frac{7}{2}$			100
21	Sc	46	45.96949	42804.08	396.77	8.6254			β^-	85. d	
21	Sc^m	46	45.96964	42804.22	396.63	8.6223				19.5 s	
21	Sc	47	46.96724	43733.12	407.23	8.6644			β^-	3.43 d	
21	Sc	48	47.96741	44664.42	415.43	8.6549			β^-	1.83 d	
21	Sc	49	48.96554	45593.82	425.54	8.6845			β^-	57.2 m	
22	Ti	45	44.97227	41875.52	385.03	8.5563			β^+, ϵ	3.10 h	
22	Ti	46	45.96695	42801.71	398.35	8.6598		(0)			7.99
22	Ti	47	46.96650	43732.43	407.13	8.6624	−0.78813	$\frac{5}{2}$			7.32

Z	El	A	Atomic mass		B/A	Magnetic moment	Spin	Decay	Half-life	Abundance
22	Ti	48	47.96312	418.65	8.7218		(0)			73.99
22	Ti	49	48.96339	426.76	8.7094	-1.1038	$\frac{7}{2}$			5.46
22	Ti	50	49.96058	437.74	8.7548		(0)			5.25
22	Ti	51	50.96266	444.17	8.7092			β^-	5.79 m	
23	V	46	45.9749	390.2	8.482		(0)	β^+	0.42 s	
23	V	47	46.96963	403.44	8.5838			β^+	31. m	
23	V	48	47.96745	413.83	8.6215			β^+, ϵ	16.1 d	
23	V	49	48.96404	425.37	8.6811			ϵ	330. d	
23	V	50	49.96312	434.59	8.6919	3.3470	6	ϵ	4.8×10^{14} y	0.25
23	V	51	50.96004	445.83	8.7417	5.1470	$\frac{7}{2}$			99.76
23	V	52	51.96118	453.13	8.7140			β^-	3.76 m	
24	Cr	48	47.9689	411.7	8.577		(0)	ϵ	23.5 h	
24	Cr	49	48.96679	422.03	8.6129			β^+	41.9 m	
24	Cr	50	49.96164	435.19	8.7038		(0)			4.31
24	Cr	51	50.96084	444.30	8.7118			ϵ	27.8 d	
24	Cr	52	51.95699	456.25	8.7740		(0)			83.76
24	Cr	53	52.95746	464.18	8.7580	-0.47439	$\frac{3}{2}$			9.55
24	Cr	54	53.95602	473.88	8.7756		(0)			2.38
24	Cr	55	54.95843	480.00	8.7273			β^-	3.52 m	
25	Mn	50	49.9700	426.6	8.533			β^+	0.28 s	
25	Mn	51	50.96430	440.30	8.6333			β^+	45. m	
25	Mn	52	51.96207	450.74	8.6680			ϵ, β^+	5.55 d	
25	Mn^m	52	51.96249	450.35	8.6605			β^+	21.3 m	
25	Mn	53	52.95813	462.77	8.7315	5.050	$\frac{7}{2}$	ϵ	$\sim 2 \times 10^{6}$ y	
25	Mn	54	53.9575	471.7	8.736			ϵ	300. d	
25	Mn	55	54.95540	482.04	8.7644	3.4677	$\frac{5}{2}$			100
25	Mn	56	55.95659	489.30	8.7375			β^-	2.58 h	
26	Fe	52	51.96445	447.74	8.6104		(0)	β^+, ϵ	8.2 h	
26	Fe	53	52.96229	458.12	8.6437		$(\frac{7}{2})$	β^+	8.9 m	
26	Fe	54	53.95664	471.74	8.7360		(0)			5.84
26	Fe	55	54.95565	481.03	8.7460			ϵ	2.94 y	
26	Fe	56	55.95264	492.20	8.7892		(0)			91.68

Z	Element Symbol[b]	A	Mass (amu)	Mass (Mev/c²)	Binding energy (Mev)	B. E. per nucleon (Mev)	Nuclear[c] magnetic moment (n. m.)	Nuclear[d] spin	Decay[e] mode	Half-life	Abundance (%)
26	Fe	57	56.95342	53031.66	499.83	8.7690	<0.05	$\frac{1}{2}$			2.19
26	Fe	58	57.95147	53960.99	510.01	8.7933		(0)			0.31
26	Fe	59	58.9536	54894.1	516.4	8.752			β^-	45.1 d	
26	Fe	60	59.9533	55825.0	525.0	8.751			β^-	~3 × 10⁵ y	
27	Co	54	53.9662	50250.1	462.1	8.557			β^+	0.2 s	
27	Co	55	54.95936	51174.91	476.79	8.6690			β^+, ϵ	18.0 h	
27	Co	56	55.95761	52104.42	486.79	8.6926	(±)3.855	4	β^+, ϵ	77. d	
27	Co	57	56.9540	53032.2	498.5	8.746	4.6	$\frac{7}{2}$	ϵ	270. d	
27	Co	58	57.95421	53963.54	506.68	8.7359	(4.05)	(2)	ϵ, β^+	72.0 d	
27	Co	59	58.9519	54892.5	517.2	8.766	4.649	$\frac{7}{2}$			100
27	Co	60	59.952851	55824.558	524.676	8.74459	3.80	5	β^-	5.27 y	
27	Co	61	60.9513	56754.3	534.5	8.762			β^-	1.65 h	
27	Co	62	61.9529	57686.9	541.4	8.732			β^-	13.9 m	
28	Ni	57	56.9575	53035.5	494.5	8.675			β^+, ϵ	37.0 h	
28	Ni	58	57.9538	53963.2	506.3	8.729		(0)			67.8
28	Ni	59	58.9531	54893.6	515.3	8.734			ϵ	8. × 10⁴ y	
28	Ni	60	59.949824	55821.739	526.713	8.77855		(0)			26.23
28	Ni	61	60.9497	56752.8	535.2	8.774	(0.1)	($\frac{3}{2}$)			1.25
28	Ni	62	61.9476	57682.0	545.5	8.799		(0)			3.66
28	Ni	63	62.9495	58614.9	552.1	8.764			β^-	80. y	
28	Ni	64	63.9481	59544.7	561.8	8.778		(0)			1.16
28	Ni	65	64.9506	60478.2	567.8	8.736			β^-	2.56 h	
29	Cu	58	57.9640	53972.7	496.0	8.552			β^+	3.0 s	
29	Cu	60	59.95656	55828.01	519.66	8.6610		2	β^+, ϵ	24. m	
29	Cu	61	60.9521	56755.0	532.2	8.724			β^+, ϵ	3.33 h	
29	Cu	62	61.9518	57685.9	540.8	8.723			β^+, ϵ	9.80 m	
29	Cu	63	62.9494	58614.8	551.4	8.753	2.2266	$\frac{3}{2}$			69.1

29	Cu	64	63.9499	59546.4	559.3	8.739	0.40	1	$\epsilon, \beta^-, \beta^+$	12.82 h	
29	Cu	65	64.9484	60476.1	569.1	8.755	2.3847	3/2			30.9
29	Cu	66	65.9498	61408.6	576.1	8.729			β^-	5.15 m	
29	Cu	67	66.9491	62339.1	585.2	8.734			β^-	59. h	
30	Zn	61	60.9576	56760.1	526.3	8.627			β^+	88.5 s	
30	Zn	62	61.9536	57687.5	538.4	8.683			ϵ, β^+	9.33 h	
30	Zn	63	62.9530	58618.1	547.3	8.687			β^+, ϵ	38.3 m	
30	Zn	64	63.9493	59545.8	559.1	8.736	–0–	(0)			48.89
30	Zn	65	64.9498	60477.4	567.0	8.723			ϵ, β^+	245. d	
30	Zn	66	65.9469	61405.9	578.1	8.758	–0–	(0)			27.81
30	Zn	67	66.9485	62338.5	584.9	8.730	0.8757	5/2			4.11
30	Zn	68	67.9465	63267.8	595.2	8.752	–0–	(0)			18.56
30	Zn	69	68.9485	64200.8	601.7	8.720			β^-	52. m	
30	Zn^m	69	68.9490	64201.2	601.2	8.713			β^-	13.8 h	
30	Zn	70	69.9474	65130.9	611.1	8.729	–0–	(0)			0.62
30	Zn	71	70.9505	66064.9	616.5	8.684			β^-	2.2 m	
30	Zn^m	71	70.9506	66065.0	616.4	8.682			β^-	3. h	
31	Ga	64	63.9572	59553.2	551.0	8.609			β^+	2.6 m	
31	Ga	65	64.95337	60480.75	562.89	8.6598			β^+, ϵ	15. m	
31	Ga	66	65.9525	61411.1	572.1	8.668			β^+, ϵ	9.45 h	
31	Ga	67	66.9496	62339.5	583.1	8.703			ϵ	78.0 h	
31	Ga	68	67.9496	63270.7	591.5	8.698		1	β^+, ϵ	68. m	
31	Ga	69	68.9476	64199.9	601.7	8.721	2.0160	3/2			60.2
31	Ga	70	69.94800	65131.45	609.71	8.7102		1	β^-	21.1 m	
31	Ga	71	70.9474	66062.0	618.6	8.713	2.5616	3/2			39.8
31	Ga	72	71.9489	66994.6	625.6	8.689			β^-	14.20 h	
31	Ga	73	72.94795	67924.83	634.85	8.6966			β^-	4.85 h	
32	Ge	67	66.9542	62343.8	578.1	8.628			β^+	18.6 m	
32	Ge	69	68.9500	64202.2	598.7	8.677			ϵ, β^+	39.6 h	
32	Ge	70	69.9464	65130.0	610.4	8.720		0			20.55
32	Ge	71	70.9476	66062.2	617.7	8.700			ϵ	12. d	
32	Ge	72	71.94446	66990.44	628.96	8.7355		0			27.43

Z	Element Symbol [b]	A	Mass (amu)	Mass (Mev/c²)	Binding energy (Mev)	B. E. per nucleon (Mev)	Nuclear [c] magnetic moment (n. m.)	Nuclear [d] spin	Decay [e] mode	Half-life	Abundance (%)
32	Ge	73	72.94653	67923.50	635.39	8.7040	0.8767	$\frac{9}{2}$			7.76
32	Ge	74	73.94459	68852.84	645.56	8.7238		0			36.74
32	Ge	75	74.94662	69785.87	652.04	8.6938			β^-	82. m	
32	Ge^m	75	74.94677	69786.01	651.90	8.6920				48. s	
32	Ge	76	75.94533	70715.81	661.60	8.7053		0			7.67
32	Ge	77	76.94802	71649.46	667.46	8.6684			β^-	12. h	
32	Ge^m	77	76.94843	71649.84	667.08	8.6634			β^-	52. s	
33	As	70	69.9534	65136.5	603.1	8.616			β^+, ϵ	52. m	
33	As	71	70.9497	66064.2	614.9	8.661			ϵ, β^+	62. h	
33	As	72	71.9493	66994.9	623.7	8.662			ϵ, β^+	26. h	
33	As	73	72.94685	67923.80	634.31	8.6892		$(\frac{3}{2})$	ϵ	76. d	
33	As	74	73.94734	68855.40	642.22	8.6787		(2)	$\epsilon, \beta^-, \beta^+$	17.5 d	
33	As	75	74.94554	69784.86	652.26	8.6968	1.4349	$\frac{3}{2}$			100
33	As	76	75.94653	70716.93	659.71	8.6803			β^-	26.6 h	
33	As	77	76.94510	71646.74	669.40	8.6935			β^-	38.8 h	
33	As	78	77.94649	72579.17	676.47	8.6727			β^-	91.0 m	
33	As	79	78.94605	73509.90	685.25	8.6740			β^-	9.0 m	
34	Se	71	70.9549	66069.0	609.3	8.582			β^+	4.5 m	
34	Se	73	72.94983	67926.58	630.76	8.6405		$(\frac{9}{2})$	β^+, ϵ	7.1 h	
34	Se	74	73.94589	68854.05	642.79	8.6864		(0)			0.87
34	Se	75	74.94633	69785.60	650.75	8.6766		$\frac{5}{2}$	ϵ	127. d	
34	Se	76	75.94334	70713.96	661.89	8.7091	$-0-$	(0)			9.02
34	Se	77	76.94436	71646.05	669.31	8.6923	0.53406	$\frac{1}{2}$			7.58
34	Se	78	77.94209	72575.08	679.79	8.7152	$-0-$	0			23.52
34	Se	79	78.94358	73507.60	686.76	8.6932	-1.018	$\frac{7}{2}$	β^-	$\leq 6 \times 10^4$ y	
34	Se^m	79	78.94368	73507.70	686.67	8.6920				3.90 m	
34	Se	80	79.9420	74437.3	696.6	8.707		0			49.82

34	Se	81	80.9436	75369.9	703.5	8.685			β^-	18.2 m	
34	Se^m	81	80.9437	75370.0	703.4	8.684				56.8 m	
34	Se	82	81.94261	76300.12	712.76	8.6922	$-0-$	(0)			9.19
35	Br	75	74.94926	69788.33	647.24	8.6298			ϵ, β^+	1.6 h	
35	Br	76	75.94863	70718.88	656.19	8.6340			β^+, ϵ	17.2 h	
35	Br	77	76.94588	71647.46	667.11	8.6638			ϵ, β^+	58.0 h	
35	Br^m	78	77.94585	72578.58	675.50	8.6603			β^+	≤6 m	
35	Br	78	77.94602	72578.74	675.35	8.6583		$\tfrac{3}{2}$		6.4 m	
35	Br	79	78.94341	73507.45	686.14	8.6853	2.1056	$\tfrac{3}{2}$			50.53
35	Br	80	79.9440	74439.1	694.0	8.674			$\beta^-, \epsilon, \beta^+$	18.5 m	
35	Br	81	80.94215	75368.55	704.04	8.6919	2.26	$\tfrac{3}{2}$			49.47
35	Br	82	81.9427	76300.2	711.9	8.682			β^-	35.9 h	
35	Br	83	82.9414	77230.1	721.5	8.692			β^-	2.33 h	
35	Br	84	83.9341	78154.5	736.6	8.769			β^-	31.8 m	
35	Br^m	84	83.9406	78160.5	730.6	8.697			β^-	6.0 m	
35	Br	85	84.9426	79093.5	737.1	8.672			β^-	3.00 m	
35	Br	87	86.9499	80962.6	747.0	8.586			β^-	55.6 s	
36	Kr	77	76.94891	71650.28	663.51	8.6170			β^+, ϵ	1.1 h	
36	Kr	78	77.94489	72577.68	675.62	8.6618	$-0-$	(0)			0.354
36	Kr	79	78.94515	73509.07	683.74	8.6549			ϵ, β^+	34.5 h	
36	Kr	80	79.9419	74437.2	695.1	8.689		(0)			2.27
36	Kr	81	80.9422	75368.6	703.2	8.682			ϵ	2.1×10^5 y	
36	Kr^m	81	80.9424	75368.8	703.0	8.679				13. s	
36	Kr	82	81.9394	76297.1	714.2	8.710	$-0-$	(0)			11.56
36	Kr	83	82.9403	77229.1	721.7	8.695	-0.969	$\tfrac{9}{2}$			11.55
36	Kr	84	83.9381	78158.2	732.1	8.716	$-0-$	(0)			56.90
36	Kr	85	84.9396	79090.7	739.1	8.695	-1.00	$\tfrac{9}{2}$	β^-	10.60 y	
36	Kr	86	85.9382	80020.6	748.8	8.707	$-0-$	(0)			17.37
36	Kr	87	86.94146	80954.76	754.09	8.6677			β^-	78. m	
36	Kr	88	87.94266	81887.02	761.34	8.6516			β^-	2.8 h	
36	Kr	89	88.9448	82820.2	767.7	8.626			β^-	3.2 m	
37	Rb	81	80.9446	75370.8	700.2	8.644	2.05	$\tfrac{3}{2}$	ϵ, β^+	4.7 h	

Z	A	Element Symbol[b]	Mass (amu)	Mass (Mev/c^2)	Binding energy (Mev)	B. E. per nucleon (Mev)	Nuclear magnetic moment (n. m.)[c]	Nuclear spin[d]	Decay[e] mode	Half-life	Abundance (%)
37	82	Rb	81.9439	76301.3	709.2	8.649			β^+	1.25 m	
37	82	Rb^m	81.9441	76301.5	709.0	8.647			ϵ, β^+	6.3 h	
37	83	Rb	82.9412	77230.0	720.1	8.676			ϵ	83. d	
37	84	Rb	83.9409	78160.8	728.7	8.675			ϵ,β^+,β^-	33.0 d	
37	84	Rb^m	83.9414	78161.3	728.3	8.670			ϵ	23. m	
37	85	Rb	84.93902	79090.20	738.85	8.6924	1.3482	$\frac{5}{2}$			72.15
37	86	Rb	85.9385	80020.9	747.7	8.694	(−)1.67	2	β^-	18.6 d	
37	86	Rb^m	85.9391	80021.4	747.1	8.688				1.02 m	
37	87	Rb	86.93687	80950.48	757.5	8.7079	2.7505	$\frac{3}{2}$	β^-	5. × 10^{10} y	27.85
37	88	Rb	87.9393	81883.9	763.7	8.678			β^-	17.8 m	
37	89	Rb	88.9405	82816.1	770.9	8.662			β^-	15.0 m	
37	90	Rb	89.9419	83748.6	778.0	8.644			β^-	2.74 m	
38	82	Sr	81.9451	76302.4	707.3	8.626			ϵ	26. d	
38	84	Sr	83.9399	78159.9	728.9	8.677		(0)			0.55
38	85	Sr	84.9400	79091.1	737.2	8.672			ϵ	65. d	
38	86	Sr	85.9366	80019.1	748.7	8.706	−0−	(0)			9.87
38	87	Sr	86.93658	80950.21	757.07	8.7020	−1.0930	$\frac{9}{2}$			7.02
38	88	Sr	87.9338	81878.8	768.0	8.728	−0−	(0)			82.56
38	89	Sr	88.93556	82811.55	774.75	8.7051			β^-	50.4 d	
38	90	Sr	89.9358	83742.9	782.9	8.699			β^-	28. y	
38	91	Sr	90.9387	84676.8	788.6	8.665			β^-	9.67 h	
38	92	Sr	91.9396	85608.7	796.1	8.653			β^-	2.60 h	
39	86	Y	85.9411	80023.3	743.7	8.648			β^+	14.6 h	
39	87	Y	86.9384	80951.9	754.6	8.674			ϵ, β^+	80. h	
39	87	Y^m	86.9388	80952.3	754.2	8.669				14.6 h	
39	88	Y	87.9378	81882.5	763.5	8.676		(4)	ϵ, β^+	105. d	
39	89	Y	88.9341	82810.2	775.3	8.712	−0.13731	$\frac{1}{2}$			100

Z	El	A	Atomic mass	Mass excess		B/A	μ	I	Decay	Half-life	Abund.
39	Y	90	89.9352	83742.4	782.6	8.696			β⁻	64.2 h	
39	Y	91	90.9358	84674.1	790.5	8.687			β⁻	58.0 d	
39	Y	92	91.9376	85606.9	797.2	8.665			β⁻	3.60 h	
39	Y	93	92.9385	86538.8	804.7	8.653			β⁻	10.2 h	
39	Y	94	93.9412	87472.5	810.5	8.623			β⁺, ε	16.5 m	
40	Zr	87	86.9422	80955.4	750.3	8.624			ε, β⁺	94. m	
40	Zr	89	88.9371	82813.0	771.8	8.671			ε, β⁺	79. h	
40	Zrᵐ	89	88.9377	82813.5	771.2	8.665			ε, β⁺	4.4 m	
40	Zr	90	89.9329	83740.2	784.0	8.711		0			51.46
40	Zr	91	90.9341	84672.5	791.3	8.695	−1.9	$\frac{5}{2}$			11.23
40	Zr	92	91.9338	85603.3	799.9	8.695		(0)			17.11
40	Zr	93	92.9353	86535.9	806.9	8.676			β⁻	1.1×10^6 y	
40	Zr	94	93.9358	87467.5	814.8	8.668		(0)			17.40
40	Zr	95	94.9379	88400.6	821.2	8.644			β⁻	63.3 d	
40	Zr	96	95.9385	89332.3	829.0	8.635		(0)	β⁻	$>2 \times 10^{16}$ y	2.80
40	Zr	97	96.9414	90266.1	834.7	8.605			β⁻	17.0 h	
41	Nb	90	89.9376	83744.6	778.9	8.654			β⁺	14.7 h	
41	Nb	91	90.9356	84673.9	789.1	8.671			ε	LONG	
41	Nb	92	91.9356	85605.0	797.5	8.668			ε	10.1 d	
41	Nb	93	92.9353	86535.9	806.1	8.668	6.1671	$\frac{9}{2}$			100
41	Nb	94	93.9365	87468.1	813.4	8.653			β⁻	$2. \times 10^4$ y	
41	Nb	95	94.9367	88399.5	821.5	8.648			β⁻	35. d	
41	Nb	96	95.9383	89332.1	828.4	8.629			β⁻	23.4 h	
41	Nb	97	96.9386	90263.5	836.5	8.624			β⁻	74. m	
42	Mo	90	89.9406	83747.4	775.3	8.614			ε, β⁺	5.7 h	
42	Mo	91	90.9395	84677.5	784.7	8.623			β⁺, ε	15.5 m	
42	Mo	92	91.9352	85604.6	797.1	8.664	−0−	(0)			15.86
42	Mo	93	92.9357	86536.2	805.0	8.655			ε	$\sim 10^4$ y	
42	Mo	94	93.9343	87466.1	814.6	8.666	−0−	(0)			9.12
42	Mo	95	94.9357	88398.5	821.7	8.649	−0.9135	$\frac{5}{2}$			15.70
42	Mo	96	95.9349	89328.9	830.8	8.654	−0−	(0)			16.50
42	Mo	97	96.9365	90261.6	837.7	8.636	−0.9327	$\frac{5}{2}$			9.45

Z	Element Symbol[b]	A	Mass (amu)	Mass (Mev/c²)	Binding energy (Mev)	B. E. per nucleon (Mev)	Nuclear magnetic moment (n. m.)[c]	Nuclear spin[d]	Decay mode[e]	Half-life	Abundance (%)
42	Mo	98	97.9366	91192.8	845.9	8.632	$-0-$	(0)			23.75
42	Mo	99	98.9400	92127.1	851.1	8.597			β^-	67.0 h	
42	Mo	100	99.9383	93056.6	861.1	8.611	$-0-$	(0)			9.62
43	Tc	92	91.9421	85611.1	789.8	8.585			β^+, ϵ	4.3 m	
43	Tc	93	92.9391	86539.4	801.0	8.613			ϵ, β^+	2.75 h	
43	Tc	94	93.9390	87470.5	809.5	8.611			β^+, ϵ	53. m	
43	Tc	95	94.9375	88400.2	819.2	8.623			ϵ	20.0 h	
43	Tc	96	95.9382	89332.0	826.9	8.614			ϵ	4.3 d	
43	Tc	98	97.9391	91195.1	842.8	8.600	5.6805	$\frac{9}{2}$	β^-	1.5×10^6 y	
43	Tc	99	98.9385	92125.7	851.8	8.604			β^-	2.12×10^5 y	
44	Ru	95	94.9397	88402.2	816.4	8.594			β^+, ϵ	98. m	
44	Ru	96	95.9379	89331.7	826.4	8.609		(0)			5.5
44	Ru	98	97.9371	91193.2	843.9	8.611		(0)			1.9
44	Ru	99	98.9382	92125.4	851.3	8.598	-0.63	$\frac{5}{2}$			12.7
44	Ru	102	101.9364	94917.16	878.02	8.6080		(0)			31.5
44	Ru	103	102.9387	95850.44	884.24	8.5848			β^-	41.0 d	
44	Ru	104	103.9378	96780.75	893.45	8.5909		(0)			18.7
44	Ru	105	104.9408	97714.68	899.02	8.5621			β^-	4.5 h	
44	Ru	106	105.9402	98645.26	907.94	8.5654			β^-	1.0 y	
45	Rh	102	101.9388	94919.40	875.00	8.5785			$\beta^-, \beta^+, (\epsilon?)$	210. d	
45	Rh	103	102.9379	95849.70	884.20	8.5845	-0.08851	$\frac{1}{2}$			100
45	Rh	104	103.93894	96781.809	891.605	8.57312		(1)	β^-	42. s	
45	Rh	105	104.9387	97712.73	900.19	8.5732			β^-	36.5 h	
45	Rh	106	105.9402	98645.26	907.15	8.5581			β^-	30. s	
45	Rhᵐ	106	105.9403	98645.36	907.06	8.5572			β^-	2. h	
45	Rh	107	106.9402	99576.40	915.53	8.5563			β^-	23.0 m	
46	Pd	102	101.9375	94918.19	875.43	8.5827		(0)			0.96

Z	El	A	mass (u)	(col 5)	(col 6)	(col 7)	μ	I	decay	$T_{1/2}$	%
46	Pd	103	102.9385	95850.26	882.87	8.5716			ϵ	17. d	
46	Pd	104	103.93632	96779.369	893.262	8.58906		(0)			10.97
46	Pd	105	104.9381	97712.17	899.97	8.5711	−0.57	$\frac{5}{2}$			22.23
46	Pd	106	105.9364	98641.72	909.91	8.5841		(0)			27.33
46	Pd	107	106.9390	99575.29	915.86	8.5594		$\frac{5}{2}$	β^-	7.5×10^6 y	
46	Pd	108	107.9378	100505.3	925.3	8.568		(0)			26.71
46	Pd	109	108.9405	101439.0	931.2	8.543			β^-	13.6 h	
46	Pd	110	109.9396	102369.3	940.4	8.549		(0)			11.81
46	Pd	111	110.9429	103303.5	945.7	8.520			β^-	22. m	
46	Pd	112	111.9428	104234.5	954.1	8.519			β^-	21. h	
47	Ag	105	104.9405	97714.40	896.95	8.5424			ϵ	40. d	
47	Ag	106	105.9396	98644.70	906.16	8.5487			β^+	24.0 m	
47	Ag	107	106.9389	99575.19	915.17	8.5530	−0.11355	$\frac{1}{2}$			51.35
47	Ag	108	107.9401	100507.4	922.4	8.541			$\beta^-, \epsilon, \beta^+$	2.3 m	
47	Ag	109	108.9393	101437.8	931.5	8.546	−0.1305	$\frac{1}{2}$			48.65
47	Ag	110	109.9414	102370.9	937.9	8.527			β^-	24.2 s	
47	Ag^m	110	109.9415	102371.0	937.8	8.526			β^-	270. d	
47	Ag	111	110.9406	103301.3	947.0	8.532	−0.145	$\frac{1}{2}$	β^-	7.50 d	
47	Ag	112	111.9424	104234.2	953.7	8.515			β^-	3.20 h	
48	Cd	104	103.9430	96785.59	885.48	8.5142			β^+	59. m	
48	Cd	105	104.9437	97717.38	893.19	8.5065			β^+, ϵ	55. m	
48	Cd	106	105.9395	98644.61	905.47	8.5422		(0)			1.21
48	Cd	107	106.9405	99576.68	912.90	8.5318			ϵ, β^+	6.7 h	
48	Cd	108	107.9382	100505.7	923.4	8.550		(0)			0.88
48	Cd	109	108.9395	101438.0	930.6	8.537			ϵ	1.30 y	
48	Cd	110	109.9383	102368.1	940.0	8.546	(0)	(0)			12.39
48	Cd	111	110.9394	103300.2	947.4	8.535	−0.5950	$\frac{1}{2}$			12.75
48	Cd	112	111.9382	104230.2	956.9	8.543	(0)	(0)			24.07
48	Cd	113	112.94036	105163.40	963.22	8.5241	−0.620	$\frac{1}{2}$	β^-	$>10^{15}$ y	12.26
48	Cd	114	113.9396	106093.8	972.3	8.529	(0)	(0)			28.86
48	Cd	115	114.9421	107027.3	978.3	8.507			β^-	53. h	
48	Cd	116	115.9418	107958.2	987.0	8.508	(0)	(0)			7.58

Z	Element Symbol[b]	A	Mass (amu)	Mass (Mev/c²)	Binding energy (Mev)	B.E. per nucleon (Mev)	Nuclear[c] magnetic moment (n. m.)	Nuclear[d] spin	Decay[e] mode	Half-life	Abundance (%)
49	In	107	106.9440	99579.94	908.86	8.4940			β^+	33. m	
49	In	109	108.9414	101439.8	928.0	8.514			ϵ, β^+	4.3 h	
49	In	110	109.9425	102372.0	935.3	8.503			β^+, ϵ	65. m	
49	In	111	110.9404	103301.2	945.7	8.520			ϵ	2.84 d	
49	In	112	111.9410	104232.8	953.5	8.513			β^+, β^-	14.5 m	
49	In^m	112	111.9402	104232.1	954.2	8.520				20.7 m	
49	In	113	112.9401	105163.2	962.7	8.519	5.5231	$\frac{9}{2}$			4.23
49	In	114	113.9416	106095.7	969.6	8.506			$\beta^-, \epsilon, \beta^+$	72. s	
49	In^m	114	113.9418	106095.9	969.5	8.504	4.7	5	ϵ	49. d	
49	In	115	114.9405	107025.8	979.0	8.513	5.5344	$\frac{9}{2}$	β^-	$6. \times 10^{14}\ y$	95.77
49	In^m	115	114.9409	107026.2	978.7	8.510			β^-	4.50 h	
49	In	116	115.9422	107958.5	985.8	8.498			β^-	13. s	
49	In	117	116.9418	108889.3	994.6	8.500			β^-	66. m	
49	In^m	117	116.9421	108889.6	994.3	8.498			β^-	1.90 h	
50	Sn	111	110.9431	103303.7	942.4	8.490			ϵ, β^+	35.0 m	
50	Sn	112	111.9403	104232.2	953.3	8.507		(0)			0.95
50	Sn	113	112.9408	105163.8	961.2	8.502			ϵ	115. d	
50	Sn	114	113.9395	106093.7	970.8	8.516		(0)			0.65
50	Sn	115	114.9400	107025.4	978.7	8.511	−0.9178	$\frac{1}{2}$			0.34
50	Sn	116	115.9390	107955.6	988.0	8.517	−0−	(0)			14.24
50	Sn	117	116.9402	108887.8	995.3	8.506	−1.000	$\frac{1}{2}$			7.57
50	Sn	118	117.9393	109818.1	1004.5	8.5124	−0−	(0)			24.01
50	Sn	119	118.94096	110750.80	1011.28	8.49819	−1.04085	$\frac{1}{2}$			8.58
50	Sn	120	119.94032	111681.35	1020.24	8.50202	−0−	0			32.85
50	Sn	121	120.9424	112614.4	1026.7	8.4848		(0)	β^-	27.5 h	
50	Sn	122	121.94222	113545.40	1035.21	8.48529					4.72
50	Sn	123	122.9446	114478.8	1041.4	8.4663			β^-	40.0 m	

50	Sn^m	123	122.9447	114478.9	1041.3	8.4655		(0)	β^-	131. d	
50	Sn	124	123.9445	115409.8	1049.8	8.4662					5.98
51	Sb^m	116	115.9440	107960.2	982.6	8.470			β^+	15. m	
51	Sb	117	116.9421	108889.6	992.7	8.485			ϵ, β^+	2.8 h	
51	Sb	118	117.9437	109822.2	999.6	8.471			ϵ	5.1 h	
51	Sb	119	118.9416	110751.4	1009.9	8.4866			ϵ	38.0 h	
51	Sb^m	120	119.9430	111683.8	1017.0	8.4747			ϵ	5.8 d	
51	Sb	121	120.9420	112614.0	1026.3	8.4815	3.3589	$\frac{5}{2}$			57.25
51	Sb	122	121.94386	113546.93	1032.90	8.46636		2	$\beta^-, \epsilon, \beta^+$	2.80 d	
51	Sb	123	122.9431	114477.4	1042.0	8.4713	2.5465	$\frac{7}{2}$			42.75
51	Sb	125	124.9449	116341.3	1057.0	8.4562			β^-	2.4 y	
52	Te	120	119.9425	111683.4	1016.6	8.4721		(0)			0.089
52	Te	122	121.94166	113544.88	1034.16	8.47674		(0)			2.46
52	Te	123	122.9434	114477.6	1040.9	8.4626	-0.732	$\frac{1}{2}$	ϵ	$>10^{14}\ y$	0.87
52	Te	124	123.9421	115407.6	1050.5	8.4716		(0)			4.61
52	Te	125	124.9441	116340.6	1057.0	8.4559	-0.8872	$\frac{1}{2}$			6.99
52	Te	126	125.9436	117271.2	1065.8	8.4588		(0)			18.71
52	Te	127	126.9457	118204.4	1072.2	8.4427	$-0-$		β^-	9.35 h	
52	Te	128	127.9461	119135.9	1080.2	8.4392		(0)			31.79
52	Te^m	129	128.9476	120068.4	1087.2	8.4278			β^-	74. m	
52	Te	129	128.9477	120068.5	1087.1	8.4270			β^-	33.0 d	
52	Te	130	129.9478	120999.7	1095.4	8.4258	$-0-$	(0)		$>10^{21}\ y$	34.49
52	Te	131	130.9500	121932.9	1101.7	8.4098			β^-	24.8 m	
52	Te	132	131.9503	122864.3	1109.8	8.4073			β^-	77.7 h	
52	Te	133	132.9528	123797.8	1115.8	8.3894			β^-	2 m	
53	I	122	121.9460	113548.9	1029.3	8.4372			β^+	3.5 m	
53	I	124	123.9456	115410.8	1046.4	8.4391			ϵ, β^+	4.5 d	
53	I	125	124.9442	116340.7	1056.1	8.4489			ϵ	60.0 d	
53	I	126	125.9458	117273.3	1063.0	8.4364	2.809	2	$\epsilon, \beta^-, \beta^+$	13.3 d	
53	I	127	126.9448	118203.5	1072.3	8.4431		$\frac{5}{2}$			100
53	I	128	127.9467	119136.4	1078.9	8.4287			β^-, β^+	24.98 m	
53	I	129	128.94593	120066.84	1087.95	8.43376	2.603	$\frac{7}{2}$	β^-	$1.6 \times 10^7\ y$	

Z	A	Element Symbol[b]	Mass (amu)	Mass (Mev/c²)	Binding energy (Mev)	B. E. per nucleon (Mev)	Nuclear[c] magnetic moment (n. m.)	Nuclear[d] spin	Decay[e] mode	Half-life	Abundance (%)
53	130	I	129.9478	120999.7	1094.6	8.4198			β^-	12.5 h	
53	131	I	130.9477	121930.8	1103.0	8.4201		$\frac{7}{2}$	β^-	8.05 d	
53	132	I	131.9498	122863.9	1109.4	8.4049			β^-	2.33 h	
53	133	I	132.9496	123794.8	1118.0	8.4060			β^-	20.8 h	
53	134	I	133.9513	124727.6	1124.8	8.3939			β^-	52.5 m	
53	136	I	135.9579	126596.0	1135.4	8.3482			β^-	86. s	
54	124	Xe	123.9454	115410.6	1045.8	8.4343		(0)			0.096
54	126	Xe	125.9445	117272.1	1063.4	8.4398		(0)			0.090
54	127	Xe	126.9459	118204.5	1070.5	8.4290			ϵ	36.4 d	
54	128	Xe	127.9445	119134.4	1080.1	8.4386		(0)			1.919
54	129	Xe	128.9456	120066.5	1087.5	8.4301	-0.7769	$\frac{1}{2}$			26.44
54	130	Xe	129.9446	120996.7	1096.8	8.4367		(0)			4.08
54	132	Xe	131.9460	122860.3	1112.2	8.4258		(0)			26.89
54	133	Xe	132.9477	123793.0	1119.0	8.4134			β^-	5.270 d	
54	134	Xe	133.9476	124724.1	1127.4	8.4138		(0)			10.44
54	136	Xe	135.9500	126588.6	1141.9	8.3966		(0)			8.87
54	137	Xe	136.9546	127524.0	1146.0	8.3651			β^-	3.8 m	
54	138	Xe	137.9569	128457.3	1152.2	8.3496			β^-	17. m	
55	126	Cs	125.9497	117276.9	1057.8	8.3951			β^+, ϵ	1.6 m	
55	127	Cs	126.9482	118206.7	1067.6	8.4059			ϵ, β^+	6.25 h	
55	128	Cs	127.9489	119138.5	1075.3	8.4005			β^+, ϵ	3.8 m	
55	129	Cs	128.9467	120067.6	1085.7	8.4161			ϵ	31. h	
55	130	Cs	129.9478	120999.7	1093.0	8.4078			$\beta^+, \epsilon, \beta^-$	30. m	
55	131	Cs	130.9470	121930.1	1102.1	8.4132	3.48	$\frac{5}{2}$	ϵ	10.0 d	
55	132	Cs	131.9479	122862.1	1109.6	8.4064		$\frac{7}{2}$	ϵ	6.2 d	
55	133	Cs	132.9472	123792.6	1118.7	8.4110	2.5789	$\frac{7}{2}$			100
55	134	Cs	133.9490	124725.4	1125.4	8.3982	2.95	4	β^-	2.3 y	

Z	El	A	Mass			B/A	μ	J^π	Decay	Half-life	Abundance
55	Cs	135	134.94867	125656.24	1134.03	8.40020	2.713	$\frac{7}{2}$	β^-	$2.0 \times 10^6\ y$	
55	Cs	137	136.9509	127520.6	1148.7	8.3846	2.850	$\frac{7}{2}$	β^-	$30.\ y$	
55	Cs	138	137.9539	128454.5	1154.3	8.3641			β^-	$32.\ m$	
56	Ba	129	128.9498	120070.4	1082.0	8.3876		$(\frac{1}{2})$	ϵ, β^+	$2.45\ h$	
56	Ba	130	129.9474	120999.4	1092.6	8.4047		(0)			0.101
56	Ba	134	133.9468	124723.4	1126.6	8.4076	0.932	(0)			2.42
56	Ba	137	136.9496	127519.4	1149.1	8.3877		$\frac{3}{2}$			11.32
56	Ba	138	137.9487	128449.7	1158.3	8.3936		(0)			71.66
56	Ba	139	138.95271	129384.57	1162.94	8.36647			β^-	$85.0\ m$	
56	Ba	140	139.9544	130317.3	1169.7	8.3553			β^-	$12.8\ d$	
57	La	134	133.9507	124727.0	1122.2	8.3747			ϵ, β^+	$6.5\ m$	
57	La	138	137.9501	128451.0	1156.2	8.3784	3.6844	5	ϵ, β^-	$1.1 \times 10^{11}\ y$	0.089
57	La	139	138.95020	129382.23	1164.49	8.37756	2.761	$\frac{7}{2}$			99.911
57	La	140	139.9530	130316.0	1170.3	8.3590			β^-	$40.20\ h$	
57	La	141	140.9543	131248.3	1177.4	8.3504			β^-	$3.7\ h$	
58	Ce	138	137.9490	128450.0	1156.5	8.3802		(0)			0.250
58	Ce	139	138.9505	129382.5	1163.4	8.3701	0.84	$\frac{3}{2}$	ϵ	$140.\ d$	
58	Ce	140	139.9489	130312.2	1173.3	8.3807		(0)			88.48
58	Ce	141	140.95290	131247.02	1177.93	8.35411	0.89	$\frac{7}{2}$	β^-	$32.5\ d$	
58	Ce	142	141.9530	132178.3	1186.2	8.3535		(0)			11.07
58	Ce	143	142.9565	133112.7	1191.3	8.3308			β^-	$33.\ h$	
58	Ce	144	143.9584	134045.6	1197.9	8.3188			β^-	$290.\ d$	
58	Ce	146	145.9643	135913.3	1209.1	8.2818			β^-	$14.0\ m$	
59	Pr	138	137.9528	128453.5	1152.1	8.3489			ϵ, β^+	$2.0\ h$	
59	Pr	140	139.9524	130315.4	1169.3	8.3518			β^+, ϵ	$3.4\ m$	
59	Pr	141	140.95228	131246.45	1177.73	8.35267	3.92	$\frac{5}{2}$			100
59	Pr	142	141.9538	132179.0	1184.7	8.3428			β^-	$19.3\ h$	
59	Pr	143	142.9550	133111.3	1191.9	8.3351			β^-	$13.7\ d$	
59	Pr	144	143.9581	134045.3	1197.4	8.3153			β^-	$17.5\ m$	
59	Pr	146	145.9632	135912.3	1209.4	8.2835			β^-	$24.4\ m$	
60	Nd	140	139.9525	130315.5	1168.4	8.3456			ϵ	$3.3\ d$	
60	Nd	141	140.95408	131248.12	1175.27	8.33523		$(\frac{3}{2})$	ϵ, β^+	$2.42\ h$	

Z	Element Symbol[b]	A	Mass (amu)	Mass (Mev/c²)	Binding energy (Mev)	B. E. per nucleon (Mev)	Nuclear[c] magnetic moment (n. m.)	Nuclear[d] spin	Decay[e] mode	Half-life	Abundance (%)
60	Nd	142	141.9515	132176.9	1186.0	8.3524		(0)			27.09
60	Nd	143	142.9541	133110.4	1192.0	8.3355	-1.1	$\frac{7}{2}$			12.14
60	Nd	144	143.9549	134042.3	1199.6	8.3305		(0)	α	$\sim 2 \times 10^{15}\, y$	23.83
60	Nd	146	145.9587	135908.1	1212.8	8.3068		(0)			17.26
60	Nd	147	146.9615	136841.9	1218.5	8.2894	0.22		β^-	11.3 d	
60	Nd	148	147.9640	137775.4	1224.6	8.2742		(0)			5.74
60	Nd	149	148.9667	138709.0	1230.4	8.2580			β^-	2. h	
60	Nd	150	149.9679	139641.3	1237.7	8.2512		(0)		$> 10^{16}\, y$	5.63
61	Pm	146	145.9590	135908.4	1211.7	8.2995			$(?\beta^-)$	$\sim 1.\, y$	
61	Pm	147	146.9605	136841.0	1218.7	8.2904		$(\frac{7}{2})$	β^-	2.52 y	
61	Pm	148	147.9642	137775.5	1223.6	8.2677			β^-	42. d	
61	Pm	149	148.9649	138707.3	1231.3	8.2640			β^-	52. h	
61	Pm	150	149.9691	139642.4	1235.8	8.2385			β^-	2.7 h	
62	Sm	144	143.9560	134043.3	1197.0	8.3126		(0)			3.16
62	Sm	146	145.9582	135907.7	1211.7	8.2993			α	$\sim 5. \times 10^7\, y$	
62	Sm	147	146.9603	135840.8	1218.1	8.2864	-0.8	$\frac{7}{2}$	α	$1.3 \times 10^{11}\, y$	15.07
62	Sm	148	147.9613	137772.8	1225.5	8.2807		(0)			11.27
62	Sm	149	148.9635	138706.0	1231.9	8.2675	-0.65	$\frac{7}{2}$			13.84
62	Sm	150	149.9634	139637.1	1240.3	8.2687		(0)			7.47
62	Sm	152	151.9673	141503.0	1253.4	8.2461		(0)			26.63
62	Sm	154	153.9705	143368.2	1267.2	8.2283		(0)			22.53
62	Sm	155	154.9735	144302.2	1272.7	8.2112			β^-	24.0 m	
62	Sm	156	155.9750	145234.7	1279.7	8.2032			β^-	$\sim 10.\, h$	
63	Eu	150	149.9662	139639.7	1236.9	8.2461			β^-	13.7 h	
63	Eu	154	153.9729	143370.5	1264.1	8.2087			β^-, ϵ	16. y	
63	Eu	155	154.9711	144300.0	1274.2	8.2205			β^-	1.7 y	
63	Eu	156	155.9741	145233.9	1279.8	8.2035			β^-	15.4 d	

Z	El	A	Mass					I	Decay	Half-life	%
63	Eu	157	156.9749	146165.8	1287.4	8.1998			β^-	15.4 h	
64	Gd	148	147.9634	137774.8	1222.0	8.2569			α (?ϵ)	>35. y	
64	Gd	150	149.9650	139638.6	1237.3	8.2484			α	>10⁵ y	
64	Gd	154	153.9697	143367.5	1266.3	8.2230	−0.30	(0)			2.15
64	Gd	155	154.9709	144299.8	1273.6	8.2167		3/2			14.73
64	Gd	156	155.9715	145231.5	1281.4	8.2140		(0)			20.47
64	Gd	157	156.9712	146162.3	1290.0	8.2168	−0.37	3/2			15.68
64	Gd	158	157.9734	147095.5	1296.4	8.2048		(0)			24.87
64	Gd	160	159.9778	148961.9	1309.0	8.1811		(0)			21.90
65	Tb	160	159.978	148962.	1308.	8.175			β^-	73.0 d	
66	Dy	160	159.9748	148959.1	1310.2	8.1889		(0)			2.29
66	Dy	162	161.977	150823.	1325.	8.178		(0)			25.53
66	Dy	164	163.980	152688.	1339.	8.164		(0)			28.18
66	Dy	165	164.982	153622.	1345.	8.154			β^-	2.32 h	
67	Ho	164	163.9828	152691.1	1335.4	8.1429			β^-, ϵ	37. m	
67	Ho	165	164.981	153621.	1345.	8.154	3.3	7/2			100
67	Ho	166	165.9835	154554.0	1351.5	8.1417			β^-	27.0 h	
68	Er	164	163.9817	152690.1	1335.7	8.1444		(0)			1.56
68	Er	166	165.9815	154552.2	1352.6	8.1482		(0)			33.4
68	Er	168	167.9839	156416.7	1367.1	8.1375		(0)			27.1
68	Er	170	169.989	158284.	1379.	8.112		(0)			14.9
70	Yb	172	171.984	160141.	1399.	8.133		(0)			21.82
70	Yb	174	173.981	162001.	1418.	8.152		(0)			31.84
71	Lu	176	175.9978	163878.8	1418.7	8.0609	2.8	(6?)	β^-	2.2 × 10¹⁰ y	2.6
72	Hf	176	175.9967	163877.7	1419.0	8.0623		(0)			5.20
72	Hf	178	178.000	165743.	1433.	8.048		(0)			27.10
72	Hf	181	181.004	168540.	1454.	8.033			β^-	46. d	0.012
73	Ta	180	180.002	167607.	1447.	8.037				>10⁷ y	99.99
73	Ta	181	181.0033	168539.6	1453.9	8.0324	2.1	7/2			
73	Ta	182	182.005	169472.	1461.	8.026			β^-	112. d	
74	W	180	180.0017	167607.0	1446.2	8.0345		0			0.135
74	W	182	182.0039	169471.3	1460.9	8.0268		0			26.4

Z	Element Symbol[b]	A	Mass (amu)	Mass (Mev/c²)	Binding energy (Mev)	B.E. per nucleon (Mev)	Nuclear[c] magnetic moment (n. m.)	Nuclear[a] spin	Decay[e] mode	Half-life	Abundance (%)
74	W	183	183.005	170403.	1468.	8.023	0.11846	$\frac{1}{2}$			14.4
74	W	184	184.006	171336.	1476.	8.020		(0)			30.6
74	W	186	186.010	173202.	1489.	8.004		(0)			28.4
74	W	187	187.012	174135.	1495.	7.996			β^-	24.00 h	
75	Re	186	186.011	173202.	1487.	7.994			β^-, ϵ	91.0 h	
75	Re	187	187.011	174134.	1495.	7.996	3.1475	$\frac{5}{2}$	β^-	$5. \times 10^{10}$ y	62.93
75	Re	188	188.016	175069.	1499.	7.974			β^-	17.0 h	
76	Os	186	186.010	173202.	1487.	7.995		(0)			1.59
76	Os	187	187.011	174134.	1495.	7.992	0.12	$\frac{1}{2}$			1.64
76	Os	188	188.0167	175070.0	1497.6	7.9659		(0)			13.3
76	Os	189	189.018	176002.	1505.	7.962	0.6559	$\frac{3}{2}$			16.1
76	Os	190	190.017	176933.	1514.	7.969		(0)			26.4
76	Os	191	191.022	177868.	1518.	7.946			β^-	16.0d	
76	Os	192	192.022	178800.	1526.	7.949		(0)			41.0
76	Os	193	193.026	179734.	1531.	7.931			β^-	31.5 h	
77	Ir	191	191.021	177867.	1518.	7.947	0.2	$\frac{3}{2}$			38.5
77	Ir	193	193.025	179733.	1531.	7.932	0.17	$\frac{3}{2}$			61.5
77	Ir	194	194.0264	180665.9	1538.0	7.9277		(2)	β^-	19.0 h	
77	Ir	195	195.0287	181599.2	1544.2	7.9189			β^-	2.3 h	
77	Ir	198	198.034	184398.	1564.	7.901			β^-	50. s	
78	Pt	192	192.023	178800.	1524.	7.936		(0)			0.78
78	Pt	193	193.0253	179733.8	1529.8	7.9267			ϵ	<500. y	
78	Pt	194	194.0240	180663.7	1539.4	7.9351		(0)			32.8
78	Pt	195	195.0264	181597.1	1545.5	7.9259	0.6060	$\frac{1}{2}$			33.7
78	Pt	196	196.0269	182528.7	1553.4	7.9257		(0)			25.4
78	Pt	197	197.029	183462.	1560.	7.918			β^-	18. h	
78	Pt	198	198.029	184393.	1568.	7.920		(0)			7.2

Z	El	A	Atomic mass				μ	I	Decay	$T_{1/2}$	Abundance
79	Au	196	196.02888	182530.53	1550.82	7.91237		2	ε, β⁻	5.60 d	
79	Au	197	197.028	183461.	1560.	7.919	0.14	3/2			100.
79	Au	198	198.030	184394.	1567.	7.912		2	β⁻	2.70 d	
79	Au	199	199.031	185326.	1574.	7.909		3/2	β⁻	3.15 d	
79	Au	200	200.0343	186260.1	1579.2	7.8962			β⁻	48. m	
79	Au	201	201.036	187193.	1586.	7.891			β⁻	26. m	
80	Hg	196	196.027	182529.	1552.	7.917		(0)			0.146
80	Hg	198	198.029	184393.	1567.	7.912		(0)			10.02
80	Hg	200	200.0319	186257.9	1580.7	7.9034	(−0−)	(0)			23.13
80	Hg	201	201.034	187191.	1587.	7.896	−0.613	3/2			13.22
80	Hg	202	202.0354	188123.4	1594.2	7.8919		(0)			29.80
80	Hg	203	203.0365	189055.6	1601.5	7.8891			β⁻	45.8 d	
80	Hg	204	204.0373	189987.5	1609.1	7.8878		(0)			6.85
80	Hg	205	205.04036	190921.49	1614.64	7.87627			β⁻	5.5 m	
81	Tl	200	200.0345	186260.3	1577.5	7.8874		2	ε, β⁺	26.1 h	
81	Tl	202	202.0364	188124.4	1592.4	7.8834			ε	12.0 d	
81	Tl	203	203.0360	189055.1	1601.2	7.8876	1.612	1/2			29.50
81	Tl	204	204.03768	189987.85	1607.98	7.88225	(±)0.08	2	β⁻, ε	4.1 y	
81	Tl	205	205.03848	190919.74	1615.59	7.88095	1.6273	1/2			70.50
81	Tl	206	206.04045	191852.71	1622.13	7.87442			β⁻	4.20 m	
81	Tl	207	207.04214	192785.43	1628.92	7.86918			β⁻	4.78 m	
81	Tl	208	208.04701	193721.10	1632.75	7.84974			β⁻	3.1 m	
81	Tl	209	209.05068	194655.66	1637.69	7.83584			β⁻	2.20 m	
81	Tl	210	210.05562	195591.40	1641.46	7.81649			β⁻	1.32 m	
82	Pbᵐ	202	202.0365	188124.5	1591.6	7.8791			ε	3.5 h	
82	Pb	203	203.0374	189056.4	1599.1	7.8773			ε	52. h	
82	Pb	204	204.03686	189987.09	1607.97	7.88220	−0−	(0)			1.5
82	Pb	205	205.03854	190919.79	1614.77	7.87691		(5/2)	ε	3.0 × 10⁷ y	
82	Pb	206	206.03883	191851.20	1622.86	7.87795		0			23.6
82	Pb	207	207.04058	192783.97	1629.60	7.87246	0.58943	1/2			22.6
82	Pb	208	208.041640	193716.101	1636.974	7.870066	−0−	(0)			52.3
82	Pb	209	209.04647	194651.74	1640.84	7.85090			β⁻	3.32 h	

Z	Element Symbol[b]	A	Mass (amu)	Mass (Mev/c²)	Binding energy (Mev)	B. E. per nucleon (Mev)	Nuclear[c] magnetic moment (n. m.)	Nuclear[d] spin	Decay[e] mode	Half-life	Abundance (%)
82	Pb	210	210.04983	195586.01	1646.07	7.83843		0	β^-	22.0 y	
82	Pb	211	211.05475	196521.73	1649.86	7.81925			β^-	36.1 m	
82	Pb	212	212.05817	197456.06	1655.04	7.80678			β^-	10.64 h	
82	Pb	214	214.06658	199326.17	1663.94	7.77542			β^-	26.8 m	
83	Bi	206	206.0427	191854.8	1618.5	7.8567			ϵ	6.4 d	
83	Bi	207	207.04238	192785.65	1627.13	7.86054			ϵ	28. y	
83	Bi	208	208.04479	193719.03	1633.26	7.85220		(4)	ϵ	$\sim 2. \times 10^4 \, y$	
83	Bi	209	209.04579	194651.11	1640.69	7.85019	4.0797	$\frac{9}{2}$	α	$> 2. \times 10^{18} \, y$	100.
83	Bi	210	210.04976	195585.94	1645.35	7.83502	0	1	β^-, α	5.00 d	
83	Bi	211	211.05326	196520.34	1650.46	7.82207			α, β^-	2.16 m	
83	Bi	212	212.05754	197455.47	1654.84	7.80586			β^-, α	60.5 m	
83	Bi	213	213.06097	198389.80	1660.01	7.79348			β^-, α	47. m	
83	Bi	214	214.06552	199325.18	1664.14	7.77633			β^-, α	19.7 m	
83	Bi	215	215.0689	200259.5	1669.4	7.7645			β^-	8. m	
84	Po	207	207.04626	192789.26	1622.75	7.83935			$\epsilon, \beta^+, \alpha$	5.7 h	
84	Po	208	208.04633	193720.47	1631.04	7.84155			α	2.93 y	
84	Po	209	209.04776	194652.94	1638.08	7.83771		$\frac{1}{2}$	α, ϵ	$\sim 100 \, y$	
84	Po	210	210.04850	195584.77	1645.75	7.83693			α	138.40 d	
84	Po	211	211.05261	196519.74	1650.29	7.82128			α	0.52 s	
84	Po	212	212.055129	197453.225	1656.305	7.812761			α	$3.04 \times 10^{-7} \, s$	
84	Po	213	213.05947	198388.41	1660.63	7.79640			α	$4.2 \times 10^{-6} \, s$	
84	Po	214	214.06211	199322.01	1666.54	7.78756			α	$1.64 \times 10^{-4} \, s$	
84	Po	215	215.06671	200257.43	1670.62	7.77031			α, β^-	$1.83 \times 10^{-3} \, s$	
84	Po	216	216.06946	201191.13	1676.43	7.76123			α	0.158 s	
84	Po	217	217.0741	202126.6	1680.5	7.7441			α	< 10 s	
84	Po	218	218.07702	203060.45	1686.11	7.73445			α, β^-	3.05 m	
85	At	210	210.0526	195588.6	1641.2	7.8150			ϵ, α	8.3 h	

Z	El	A	Mass				Decay	Half-life
85	At	211	211.05345	196520.52	1648.72	7.81386	ϵ, α	$7.20\ h$
85	At	212	212.0569	197454.9	1653.9	7.8013	α	$0.22\ s$
85	At	213	213.05975	198388.67	1659.58	7.79146	α	$\sim 10^{-6}\ s$
85	At	214	214.06325	199323.07	1664.69	7.77894	α	$\sim 2 \times 10^{-6}\ s$
85	At	215	215.06589	200256.67	1670.60	7.77022	α	$\sim 10^{-4}\ s$
85	At	216	216.06995	201191.59	1675.18	7.75546	α	$3. \times 10^{-4}\ s$
85	At	217	217.07251	202125.11	1681.17	7.74731	α	$0.018\ s$
85	At	218	218.0766	203060.1	1685.7	7.7327	α, β^-	$\sim 2\ s$
86	Em	212	212.05706	197455.02	1652.94	7.79690	α, ϵ	$23.\ m$
86	Em	215	215.06589	200256.67	1669.82	7.76658	α	$\sim 10^{-6}\ s$
86	Em	216	216.06777	201189.56	1676.43	7.76123	α	$\sim 10^{-4}\ s$
86	Em	217	217.07182	202124.47	1681.02	7.74662	α	$\sim 1 \times 10^{-3}\ s$
86	Em	218	218.07379	203057.45	1687.55	7.74107	α	$0.019\ s$
86	Em	219	219.07804	203992.55	1691.96	7.72583	α	$3.92\ s$
86	Em	220	220.08021	204925.71	1698.30	7.71954	α	$52.\ s$
86	Em	221	221.0845	205860.8	1702.7	7.7044	β^-, α	$25.\ m$
86	Em	222	222.08690	206794.22	1708.80	7.69731	α	$3.825\ d$
87	Fr	217	217.07271	202125.30	1679.42	7.73924	α	very short
87	Fr	218	218.07572	203059.24	1684.97	7.72924	α	$5. \times 10^{-3}\ s$
87	Fr	219	219.07776	203992.28	1691.45	7.72350	α	$\sim 0.02\ s$
87	Fr	220	220.08114	204926.57	1696.66	7.71209	α	$27.5\ s$
87	Fr	221	221.08328	205859.71	1703.03	7.70601	α	$4.8\ m$
87	Fr	222	222.0871	206794.4	1707.8	7.6930	β^-, α	$14.8\ m$
87	Fr	223	223.08960	207727.87	1713.88	7.68555	β^-, α	$21.\ m$
88	Ra	219	219.07852	203992.99	1689.95	7.71665	α	$10^{-3}\ s$
88	Ra	220	220.07978	204925.31	1697.14	7.71429	α	$3. \times 10^{-2}\ s$
88	Ra	221	221.08304	205859.48	1702.47	7.70349	α	$30.\ s$
88	Ra	222	222.08483	206792.29	1709.17	7.69894	α	$38.\ s$
88	Ra	223	223.08832	207726.68	1714.29	7.68738	α	$11.68\ d$
88	Ra	224	224.09030	208659.67	1720.80	7.68216	α	$3.64\ d$
88	Ra	225	225.09388	209594.14	1725.83	7.67037	β^-	$14.8\ d$
88	Ra	226	226.09600	210527.26	1732.22	7.66469	α	$1.622 \times 10^3\ y$

Z	Element Symbol[b]	A	Mass (amu)	Mass (Mev/c²)	Binding energy (Mev)	B. E. per nucleon (Mev)	Nuclear magnetic moment (n. m.)[c]	Nuclear spin[d]	Decay mode[e]	Half-life	Abundance (%)
88	Ra	227	227.10018	211462.29	1736.70	7.65066			β^-	41.2 m	
88	Ra	228	228.10256	212395.65	1742.84	7.64405			β^-	6.7 y	
88	Ra	229	229.1064	213330.4	1747.6	7.6316			β^-	short	
89	Ac	221	221.0849	205861.2	1700.0	7.6922			α	<1 s	
89	Ac	222	222.08721	206794.51	1706.18	7.68548			α	5.5 s	
89	Ac	223	223.08890	207727.22	1712.96	7.68145			α, ϵ	2.2 m	
89	Ac	224	224.09176	208661.03	1718.67	7.67264			ϵ, α	2.9 h	
89	Ac	225	225.09350	209593.79	1725.41	7.66850			α	10.0 d	
89	Ac	226	226.0969	210528.1	1730.6	7.6576			β^-	29. h	
89	Ac	227	227.09888	211461.08	1737.13	7.65254	1.1	$\frac{3}{2}$	β^-, α	21.8 y	
89	Ac	228	228.10251	212395.60	1742.12	7.64087			β^-	6.13 h	
89	Ac	229	229.1045	213328.6	1748.6	7.6359			β^-	66. m	
89	Ac	230	230.1082	214263.2	1753.5	7.6241			β^-	<1 m	
90	Th	223	223.0907	207728.9	1710.5	7.6704			α	0.9 s	
90	Th	224	224.09145	208660.74	1718.17	7.67040			α	1.05 s	
90	Th	225	225.09414	209594.38	1724.04	7.66238			α, ϵ	8.0 m	
90	Th	226	226.09564	210526.92	1731.00	7.65929			α	30.9 m	
90	Th	227	227.09879	211460.99	1736.43	7.64947			α	18.4 d	
90	Th	228	228.10011	212393.36	1743.56	7.64720			α	1.91 y	
90	Th	229	229.10325	213327.43	1749.01	7.63759		$(\frac{5}{2})$	α	7.34×10^3 y	
90	Th	230	230.10500	214260.20	1755.74	7.63366		(0)	α	8.0×10^4 y	
90	Th	231	231.10861	215194.70	1760.74	7.62226			β^-	25.64 h	
90	Th	232	232.11030	216127.88	1767.07	7.61669			α	1.39×10^{10} y	100.
90	Th	233	233.11432	217062.30	1772.16	7.60582			β^-	23.5 m	
90	Th	234	234.11678	217995.73	1778.23	7.59926			β^-	24.10 d	
91	Pa	225	225.0956	209596.7	1721.0	7.6487			α	2.0 s	
91	Pa	226	226.0999	210530.9	1726.3	7.6383			α	1.8 m	

Z	El	A	Mass				Spin	Decay	Half-life	Abundance
91	Pa	227	227.09984	211461.97	1734.67	7.64171		α, ϵ	38.3 m	
91	Pa	228	228.10230	212395.40	1740.74	7.63483		ϵ, α	22.h	
91	Pa	229	229.10359	213327.75	1747.90	7.63275		ϵ, α	1.5 d	
91	Pa	230	230.1066	214261.7	1753.5	7.6238		$\epsilon, \beta^-, \beta^+, \alpha$	17.7 d	
91	Pa	231	231.10827	215194.39	1760.28	7.62024	$\frac{3}{2}$	α	3.43×10^4 y	
91	Pa	232	232.11118	216128.24	1765.93	7.61176		β^-	1.32 d	
91	Pa	233	233.11300	217061.07	1772.60	7.60774		β^-	27.4 d	
91	Pa	234	234.1166	217995.6	1777.6	7.5966		β^-	6.66 h	
91	Pa	235	235.1190	218928.9	1783.7	7.5904		β^-	23.7 m	
91	Pa	237	237.1251	220796.9	1794.8	7.5730	$\left(\frac{3}{2}\right)$	β^-	39. m	
92	U	227	227.1020	211464.0	1731.9	7.6294		α	1.3 m	
92	U	228	228.10262	212395.70	1739.67	7.53013		α, ϵ	9.3 m	
92	U	229	229.10499	213329.05	1745.82	7.62369		ϵ, α	58. m	
92	U	230	230.10595	214261.08	1753.29	7.62301		α	20.8 d	
92	U	231	231.10863	215194.72	1759.17	7.61544		ϵ, α	4.3 d	
92	U	232	232.10980	216126.95	1766.44	7.61396		α	74. y	
92	U	233	233.11240	217060.51	1772.38	7.60678	$\frac{5}{2}$	α	1.62×10^5 y	
92	U	234	234.11408	217993.22	1779.19	7.60336		α	2.48×10^5 y	0.0058
92	U	235	235.11750	218927.54	1784.36	7.59304	$\frac{7}{2}$	α	7.15×10^8 y	0.720
92	U	236	236.11959	219860.63	1790.78	7.58805		α	2.39×10^7 y	
92	U	237	237.12275	220794.71	1796.21	7.57894	$\left(\frac{1}{2}\right)$	β^-	6.75 d	
92	U	238	238.12522	221728.16	1802.27	7.57256		α	4.51×10^9 y	99.274
92	U	239	239.12916	222662.97	1806.96	7.56051		β^-	23.5 m	
92	U	240	240.13181	223596.57	1812.86	7.55357	0	β^-	14.1 h	
93	Np	231	231.11058	215196.54	1756.56	7.60416		α, ϵ	50. m	
93	Np	232	232.11264	216129.60	1763.01	7.59919		ϵ	~13 m	
93	Np	233	233.11352	217061.56	1770.56	7.59895		ϵ, α	35. m	
93	Np	234	234.1164	217995.4	1776.2	7.5907		$\epsilon, \beta^+, \alpha$	4.40 d	
93	Np	235	235.11767	218927.70	1783.42	7.58904		ϵ, α	1.12 y	
93	Np^m	236	236.12050	219861.48	1789.15	7.58114	$\frac{5}{2}$	β^-, ϵ	22. h	
93	Np	237	237.12220	220794.20	1795.93	7.57776		α	2.20×10^6 y	6.
93	Np	238	238.12536	221728.29	1801.36	7.56873		β^-	2.10 d	

Z	Element Symbol[b]	A	Mass (amu)	Mass (Mev/c^2)	Binding energy (Mev)	B.E. per nucleon (Mev)	Nuclear[c] magnetic moment (n. m.)	Nuclear[d] spin	Decay[e] mode	Half-life	Abundance (%)
93	Np	239	239.12777	222661.67	1807.48	7.56266		$\frac{1}{2}$	β^-	2.33 d	
93	Np^m	240	240.13142	223596.21	1812.44	7.55182			β^-	7.3 m	
93	Np	241	241.1336	224529.4	1818.8	7.5468		$(\frac{5}{2})$	β^-	16. m	
94	Pu	232	232.11370	216130.58	1761.24	7.59157			ϵ, α	36. m	
94	Pu	233	233.11585	217063.73	1767.61	7.58632			ϵ, α	20. m	
94	Pu	234	234.11660	217995.57	1775.28	7.58665			ϵ, α	9.0 h	
94	Pu	235	235.11890	218928.85	1781.50	7.58083			ϵ, α	26. m	
94	Pu	236	236.11996	219860.98	1788.88	7.58000			α	2.7 y	
94	Pu	237	237.12243	220794.42	1794.94	7.57359			ϵ, α	45. d	
94	Pu	238	238.12396	221726.98	1801.88	7.57092			α	89.6 y	
94	Pu	239	239.12700	222660.95	1807.42	7.56242	0.4	$\frac{1}{2}$	α	2.44 × 10^4 y	
94	Pu	240	240.12910	223594.05	1813.83	7.55761			α	6.6 × 10^3 y	
94	Pu	241	241.13215	224528.03	1819.35	7.54916	1.4	$\frac{5}{2}$	β^-, α	13.2 y	
94	Pu	242	242.13445	225461.31	1825.57	7.54367			α	3.8 × 10^5 y	
94	Pu	243	243.13809	226395.84	1830.55	7.53312			β^-	4.98 h	
94	Pu	244	244.1406	227329.3	1836.6	7.5269			α	7. × 10^7 y	
94	Pu	245	245.1441	228263.7	1841.7	7.5170			β^-	11. h	
94	Pu	246	246.1471	229197.7	1847.3	7.5092			β^-	11. d	
95	Am	237	237.12396	220795.84	1792.74	7.56428			ϵ, α	~1.3 h	
95	Am	238	238.1266	221729.4	1798.6	7.5573			ϵ	1.86 h	
95	Am	239	239.12784	222661.74	1805.85	7.55584			ϵ, α	12. h	
95	Am	240	240.13056	223595.41	1811.68	7.54868			ϵ	50. h	
95	Am	241	241.13213	224528.01	1818.58	7.54599	1.4	$\frac{5}{2}$	α	462. y	
95	Am	242	242.13523	225462.04	1824.06	7.53743		1	β^-, ϵ	16.0 h	
95	Am	243	243.13748	226395.28	1830.33	7.53220		$\frac{5}{2}$	α	8. × 10^3 y	
95	Am	244	244.14092	227329.62	1835.49	7.52251			β^-, ϵ	26. m	
95	Am	245	245.14283	228262.54	1842.08	7.51868			β^-	2.0 h	

Z	El	A	mass					decay	half-life
95	Am	246	246.1468	229197.4	1846.7	7.5071		β^-	25. m
96	Cm	238	238.12757	221730.34	1796.95	7.55022		ϵ, α	2.5 h
96	Cm	239	239.1298	222663.6	1803.2	7.5449		ϵ	~3 h
96	Cm	240	240.13066	223595.50	1810.80	7.54500		α	26.8 d
96	Cm	241	241.1331	224528.9	1816.9	7.5390		ϵ, α	35. d
96	Cm	242	242.13451	225461.37	1823.95	7.53697		α	162.5 d
96	Cm	243	243.13748	226395.28	1829.54	7.52898		α	~35 y
96	Cm	244	244.13931	227328.12	1836.20	7.52541		α	18.4 y
96	Cm	245	245.14283	228262.54	1841.29	7.51549		α	$2. \times 10^4$ y
96	Cm	246	246.14413	229194.89	1848.45	7.51400		α	6.6×10^3 y
96	Cm	247	247.14750	230129.17	1853.67	7.50473		α	$>10^6$ y
96	Cm	248	248.1501	231062.7	1859.6	7.4985	(0)	α	4.2×10^5 y
96	Cm	249	249.15355	231997.09	1864.77	7.48903		β^-	64 m.
96	Cm	250	250.1566	232931.1	1870.3	7.4812		β^-	<130 y
97	Bk	243	243.13905	226396.74	1827.31	7.51979		ϵ, α	4.5 h
97	Bk	244	244.1415	227330.2	1833.4	7.5139		ϵ, α	4.4 h
97	Bk	245	245.14292	228262.62	1840.43	7.51195		ϵ, α	5.0 d
97	Bk	246	246.1457	229196.4	1846.2	7.5049		ϵ	1.9 d
97	Bk	247	247.1476	230129.3	1852.8	7.5012		α	$7. \times 10^3$ y
97	Bk	248	248.1507	231063.3	1858.3	7.4931		β^-, ϵ	18. h
97	Bk	249	249.15261	231996.21	1864.87	7.48944	(2)	β^-, α	2.9×10^2 d
97	Bk	250	250.15664	232931.10	1869.48	7.47792		β^-	3.22 h
98	Cf	244	244.14235	227330.95	1831.82	7.50744		α, ϵ	25. m
98	Cf	245	245.1446	228264.2	1838.1	7.5024		ϵ, α	44. m
98	Cf	246	246.14575	229196.40	1845.37	7.50151		α	35.7 h
98	Cf	247	247.1485	230130.1	1851.2	7.4947		ϵ	2.4 h
93	Cf	248	248.15002	231062.66	1858.13	7.49246		α	2.5×10^2 d
98	Cf	249	249.1525	231996.1	1864.2	7.4867		α	4.7×10^2 y
98	Cf	250	250.15460	232929.20	1870.60	7.48239		α	10. y
98	Cf	251	251.1580	233863.5	1875.8	7.4733		α	~700 y
98	Cf	252	252.1607	234797.2	1881.6	7.4668		α	2.2 y
98	Cf	253	253.1639	235731.3	1887.0	7.4586		β^-	18. d

Z	Element Symbol[b]	A	Mass (amu)	Mass (Mev/c²)	Binding energy (Mev)	B. E. per nucleon (Mev)	Nuclear[c] magnetic moment (n. m.)	Nuclear[d] spin	Decay[e] mode	Half-life	Abundance (%)
98	Cf	254	254.1668	236665.1	1892.7	7.4515				60. d	
99	E	246	246.1502	229200.5	1840.5	7.4815			α, ϵ	7.3 m	
99	E	248	248.1531	231065.5	1854.5	7.4778			ϵ, α	25. m	
99	E	249	249.1542	231997.7	1861.8	7.4772			ϵ, α	2. h	
99	E	250	250.1567	232931.2	1867.9	7.4714			$\epsilon(\alpha?)$	8. h	
99	E	251	251.1586	233864.1	1874.5	7.4680			ϵ, α	1.5 d	
99	E	252	252.1617	234798.1	1879.9	7.4601			$\alpha(\epsilon?)$	~140 d	
99	E	253	253.1637	235731.1	1886.4	7.4563			α	20.0 d	
99	E	254	254.1673	236665.6	1891.5	7.4467			α	$3. \times 10^2$ d	
99	E^m	254	254.1675	236665.8	1891.3	7.4459			β^-, ϵ	38. h	
99	E	255	255.1698	237599.1	1897.5	7.4411			β^-	30. d	
99	E	256	256.1742	238534.3	1901.8	7.4287			β^-	short	
100	Fm	248	248.1548	231067.1	1852.1	7.4682			α	37. s	
100	Fm	249	249.1569	232000.2	1858.5	7.4640			α	~150 s	
100	Fm	250	250.1577	232932.1	1866.1	7.4646			α, ϵ	30. m	
100	Fm	251	251.1600	233865.4	1872.4	7.4596			α, ϵ	7.5 h	
100	Fm	252	252.1616	234798.0	1879.2	7.4573			α	36. h	
100	Fm	253	253.1642	235731.6	1885.2	7.4513			ϵ, α	5. d	
100	Fm	254	254.1663	236664.7	1891.6	7.4472			α	3.38 h	
100	Fm	255	255.1696	237598.9	1896.9	7.4388			α	21.5 h	
100	Fm	256	256.1721	238532.4	1902.9	7.4333				3.1 h	
101	Mv	255	255.1709	237600.1	1894.9	7.4309			$\epsilon(\alpha?)$	~0.5 h	
101	Mv	256	256.1738	238533.9	1900.6	7.4241			ϵ	1. h	

(a) Except for H¹ and the neutron, all data is taken from "Trilinear Chart of Nuclides," by William H. Sullivan, U.S. Government Printing Office (1957). According to Everling, König, Mattauch and Wapstra [Nuclear Physics 15, 342 (1960)] 1 u (C¹² = 12) = 1.000 317 917 amu (O¹⁶ = 16). The latter authors [Nuclear Physics 18, 529 (1960)] also give a complete new table of nuclidic masses in u and in Kev/c².

(b) Superscript m on element symbol denotes isomeric state.

(c) Nuclear magnetic moments are given in nuclear magnetons. A parenthesis around the value indicates that there is some doubt about this value. A parenthesis around the sign means that the sign is uncertain. (±) means that the sign is not known.

(d) A parenthesis around the spin value means that the spin was not actually measured.

(e) Orbital electron capture is denoted by ε. Gamma rays are not shown. In the case of isomeric nuclei where no decay particle is shown, it may be inferred that one or more gamma rays are emitted in transition to the ground state. The predominant decay mode is given first. The other decay modes are given in order of decreasing frequency of occurrence.

CONSTANTS AND CONVERSION FACTORS

F-1 Fundamental Constants

Avogadro's number .. $\begin{cases} (6.02486 \pm 0.00016) \times 10^{23} \text{ (physical scale)} \\ (6.02338 \pm 0.00043) \times 10^{23} \text{ (chemical scale)} \end{cases}$

Boltzmann's constant . 8.6167×10^{-11} Mev/C deg

Chemical scale to
physical scale ratio
(i.e., unit atomic wt/
unit isotopic mass) . 1.000272 ± 0.000005

Faraday $\dots\dots\dots$ $\begin{cases} 2.89366 \times 10^{14} \text{ esu/gm-mole (physical scale)} \\ 9652.18 \text{ emu/gm-mole (physical scale)} \end{cases}$

Fine structure constant
$(= e^2/\hbar c)\dots\dots\dots$ $1/137.0391$

Planck's constant $\dots$ $\begin{cases} (h)\ 6.62391 \times 10^{-27} \text{ erg-sec} \\ (\hbar)\ 1.05423 \times 10^{-27} \text{ erg-sec} \\ (\hbar)\ 6.58050 \times 10^{-22} \text{ Mev-sec} \end{cases}$

Velocity of light in
vacuum .... (c) $(2.99793 \pm 0.000003) \times 10^{10}$ cm/sec

F-2 Some Particle Properties

Electron charge ...... 4.80273×10^{-10} statcoulomb (esu)

Electron mass $\begin{cases} 9.1082 \times 10^{-28} \text{ gm} \\ 0.00054876 \text{ amu} \\ 0.51097 \text{ Mev}/c^2 \end{cases}$

Neutron mass .... $\begin{cases} 1.67470 \times 10^{-24} \text{ gm} \\ 1.008983 \text{ amu} \\ 939.5054 \text{ Mev}/c^2 \end{cases}$

Proton mass .... $\begin{cases} 1.67240 \times 10^{-24} \text{ gm} \\ 1.007595 \text{ amu} \\ 938.213 \text{ Mev}/c^2 \\ 1836.13m \end{cases}$

F-3 Some Special Units of Measurement

Bohr radius for an
infinitely massive
nucleus .... $(= \hbar^2/me^2)$ 0.52917 Å

Bohr magneton ...... $(= e\hbar/2mc)$ $\begin{cases} (0.92731 \pm 0.00002) \times 10^{-20} \text{ erg/gauss} \\ 0.57883 \times 10^{-14} \text{ Mev/gauss} \end{cases}$

Compton wavelength . $(\lambda_c = h/mc)$ 2.4261×10^{-10} cm
$(\hat{\lambda}_c = \hbar/mc)$ 3.8612×10^{-11} cm

Electron cyclotron
frequency .... $(\omega_e = e/mc)$ 8.7945×10^6 rad sec^{-1}/gauss

Electron radius
(classical) .... $(= e^2/mc^2)$ 2.81785 fermi

Nuclear magneton ... $(= e\hbar/2M_p c)$ $\begin{cases} 5.0504 \times 10^{-24} \text{ erg/gauss} \\ 3.1524 \times 10^{-18} \text{ Mev/gauss} \end{cases}$

Proton cyclotron
frequency .... $(\omega_p = e/M_p c)$ 9.5792×10^3 rad sec^{-1}/gauss

Rydberg .... $(= me^4/2\hbar^2)$ 13.605 ev

F-4 Radiation Units (see Glossary for definitions)

Curie .... 3.700×10^{10} disintegrations/sec

RAD .... 100 ergs/gm

REP............... 1.6×10^{12} ion-pairs/gm tissue

Roentgen (r unit) .... 2.083×10^9 ion pairs/cm^3 air at NTP

Rutherford .... 10^6 disintegrations/sec

F-5 Conversion Factors

*Electrical**

Capacitance ....
$$\begin{cases} 1 \text{ farad} = 10^{-9}c^2 \text{ statfarad}\dagger \text{ (esu)} \\ 1 \text{ abfarad (emu)} = 10^9 \text{ farad} \\ 1 \text{ abfarad} = c^2 \text{ statfarad} \end{cases}$$

Charge ....
$$\begin{cases} 1 \text{ coulomb} = 10^{-1}c \text{ statcoulomb (esu)} \\ 1 \text{ abcoulomb (emu)} = 10 \text{ coulomb} \\ 1 \text{ abcoulomb} = c \text{ statcoulomb} \end{cases}$$

Current ....
$$\begin{cases} 1 \text{ ampere} = 3 \times 10^9 \text{ statampere} \\ 1 \text{ abampere} = 10 \text{ ampere} \\ 1 \text{ abampere} = c \text{ statampere} \end{cases}$$

Electric intensity ...
$$\begin{cases} 1 \text{ statvolt/cm (esu)} = 1 \text{ dyne/statcoulomb} = \\ \qquad 10^{-6}c \text{ volt/meter} = 10^{-6}c \text{ newton/coulomb} \\ 1 \text{ abvolt/cm (emu)} = 1 \text{ dyne/abcoulomb} \\ \qquad\qquad\qquad\qquad = 10^{-6} \text{ volt/meter} \\ 1 \text{ statvolt/cm} = c \text{ abvolt/cm} \end{cases}$$

Magnetic flux ..... 1 weber $= 10^8$ maxwell (emu)

Magnetic flux
density......... 1 weber/m^2 $= 10^4$ maxwell/cm^2 $= 10^4$ gauss (emu)

Permeability .... 1 henry/m $= 10^7/4\pi$ emu

Permittivity .... 1 farad/m $= 4\pi \times 10^{-11}c^2$ statcoulomb^2/dyne-cm^2 (esu)

Potential difference .
$$\begin{cases} 1 \text{ statvolt (esu)} = 10^{-8}c \text{ volt} \\ 1 \text{ abvolt (emu)} = 10^{-8} \text{ volt} \\ 1 \text{ statvolt} = c \text{ abvolt} \end{cases}$$

Energy ....
$$\begin{cases} 1 \text{ ev} = 1 \text{ electron volt} = (1.60206 \pm 0.00003) \times 10^{-12} \\ \qquad\qquad\qquad\qquad\qquad\qquad\qquad\qquad\qquad \text{erg} \\ 1 \text{ Mev} = 1.60206 \times 10^{-6} \text{ erg} = 1.60206 \times 10^{-13} \text{ joule} \\ 1 \text{ joule} = 10^7 \text{ erg} = 0.7376 \text{ ft-lb} = 6.2420 \times 10^{12} \text{ Mev} \\ 1 \text{ kw-hr} = 3413 \text{ Btu} = 1.341 \text{ hp-hr} \\ \qquad\qquad\qquad = 3.6 \times 10^6 \text{ joule} = 8.601 \times 10^5 \text{ cal} \end{cases}$$

Force .... 1 newton $= 10^5$ dyne $= 0.2248$ lb-wt

Length ....
$$\begin{cases} 1 \text{ foot} = 0.3048 \text{ m} \\ 1 \text{ inch} = 2.54 \text{ cm} \\ 1 \text{ meter} = 39.37 \text{ in.} = 3.281 \text{ ft} \\ 1 \text{ micron} = 10^{-6} \text{ m} = 10^{-3} \text{ mm} \\ 1 \text{ Angstrom (Å)} = 10^{-10} \text{ m} = 10^{-8} \text{ cm} \\ 1 \text{ fermi} = 10^{-15} \text{ m} = 10^{-13} \text{ cm} \end{cases}$$

* In the electrical conversion units, c is numerically equal to the velocity of light in vacuum in cm/sec.

† The statfarad is sometimes called a cm.

Mass . . . . $\begin{cases} \text{1 atomic mass unit (amu)} = (1.65979 \pm 0.00004) \\ \qquad\qquad\qquad \times\ 10^{-24}\ \text{gm} = 931.141 \pm 0.010\ \text{Mev}/c^2 \\ \text{1 gram} = 2.205 \times 10^{-3}\ \text{lb} = 10^{-3}\ \text{kg} \\ \qquad\qquad\qquad\qquad\qquad\quad = 6.852 \times 10^{-5}\ \text{slug} \\ \text{1 pound} = 0.4536\ \text{kg} \\ \text{1 slug} = 14.59\ \text{kg} = 32.17\ \text{lb} \end{cases}$

GLOSSARY

actinium A. Po^{215}.

actinium B. Pb^{211}.

actinium C. Bi^{211}.

actinium C'. Po^{211}.

actinium C". Tl^{207}.

actinium K. Fr^{223}.

actinium-uranium. U^{235}.

actinium X. Ra^{223}.

actinon. Rn^{219}.

activity. A measure of the intensity of radiation from a substance. Sometimes used in the more restricted sense of number of disintegrations per unit time. See Sec. 1-2.

age. See *slowing-down length*.

alpha particle. A He^4 nucleus.

americium. Element 95.

amu. Atomic mass unit.

angular distribution. Number of events observed per unit angle $(dN/d\theta)$ as a function of the angle (θ). Also the number of events per unit solid angle $(dN/d\Omega)$ as a function of the angle (θ).

annihilation radiation. Gamma radiations resulting from combination of a positron with a negatron in which the masses of the two particles are completely converted to radiant energy.

anticoincidence circuit. A type of coincidence circuit in which a coincidence results in no output pulse if there are simultaneous input pulses from one or more anticoincidence tubes.

antineutrino. A hypothetical antiparticle associated with the neutrino. This name is usually given to the neutral particle emitted in negatron decay. It corresponds to a hole in a negative-energy neutrino sea. It should thus have a magnetic moment, if any, opposite in sign to that of the neutrino.

antineutron. A neutral antiparticle which can undergo annihilation when it interacts with a neutron.

antiproton. A negative proton. A particle bearing the same relationship to a proton that a positron bears to a negatron.

atomic mass unit. One-sixteenth the mass of an O^{16} atom. $(1.65979 \pm 0.00004) \times 10^{-24}$ gm.

atomic number. The number of positive charges on the nucleus of an atom. Also, therefore, the number of orbital electrons.

Auger electron. An electron emitted by an atom when another electron drops from a higher to a lower energy orbit without photon emission. For example, an electron may drop from the L shell of an atom to a vacant site in the K shell. This loss of energy may be sufficient to cast an electron out of the M shell with a considerable amount of kinetic energy.

autoradiography. Production of a developable image in a photographic emulsion by placing a material (such as a tissue section) which contains radioisotopes in contact with it.

Avogadro's number. The number of atoms in one gram-atomic weight of an element. $(6.02486 \pm 0.00016) \times 10^{23}$ (physical scale).

babe. 20 Kev.

barn. A unit of area equal to 10^{-24} cm^2. Nuclear cross sections are commonly expressed in barns.

baryon. Any particle whose mass is equal to or greater than that of the proton. The only such particles recognized thus far have a "baryon number" of $+1$. Antibaryons corresponding to these particles have a baryon number of -1.

berkelium. Element 97.

beta particle. An electron ejected from the nucleus of a radioisotope.

beta ray. A beta particle.

betatron. An induction accelerator used to accelerate electrons. A varying magnetic field holds the electron in an orbit of constant radius, while the changing flux through the orbit provides the accelerating emf.

Bev. 10^9 ev (one billion electron volts). Also called *Gev*.

Bevatron. A 6.2-Bev proton synchrotron located at the University of California in Berkeley.

binding energy. Energy required completely to separate all the component particles in a stable configuration of particles. Nuclear binding energy, strictly speaking, is the sum of the masses of the neutrons and protons composing the nucleus less the actual nuclear mass, the difference being expressed in energy units. In practice, because atomic rather than nuclear masses are usually measured, an inexact value of the nuclear binding energy is computed from the equation

$$W_B = zM_H + (A - Z)M_N - M,$$

where M_H, M_N, and M are the isotopic masses of hydrogen, the neutron, and the nuclide in question, all expressed in Mev. The binding energy per nucleon is the binding energy, W_B, divided by the mass number, A.

binding fraction. Binding energy per nucleon.

Bohr magneton. Magnetic moment of an orbital electron having an angular momentum of $\hbar$. Equals $(0.92731 \pm 0.00002) \times 10^{-20}$ erg/gauss.

boson. A typical particle in an ensemble of particles which obeys the Bose-Einstein quantum statistics. For example, any nuclide of even mass number.

branching ratio. The ratio of the number, per unit of time, of atoms of a particular nuclear species undergoing decay of one type to the number undergoing decay of another type. For example, the ratio of β particles to α particles emitted per second by Bi^{214}.

breeding. The production, within a nuclear reactor, of new thermally fissionable nuclei of the same kind as those used for fuel. For example, the production of Pu^{239} from U^{238} in a reactor using Pu^{239} as fuel. If the newly produced thermally fissionable nuclei differ from the fuel nuclei, the process is termed *conversion*.

bremsstrahlung. Radiation produced by acceleration or deceleration of a charged particle.

burn-up. The fractional loss, caused by fission, of the original fissionable material in a reactor.

californium. Element 98.

canal rays. Rays of, or beams of, positive ions produced by electrical discharge through a gas.

carbon cycle. The cycle of nuclear reactions postulated by Bethe to account for the production of the enormous amount of energy being radiated by the sun each year. The reactions are

$$_6C^{12} + {}_1H^1 \longrightarrow {}_7N^{13} + \gamma$$
$$_7N^{13} \longrightarrow {}_6C^{13} + e^+$$
$$_6C^{13} + {}_1H^1 \longrightarrow {}_7N^{14} + \gamma$$
$$_7N^{14} + {}_1H^1 \longrightarrow {}_8O^{15} + \gamma$$
$$_8O^{15} \longrightarrow {}_7N^{15} + e^+$$
$$_7N^{15} + {}_1H^1 \longrightarrow {}_6C^{12} + {}_2He^4$$

The result is the continuous conversion of hydrogen to helium without consuming carbon.

cascade unit. See *radiation length*.

centrifugal barrier. When the potential, $U(r)$, of a particle is a function only of the radial coordinate, r, the wave function may be broken down into a product of two functions, one a function of the angular position only and the other a function of r only. The differential equation of the latter function, $[R(r)]$, is

$$\frac{1}{r^2}\frac{d}{dr}\left[r^2\frac{dR(r)}{dr}\right] + \frac{2M}{\hbar^2}\left[W - U(r) - \frac{l(l+1)}{2Mr^2}\hbar^2\right]R(r) = 0.$$

The term $\frac{l(l+1)}{2Mr^2}\hbar^2$, in which $l(l+1)\hbar^2$ is the square of the total angular momentum of the particle, is just the rotational kinetic energy of a particle of reduced mass M with angular momentum $\sqrt{l(l+1)}\,\hbar$. Since

$$-\frac{d}{dr}\left[\frac{l(l+1)}{2Mr^2}\hbar^2\right]$$

is equal to the centrifugal force, the quantity $\frac{l(l+1)}{2Mr^2}\hbar^2$ is called a centrifugal potential. The problem of finding the probability of barrier penetration when a particle has orbital motion reduces to that of a particle without such orbital motion penetrating a barrier

$$U' \equiv U + \frac{l(l+1)}{2Mr^2}\hbar^2.$$

The orbital motion, then, has the effect of making the potential barrier seem to rise more rapidly than normal with decreasing r.

Čerenkov counter. A particle detector in which a photomultiplier tube is activated by the Čerenkov radiation produced by a charged particle passing through a transparent dielectric adjacent to the tube.

Čerenkov radiation. Radiation into a cone whose axis is in the direction of motion of the charged particle responsible for the radiation. Occurs when the velocity of a charged particle exceeds the phase velocity of a light wave in the dielectric medium through which the particle is moving.

circular wavelength. Wavelength divided by 2π.

Cockcroft-Walton generator. A voltage-multiplier circuit consisting of capacitors and diodes fed by a high-voltage transformer. The potential difference is usually less than 1 Mev.

coincidence circuit. An electronic circuit in which an output pulse occurs only when a given number of input pulses (as from three Geiger tubes, for example) occur "simultaneously" (i.e., within some small time interval $\varDelta t$).

compound nucleus. An excited nucleus which exists for a short time as an intermediate state in a nuclear reaction.

Compton effect. Change in wavelength of a photon when it suffers elastic collision with a free electron.

Compton recoil electron. The electron recoiling from elastic impact of a photon.

Compton wavelength. The wavelength of a photon whose energy is equal to the rest energy (mc^2) of an electron. $\lambda_c = h/mc = 2.426 \times 10^{-10}$ cm.

Cosmotron. The 3-Bev Brookhaven proton synchrotron.

coulomb field. An electric field in which the force exerted on a charged particle varies as the inverse square of the distance from some point.

cross-over gamma ray. A gamma ray emitted in a cross-over transition, that is, a single-step transition from a higher to a lower energy level where a two-step transition via an intermediate energy level is allowed.

cross section. The effective target area of a nucleus for a particular type of interaction with a bombarding particle, the latter being treated as a geometric point. A measure of the probability per target nucleus that a given reaction will be produced by a specific bombarding particle.

crystal counter. A counter utilizing the pulse of electrical current that flows through a crystal in which an unusual number of charge carriers have been released by movement of an energetic charged particle within the crystal.

curie. That quantity of a radioisotope undergoing exactly 3.700×10^{10} disintegrations per second.

curium. Element 96.

cyclotron. A magnetic resonance particle accelerator in which the particle path is a series of semicircles because of deflection of the particle by a nearly uniform transverse magnetic field. The particle is accelerated every half cycle by a constant frequency alternating potential difference.

decay constant. Ratio of number of disintegrations per unit time to the total number of radioactive atoms present at that time. Also the probability, per unit time, that a nucleus will decay.

delta rays. Low-energy electrons moving away in random directions from a collimated beam of photons or from the path of a charged particle. These can occur, of course, only in an ionizable medium.

deuterium. Hydrogen of mass number two.

deuteron. A deuterium nucleus.

differential cross section. Effective target area of a nucleus, per unit angle or per unit solid angle, for those specific interactions in which some entity is observed at a given angle with respect to some specified direction such as the direction of motion of an incident bombarding particle. See Sec. 4-3.

diffusion length. The square root of one-sixth the mean square of the displacement of neutrons from the points where they begin diffusing as thermal neutrons in a nuclear reactor to the points where they are absorbed.

di-neutron. A hypothetical transient particle consisting of two closely bound neutrons.

Dirac hole theory. See *hole.*

disintegration constant. Decay constant.

disintegration energy. Q value of a nuclear disintegration.

dollar. The reactivity necessary to make a reactor prompt-critical. A "cent" is one one-hundredth of this amount.

electronic charge. Absolute value of the charge borne by a proton or an electron.

electron-volt. An energy unit equal in magnitude to the energy given to a particle with a single electronic charge when it falls through a potential difference of one volt. Equals 1.6×10^{-12} erg.

endoergic reaction. A reaction which requires more kinetic energy input than is obtained from the reaction products.

epithermal neutron. A neutron having appreciably more energy than the average energy of a thermal neutron.

excess multiplication. The amount by which the multiplication factor exceeds unity. $\Delta k = k - 1$.

exchange force. Force arising from the sharing of a particle by two or more other particles. A quantum mechanical effect with no classical analog.

excitation energy. Amount by which the energy of a nucleus in an excited state exceeds its energy in the ground state.

exclusion principle. A rule which states that two or more identical particles may not occupy a given quantum state.

exoergic reaction. A reaction in which more kinetic energy is liberated than was put into the reaction.

fast effect. The release, in a nuclear reactor, of more neutrons than expected on the basis of thermal fissions only.

fast fission factor. The ratio of the total number of fast neutrons produced in a reactor to the number of fast neutrons liberated in thermal fissions.

fast neutron. A neutron having appreciably more energy than the average energy of a thermal neutron.

fast reactor. A nuclear reactor in which the average neutron energy at which fission occurs exceeds 100 Kev.

fermi. 10^{-13} cm.

fermion. A typical particle in an ensemble of particles which obeys the Fermi-Dirac quantum statistics. Electrons, protons, and neutrons are examples of such particles.

fine structure constant. $e^2/\hbar c = \frac{1}{137.0391}$.

fission. Splitting of a nucleus into two or more parts of comparable mass.

flux. In nuclear reactor theory, the product of the neutron concentration (free neutrons per unit volume) and the average speed of the neutrons.

francium. Element 87.

fusion. The combining of light nuclei to form heavier nuclei.

gamma ray. An electromagnetic radiation of greater quantum energy than is usually associated with x-rays. Usually applied to photons of nuclear origin.

Geiger-Müller tube. A gas-filled tube in which gas amplification gives an easily detectable electrical pulse when a charged particle passes through. Usually refers to such a tube operated in the "Geiger region," but see *proportional counter*.

Geiger-Nuttall relation. An empirical rule that the logarithms of the decay constants of certain groups of α emitters bear a linear relation to the logarithms of the ranges of the emitted α particles (i.e., $\log R = a + b \log \lambda$).

Gev. Same as Bev.

ground state. Lowest and most stable energy state, as of a nucleus.

half-life. The time required for one-half of an initial given number of identical radioactive particles to decay.

half-thickness. The thickness of an absorber required to reduce the intensity of radiation to one-half of its original value. Sometimes expressed in grams/cm^2 rather than in cm.

heavy hydrogen. Deuterium.

heavy water. D_2O.

Heisenberg uncertainty principle. See *uncertainty principle*.

helicity. Cosine of the angle between the spin vector and propagation vector.

hole. The absence of a particle from a normally filled energy state. The positron is supposed to be a hole in the "negative-electron, negative-energy sea."

hyperfragment. A nuclear entity in which a lambda hyperon replaces a neutron.

hypernucleus. A hyperfragment.

hyperon. An unstable particle more massive than a neutron.

impact parameter. The closest distance to which one particle would approach another particle in the absence of any interaction between them (see Appendix D).

intermediate reactor. A nuclear reactor in which the average neutron energy at which fission occurs lies between the average energy of a thermal neutron and 100 Kev.

internal conversion. The ejection, associated with de-excitation of the nucleus, of an orbital electron from an atom. The process commonly competes with gamma-ray emission.

internal conversion coefficient. The ratio of the number of internal conversion electrons to the number of γ rays emitted per unit time.

ionium. Th^{230}.

ionization potential. The energy required to remove an orbital electron to infinity.

ion pair. A positive and a negative ion resulting from the ionization of a neutral atom or molecule.

isobar. One of two or more nuclides of different atomic number, Z, which have the same mass number, A.

isobaric spin. A quantum number characterizing a group of nucleons. The proton and neutron belong to an isobaric spin multiplet with $T = \frac{1}{2}$. The projection of the T "vector" on some preferred axis in isobaric spin space gives the charge of the substate. Thus $T_\zeta = \frac{1}{2}$ represents the neutron and $T_\zeta = -\frac{1}{2}$ represents the proton. In general, $T_\zeta = \frac{1}{2}(A - 2Z)$. Sometimes called "isotopic spin," but in this text the latter term is reserved for a closely related usage.

isodiasphere. A nuclide having the same isotopic number as another nuclide.

isomer. A nucleus differing from another nucleus only in energy. An excited nucleus. In common usage, the term is restricted to excited nuclei with lifetimes long enough to be measurable.

isospin. See *isobaric spin*.

isotone. A nuclide having the same isotonic number as another nuclide. According to present concepts of nuclear structure, isotones are nuclides with equal numbers of neutrons.

isotonic number. Difference between mass number and atomic number. Also called *neutron number*.

isotope. A nucleus whose mass number, A, is different from that of another nucleus of the same element. Isotopes of an element have the same atomic number but different mass numbers.

isotopic abundance. The ratio of the number of atoms of a particular isotope, in a representative sample of an element, to the total number of atoms of the element in question in the sample.

isotopic mass. The mass of an atom of a particular isotope in amu.

isotopic number. The difference between the isotonic number and the atomic number of a nuclide.

isotopic spin. A quantum number characterizing charge multiplets of a given type of particle. Pions are members of an isotopic spin triplet with $T = 1$. The projection of T on some preferred axis in isotopic spin space gives the charge. Thus $T_\zeta = +1$ for π^+, $T_\zeta = 0$ for π^0, and $T_\zeta = -1$ for π^-. In general, $T_\zeta = q/e - \frac{1}{2}Y$, where q is the charge, e is the electronic charge, and Ye is the sum of the charges in the different charge states of the multiplet. The term is also used for the quantity which is called "isobaric spin" in this text.

isotopic weight. Same as isotopic mass.

I spin. See *isobaric spin*.

jerk. 10^{16} ergs.

kaon. K-meson.

K capture. Radioactive decay of an atom in which the nucleus absorbs an orbital electron from the K shell.

K conversion. Internal conversion in which a K-shell electron is emitted.

K-meson. A charged ($\pm$) or neutral particle with a mass of about 970 electron masses.

knock-on electron. Electron given a large forward momentum from a central or nearly central blow by a high-energy particle. Most often used to designate the secondary electrons produced by impinging cosmic-ray mesons.

lambda hyperon. A neutral unstable particle with a mass of about $2183m$.

Laue diffraction pattern. Pattern resulting from diffraction of a polychromatic or heteroergic beam by a single crystal.

L conversion. Internal conversion in which an L-shell electron is ejected.

lepton. An $e^{\pm}$, a $\mu^{\pm}$, a neutrino or an antineutrino.

lethargy. A dimensionless measure of energy used in reactor analysis. The natural logarithm of the ratio of initial (or other arbitrary reference) energy to the energy in question. $u = \ln(W_0/W)$.

level width. The quantum mechanical uncertainty in the energy of a nuclear energy level. It is defined by $\Gamma = \hbar/t_a$, where Γ is the level width and t_a is the mean lifetime of the state. If there is more than one mode of decay, one speaks of the "partial level width" ascribable to each mode. Then $\Gamma_i = \hbar\lambda_i$, where λ_i is the decay constant for the ith mode of decay. Hence

$$\Gamma = \sum_i \Gamma_i = \hbar \sum_i \lambda_i = \frac{\hbar}{t_a} \qquad \text{since } t_a = \frac{1}{\lambda} = \frac{1}{\sum_i \lambda_i}.$$

linac. A linear accelerator for protons.

macroscopic cross section. The product of ordinary or microscopic cross section for a given process and the number of nuclei per unit volume which can participate in the process.

magic number. One of several numbers of protons (2, 8, 20, 28, 50, 82) or neutrons (2, 8, 20, 28, 50, 82, 126) which seem to give nuclei of unusual stability.

magnetic rigidity. A measure of the ratio of momentum to charge. Equal to the product of the radius of curvature of the particle path and the component of magnetic intensity at right angles to the velocity vector. Given as $B\rho$ (or $H\rho$) in the literature.

magneton. See *Bohr magneton* and *nuclear magneton*.

mass defect. Isotopic mass minus mass number. This is sometimes called *mass decrement*, in which case the term *mass defect* is used for the nuclear binding energy expressed in amu.

mass number. The integer nearest the isotopic mass of a nuclide. According to present concepts of nuclear structure, equal to the total number of nucleons in the nucleus of an atom.

mass unit. One-sixteenth of the mass of an O^{16} atom. One amu.

mean free path. The average distance traveled by a particle between events. It is customary to specify the type of event. The mean free path is then the average distance traveled by a particle between events of the specified type (such as elastic scattering).

mean life. The average lifetime of a radionuclide. The time in which the number of nuclei is reduced to $1/e$ of the original number. The reciprocal of the decay constant.

mesic atom. An atom consisting of a nucleus and an orbital μ^--meson (a mu-mesic atom) or an orbital π^--meson (a pi-mesic atom).

meson. A particle intermediate in mass between the mass of an electron and the mass of a proton.

mesothorium I. Ra^{228}.

mesothorium II. Ac^{228}.

mesotron. A meson.

metastable state. An excited state of longer than usual lifetime. This implies that transitions to all lower energy states are quantum mechanically forbidden, that is, they are transitions which violate certain selection rules.

migration area. One-sixth of the mean square displacement of neutrons from the points where they are released by fission in a nuclear reactor to the points where they are absorbed as thermal neutrons. The sum of the squares of the slowing-down length and the diffusion length.

migration length. The square root of the migration area.

mirror nucleus. A nucleus having the same mass number as another nucleus, but having as many protons as the other nucleus has neutrons.

moderator. A material to slow the fast neutrons, released in fission, down to thermal speeds.

multiplication factor. The ratio of the number of thermal neutrons absorbed by fissionable nuclei in a reactor in one generation to the number absorbed in the previous generation.

mu-mesic atom. An atom with a negative muon in a Bohr orbit.

mu-meson. A charged meson ($\mu^{\pm}$) having a mass of about 207 electron masses.

muon. A μ-meson.

muonium. A hydrogenlike atom consisting of a positive muon and an electron.

nanosecond. 10^{-9} sec.

negaton. A negatron. (An infelicitous spelling in the age of the megaton.)

negatron. A negatively charged electron.

neutretto. A neutral meson.

neutrino. A neutral particle of rest mass much smaller than that of an electron having a magnetic moment which is extremely small if not zero, and having a spin of $\frac{1}{2}$.

neutron. A particle having a mass very nearly equal to that of H^1, but bearing no electric charge.

neutron number. See *isotonic number*.

nuclear emulsion. A photographic-type emulsion 25 to 600 or more microns thick which contains an abnormally high concentration of AgBr (about 80%) and which is especially sensitive to traversal by charged particles.

nuclear isomer. See *isomer*.

nuclear magneton. A unit of magnetic moment appropriate to expression of magnetic moments of nuclei and nucleons. Magnitude given by $e\hbar/2M_p c = 5.0504 \times 10^{-24}$ erg/gauss, where M_p is the mass of a proton.

nucleons. Neutrons and protons.

nuclide. A particular nuclear species. Often used synonymously with *isotope*, but a given isotope may exist in different energy states, each of which is considered to be a separate nuclide.

Oppenheimer-Phillips process. Separation, in the nuclear field of a target atom, of a bombarding deuteron into a neutron and proton, the neutron being absorbed by the target nucleus and the proton scattered by the coulomb field.

packing fraction. [(Isotopic mass − mass number)/(mass number)] $\times 10^4$. For a better definition, see Sec. 2-4.

pair production. Production of a positron-negatron pair by a γ ray.

Panofsky ratio. [Rate of $(\pi^- + p \rightarrow n + \pi^0)$]/[rate of $(\pi^- + p \rightarrow n + \gamma)$].

parity. A characterization of a wave function. If, when all coordinates of a system are replaced by their negatives, the wave function remains unchanged in sign, the wave function is said to possess even parity. If, on the other hand, it changes sign under this operation, it is said to possess odd parity.

Pauli exclusion principle. See *exclusion principle*.

period. In reactor analysis, the time required for the power level to change by a factor e.

photodisintegration. Nuclear disintegration induced by absorption of a photon.

photofission. Fission induced by absorption of a γ ray.

photon. A quantum of electromagnetic energy.

photoneutron source. A neutron source in which a γ emitter produces neutrons by a (γ, n) reaction on some element such as Be.

pile. A nuclear reactor.

pi-meson. A particle with a mass of about 273 electron masses if charged and a mass of about 264 electron masses if neutral.

pion. A π-meson.

plutonium. Element 94.

positon. A positron.

positron. A particle having the same mass as an electron, but having a positive charge.

positronium. A hydrogenlike atom consisting of a positron and an electron.

prometheum. Element 61.

proportional counter. A gaseous discharge tube in which the size of the output pulse is proportional to the amount of primary ionization produced by the passage of a charged particle through it.

proton. A hydrogen nucleus of mass number unity.

proton synchrotron. A proton accelerator in which the orbit radius is held constant by a varying magnetic field while the particle is accelerated by repeated passages through an alternating electric field whose frequency changes with time in such a way that it remains in synchronism with the particle's orbit frequency.

quadrupole moment. The electrical quadrupole moment of a nucleus is a measure of that component of the electrical potential of a nucleus which varies as r^{-3}. It is defined by

$$Q = \frac{1}{q} \int (3z^2 - r^2) D(r, \theta)\, dV,$$

where q is the total nuclear charge, $D(r, \theta)$ is the charge density at (r, θ, ϕ), r is the radial distance from the center of the nucleus, z is the projection of r along the spin axis, and dV is an element of volume. The integration extends over the entire nuclear volume. Q has the dimensions of an area. (See Sec. 2-6.)

Q-value. The difference between the mass energy of the reactants and that of the products of a nuclear reaction.

rad. A radiation dose in which 100 ergs are deposited per gram of material.

radiation length. The average distance (usually expressed as gm/cm^2) an electron travels before its energy falls to $1/e$ of its original value because of loss through bremsstrahlung. The earth's atmosphere is about 20 radiation lengths thick. Also called a "cascade unit."

radio actinium. Th^{227}.

radio thorium. Th^{228}.

radium A. Po^{218}.

radium B. Pb^{214}.

radium C. Bi^{214}.

radium C'. Po^{214}.

radium C". Tl^{210}.

radium D. Pb^{210}.

radium E. Bi^{210}.

radium F. Po^{210}.

radon. Rn^{222} in older literature.

range. Distance a given charged particle with a specified kinetic energy will travel through a medium before being brought to rest, or, more accurately, before it ceases to produce ionization. Use of the term implies that the particle does not lose an appreciable fraction of its energy in any single encounter, as often happens, for example, in collisions of protons with light nuclei. In the case of electrons, which are easily deflected from their original path, the range is usually taken to be the greatest distance of penetration into the medium rather than the actual path length.

reactivity. The ratio of excess multiplication to multiplication factor.

reflector. A material used to scatter as many escaping neutrons as possible back into the core of a reactor. A good reflector must have a large ratio of scattering to absorption cross sections.

rem. Roentgen equivalent man. An amount of radiation of any kind which, when absorbed by man, produces an effect equivalent to that produced by absorption of one roentgen of x- or γ-radiation.

rep. Roentgen equivalent physical. That quantity of ionizing radiation which will produce 1.6×10^{12} ion-pairs per gram of tissue.

residual range. The path length from a point on the path of a charged particle to the point where the particle ceases to ionize.

resonance capture. A wave-mechanical effect distinguished experimentally by an abnormally high capture cross section over a narrow energy band.

resonance escape probability. The probability that a fast neutron released within a reactor will be slowed down to thermal velocities without being captured.

rhm. Roentgen per hour at one meter. (Used for γ emitters where disintegration rate cannot be determined.)

rho-meson. A term used at one time to designate a light meson which comes to rest in a non-electron sensitive nuclear emulsion without visible secondary tracks to indicate decay or nuclear interaction.

roentgen unit. One r unit is defined as that quantity of x-radiation which will produce 2.083×10^9 ion pairs/cm^3 of air at NTP.

r unit. See *roentgen unit.*

rutherford. (1) That quantity of a radioisotope undergoing 10^6 disintegrations per second. (2) A unit of activity equal to 10^6 disintegrations per second.

rydberg (ry). A unit of energy equal to -13.52 ev.

sargent diagram. A plot of log (maximum β energy) *vs.* log (decay constant) which gives an approximate straight-line relationship for certain groups of β emitters.

scattering length. Same as "coherent scattering amplitude." Equals $(\sigma_{coh}/4\pi)^{1/2}$.

scintillation counter. A scintillator combined with a photomultiplier tube. Light from a scintillation, produced by the passage of a charged particle, releases photoelectrons from the photocathode of the photomultiplier tube. This pulse of electrons is amplified in the dynode structure of the tube so that an electrical output pulse is produced of sufficient magnitude to be amplified and operate a mechanical register or other counting device.

scintillator. A material which emits light as a consequence of ionization produced in it by motion of a charged particle. A gamma ray may eject a Compton electron or a photo-electron, either of which can produce a scintillation.

self-absorption. Absorption of a part of the radiation from a radioisotope before it can escape from a thick layer of material containing the radioisotope.

shake. 10^{-8} sec.

shed. 10^{-24} barn or 10^{-48} cm^2.

sigma-hyperon. The Σ^- has a mass of about $2341m$, the Σ^+, about $2328m$, and the Σ^0 about $2332m$.

sigma-meson. A term used at one time to designate a light meson which produces a star at the end of its range.

slowing-down length. The square root of one-sixth the mean square of the displacement of neutrons from the points where they are released by fission in a nuclear reactor to the points where they reach mean thermal velocity. In Fermi-age theory, the square of the slowing-down length is called the "age."

spallation. Chipping off of nuclear fragments by bombardment.

specific activity. Number of disintegrations per unit time per unit mass of radioisotope.

spin. Angular momentum of a particle about an axis of rotation fixed in the particle. Also used for total angular momentum of a nucleus. The spin quantum number is spoken of loosely as *spin*.

s-state. A quantum state of zero orbital angular momentum.

statitron. An electrostatic particle accelerator of the Van de Graaff type.

stopping power. In modern usage, the space-rate of energy loss, dW/dR.

stopping power (relative). The ratio of the decrease in air (at NTP) range, caused by traversing a thin sheet of some material, to the thickness of the sheet of material.

straggling. Random variations in the ranges of identical particles having the same initial energy traceable to the statistical nature of the energy-loss process is called "range straggling."

strangeness. A quantum number introduced to characterize families of particles. The strangeness, S, is defined by $S = Y - N$ where Y is the sum of the charges (measured in electronic charge units) of the various substates of an isotopic spin multiplet, and N is the baryon number.

stripping. The removal of either a neutron or a proton from a high-energy deuteron as it passes through matter.

s-wave. A quantum-mechanical wave which has spherical symmetry (i.e., is a function of radial distance only). The object represented by an *s*-wave can carry away no angular momentum.

synchrocyclotron. A cyclotron in which the frequency of the radio-frequency potential difference applied to the dees is decreased as the energy of the particle being accelerated increases, thus correcting for the relativistic momentum increase. A frequency-modulated cyclotron.

synchrotron. A charged-particle accelerator in which the orbit radius is held constant by varying the magnetic field. Acceleration is produced by a constant radio-frequency electric field. The name is ordinarily applied only to electron accelerators.

Szilard-Chalmers reaction. A separation of radioisotopes from material which has been bombarded, made possible by the recoil energy of the nucleus being great enough to disrupt the chemical bond.

tamper. Heavy material (usually Pb) placed around an atomic bomb to allow the fission of as many nuclei as possible before the expansion of the products stops the reaction.

tau-meson. A charged kaon which decays into three charged pions.

technetium. Element 43.

thermal neutron. A neutron having a kinetic energy near the average kinetic energy of a monatomic gas atom at ordinary temperature (about $\frac{1}{30}$ ev).

thermal reactor. A nuclear reactor in which thermal neutrons are responsible for the preponderant fraction of fissions.

thermal utilization factor. The fraction of thermal neutrons absorbed which are absorbed in the reactor fuel.

thermonuclear reaction. A nuclear reaction in which the bombardment energy comes from the thermal motions of the colliding particles.

theta-meson. A neutral kaon which decays into two oppositely charged pions.

thorium A. Po^{216}.

thorium B. Pb^{212}.

thorium C. Bi^{212}.

thorium C'. Po^{212}.

thorium C″. Tl^{208}.

thorium X. Ra^{224}.

thoron. Rn^{220}.

threshold energy. The minimum kinetic energy required for an impinging particle to produce a given nuclear reaction if it strikes a second particle which is initially at rest. Sometimes incorrectly equated with the Q-value where the latter is negative. Conservation of momentum demands that the threshold energy must always exceed the absolute magnitude of Q if Q is negative.

tralphium. He^3.

trident. Phenomenologically, the occurrence of three outgoing electron tracks with only one incident electron track. Some of these events are undoubtedly due to direct production of an electron pair, a process which competes with bremsstrahlung.

tritium. Hydrogen of mass number three.

triton. A tritium nucleus.

tunnel effect. Name given to the wave-mechanical effect in which there is a certain probability that a particle in a nuclear metastable state "leaks out" through the potential barrier.

uncertainty principle. A principle enunciated by Heisenberg which says, for example, that the momentum and position of a particle can only be determined to an uncertainty given by $\Delta x \, \Delta p \simeq \hbar$, where Δx is the uncertainty in the position of a particle and Δp is the uncertainty in its momentum.

uranium X-I. Th^{234}.

uranium X-II. Pa^{234m}.

uranium Y. Th^{231}.

uranium Z. Pa^{234} in its ground state.

vacuum polarization. An electrical charge is pictured as surrounding itself with a cloud of virtual positron-electron pairs, pairs that are constantly being destroyed and recreated. The charge repels particles of like charge and attracts those of opposite charge, thus producing a partial charge separation or polarization of the virtual pair cloud. At distances greater than one Compton wavelength from the charge, the effect of this polarization rapidly becomes negligible. In μ-mesonic atoms, the meson moves inside the polarization region surrounding the nucleus and therefore sees a smaller effective nuclear charge than does an orbital electron. The energy of an orbital state is therefore greater than it would be in the absence of vacuum polarization, the effect being greater for orbits of smaller radius. The energy of the $3D$ state of a μ-mesonic lead nucleus, for example, is raised about 9200 ev by vacuum polarization.

Van de Graaff generator. A high potential-difference electrostatic generator widely used in nuclear physics to accelerate charged particles because it maintains a very steady potential difference.

Wigner effect. Disruption of a crystal lattice by neutron bombardment, resulting in changes in its electrical and thermal conductivity.

Wigner nuclides. Mirror nuclides in which the atomic number differs from the neutron number by ± 1.

Wilson chamber. A cloud chamber.

xi-hyperon. The negative Ξ has a mass of about $2580m$. Believed to occur also in the neutral state.

X-unit. 10^{-11} cm, or 10^{-3} Å.

zerk. 10^{25} ergs.

Index

(For items not listed see Table of Contents and Glossary)

Straggling, 75, 571
Superallowed transitions, 238
Swimming-pool reactor, 177
Symmetric fission, 175
Synchrocyclotron, 454, 572
Synchrotron, 456, 572

Tandem Van de Graaff generator, 437
Tensor coupling constant, 229
Thermal fission neutrons, energy spectrum of, 472
Thermal neutron: absorption cross sections, 292; activation cross sections, 292
Thermal neutrons, 174, 572
Thomson atom model, 21
Thomson scattering, 262
Thorium decay series, 37
Threshold detector, 203
Threshold energy, 205, 337, 573
Time-of-flight spectrometer, 202
Triplet state of deuteron, 190

u, 31, 552
Unique forbidden beta decay, 239, 240, 241
Uranium–actinium decay series, 36
Uranium–radium decay series, 35
U^{238} total cross section, 473

Van de Graaff generator, 436, 574
Vector coupling constant, 229
Velocity selector, 201

Weizsäcker semi-empirical mass formula, 311

Ξ hyperons, 401, 420, 574
x-rays: absorption edge, 263, 264; following orbital electron capture, 219
x-ray spectra, Moseley's, 25

Zero-zero internal pair creation, 258
Zero-zero transitions, internal conversion, 150